Permian Brachiopods of West Texas, VI

G. Arthur Cooper
and Richard E. Grant

SMITHSONIAN INSTITUTION PRESS

City of Washington

1977

ABSTRACT

Cooper, G. Arthur, and Richard E. Grant. Permian Brachiopods of West Texas, VI. *Smithsonian Contributions to Paleobiology*, number 32, pages 3161–3370, 2 tables, 1977.—The sixth and final part of a monograph of Permian strata and faunas of West Texas and adjacent parts of New Mexico, this volume consists primarily of faunal lists and a taxonomic index of the previous five parts. A list of brachiopods grouped according to R. E. King's localities and compiled from King's data by the authors is followed by the author's compilation of lists of brachiopods found at the localities designated by the United States Geological Survey, the American Museum of Natural History, Kansas University, and the National Museum of Natural History. The list pertaining to the last three groups of localities carries a code indicating the approximate number of specimens of each taxon in the museum collections. A list of the authors' collection of ammonites is included, followed by lists of their fusulinids; these are appended to this monograph on brachiopods because they have important implications for dating and correlation. Also included are Corrigenda (with reference to the previously published parts) and suggestions for future related research.

Permian Brachiopods of West Texas, I. *Smithsonian Contributions to Paleobiology*, number 14, 231 pages, 39 figures, 23 plates. Issued 29 December 1972.

Permian Brachiopods of West Texas, II. *Smithsonian Contributions to Paleobiology*, number 15, pages 233–793, figure 40, plates 24–191. Issued 16 April 1974.

Permian Brachiopods of West Texas, III. *Smithsonian Contributions to Paleobiology*, number 19 (part 1: text; part 2: plates), pages 795–1921, plates 192–502. Issued 29 December 1975.

Permian Brachiopods of West Texas, IV. *Smithsonian Contributions to Paleobiology*, number 21 (part 1: text; part 2: plates), pages 1923–2607, figure 41, plates 503–662, table 1. Issued 12 February 1976.

Permian Brachiopods of West Texas, V. *Smithsonian Contributions to Paleobiology*, number 24, pages 2609–3159, figure 42, plates 663–780. Issued 15 October 1976.

Library of Congress Cataloging in Publication Data
Cooper, Gustav Arthur, 1902–
Permian brachiopods of West Texas.
(Smithsonian contributions to paleobiology, no. 14–15, 19, 21, 24, 32)
Includes bibliographies.
Supt. of Docs. no.: SI 1.30:32
1. Brachiopoda, Fossil. 2. Paleontology—Permian. 3. Paleontology—Texas. I. Grant, Richard E., joint author. II. Title. III. Series: Smithsonian Institution. Smithsonian contributions to paleobiology, no. 14 [etc.]
QE701.S56 no. 14, etc.   560′.8s   [564′.8′097649]   72-4218

Contents

TABLES

Permian Brachiopods
of West Texas, VI

G. Arthur Cooper
and Richard E. Grant

Introduction

Detailed study of the brachiopods of West Texas requires lists that consolidate the known data concerning associations of genera and species at the various localities. A summary showing the stratigraphic distribution of the species and genera also is essential. These items (comprising faunal lists and Tables 2 and 3) are furnished in this part six of our study of the Permian brachiopods of West Texas. Also included are miscellanea that we believe will be useful to students of the Permian.

During our extensive field and laboratory work stretching over more than a quarter century we collected many specimens of other phyla in addition to the brachiopods. We also amassed specimens of other shells from the residues of the solution program. Many of these will be useful in other studies. Realizing the value of the Fusulinacea and Ammonoidea in dating and correlating strata, we made special effort to collect specimens of these important fossils. We found fusulinids at 366 localities and ammonites at 157 places. At a few localities both of these were taken in addition to the brachiopods.

In correlating strata, especially those in separated areas, it is desirable to have as full a representation of the faunas as can be obtained. It is of considerable interest and concern that establishing correlation and dating in terms of only one phylum may produce results conflicting with those obtained in using other phyla. Inasmuch as many of the stratigraphic divisions of the Permian of West Texas were established on the basis of fusulinids through the classic work of Dunbar and Skinner (1937), it is important to record as much information on this fauna as possible. We were helped immeasurably in attaining this goal by the generous assistance of Dr. C. O. Dunbar, formerly at Yale University, Mr. Garner Wilde of the Exxon Company, Midland, Texas, and Dr. Charles A. Ross, Western Washington State College, Bellingham, Washington. Each identified our fusulinids from different parts of the Glass Mountains. Wilde, who identified lots from 279 localities, also examined our fusulinids from the Chinati Mountains.

Ammonite and fusulinid dating in the Glass Mountains has usually been in close accordance, but some conflict in dating Bed 2 of P. B. King's section in the Wolfcamp Hills is now evident. Our ammonites were identified by Dr. Arthur K. Miller, University of Iowa and, after his untimely death, by Drs. William M. Furnish and Brian G. Glenister, both of the University of Iowa.

All these data will supplement the brachiopod information and put many key fossils in their proper association. To enrich the lists presented below, further reference to other works on the

G. Arthur Cooper and Richard E. Grant, Department of Paleobiology, National Museum of Natural History, Smithsonian Institution, Washington, D.C. 20560.

Permian faunas of West Texas and the Glass Mountains can be made: Finks (1960) for sponges, Kier (1958) for echinoids, Yochelson (1956, 1960) and Batten (1958) for gastropods, Newell and Boyd (1970, 1975) for bivalves, Allyn Smith (1976) for chitons, and Elias and Condra (1957) for bryozoa. Studies on Glass Mountains fossils by Jerzy Federowski on the tetracorals and by Harrel Strimple on crinoids are pending. A fair number of trilobites have been collected but there is no worker studying them.

In this final part we correct errors in the lists of localities appearing in the first part of our study (pages 128–164) and record additional localities. We also include revisions of the lists of locations arranged by formations that appear in Part I (pages 165–166). Throughout each part we have recorded the localities for each species. Occasional citations now prove erroneous. Consequently the lists included in this last part of the monograph are final for each species. If a name appears herein in the faunal list under a given locality but the locality citation does not appear in the description, this signifies an addition. Contrariwise, if a locality number appears in a description but the species is not recorded in the faunal list under that locality, this constitutes a deletion of the locality for that species. In any case the lists herein represent our final checking of the fauna.

FURTHER ACKNOWLEDGMENTS.—Over the four years in which the various parts of this work have appeared, we have been assisted by persons whose names are not mentioned in the first part. Dr. Porter M. Kier, Director of the National Museum of Natural History, has taken an interest in the study, has participated in part of it, and has facilitated its publication. We give our thanks to him for making early publication possible. We are much indebted to Mr. Albert L. Ruffin, Jr., Series Managing Editor, who took a personal interest in the project and edited the first two parts and set the format of the books. Mr. John S. Lea, formerly of the editorial staff, edited Parts III, IV, and V. We are most grateful for his enthusiastic help. Mrs. Barbara Spann, editor of Part VI, brought the structure and numerous details of this final volume into a more coherent and useful format. To Mr. Vern Shaffer, Series Production Manager, watchdog over the illustrations, we owe much for his insistence on the highest quality of reproduction of often difficult subjects. To all of these members of the Smithsonian Institution Press we give our thanks.

We are also indebted to and thank Mr. Rex A. Doescher, Research Assistant, Department of Paleobiology, for preparing the index, ferreting out inconsistencies and errors in the manuscripts, and taking an interest in the publication.

Faunal Lists

Brachiopods

R. E. King Localities

The subjoined list of brachiopods has been compiled from R. E. King, "The Geology of the Glass Mountains, Texas, Part II: Faunal Summary and Correlation of the Permian Formations with Description of Brachiopoda" (1931) and arranged according to the Glass Mountains locality numbers used by King in that work. Emendations are included where necessary to supplement the descriptions of those localities given in Part I, pages 128–134, of the present monograph. In addition to listing the data extracted from King, we give the modern generic name or corrected specific name when we can be certain of it. Species marked with an asterisk were examined by Cooper at Yale University. Re-examination of these specimens enabled us to revise some names in the list that appeared in conflict with current views. For example, *Uncinuloides* (now *Torynechus*) is recorded by King (1931:119) from the Wolfcamp formations through the members of the Word Formation, as well as from the Hess and Leonard. We found it only in a narrow zone that straddles the boundary between the upper Skinner Ranch Formation and the lower Cathedral Mountain Formation. King occasionally confused it with *Rhynchopora,* a similar appearing genus.

Many of Girty's species described originally in his "Guadalupian Fauna" (1909) are identified by R. E. King at levels far below those of the Guadalupe Mountains whence they originally came. *Martinia rhomboidalis* Girty is an example. This is identified by King all through the Glass Mountains sequence but we were unable to find this Capitan species. These Girty names are often marked "doubtful" by us. Some other Guadalupe names are listed frequently and these, together with some common but uncertain Glass Mountains species, are listed without change. These names are recorded and explained below.

Aulosteges magnicostatus GIRTY.—The type speci-men of this species is poorly preserved, immature, and of uncertain locality, yet its name appears in many sections of the list. It belongs to the genus *Chonosteges,* which occurs throughout the Skinner Ranch and Cathedral Mountain formations. Stripped of its spines and with other details obscured by weathering (a problem common to other specimens of the genus due to its usually being found on the outcrop), it is impossible to identify specifically; consequently this name only indicates the presence of the genus.

Aulosteges medlicottianus WAAGEN.—This is an asiatic species not properly identified in the Glass Mountains. The weathered specimens figured by King evidently belong to *Edriosteges.* In the list we refer this to a species only where that species is the lone occurrence of the genus.

Camarophoria venusta GIRTY.—A variety of specimens from Wolfcamp formations through the Word members are so identified. The name is qualified by us in the rare cases in which we could be sure of the species. The listing, therefore, in most examples, does no more than indicate the presence of a species of *Stenoscisma.*

Composita subtilita (HALL).—This is a Pennsylvanian species widely identified in that period and in the Permian. Weathered specimens in small number are difficult to identify correctly, and the unqualified name stands as a record of the genus.

Derbyia nasuta GIRTY.—This is a large *Derbyia* of poor preservation and thus of uncertain specific character. It is not further qualified in the list.

Hustedia meekana (SHUMARD).—This name occurs in many sections of the list. It is a species name that we were unable satisfactorily to re-establish. *Hustedia* is so generalized that we cannot offer corrected specific names for most of its citations.

Hustedia mormoni (MARCOU).—This is a common Pennsylvanian species smaller than any that we found in the *Uddenites*-bearing Shale Member of the Gaptank Formation or in the formations of the Wolfcamp. We are unable to reassign King's listed examples.

Linoproductus cora (D'ORBIGNY).—This is a large South American species, the identification of which in Texas is doubtful. In most cases it is qualified only as *L.* sp.?.

Lyttonia nobilis americanus (GIRTY).—This is a Capitan species described by Girty as *Leptodus americanus,* a name used by R. E. King throughout the Glass Mountains sequence. Wolfcamp and Skinner Ranch specimens so referred usually belong to *Eolyttonia* and those from higher in the column are referrable to *Collemataria*. Most of King's material is fragmentary and not specifically identifiable. His names are qualified only in portions of the list pertaining to localities that were the origin of specimens that we can identify with certainty. *Lyttonia* is a synonym of *Leptodus* and now not in use.

Marginifera? cristobalensis GIRTY.—The type specimen of this species is generically unidentifiable. It has some features of *Echinauris* but its spines are not preserved and their bases are obscured. Inasmuch as the type specimen is an uncertain entity, so will be anything identified with it. Certain names in the subjoined list can be qualified, but the name indicates only the presence of a small productid.

Marginifera manzanica GIRTY.—The same remarks as those dealing with *M. cristobalensis* are apt here also. This is not a *Marginifera*; it is represented by a stripped and worn specimen possibly belonging to a species of *Echinauris* of small size. The name is usually not qualified.

Martinia rhomboidalis GIRTY.—This is a common species of the high Guadalupian (Capitan Formation and Bell Canyon Formation, Lamar Member) in the Guadalupe Mountains and Delaware Basin. King identified it at many levels in the Glass Mountains. In our experience, *Martinia* is very rare in the Glass Mountains and none of the listed occurrences can be so identified. Examination of some of King's specimens reveal what appear to be poorly preserved examples of *Composita* and *Neophricadothyris*, both of which can easily be mistaken for *Martinia*. The name is qualified in a few instances only. Specimens identified by King from his locality 57 (Altuda Formation) are probably correctly identified as *M. rhomboidalis*. Another

Guadalupian species, *Squamularia guadalupensis* (Shumard) is also probably correctly assigned at this locality.

Meekella attenuata GIRTY AND *M. difficilis* GIRTY.—These names occur in the list at many different levels. Since they cannot be placed specifically, they are not qualified but they certify the presence of one or more meekellas in the fauna.

Neospirifer triplicatus (HALL).—This is a fairly common Late Pennsylvanian species of uncertain occurrence in the Glass Mountains Permian.

Neospirifer pseudocameratus (GIRTY).—The type specimen is a small narrow form having the appearance of *Spiriferella*, quite unlike the wide fasciculate specimens referred by King to this species from several levels in the Glass Mountains sequence. The species name is qualified only when we are certain of the reassignment.

Productus hermosanus GIRTY.—This is a Pennsylvanian species that, in the Glass Mountains, is usually represented by fragmentary and worn specimens that if well preserved would probably be referable to a species of *Reticulatia*.

Prorichthofenia.—All of the citations of this genus must be referred to other names because of the uncertainty of the status of *Prorichthofenia* as a genus (see Part III, page 939). We qualify this genus and its species only for cases in which we are sure of the change.

Pugnoides bidentatus (GIRTY).—This is a small species that we were unable to identify in the Glass Mountains. In the absence of interior details it is impossible properly to place King's citations.

Pugnoides pinguis (GIRTY).—This is a large species from the Bell Canyon Formation and all citations of it in the Glass Mountains are below this level. We are unable to assess most of the records of it in King's lists; thus such records are unqualified.

1. SKINNER RANCH FORMATION
    Aulosteges magnicostatus Girty
    A. medlicottianus Waagen
    Camarophoria venusta Girty
    Composita mexicana (Hall)
    Enteletes liumbonus King [doubtful]
    Linoproductus cora angustus King
    Prorichthofenia likharewi King
    Rhipidomella hessensis King
    Squamularia guadalupensis (Shumard) = *Neophricadothyris* sp.?
    Striatifera pinniformis (Girty) = *Compressoproductus* sp.

2. LENOX HILLS FORMATION

Linoproductus cora (d'Orbigny) = *L.* sp.?
Orthotetella wolfcampensis King?
Productus wolfcampensis King? = *Limbella wolfcampensis* (King)

3. SKINNER RANCH FORMATION

Chonetes subliratus Girty = *Dyoros (Dyoros)* sp.?
Composita subtilita (Hall)
Enteletes liumbonus King [doubtful]
Marginifera cristobalensis Girty = *Oncosarina* sp.?
M. reticulata King = *Spyridiophora reticulata* (King)
Prorichthofenia likharewi King
Rhipidomella hessensis King
Uncinuloides guadalupensis (Shumard) = *Torynechus caelatus* Cooper and Grant
Waagenoncha montpelierensis (Girty) [doubtful]

4. SKINNER RANCH FORMATION

Aulosteges magnicostatus Girty
A. medlicottianus Waagen
Camarophoria venusta Girty
Composita subtilita (Hall)
Derbyia nasuta Girty
Hustedia meekana (Shumard)
Lyttonia nobilis americanus (Girty)
Marginfera manzanica Girty = *Oncosarina spinicostata* Cooper and Grant
M. reticulata King = *Spyridiophora reticulata* (King)
M. r. angusta King = *Glyptosteges angustus* (King)
M. sublaevis King [doubtful]
Meekella difficilis Girty
Productus ivesi Newberry = *Peniculauris* sp.?
P. leonardensis King [immature-doubtful]
Prorichthofenia likharewi King = *Hercosia* sp.?
Pugnoides bidentatus (Girty)
Rhipidomella transversa King = *Acosarina* sp.?
Scacchinella gigantea Schellwien [not *Scacchinella*] = ?
Spiriferina hilli Girty = *Paraspiriferina* sp.?

5. CATHEDRAL MOUNTAIN FORMATION

Meekella attenuata Girty
Neospirifer mexicanus latus King = *Cartorhium latum* (King)

6. ROAD CANYON FORMATION (LOWER)

Chonetes permianus Shumard [doubtful]
Hustedia mormoni papillata (Shumard) [doubtful]
Lyttonia nobilis americanus (Girty)
Marginifera popei (Shumard) [doubtful]
Martinia rhomboidalis Girty
Meekella skenoides Girty
Neospirifer pseudocameratus (Girty)
Productus multistriatus Meek = *Yakovlevia* sp.?
Rhynchopora taylori Girty = *Rhynchopora* sp.?

7. CATHEDRAL MOUNTAIN FORMATION

Composita subtilita (Hall)
Hustedia meekana (Shumard)

Lyttonia hortoni King = *Coscinophora hortoni* (King)
Marginifera cristobalensis Girty = *Oncosarina* sp.?
Neospirifer bakeri King [doubtful]
Productus ivesi Newberry = *Peniculauris* sp.?
P. leonardensis King = *Institella leonardensis* (King)
P. occidentalis Newberry = *Rugatia* sp.?
Prorichthofenia likharewi King = *Hercosia uddeni* (Böse)
P. uddeni (Böse) = *Hercosia uddeni* (Böse)
Squamularia guadalupensis (Shumard) = *Neophricadothyris* sp.?
Uncinuloides guadalupensis (Shumard) = *Torynechus* sp.?

8. SKINNER RANCH FORMATION AND CATHEDRAL MOUNTAIN FORMATION [mixture]

Aulosteges magnicostatus Girty
A. triagonalis King = *Agelesia triagonalis* (King)
Camarophoria venusta Girty
Chonetes permianus Shumard [doubtful]
Composita subtilita (Hall)
Derbyia nasuta Girty
Enteletes liumbonus King [doubtful]
E. plummeri King
Hustedia meekana (Shumard)
Linoproductus waagenianus (Girty) = *Megousia* sp.?
Lyttonia nobilis americanus (Girty)
Marginifera cristobalensis Girty
Martinia rhomboidalis Girty
Meekella grandis King = *M. occidentalis* (Newberry)
Neospirifer mexicanus latus (King) = *Cartorhium latum* (King)
N. pseudocameratus (Girty)
Productus leonardensis King = *Institella leonardensis* (King)
Prorichthofenia likharewi King = *Hercosia uddeni* (Böse)
P. uddeni (Böse) = *Hercosia uddeni* (Böse)
Rhipidomella hessensis King
Squamularia guadalupensis (Shumard) = *Neophricadothyris* sp.?
Striatifera pinniformis (Girty) = *Compressoproductus* sp.?

9. CATHEDRAL MOUNTAIN FORMATION

Aulosteges triagonalis King = *Agelesia triagonalis* (King)
Camarophoria venusta Girty
Chonetes permianus Shumard [doubtful]
Composita subtilita (Hall)
Lyttonia nobilis americanus (Girty)
Marginifera manzanica Girty
Martinia rhomboidalis Girty
Meekella grandis King = *M.* sp.?
Productus ivesi Newberry = *Peniculauris* sp.?
P. leonardensis King = *Institella leonardensis* (King)
P. schucherti King = *Xestosia schucherti* (King)
Prorichthofenia likharewi King = *Hercosia uddeni* (Böse)
P. uddeni (Böse) = *Hercosia uddeni* (Böse)

Squamularia guadalupensis (Shumard) = *Neophricado-thyris* sp.?

10. CATHEDRAL MOUNTAIN FORMATION

Camarophoria venusta Girty
Chonetes permianus Shumard [doubtful]
Composita subtilita (Hall)
Lyttonia nobilis americanus (Girty)
Martinia rhomboidalis Girty
Meekella grandis King = *M.* sp.?
*Productus leonardensis King = *Institella leonardensis* (King)
Prorichthofenia likharewi King = *Hercosia uddeni* (Böse)
P. uddeni (Böse) = *Hercosia uddeni* (Böse)
Squamularia guadalupensis (Shumard) = *Neophricado-thyris* sp.?

11. CATHEDRAL MOUNTAIN FORMATION

Camarophoria venusta Girty
Chonetes permianus Shumard [doubtful]
Composita subtilita (Hall)
Lyttonia nobilis americanus (Girty)
Martinia rhomboidalis Girty
Meekella grandis King = *M.* sp.?
*Productus leonardensis King = *Institella leonardensis* (King)
Prorichthofenia likharewi King = *Hercosia uddeni* (Böse)
P. uddeni (Böse) = *Hercosia uddeni* (Böse)
Squamularia guadalupensis (Shumard) = *Neophricado-thyris* sp.?

12. CATHEDRAL MOUNTAIN FORMATION

Ambocoelia guadalupensis Girty = *Crurithyris* sp.?
Camarophoria venusta Girty
Chonetes permianus Shumard [doubtful]
C. subliratus Girty [doubtful]
Composita subtilita (Hall)
Hustedia meekana (Shumard)
Linoproductus waagenianus (Girty) = *Megousia* sp.?
Lyttonia nobilis americanus (Girty)
Marginifera cristobalensis Girty
M. reticulata angusta King [doubtful]
M. sublaevis King = *Anemonaria sublaevis* (King)
Martinia rhomboidalis Girty
Meekella attenuata Girty
M. grandis King = *M.* sp.?
Neospirifer mexicanus latus King = *Cartorhium latum* (King)
Productus leonardensis King = *Institella leonardensis* (King)
P. schucherti King = *Xestosia schucherti* (King)
Prorichthofenia likharewi King = *Hercosia uddeni* (Böse)
P. uddeni (Böse) = *Hercosia uddeni* (Böse)
Pugnoides bidentatus (Girty)
Rhipidomella leonardensis King = *Acosarina meso-platys* (King)

Squamularia guadalupensis (Shumard) = *Neophricado-thyris* sp.?

13. CATHEDRAL MOUNTAIN FORMATION

Camarophoria venusta Girty = *Stenoscisma triquetrum* Cooper and Grant
Chonetes permianus Shumard [doubtful]
Composita mira (Girty) [doubtful]
C. subtilita (Hall)
Linoproductus girtyi King = *Megousia* sp.?
Lyttonia nobilis americanus (Girty)
Marginifera cristobalensis Girty
Martinia rhomboidalis Girty
Meekella difficilis Girty
M. grandis King = *M.* sp.
*Productus leonardensis King = *Institella leonardensis* (King)
P. schucherti King = *Xestosia schucherti* (King)
Prorichthofenia likharewi King = *Hercosia uddeni* (Böse)
P. uddeni (Böse) = *Hercosia uddeni* (Böse)
Squamularia guadalupensis (Shumard) = *Neophricado-thyris* sp.?
Waagenoconcha montpelierensis (Girty) = *W.* sp.?

14. CATHEDRAL MOUNTAIN FORMATION

Camarophoria venusta Girty
Chonetes permianus Shumard [doubtful]
Composita subtilita (Hall)
Lyttonia nobilis americanus (Girty)
Martinia rhomboidalis Girty
Meekella attenuata Girty
M. grandis King = *M.* sp.?
Prorichthofenia likharewi King = *Hercosia uddeni* (Böse)
P. uddeni (Böse) = *Hercosia uddeni* (Böse)
Squamularia guadalupensis (Shumard) = *Neophricado-thyris* sp.?

15. SKINNER RANCH AND CATHEDRAL MOUNTAIN FORMATIONS [mixed]

Aulosteges medlicottianus Waagen
Camarophoria venusta Girty
Chonetes permianus Shumard [doubtful]
Composita subtilita (Hall)
Hustedia meekana (Shumard)
Linoproductus cora angustus King = *L. angustus* King
Lyttonia nobilis americanus (Girty)
Marginifera manzanica Girty
M. popei (Shumard) [doubtful]
M. reticulata angusta King [doubtful]
Meekella difficilis Girty
Neospirifer pseudocameratus (Girty)
*Parakeyserlingina fredericksi King = *Sceletonia crassa* Cooper and Grant
Productus ivesi Newberry = *Peniculauris* sp.?
P. leonardensis King = *Institella leonardensis* (King)
Pugnoides elegans (Girty) [doubtful]
Rhipidomella hessensis King

Scacchinella gigantea Schellwien = *S. titan* Cooper and Grant
Squamularia guadalupensis (Shumard) = *Neophricadothyris* sp.?
Waagenoconcha leonardensis King = *Rhamnaria leonardensis* (King)

16. SKINNER RANCH FORMATION

Camarophoria venusta Girty
Chonetes subliratus Girty [doubtful]
Composita subtilita (Hall)
Enteletes leonardensis King [doubtful]
Linoproductus girtyi King = *Megousia* sp.?
Marginifera cristobalensis Girty = *Oncosarina* sp.?
M. reticulata King = *Spyridiophora reticulata* (King)
Martinia rhomboidalis Girty
Prorichthofenia likharwei King = *Hercosia* sp.?
Pugnoides bidentatus (Girty)
Striatifera pinniformis (Girty) = *Compressoproductus* sp.?
*Uncinuloides guadalupensis (Shumard) = *Torynechus caelatus* Cooper and Grant

This location is not in accordance with that given on R. E. King's map. The map location is near the base of the hill, at the west end, 0.9 mi S 6° W of the top of hill 5021, which is the third hill west of Iron Mountain. The faunal list suggests the same level as that at King's locality 3 which is on the line of section 15 or very close to it, probably at the top of the Skinner Ranch Formation.

17. SKINNER RANCH FORMATION (SULLIVAN PEAK MEMBER) = USNM 707

Enteletes liumbonus King
Geyerella americana Girty = *G. hessi* Cooper and Grant
Meekella hessensis King
Productus ivesi Newberry = *Peniculauris* sp.?
Streptorhynchus undulatum King = *Tropidelasma undulatum* (King)

17a. SKINNER RANCH FORMATION (SULLIVAN PEAK MEMBER) = USNM 707

Hustedia meekana (Shumard)
Linoproductus waagenianus (Girty) = *Megousia* sp.?
Marginifera? whitei King = *Oncosarina* sp.?
Rhipidomella transversa King = *Acosarina mesoplatys* (King)
Scacchinella gigantea Schellwien = *S. titan* Cooper and Grant

17b. SKINNER RANCH FORMATION (SULLIVAN PEAK MEMBER)

Lyttonia hortoni King = *Coscinophora* sp.?
Prorichthofenia likharwei King = ?
Pugnoides pinguis (Girty) = *Antronaria* sp.?

17c. SKINNER RANCH FORMATION (SULLIVAN PEAK MEMBER)

Pugnoides pinguis (Girty) = *Antronaria* sp.?

19. SKINNER RANCH FORMATION (POPLAR TANK MEMBER)

Composita subtilita (Hall)
Hustedia meekana (Shumard)
*Parakeyserlingina fredericksi King = *Eolyttonia* sp.?

20. SKINNER RANCH FORMATION (POPLAR TANK MEMBER)

Chonetes subliratus Girty = *Dyoros* sp.?
Composita subtilita (Hall)
Marginifera manzanica Girty = *Oncosarina* sp.
M. wabashensis (Norwood and Pratten) [doubtful]
Meekella difficilis Girty
Prorichthofenia uddeni (Böse) = *Hercosia uddeni* (Böse)
Rhipidomella mesoplatys King = *Acosarina* sp.?

21. CATHEDRAL MOUNTAIN FORMATION (THIRD AND FOURTH LIMESTONE MEMBERS)

Composita mira (Girty) [doubtful]
Marginifera cristobalensis Girty
M. manzanica Girty
Martinia rhomboidalis Girty
Productus ivesi Newberry = *Peniculauris* sp.?
P. leonardensis King [doubtful]
Prorichthofenia uddeni (Böse) = *Hercosia uddeni* (Böse)
Striatifera pinniformis (Girty) = *Compressoproductus* sp.?

22. CATHEDRAL MOUNTAIN FORMATION

Camarophoria venusta Girty
Meekella attenuata Girty
M. difficilis Girty
Productus ivesi Newberry = *Peniculauris subcostata* (King)
Waagenoconcha leonardensis King = *Rhamnaria leonardensis* (King)

23. CATHEDRAL MOUNTAIN FORMATION

Aulosteges medlicottianus Waagen
Composita subtilita (Hall)
Linoproductus girtyi King = *Megousia* sp.?
Marginifera cristobalensis Girty
Prorichthofenia likharewi King = ?

24. SKINNER RANCH FORMATION

Composita subtilita (Hall)
Linoproductus girtyi King = *Megousia* sp.?
Lyttonia nobilis americanus (Girty)
*Marginifera manzanica Girty = *Oncosarina* sp.
*M. reticulata King = *Spyridiophora reticulata* (King)
M. r. angusta King = *Glyptosteges angustus* (King)
Meekella attenuata Girty
M. difficilis Girty
Neospirifer costella King = *Lepidospirifer costellus* (King)
Productus ivesi Newberry = *Peniculauris* sp.?
Prorichthofenia uddeni (Böse) = *Hercosia uddeni* (Böse)
Pugnoides bidentatus (Girty)

Squamularia guadalupensis (Shumard) = *Neophricadothyris* sp.?

**Uncinuloides guadalupensis* (Shumard) = *Torynechus caelatus* Cooper and Grant

25. CATHEDRAL MOUNTAIN FORMATION

Ambocoelia guadalupensis Girty = *Crurithyris* sp.?
Aulosteges magnicostatus Girty
Hustedia meekana (Shumard)
Linoproductus waagenianus (Girty) = *Megousia* sp.?
Pugnoides bidentatus (Girty)

26. CATHEDRAL MOUNTAIN FORMATION

Aulosteges magnicostatus Girty
Camarophoria venusta Girty
Hustedia meekana (Shumard)
Lyttonia nobilis americanus (Girty)
Marginifera cristobalensis Girty
Neospirifer pseudocameratus (Girty)
Pugnoides pinguis (Girty)

26s. CATHEDRAL MOUNTAIN FORMATION

Aulosteges magnicostatus Girty
Buxtonia victorioensis King = *Kochiproductus* sp.?
Camarophoria venusta Girty
Chonetes permianus Shumard [doubtful]
Composita subtilita (Hall)
Enteletes leonardensis King
Marginifera manzanica Girty
M. reticulata King = *Spyridiophora reticulata* (King)
M. r. angusta King = *Glyptosteges angustus* (King)
Martinia rhomboidalis Girty
Meekella difficilis Girty
Neospirifer mexicanus latus King = *Cartorhium latum* (King)
N. pseudocameratus (Girty)
Prorichthofenia likharewi King = *Hercosia* sp.?
Pugnoides bidentatus (Girty)
Rhipidomella leonardensis = *Acosarina mesoplatys* (King)
R. mesoplatys King = *Acosarina mesoplatys* (King)
Squamularia guadalupensis (Shumard) = *Neophricadothyris* sp.?
Streptorhynchus pygmaeum Girty [doubtful]
Striatifera pinniformis (Girty) = *Compressoproductus* sp.?

27. CATHEDRAL MOUNTAIN FORMATION

Aulosteges magnicostatus Girty
Marginifera manzanica Girty
Meekella difficilis Girty

28. CATHEDRAL MOUNTAIN FORMATION

Aulosteges magnicostatus Girty
Enteletes leonardensis King

29. CATHEDRAL MOUNTAIN FORMATION

Aulosteges magnicostatus Girty

30. CATHEDRAL MOUNTAIN FORMATION

Camarophoria venusta Girty
Uncinuloides guadalupensis (Shumard) = *Torynechus caelatus* Cooper and Grant

31. CATHEDRAL MOUNTAIN FORMATION = USNM 710f

Ambocoelia guadalupensis Girty = *Crurithyris* sp.?
Aulosteges magnicostatus Girty
Avonia subhorrida rugatula (Girty) = *Echinauris* sp.?
Camarophoria venusta Girty
Chonetes permianus Shumard [doubtful]
C. subliratus Girty [doubtful]
Composita subtilita (Hall)
Lyttonia nobilis americanus (Girty)
Marginifera cristobalensis Girty
Meekella attenuata Girty
Productus ivesi Newberry = *Peniculauris subcostata* (King)
**P. leonardensis* King = ?
**P. schucherti* King = ?
Prorichthofenia likharewi King = *Hercosia uddeni* (Böse)
Uncinuloides guadalupensis (Shumard) = *Torynechus caelatus* Cooper and Grant

32. ROAD CANYON FORMATION

Lyttonia nobilis americanus (Girty)

33. [Formation uncertain]

Lyttonia nobilis americanus (Girty)

34. [Formation uncertain]

Martinia rhomboidalis Girty
Prorichthofenia likharewi King = *Hercosia uddeni* (Böse)
Striatifera pinniformis (Girty) = *Compressoproductus* sp.?

35. SKINNER RANCH FORMATION (DECIE RANCH MEMBER) = part of USNM 707a

Aulosteges magnicostatus Girty
Composita subtilita (Hall)
Enteletes dumblei Girty = *E. rotundobesus* Cooper and Grant
Geyerella americana Girty = *G. hessi* Cooper and Grant
Marginifera cristobalensis Girty = *Oncosarina rotundata* Cooper and Grant
M. manzanica Girty = *Oncosarina* sp.
Meekella attenuata Girty = *M. hessensis* (King)
Prorichthofenia likharewi King = *Cyclacantharia gigantea* Cooper and Grant
Scacchinella gigantea Schellwien = *S. titan* Cooper and Grant

37. CATHEDRAL MOUNTAIN FORMATION

**Aulosteges triagonalis* King = *Agelesia triagonalis* (King)
Composita subtilita (Hall)
Enteletes leonardensis King

Hustedia meekana (Shumard)
Linoproductus girtyi King = *Megousia* sp.?
L. waagenianus (Girty) = *Megousia* sp.?
Lyttonia nobilis americanus (Girty)
Marginifera cristobalensis Girty
M. manzanica Girty
Meekella attenuata Girty
Neospirifer pseudocameratus (Girty)
Productus ivesi Newberry = *Peniculauris subcostata* (King)
P. leonardensis King = probably *Institella*
Prorichthofenia likharewi King = *Hercosia uddeni* (Böse)
Striatifera pinniformis (Girty) = *Compressoproductus thomasi* Cooper and Grant
Uncinuloides guadalupensis (Shumard) = *Torynechus caelatus* Cooper and Grant

38. SKINNER RANCH FORMATION AND CATHEDRAL MOUNTAIN FORMATION [mixed] = approximately USNM 708e

Aulosteges magnicostatus Girty
A. medlicottianus Waagen
Composita subtilita (Hall)
Derbyia nasuta Girty
Lyttonia nobilis americanus (Girty)
Marginifera manzanica Girty
M. popei (Shumard) [doubtful]
M. reticulata angusta King [doubtful]
Meekella difficilis Girty
Productus ivesi Newberry = *Peniculauris* sp.?
P. schucherti King = *Xestosia* sp.?
Prorichthofenia likharewi King = *Hercosia uddeni* (Böse)
Pugnoides bidentatus (Girty)
Striatifera pinniformis (Girty) = *Compressoproductus* sp.?
Waagenoconcha leonardensis King = *Rhamnaria leonardensis* (King)

39. SKINNER RANCH FORMATION (DECIE RANCH MEMBER) = approximately USNM 727u

Derbyia nasuta Girty
Linoproductus waagenianus (Girty) = *Megousia* sp.?
Marginifera reticulata angusta King = *Glyptosteges angustus* (King)?
Productus ivesi Newberry = *Peniculauris* sp.?
Prorichthofenia likharewi King = *Hercosia* sp.?

42. CAPITAN FORMATION (ALTUDA MEMBER)

Hustedia meekana (Shumard) [doubtful]

43. CAPITAN FORMATION (ALTUDA MEMBER)

Composita emarginata affinis Girty
Hustedia meekana (Shumard)
Marginifera popei (Shumard)
Martinia rhomboidalis Girty
Punctospirifer billingsi (Shumard)

44. ROAD CANYON FORMATION = approximately USNM 731v

Aulosteges medlicottianus Waagen = *Edriosteges multispinosus* Muir-Wood and Cooper
Avonia subhorrida rugatula (Girty) = *Costispinifera rugatula* (Girty)
Camarophoria venusta Girty
Chonetes subliratus Girty [doubtful]
Composita mira (Girty) [doubtful]
Hustedia meekana (Shumard)
H. pusilla (Girty) [doubtful]
Meekella skenoides Girty
Neospirifer pseudocameratus (Girty)
Prorichthofenia permiana (Shumard) = *Cyclacantharia* sp.?

45. ROAD CANYON FORMATION

Camarophoria venusta Girty = *Stenoscisma* sp.?
Composita mira (Girty) [doubtful]
Hustedia meekana (Shumard)
H. pusilla (Girty) [doubtful]
Linoproductus waagenianus (Girty) = *Megousia* sp.?
Meekella skenoides Girty
Neospirifer pseudocameratus (Girty) = *N. bakeri* King
Prorichthofenia permiana (Shumard) = *Cyclacantharia* sp.?

46. ROAD CANYON FORMATION = USNM 707e

Aulosteges medlicottianus Waagen = *Edriosteges multispinosus* Muir-Wood and Cooper
Avonia? incurvata King = *Rugatia incurvata* (King)
A. subhorrida rugatula (Girty) = *Costispinifera rugatula* (Girty)
A. walcottiana (Girty) = *Echinauris* sp.?
Camarophoria venusta Girty
Cancrinella phosphatica (Girty) [doubtful]
Chonetes subliratus Girty = *Dyoros (Dyoros)* sp.?
Composita mira (Girty) [doubtful]
Derbyia nasuta Girty
Dielasma spatulatum Girty [doubtful]
Hustedia meekana (Shumard)
H. mormoni papillata (Shumard) [doubtful]
H. pusilla (Girty) [doubtful]
Linoproductus waagenianus (Girty) = *Megousia auriculata* Muir-Wood and Cooper
Marginifera popei (Shumard) = *Liosotella costata* Cooper and Grant
Meekella attenuata Girty
M. skenoides Girty = *M. calathica* Cooper and Grant
Neospirifer bakeri King = *N. bakeri bakeri* King
N. pseudocameratus (Girty) = *N. bakeri* King
Productus dartoni sullivanensis King = *Kutorginella sullivanensis* (King)
P. indicus Waagen = *Rugatia mckeei* Cooper and Grant
Prorichthofenia permiana (Shumard) = *Cyclacantharia* sp.?
Rhynchopora taylori Girty = *R. sphenoides* Cooper and Grant

Spiriferina laxa Girty = *Metriolepis* sp.?

Squamularia guadalupensis (Shumard) = *Neophricado-thyris cordata* Cooper and Grant

47. **WORD FORMATION (WILLIS RANCH MEMBER)**

Composita emarginata affinis Girty [doubtful]

Derbyia nasuta Girty

Neospirifer pseudocameratus (Girty) = *N. amphigyus* Cooper and Grant

48. **WORD FORMATION (WILLIS RANCH MEMBER)**

Lyttonia nobilis americanus (Girty)

Productus leonardensis King = *Institella leonardensis* (King)

50. **CAPITAN FORMATION**

Avonia subhorrida rugatula (Girty) = *Costispinifera rugatula* (Girty)

Composita emarginata affinis Girty [doubtful]

Hustedia meekana (Shumard)

Marginifera opima (Girty) [doubtful]

Punctospirifer billingsi (Shumard) [doubtful]

51. **ROAD CANYON FORMATION = near USNM 724a**

Composita mira (Girty) [doubtful]

Hustedia meekana (Shumard)

H. pusilla (Girty) [doubtful]

Lyttonia nobilis americanus (Girty)

Meekella attenuata Girty

Uncinuloides guadalupensis (Shumard) = *Rhyncho-pora* sp.?

53. **ROAD CANYON FORMATION = USNM 710m**

Aulosteges beedei King = *Echinosteges tuberculatus* (King)

Hustedia pusilla (Girty) [doubtful]

54. **ROAD CANYON FORMATION**

Avonia subhorrida rugatula (Girty) = *Costispinifera rugatula* (Girty)

Chonetes subliratus Girty

Composita mira (Girty) [doubtful]

Derbyia? crenulata Girty [doubtful]

Hustedia meekana (Shumard)

H. mormoni papillata (Shumard) [doubtful]

H. pusilla (Girty) [doubtful]

Linoproductus girtyi King = *Megousia* sp.?

L. waagenianus (Girty) = *Megousia auriculata* Muir-Wood and Cooper

Lyttonia nobilis americanus (Girty)

L. hortoni King = *Coscinophora magnifica* Cooper and Grant

Marginifera opima (Girty) [doubtful]

M. popei (Shumard) [doubtful]

Meekella attenuata Girty

Neospirifer pseudocameratus (Girty) = *N. bakeri* King

Prorichthofenia permiana (Shumard) = *Cyclacantharia* sp.?

Punctospirifer billingsi (Shumard) [doubtful]

Rhynchopora taylori Girty = *R. sphenoides* Cooper and Grant

Rhipidomella mesoplatys King [doubtful]

Squamularia guadalupensis (Shumard) = *Neophricado-thyris cordata* Cooper and Grant

Uncinuloides guadalupensis (Shumard) = *Rhynchopora* sp.?

55. **WORD FORMATION (UPPER)**

Avonia walcottiana costata King? = *Costispinifera* sp.?

Composita persinuata (Meek) [doubtful]

Derbyia nasuta Girty

Hustedia meekana (Shumard)

Lyttonia nobilis americanus (Girty)

Marginifera popei (Shumard) = *Liosotella* sp.?

Meekella attenuata Girty

Prorichthofenia permiana (Shumard) = *Cyclacantharia* sp.?

57. **CAPITAN FORMATION (ALTUDA MEMBER) = USNM 718a.**

Camarophoria? indentata (Shumard) [doubtful]

Lyttonia nobilis americanus (Girty)

Martinia rhomboidalis Girty

Squamularia guadalupensis (Shumard)

58. **ROAD CANYON FORMATION**

Aulosteges guadalupensis Shumard = *Rhamnaria* sp.?

Lyttonia nobilis americanus (Girty)

Neospirifer bakeri King

N. pseudocameratus (Girty) = *N. bakeri* King

Productus indicus Waagen = *Rugatia mckeei* Cooper and Grant

70. **LENOX HILLS FORMATION = USNM 708n**

Aulosteges medlicottianus Waagen = *Limbella wolf-campensis* (King)

Meekella irregularis texana King = *M. texana* King

71. **SKINNER RANCH FORMATION (DECIE RANCH MEMBER) = USNM 707g, 707v**

Aulosteges wolfcampensis King = *Limbella wolfcam-pensis* (King)

Orthotetina cf. *Orthotetes mutabilis* Girty? = young *Geyerella* sp.?

Parakeyserlingina fredericksi King = *Eolyttonia* sp.?

Scacchinella gigantea Schellwien = *S. titan* Cooper and Grant

Teguliferina bösei King = *Acritosia* sp.?

75. **GAPTANK FORMATION**

Buxtonia occidentalis King = *Kochiproductus occidentalis* (King)

Chonetes verneuilianus Norwood and Pratten [doubtful]

Hustedia mormoni (Marcou)

Linoproductus (Cancrinella) villiersi (d'Orbigny) = *Cancrinella* sp.?

L. cora (d'Orbigny) = *L.* sp.?

Marginifera wabashensis (Norwood and Pratten) = *Hystriculina* sp.?

*Martinia wolfcampensis King = *Composita* sp.?

Meekella attenuata Girty

Neospirifer triplicatus (Hall)

Orthotetina cf. *Orthotetes mutabilis* Girty = ?

Rhipidomella carbonaria (Swallow) = *R.* sp.?

76. LENOX HILLS FORMATION

Camarophoria venusta Girty

77. LENOX HILLS FORMATION

Martinia rhomboidalis Girty

Neospirifer triplicatus (Hall)

82. CATHEDRAL MOUNTAIN FORMATION

Camarophoria venusta Girty

Chonetes subliratus Girty

Composita subtilita (Hall)

Hustedia meekana (Shumard)

Marginifera cristobalensis Girty

M. sublaevis King = *Anemonaria sublaevis* (King)

*Productus leonardensis King = *Institella leonardensis* (King)

Rhipidomella leonardensis King = *Acosarina* sp.?

Squamularia guadalupensis (Shumard) = *Neophricadothyris* sp.?

83. CATHEDRAL MOUNTAIN FORMATION

Leonard:

*Aulosteges triagonalis King = [not this species = ?]

Chonetes subliratus Girty

Composita subtilita (Hall)

Linoproductus waagenianus (Girty) = *Megousia* sp.?

Marginifera cristobalensis Girty

M. sublaevis King = *Anemonaria sublaevis* (King)

Productus ivesi Newberry = *Peniculauris* sp.?

*P. leonardensis King = *Institella leonardensis* (King)

Prorichthofenia likharewi King = *Hercosia uddeni* (Böse)

Streptorhynchus lamellatum King = *Diplanus lamellatus* (King)

*Uncinuloides guadalupensis (Shumard) = *Rhynchopora* sp.?

Waagenoconcha leonardensis King = *Rhamnaria leonardensis* (King)

Wolfcamp:

Hustedia meekana (Shumard)

Productus wolfcampensis King = *Limbella wolfcampensis* (King)

Squamularia guadalupensis (Shumard) = *Neophricadothyris* sp.?

85. LENOX HILLS FORMATION

Aulosteges wolfcampensis King = *Limbella wolfcampensis* (King)

Geyerella americana Girty = *G. kingorum* Cooper and Grant

Orthotetella wolfcampensis King

Spirifer condor d'Orbigny = *Gypospirifer anancites* Cooper and Grant

Teguliferina bösei King = *T. boesei* King

86. LENOX HILLS FORMATION

Aulosteges wolfcampensis King = *Limbella wolfcampensis* (King)

Rhipidomella carbonaria (Swallow) = *R.* sp.?

87. NEAL RANCH FORMATION = USNM 701d

Aulosteges wolfcampensis King = *Limbella wolfcampensis* (King)

Avonia boulei (Kozlowski) = *Echinauris interrupta* Cooper and Grant

Chonetes verneuilianus Norwood and Pratten [doubtful]

Hustedia mormoni (Marcou)

Linoproductus cora (d'Orbigny) = *L.* sp.?

Martinia wolfcampensis King

Meekella striatocostata (Cox) = *M. prionota* Cooper and Grant

Neospirifer triplicatus (Hall)

Orthotetella wolfcampensis King

Parakeyserlingina fredericksi King = *Eolyttonia* sp.?

Productus semireticulatus hermosanus Girty = *Reticulatia* sp.?

Rhipidomella carbonaria (Swallow) = *R.* sp.?

Strophalosia hystricula Girty [doubtful]

Teguliferina bösei King = *T. boesei* King

88. GAPTANK FORMATION (*Uddenites*-BEARING SHALE MEMBER)

Ambocoelia planoconvexa (Shumard) = *Crurithyris tumibilis* Cooper and Grant

Aulosteges wolfcampensis King = *Limbella wolfcampensis* (King)

Chonetes granulifer Owen = *Neochonetes* sp.?

Composita subtilita (Hall)

Hustedia mormoni (Marcou)

Linoproductus (*Cancrinella*) *villiersi* (d'Orbigny) = *Cancrinella* sp.?

Marginifera capaci (d'Orbigny) = *Kozlowskia* sp.?

M. lasallensis (Worthen) = *Kutorginella uddeni* Cooper and Grant

Martinia wolfcampensis King

Meekella irregularis texana King = *M. texana* King

Neospirifer triplicatus (Hall)

N. texanus (Meek) = *Eridmatus marathonensis* Cooper and Grant

Orthotetella wolfcampensis King

Overtonia cristato-tuberculata (Kozlowski)? = *Fimbrinia plummeri* (R. H. King)

Parenteletes cooperi King

Productus semireticulatus hermosanus Girty = *Reticulatia* sp.?

Pustula semipunctata (Shepard) = *Echinaria* sp.?

Rhipidomella carbonaria (Swallow) = *R.* sp.?

Spirifer condor d'Orbigny = *Gypospirifer* sp.?

Streptorhynchus pyramidale King = *Chelononia straminea* Cooper and Grant

Teguliferina bösei King = *T. boesei* King

88s. GAPTANK FORMATION (*Uddenites*-BEARING SHALE MEMBER) = approximately USNM 701p

Wolfcamp: *Uddenites* zone at Wolfcamp

Ambocoelia planoconvexa (Shumard) = *Crurithyris tumibilis* Cooper and Grant

Aulosteges wolfcampensis King = *Limbella wolfcampensis* (King)

Chonetes granulifer Owen = *Neochonetes* sp.?

Linoproductus cora (d'Orbigny) = *L.* sp.?

Marginifera lasallensis (Worthen) = *Kutorginella uddeni* Cooper and Grant

M. capaci (d'Orbigny) [doubtful]

M. wabashensis (Norwood and Pratten) = *Hystriculina* sp.?

Martinia wolfcampensis King

Meekella irregularis texana King = *M. texana* King

Neospirifer triplicatus (Hall) = *N.* sp.

Productus semireticulatus hermosanus Girty = *Reticulatia* sp.?

P. semistriatus Meek = *Nudauris reticulata* Cooper and Grant

Pustula semipunctata (Shepard) = *Echinaria* sp.?

Rhynchopora illinoisensis (Worthen) = *R. molina* Cooper and Grant

Spirifer (Neospirifer) texanus (Meek) = *Eridmatus marathonensis* Cooper and Grant

Squamularia perplexa (McChesney) = *Neophricadothyris transversa* Cooper and Grant

89. NEAL RANCH FORMATION

Chonetes granulifer Owen = *Neochonetes* sp.?

Composita subtilita (Hall)

Hustedia mormoni (Marcou)

Marginifera wabashensis (Norwood and Pratten) = *Hystriculina* sp.?

Neospirifer triplicatus (Hall)

N. texanus (Meek) = *Eridmatus marathonensis* Cooper and Grant

Orthotetella wolfcampensis King

Parenteletes cooperi King

Productus semireticulatus hermosanus Girty = *Reticulatia* sp.?

Punctospirifer kentuckyensis (Shumard) = *Reticulariina* sp.?

90. NEAL RANCH FORMATION

Aulosteges wolfcampensis King = *Limbella wolfcampensis* (King)

Composita subtilita (Hall)

Hustedia mormoni (Marcou)

Linoproductus cora (d'Orbigny) = *L.* sp.?

Meekella grandis King = *M. magnifica* Cooper and Grant

M. irregularis texana King = *M. texana* King

Orthotetella wolfcampensis King

Orthotichia kozlowskii King

Productus semistriatus Meek = *Nudauris* sp.?

Rhipidomella carbonaria (Swallow) = *R.* sp.?

Rhynchopora illinoisensis (Worthen) = *R. molina* Cooper and Grant

Squamularia perplexa (McChesney) = *Neophricadothyris transversa* Cooper and Grant

Teguliferina bösei King = *T. boesei* King

91. NEAL RANCH FORMATION

Buxtonia occidentalis King = *Kochiproductus occidentalis* (King)

Chonetes spinoliratus King = *Chonetinella spinolirata* (King)

Derbyia buchi (d'Orbigny) = *D. carteri* Cooper and Grant

Dielasma bovidens (Morton) = *Beecheria* sp.?

Hustedia mormoni (Marcou)

Marginifera capaci (d'Orbigny) = *Kozlowskia* sp.?

Neospirifer triplicatus (Hall)

N. texanus (Meek) = *Eridmatus marathonensis* Cooper and Grant

Orthotetina cf. *Orthotetes mutabilis* Girty = *Geyerella kingorum* Cooper and Grant

Productus semireticulatus hermosanus Girty = *Reticulatia* sp.?

92. NEAL RANCH FORMATION = USNM 701c

Aulosteges wolfcampensis King = *Limbella wolfcampensis* (King)

Chonetes spinoliratus King = *Chonetinella spinolirata* (King)

Composita subtilita (Hall)

Linoproductus cora (d'Orbigny) = *L.* sp.?

Marginifera capaci (d'Orbigny) = *Kozlowskia* sp.?

Meekella irregularis texana King = *M. texana* King

Neospirifer texanus (Meek) = *Eridmatus marathonensis* Cooper and Grant

Orthotetella wolfcampensis King

Orthotichia kozlowskii King

Productus semireticulatus hermosanus Girty = *Reticulatia* sp.?

P. semistriatus Meek = *Nudauris reticulata* Cooper and Grant

93. NEAL RANCH FORMATION

Aulosteges wolfcampensis King = *Limbella wolfcampensis* (King)

Avonia boulei (Kozlowski) = *Echinauris interrupta* Cooper and Grant

Buxtonia occidentalis King = *Kochiproductus occidentalis* (King)

Camarophoria theveneni Kozlowski = *Stenoscisma* sp.?

Composita subtilita (Hall)

Derbyia buchi (d'Orbigny) = *D. carteri* Cooper and Grant

Enteletes dumblei Girty [doubtful]

E. wolfcampensis King

Hustedia mormoni (Marcou) = *H. trita* Cooper and Grant

Linoproductus cora (d'Orbigny) = *L.* sp.?

Marginifera capaci (d'Orbigny) = *Kozlowskia* sp.?

Martinia wolfcampensis King

Meekella irregularis texana King = *M. texana* King

M. striatocostata (Cox) = *M. prionota* Cooper and Grant

Neospirifer triplicatus (Hall)

Orthotetella wolfcampensis King

Parakeyserlingina fredericksi King = *Eolyttonia* sp.

Productus gratiosus occidentalis Schellwien = *Spyridiophora distincta* Cooper and Stehli

P. semireticulatus hermosanus Girty = *Reticulatia* sp.

P. semistriatus Meek? = *Nudauris splendens* Cooper and Grant

Rhipidomella carbonaria (Swallow) = *R.* sp.?

Squamularia guadalupensis (Shumard) = *Neophricadothyris* sp.?

Streptorhynchus pyramidale King = *Chelononia straminea* Cooper and Grant

Teguliferina bösei King = *T. boesei* King

93s. NEAL RANCH FORMATION

Aulosteges wolfcampensis King = *Limbella wolfcampensis* (King)

Avonia boulei (Kozlowski) = *Echinauris interrupta* Cooper and Grant

Derbyia buchi (d'Orbigny) = *D. carteri* Cooper and Grant

Enteletes wolfcampensis King

Linoproductus cora (d'Orbigny) = *L.* sp.?

Marginifera capaci (d'Orbigny) = *Kozlowskia* sp.?

Meekella irregularis texana King = *M. texana* King

M. striatocostata (Cox) = *M. prionota* Cooper and Grant

Neospirifer triplicatus (Hall)

Productus semistriatus Meek = *Nudauris* sp.?

Pustula semipunctata (Shepard) = *Echinaria* sp.?

Squamularia guadalupensis (Shumard) = *Neophricadothyris transversa* Cooper and Grant

Strophalosia hystricula Girty = *Heteralosia?* sp.?

94. GAPTANK FORMATION (*Uddenites*-BEARING SHALE MEMBER)

Ambocoelia planoconvexa (Shumard) = *Crurithyris tumibilis* Cooper and Grant

Aulosteges wolfcampensis King = *Linoproductus* sp.?

Camarophoria venusta Girty

Chonetes verneuilianus Norwood and Pratten = *Chonetinella* sp.?

Hustedia mormoni (Marcou)

Marginifera wabashensis (Norwood and Pratten) = *Hystriculina* sp.?

Martinia wolfcampensis King

Meekella irregularis texana = *M. texana* King

Neospirifer triplicatus (Hall)

Overtonia cristato-tuberculata (Kozlowski)? = *Fimbrinia plummeri* (R. H. King)

Parenteletes cooperi King

Productus semireticulatus hermosanus Girty = *Reticulatia* sp.

P. semistriatus Meek = *Nudauris splendens* Cooper and Grant

95. GAPTANK FORMATION (*Uddenites*-BEARING SHALE MEMBER) = USNM 721-1

Avonia boulei (Kozlowski) = *Echinauris interrupta* Cooper and Grant

Chonetes granulifer Owen = *Neochonetes* sp.?

Composita subtilita angusta King

Dielasma bovidens (Morton) = *Beecheria* sp.?

Marginifera lasallensis (Worthen) = *Kutorginella uddeni* Cooper and Grant

M. wabashensis (Norwood and Pratten) = *Hystriculina* sp.?

Martinia wolfcampensis King

Meekella irregularis texana King = *M. texana* King

Orthotetella wolfcampensis King

Parenteletes cooperi King

Squamularia perplexa (McChesney) = *Neophricadothyris transversa* Cooper and Grant

Teguliferina bösei King = *T. boesei* King

96. NEAL RANCH FORMATION

Martinia wolfcampensis King

98. SKINNER RANCH FORMATION (DECIE RANCH MEMBER)

Derbyia nasuta Girty

Linoproductus cora angustus King [doubtful]

Marginifera popei (Shumard) [doubtful]

Martinia rhomboidalis Girty

Meekella attenuata Girty

Rhipidomella hessensis King

100. SKINNER RANCH FORMATION (DECIE RANCH MEMBER)

Composita subtilita (Hall)

102. CATHEDRAL MOUNTAIN FORMATION

Lyttonia nobilis americanus (Girty)

Productus ivesi Newberry = *Peniculauris* sp.?

P. leonardensis King = *Institella leonardensis* (King)

Prorichthofenia likharewi King = *Hercosia uddeni* (Böse)

Pustula semipunctata (Shepard) [doubtful]

103. [Formation uncertain]

Lyttonia nobilis americanus (Girty)

Prorichthofenia likharewi King = *Hercosia* sp.?

104. CATHEDRAL MOUNTAIN FORMATION = USNM 713t

Aulosteges magnicostatus Girty

Camarophoria venusta Girty = *Stenoscisma triquetrum* Cooper and Grant

Composita subtilita (Hall)

Enteletes plummeri King

Marginifera cristobalensis Girty = *Echinauris irregularis* Cooper and Grant

M. manzanica Girty

Meekella difficilis Girty

Neospirifer huecoensis King [doubtful]

N. mexicanus latus (King) = *Cartorhium latum* (King)

Productus ivesi Newberry = *Peniculauris subcostata* (King)

*P. leonardensis King = Institella leonardensis (King)

Prorichthofenia likharewi King = Hercosia uddeni (Böse)

Pugnoides elegans (Girty) [doubtful]

Squamularia guadalupensis (Shumard) = Neophricadothyris bullata Cooper and Grant

*Uncinuloides guadalupensis (Shumard) = Torynechus caelatus Cooper and Grant

105. SKINNER RANCH FORMATION = approximately USNM 716s

Camarophoria venusta Girty

Enteletes liumbonus King [doubtful]

Hustedia hessensis King

H. meekana (Shumard)

Linoproductus cora angustus King = L. angustus King

Lyttonia nobilis americanus (Girty)

Marginifera cristobalensis Girty

Meekella grandis King = M. enormis Cooper and Grant

Productus ivsei Newberry = Peniculauris sp.?

Prorichthofenia teguliferoides King = Acritosia teguliferoides (King)

Pugnoides texanus (Shumard) [doubtful]

Rhipidomella hessensis King

Streptorhynchus lamellatum King = Diplanus lamellatus (King)

S. undulatum King = Tropidelasma sp.?

106. SKINNER RANCH FORMATION

Camarophoria venusta Girty

Composita subtilita (Hall)

Enteletes liumbonus King?

Hustedia hessensis King

Lyttonia nobilis americanus (Girty)

Marginifera manzanica Girty

M. sublaevis King [doubtful]

Productus hessensis King = Antiquatonia hessensis (King)

P. ivesi Newberry = Peniculauris sp.?

Prorichthofenia likharewi King [doubtful]

Pugnoides elegans (Girty) [doubtful]

Rhipidomella hessensis King

Scacchinella gigantea Schellwien = S. titan Cooper and Grant

Spiriferina angulata King = Crenispirifer angulatus (King)

Squamularia guadalupensis (Shumard) = Neophricadothyris sp.?

107. HESS FORMATION (TAYLOR RANCH MEMBER) = USNM 702d

Aulosteges medlicottianus Waagen = Edriosteges sp.?

Camarophoria venusta Girty = Stenoscisma pyraustoides Cooper and Grant

Chonetes hessensis King = Rugaria hessensis (King)

Composita subtilita (Hall)

Enteletes dumblei Girty = E. subcircularis Cooper and Grant

Hustedia meekana (Shumard) = H. cepacea Cooper and Grant

Linoproductus cora angustus King = L. undatus Cooper and Grant

Marginifera? whitei King = Oncosarina whitei (King)

Meekella attenuata Girty

Neospirifer huecoensis King = N. notialis Cooper and Grant

Productus hessensis King = Thamnosia silicica Cooper and Grant

P. ivesi Newberry = Peniculauris imitata Cooper and Grant

P. semireticulatus hermosanus Girty = Peniculauris sp.?

Prorichthofenia likharewi King = Hercosia sp.?

Pugnoides transversus King = Antronaria transversa (King)

Rhipidomella hessensis King

108. HESS FORMATION (TAYLOR RANCH MEMBER) = USNM 702m

Aulosteges medlicottianus Waagen = Edriosteges sp.?

Enteletes dumblei Girty = S. subcircularis Cooper and Grant

Lyttonia nobilis americanus (Girty)

Pugnoides elegans (Girty) = Antronaria speciosa Cooper and Grant

Scacchinella gigantea Schellwien = S. titan Cooper and Grant

112. HESS FORMATION

Composita mexicana (Hall) [doubtful]

113. LENOX HILLS FORMATION

Composita mexicana (Hall) [doubtful]

Linoproductus cora angustus King = L. angustus King

Productus ivesi Newberry [doubtful]

117. HESS FORMATION

Prorichthofenia likharewi King = ?

119. CATHEDRAL MOUNTAIN FORMATION

Composita subtilita (Hall)

Derbyia nasuta Girty

Productus ivesi Newberry = Peniculauris subcostata (King)

*P. leonardensis King = Institella leonardensis (King)

*P. schucherti King = Xestosia schucherti (King)

120. CATHEDRAL MOUNTAIN FORMATION = approximately USNM 721u

Aulosteges magnicostatus Girty = Chonosteges variabilis Cooper and Grant

A. medlicottianus Waagen = Edriosteges sp.?

A. subcostatus King = Peniculauris subcostata (King)

Camarophoria venusta Girty = Stenoscisma triquetrum Cooper and Grant

Composita subtilita (Hall)

Enteletes leonardensis King

Hustedia meekana (Shumard)

Linoproductus cora angustus King = *L. angustus* King
L. waagenianus (Girty) = *Megousia* sp.?
Lyttonia nobilis americanus (Girty)
*Marginifera cristobalensis Girty = *Echinauris irreg-ularis* Cooper and Grant
M. sublaevis King = *Anemonaria sublaevis* (King)
Martinia rhomboidalis Girty = *M. miranda* Cooper and Grant
Meekella attenuata Girty
M. difficilis Girty
Neospirifer mexicanus latus King = *Cartorhium latum* (King)
N. pseudocameratus (Girty) = *N. mansuetus* Cooper and Grant
Productus ivesi Newberry = *Peniculauris subcostata* (King)
*P. leonardensis King = *Institella leonardensis* (King)
*P. schucherti King = *Xestosia schucherti* (King)
Prorichthofenia likharewi King = *Hercosia uddeni* (Böse)
P. uddeni (Böse) (part) = *Hercosestria cribrosa* Cooper and Grant
Pugnoides pinguis (Girty) [doubtful]
P. bidentatus (Girty)
Rhipidomella leonardensis King = *Acosarina meso-platys* (King)
Squamularia guadalupensis (Shumard) = *Neophri-cadothyris bullata* Cooper and Grant
Striatifera pinniformis (Girty) = *Compressoproductus thomasi* Cooper and Grant
*Uncinuloides guadalupensis (Shumard) = *Torynechus caelatus* Cooper and Grant
Waagenoconcha leonardensis King = *Rhamnaria leonardensis* (King)
W. montpelierensis (Girty) = *Waagenoconcha* sp.?

121.   CATHEDRAL MOUNTAIN FORMATION

Aulosteges medlicottianus Waagen = *Edriosteges mul-tispinosus* Muir-Wood and Cooper
Lyttonia nobilis americanus (Girty)
Neospirifer pseudocameratus (Girty) = *N. thescelus* Cooper and Grant
Productus ivesi Newberry = *Peniculauris* sp.?
Prorichthofenia uddeni (Böse) = *Hercosia uddeni* (Böse)
Squamularia guadalupensis (Shumard) = *Neophri-cadothyris* sp.?

122.   SKINNER RANCH FORMATION

Meekella hessensis King
Spirifer marcoui infraplica King = *Gypospirifer in-fraplicus* (King)

123.   CATHEDRAL MOUNTAIN FORMATION = USNM 711q

Aulosteges beedei King = *Echinosteges beedei* (King)
A. magnicostatus Girty = *Chonosteges variabilis* Cooper and Grant
A. subcostatus King = *Peniculauris subcostata* (King)
Avonia subhorrida rugatula (Girty) = *Echinauris ir-regularis* Cooper and Grant

Camarophoria theveneni Kozlowski = *Stenoscisma doricranum* Cooper and Grant
Chonetes subliratus Girty
Composita mexicana (Hall) = *C. bucculenta* Cooper and Grant
C. mira (Girty) [doubtful]
Derbyia nasuta Girty
Enteletes leonardensis King
Hustedia meekana (Shumard)
Linoproductus waagenianus (Girty) = *Megousia* sp.?
Lyttonia nobilis americanus (Girty)
Marginifera cristobalensis Girty
M. sublaevis King = *Anemonaria sublaevis* (King)
Martinia rhomboidalis Girty
Meekella attenuata Girty
M. difficilis Girty
Neospirifer costella King = *Lepidospirifer costellus* (King)
N. mexicanus latus King = *Cartorhium latum* (King)
Productus ivesi Newberry = *Peniculauris subcostata* (King)
P. leonardensis King = *Institella leonardensis* (King)
P. occidentalis Newberry = *Rugatia paraindica* (McKee)
*P. schucherti King = *Xestosia schucherti* (King)
Prorichthofenia likharewi King = *Hercosia uddeni* (Böse)
Rhipidomella leonardensis King = *Acosarina meso-platys* (King)
R. mesoplatys King = *Acosarina mesoplatys* (King)
R. transversa King = *Acosarina mesoplatys* (King)
Spiriferina hilli Girty = *Paraspiriferina* sp.?

124.   CATHEDRAL MOUNTAIN FORMATION

Aulosteges medlicottianus Waagen = *Edriosteges* sp.?
Camarophoria venusta Girty = *Stenoscisma triquetrum* Cooper and Grant
Chonetes subliratus Girty
Composita mira (Girty) [doubtful]
C. subtilita angusta King
Derbyia nasuta Girty
Hustedia meekana (Shumard)
H. mormoni papillata (Shumard) [doubtful]
Lyttonia nobilis americanus (Girty)
Marginifera cristobalensis Girty
M. popei (Shumard) = *Liosotella* sp.?
M. sublaevis King = *Anemonaria sublaevis* (King)
Martinia rhomboidalis Girty
Meekella difficilis Girty
Neospirifer pseudocameratus (Girty) = *N. mansuetus* Cooper and Grant
Productus ivesi Newberry = *Peniculauris subcostata* (King)
*P. schucherti King = *Kutorginella* sp.?
Prorichthofenia likharewi King = *Hercosia uddeni* (Böse)
Pugnoides pinguis (Girty) = *Pontisia stehlii* Cooper and Grant
Squamularia guadalupensis (Shumard) = *Neophricado-thyris* sp.?

Waagenoconcha montpelierensis (Girty) = *Waagenoconcha* sp.?

125. CATHEDRAL MOUNTAIN FORMATION

Lyttonia nobilis americanus (Girty)
Linoproductus waggenianus (Girty) = *Megousia auriculata* Muir-Wood and Cooper
Marginifera cristobalensis Girty = *Echinauris irregularis* Cooper and Grant
M. sublaevis King = *Anemonaria sublaevis* (King)
Neospirifer pseudocameratus (Girty) = *N. mansuetus* Cooper and Grant

126. CATHEDRAL MOUNTAIN FORMATION

Composita mira (Girty) [doubtful]
Neospirifer costella King = *Lepidospirifer costellus* (King)
N. mexicanus latus King = *Cartorhium latum* (King)
Productus ivesi Newberry = *Peniculauris* sp.?
Prorichthofenia likharewi King = *Hercosia uddeni* (Böse)

127. CATHEDRAL MOUNTAIN FORMATION

Camarophoria venusta Girty
Meekella difficilis Girty

128. CATHEDRAL MOUNTAIN FORMATION = USNM 702

Aulosteges magnicostatus Girty = *Chonosteges variabilis* Cooper and Grant
Camarophoria venusta Girty = *Stenoscisma triquetrum* Cooper and Grant
Chonetes permianus Shumard [doubtful]
Composita mira (Girty) [doubtful]
Derbyia nasuta Girty
Enteletes leonardensis King
E. plummeri King
Hustedia meekana (Shumard)
H. mormoni papillata (Shumard) [doubtful]
Leiorhynchus bisulcatum (Shumard) [doubtful]
Lyttonia nobilis americanus (Girty) = *Collemataria gregaria* Cooper and Grant
Marginifera cristobalensis Girty = *Echinauris* sp.?
Meekella attenuata Girty
M. difficilis Girty
M. globosa King = *Niviconia globosa* (King)
Neospirifer mexicanus latus King = *Cartorhium latum* (King)
N. pseudocameratus (Girty) = *N. mansuetus* Cooper and Grant
Productus ivesi Newberry = *Peniculauris subcostata* (King)
*P. leonardensis King = *Institella leonardensis* (King)
*P. occidentalis Newberry = *Rugatia paraindica* (McKee)
*P. schucherti King = *Xestosia schucherti* (King)
Prorichthofenia likharewi King = *Hercosia uddeni* (Böse)
P. uddeni (Böse) = *Hercosia uddeni* (Böse)
Pugnoides bidentatus (Girty)

Squamularia guadalupensis (Shumard) = *Neophricadothyris bullata* Cooper and Grant
Strophalosia hystricula Girty = *Echinauris irregularis* Cooper and Grant
Uncinuloides guadalupensis (Shumard) = *Torynechus caelatus* Cooper and Grant

129. CATHEDRAL MOUNTAIN FORMATION

Chonetes subliratus Girty
Neospirifer pseudocameratus (Girty) = *N. mansuetus* Cooper and Grant

132. ROAD CANYON FORMATION

Meekella skenoides Girty
Productus dartoni sullivanensis King = *Kutorginella sullivanensis* (King)
Squamularia guadalupensis (Shumard) = *Neophricadothyris* sp.?

135. WORD FORMATION (WILLIS RANCH MEMBER)

Prorichthofenia permiana (Shumard) = *Cyclacantharia kingorum* Cooper and Grant

136. WORD FORMATION (WILLIS RANCH MEMBER)

Prorichthofenia permiana (Shumard) = *Cyclacantharia kingorum* Cooper and Grant

137. WORD FORMATION (WILLIS RANCH MEMBER)

Avonia subhorrida rugatula (Girty) = *Echinauris lateralis* Cooper and Grant
Enteletes dumblei Girty = *E. wordensis* King
Striatifera pinniformis (Girty) = *Compressoproductus* sp.?

138. WORD FORMATION (WILLIS RANCH MEMBER)

Avonia signata (Girty) = *Grandaurispina kingorum* Muir-Wood and Cooper
A. subhorrida rugatula (Girty) = *Costispinifera rugatula* (Girty)
Derbyia? crenulata Girty = ?
Linoproductus nasutus King
Neospirifer pseudocameratus (Girty) = *N. amphigyus* Cooper and Grant
Prorichthofenia permiana (Shumard) = *Cyclacantharia kingorum* Cooper and Grant

139. [Formation uncertain]

Chonetes subliratus Girty
Prorichthofenia permiana (Shumard) = *Cyclacantharia kingorum* Cooper and Grant

141. ROAD CANYON FORMATION

Enteletes dumblei Girty [doubtful]
Productus indicus Waagen = *Rugatia mckeei* Cooper and Grant
P. ivesi Newberry = *Peniculauris* sp.?
Squamularia guadalupensis (Shumard) = *Neophricadothyris* sp.?

142. WORD FORMATION (APPEL RANCH MEMBER)

Prorichthofenia permiana (Shumard) = *Cyclacantharia kingorum* Cooper and Grant
Spiriferina laxa Girty = *Reticulariina* sp.?

143. WORD FORMATION (APPEL RANCH MEMBER)

Avonia signata (Girty) = *Grandaurispina* sp.?
Hustedia mormoni papillata (Shumard) [doubtful]
Marginifera opima (Girty) = *Paucispinifera* sp.?
M. popei (Shumard) [doubtful]
Meekella skenoides Girty
Productus arcticus Whitfield = *Thamnosia phragmophora* Cooper and Grant

144. WORD FORMATION (WILLIS RANCH MEMBER) = approximately USNM 706e

Ambocoelia guadalupensis Girty = *Crurithyris tholiaphor* Cooper and Grant
Aulosteges guadalupensis Shumard = *Rhamnaria kingorum* Cooper and Grant
A. medlicottianus Waagen [doubtful]
A. tuberculatus King = *Echinosteges tuberculatus* (King)
Avonia meekana (Girty) = *Grandaurispina meekana* (Girty)
A. signata (Girty) = *Grandaurispina* sp.
A. walcottiana (Girty) = *Echinauris lateralis* Cooper and Grant
Camarophoria venusta Girty = *Stenoscisma renode* Cooper and Grant
Chonetes subliratus Girty = *Dyoros (Dyoros) extensus* Cooper and Grant
Composita emarginata affinis Girty = *C. enormis* Cooper and Grant
C. mira (Girty) [doubtful]
Derbyia nasuta Girty
Dielasma problematicum wordense King = *Texarina wordensis* (King) [not from this formation; see text page 2836]
D. schucherti minor King = *Pseudodielasma minor* (King)
D. spatulatum Girty [doubtful]
Elivina sulcifer (Shumard) = *Spiriferella gravis* Cooper and Grant
Hustedia meekana (Shumard) = *H. pugilla* Cooper and Grant
H. mormoni papillata (Shumard) [doubtful]
Leiorhynchus weeksi nobilis (Girty) = *Leiorhynchoidea amygdaloidea* Cooper and Grant
Linoproductus waagenianus (Girty) = *Megousia definita* Cooper and Grant
Lyttonia nobilis americanus (Girty) = *Collemataria elongata* Cooper and Grant
Marginifera opima (Girty) = *Paucispinifera auriculata* Muir-Wood and Cooper
M. popei (Shumard) = *Liosotella* sp.?
Meekella attenuata Girty
M. skenoides Girty

Neospirifer pseudocameratus (Girty) = *N. amphigyus* Cooper and Grant
Productus comancheanus Girty = *Paucispinifera* sp.?
P. multistriatus Meek = *Yakovlevia hessorum* Cooper and Grant
P. occidentalis Newberry [doubtful]
Prorichthofenia permiana (Shumard) = *Cyclacantharia kingorum* Cooper and Grant
Pugnoides swallovianus (Shumard) = *Wellerella girtyi* Cooper and Grant
Punctospirifer billingsi (Shumard) [doubtful]
Rhynchopora taylori Girty = *R. palumbula* Cooper and Grant
Spiriferina laxa Girty = *Reticulariina cerina* Cooper and Grant
Strophalosia hystricula Girty = *Heteralosia hystricula* (Girty)

145. WORD FORMATION (CHINA TANK MEMBER)

Chonetes quadratus King = *Dyoros (Tetragonetes) quadrangulatus* Cooper and Grant
C. subliratus Girty
Composita emarginata affinis Girty = *C. enormis* Cooper and Grant
Derbyia nasuta Girty
Linoproductus nasutus King
Lyttonia nobilis americanus (Girty) = *Collemataria elongata* Cooper and Grant
Marginifera opima (Girty) = *Liosotella* sp.?
Prorichthofenia permiana (Shumard) = *Cyclacantharia kingorum* Cooper and Grant

146. WORD FORMATION (WILLIS RANCH MEMBER)

Aulosteges guadalupensis Shumard = *Rhamnaria kingorum* Muir-Wood and Cooper
A. tuberculatus King = *Echinosteges tuberculatus* (King)
Avonia signata (Girty) = *Grandaurispina kingorum* Muir-Wood and Cooper
Elivina sulcifer (Shumard) = *Spiriferella gravis* Cooper and Grant
Lyttonia nobilis americanus (Girty) = *Collemataria elongata* Cooper and Grant
Neospirifer pseudocameratus (Girty) = *N. amphigyus* Cooper and Grant
Prorichthofenia permiana (Shumard) = *Cyclacantharia kingorum* Cooper and Grant
Waagenoconcha montpelierensis (Girty) = *W. magnifica* Cooper and Grant

147. ROAD CANYON FORMATION

Lyttonia nobilis americanus (Girty) = *Collemataria* sp.?
Meekella skenoides Girty

148. WORD FORMATION (APPEL RANCH MEMBER)

Aulosteges guadalupensis Shumard = *Rhamnaria kingorum* Muir-Wood and Cooper
Avonia signata (Girty) = *Grandaurispina kingorum* Muir-Wood and Cooper

Chonetes permianus Shumard [doubtful]
Dielasma spatulatum Girty [doubtful]
Elivina sulcifer (Shumard) = *Spiriferella clypeata* Cooper and Grant
Hustedia meekana (Shumard)
Lyttonia nobilis americanus (Girty)
Marginifera opima (Girty) [doubtful]
M. popei (Shumard) = *Liosotella* sp.?
Meekella attenuata Girty [doubtful]
M. skenoides Girty
Neospirifer pseudocameratus (Girty)
Productus guadalupensis Girty = *Yakovlevia indentata* Cooper and Grant
Prorichthofenia permiana (Shumard) = *Cyclacantharia kingorum* Cooper and Grant
Pugnoides swallovianus (Shumard) [doubtful]

150. WORD FORMATION (APPEL RANCH MEMBER)

Avonia signata (Girty) = *Grandaurispina* sp.?
A. subhorrida rugatula (Girty) = *Echinauris* sp.?
Camarophoria venusta Girty
Composita emarginata affinis Girty [doubtful]
Derbyia? crenulata Girty
Elivina sulcifer (Shumard) = *Spiriferella* sp.?
Meekella attenuata Girty
Neospirifer pseudocameratus (Girty)

151. CATHEDRAL MOUNTAIN FORMATION

Meekella globosa King = *Niviconia globosa* (King)

152. WORD FORMATION (APPEL RANCH MEMBER)

Aulosteges tuberculatus King = *Echinosteges tuberculatus* (King)
Lyttonia nobilis americanus (Girty)
Productus arcticus Whitfield = *Thamnosia phragmophora* Cooper and Grant
Prorichthofenia permiana (Shumard) = *Cyclacantharia kingorum* Cooper and Grant

153. ROAD CANYON FORMATION

Avonia signata (Girty) = *Grandaurispina* sp.?
Composita mira (Girty) [doubtful]
Derbyia? crenulata Girty = ?
Meekella attenuata Girty
M. skenoides Girty
Prorichthofenia permiana (Shumard) = *Cyclacantharia* sp.?

154. WORD FORMATION (UPPER)

Avonia signata (Girty) = *Grandaurispina* sp.?
Elivina sulcifer (Shumard) = *Spiriferella* sp.?
Enteletes dumblei Girty = *Enteletes wordensis* King
E. wordensis King
Hustedia meekana (Shumard)
Lyttonia nobilis americanus (Girty)
Marginifera opima (Girty) = *Paucispinifera* sp.?
M. popei (Shumard) = *Liosotella* sp.
Pugnoides elegans (Girty) [doubtful]

155. WORD FORMATION (UPPER)

Camarophoria venusta Girty
Composita persinuata (Meek) [doubtful]
Neospirifer pseudocameratus (Girty)
Productus guadalupensis Girty = *Yakovlevia* sp.?

158. WORD FORMATION (UPPER) [chert on hill 4732, Hess Canyon Quadrangle]

Elivina sulcifer (Shumard) = *Spiriferella* sp.?
Lyttonia nobilis americanus (Girty)

159. WORD FORMATION (UPPER)

Composita emarginata affinis Girty [doubtful]

162. WORD FORMATION (APPEL RANCH MEMBER)

Avonia signata (Girty) = *Grandaurispina* sp.?
Camarophoria venusta Girty
Composita emarginata affinis Girty [doubtful]
Hustedia meekana (Shumard)
Marginifera opima (Girty) = *Paucispinifera* sp.?
M. popei (Shumard) = *Liosotella* sp.?
M.? wordensis King = *Liosotella wordensis* (King)
Meekella skenoides Girty
Pugnoides swallovianus (Shumard) [doubtful]

168. NEAL RANCH FORMATION

Composita subtilita angusta King
Hustedia meekana (Shumard)

169a. NEAL RANCH FORMATION

Derbyia cymbula Hall and Clarke = *D. profunda* Cooper and Grant
Meekella irregularis texana King = *M. texana* King
Pustula semipunctata (Shepard) [doubtful]

170. WORD FORMATION (UPPER)

Meekella attenuata Girty
Squamularia guadalupensis (Shumard) = *Neophricadothyris* sp.?

171. ROAD CANYON FORMATION

Camarophoria venusta Girty
Dielasma spatulatum Girty [doubtful]
Lyttonia nobilis americanus (Girty)
Prorichthofenia permiana (Shumard) = *Cyclacantharia* sp.?

174. CATHEDRAL MOUNTAIN FORMATION

Camarophoria venusta Girty = *Stenoscisma triquetrum* Cooper and Grant
Composita mira (Girty) [doubtful]
Derbyia nasuta Girty
Marginifera sublaevis King = *Anemonaria sublaevis* (King)
Meekella grandis King = *M. occidentalis* (Newberry)
Neospirifer costella King = *Lepidospirifer costellus* (King)
N. pseudocameratus (Girty) = *N. mansuetus* Cooper and Grant

Productus ivesi Newberry = *Peniculauris subcostata* (King)

*P. occidentalis Newberry = *Rugatia occidentalis parvauris* Cooper and Grant

*P. schucherti King = *Xestosia schucherti* (King)

Squamularia guadalupensis (Shumard) = *Neophricadothyris* sp.?

Waagenoconcha montpelierensis (Girty) = *W.* sp.?

175. GAPTANK FORMATION (*Uddenites*-BEARING SHALE MEMBER)

Linoproductus cora (d'Orbigny) = *L.* sp.?
Neospirifer triplicatus (Hall)
Orthotetella wolfcampensis King
Orthotichia kozlowskii King
Productus semireticulatus hermosanus Girty = *Reticulatia* sp.?
Pustula semipunctata (Shepard) [doubtful]

175a. GAPTANK FORMATION (*Uddenites*-BEARING SHALE MEMBER)

Chonetes spinoliratus King = *Chonetinella spinolirata* (King)
Linoproductus cora (d'Orbigny) = *L.* sp.?
*Martinia wolfcampensis King = *Composita* sp.?
Meekella irregularis texana King = *M. texana* King
Neospirifer triplicatus (Hall)

192. WORD FORMATION (APPEL RANCH MEMBER)

Chonetes quadratus King = *Dyoros* (*Tetragonetes*) *quadrangulatus* Cooper and Grant
Composita emarginata affinis Girty [doubtful]
Derbyia nasuta Girty
Hustedia meekana (Shumard)
Lyttonia nobilis americanus (Girty)
Marginifera popei (Shumard) = *Liosotella* sp.?
Meekella attenuata Girty
M. skenoides Girty
Neospirifer pseudocameratus (Girty)
Prorichthofenia permiana (Shumard) = *Cyclacantharia* sp.?
Punctospirifer billingsi (Shumard) [doubtful]
Spiriferina laxa Girty = *Reticulariina cerina* Cooper and Grant

193. LENOX HILLS FORMATION

Aulosteges wolfcampensis King = *Limbella wolfcampensis* (King)
Avonia boulei (Kozlowski) = *Echinauris interrupta* Cooper and Grant
A. meekana Girty = *Cancrinella* sp.?
Camarophoria venusta Girty
Chonetes biplicatus King [doubtful]
Composita subtilita angusta King
Hustedia mormoni (Marcou)
Linoproductus (*Cancrinella*) *villiersi* (d'Orbigny) = *Cancrinella* sp.?
Marginifera dugoutensis King = *Hystriculina dugoutensis* (King)
Neospirifer triplicatus (Hall)

Productus huecoensis King = *Reticulatia* sp.?
Teguliferina bösei King = *T. boesei* King

194. LENOX HILLS FORMATION [probable]

Parakeyserlingina fredericksi King [doubtful]
Spirifer condor d'Orbigny = *Gypospirifer anancites* Cooper and Grant

195. NEAL RANCH FORMATION

Ambocoelia planoconvexa (Shumard) = *Crurithyris* sp.?
Camarophoria theveneni Kozlowski = *Stenoscisma* sp.?
Chonetes biplicatus King = *Chonetinella* sp.?
C. granulifer Owen = *Neochonetes* sp.?
C. verneuilianus Norwood and Pratten [doubtful]
Hustedia pusilla (Girty) [doubtful]
Linoproductus (*Cancrinella*) *villiersi* (d'Orbigny) = *Cancrinella* sp.?
Marginifera wabashensis (Norwood and Pratten) = *Hystriculina* sp.?
Orthotetella wolfcampensis King
Productus semireticulatus hermosanus Girty = *Reticulatia* sp.?
P. wolfcampensis King = *Dasysaria wolfcampensis* (King)

196. LENOX HILLS FORMATION = USNM 716r

Aulosteges wolfcampensis King = *Limbella wolfcampensis* (King)
Chonetes granulifer Owen = *Neochonetes* sp.?
Composita subtilita (Hall)
Enteletes wolfcampensis King
Hustedia mormoni (Marcou)
Linoproductus cora (d'Orbigny) = *L.* sp.?
Marginifera capaci (d'Orbigny) [doubtful]
*Martinia wolfcampensis King = *Composita* sp.?
Meekella irregularis texana King = *M. texana* King
Neospirifer triplicatus (Hall)
Orthotetina cf. *Orthotetes mutabilis* Girty = young *Geyerella* sp.?
Orthotichia kozlowskii King
Productus semistriatus Meek = *Nudauris* sp.?
P. wolfcampensis King = *Dasysaria wolfcampensis* (King)
Rhipidomella carbonaria (Swallow) = *R.* sp.?
Spirifer condor d'Orbigny = *Gypospirifer* sp.?
Squamularia guadalupensis (Shumard) = *Neophricadothyris* sp.?
*Uncinuloides guadalupensis (Shumard) = *Rhynchopora* sp.?

197. LENOX HILLS FORMATION

Derbyia buchi (d'Orbigny) = *D. carteri* Cooper and Grant
Orthotichia kozlowskii King

198. LENOX HILLS FORMATION

Aulosteges wolfcampensis King = *Limbella wolfcampensis* (King)

Derbyia buchi (d'Orbigny) = *D. carteri* Cooper and Grant

Linoproductus cora (d'Orbigny) = *L.* sp.?

Neospirifer triplicatus (Hall)

Productus wolfcampensis King = *Dasysaria wolfcampensis* (King)

Rhipidomella carbonaria (Swallow) = *R.* sp.?

Squamularia guadalupensis (Shumard) = *Neophricadothyris* sp.?

199. GAPTANK FORMATION (*Uddenites*-BEARING SHALE MEMBER) = USNM 701f

Composita subtilita angusta King

Dielasma bovidens (Morton) = *Beecheria* sp.?

Meekella irregularis texana King = *M. texana* King

Parenteletes cooperi King

Scacchinella gigantea Schellwien = *S. triangulata* Cooper and Grant

201. GAPTANK FORMATION

Aulosteges wolfcampensis King = *Limbella wolfcampensis* (King)

Composita subtilita (Hall)

C. subtilita angusta King

Dielasma bovidens (Morton) = *Beecheria* sp.?

Linoproductus cora (d'Orbigny) = *L.* sp.?

Marginifera dugoutensis King = *Hystriculina dugoutensis* (King)

M. wabashensis (Norwood and Pratten) = *Hystriculina* sp.?

Martinia wolfcampensis King = *Composita* sp.?

Meekella irregularis texana King = *M. texana* King

Neospirifer triplicatus (Hall)

Orthototella wolfcampensis King

Parenteletes cooperi King

Productus semireticulatus hermosanus Girty = *Reticulatia* sp.?

Squamularia perplexa (McChesney) = *Neophricadothyris* sp.?

202. GAPTANK FORMATION (*Uddenites*-BEARING SHALE MEMBER)

Composita subtilita (Hall)

Martinia wolfcampensis King = *Composita* sp.?

Meekella irregularis texana King = *M. texana* King

203. GAPTANK FORMATION

Aulosteges wolfcampensis King = *Limbella wolfcampensis* (King)

Buxtonia occidentalis King = *Kochiproductus occidentalis* (King)

Composita subtilita (Hall)

Dielasma bovidens (Morton) = *Beecheria* sp.?

Isogramma millepunctata (Meek and Worthen) = *I. vidriense* Cooper and Grant

Linoproductus cora (d'Orbigny) = *L.* sp.?

Marginifera capaci (d'Orbigny) [doubtful]

Squamularia preplexa (McChesney) = *Neophricadothyris* sp.?

Teguliferina bösei King = *T. boesei* King

204. NEAL RANCH FORMATION

Marginifera capaci (d'Orbigny) [doubtful]

205. SKINNER RANCH FORMATION (DECIE RANCH MEMBER)

Meekella irregularis texana King = *M. texana* King

206. SKINNER RANCH FORMATION (DECIE RANCH MEMBER)

Productus ivesi Newberry [doubtful]

207. SKINNER RANCH FORMATION = approximately USNM 714a

Aulosteges magnicostatus Girty

Camarophoria venusta Girty

Chonetes permianus Shumard [doubtful]

C. subliratus Girty

Composita subtilita (Hall)

Lyttonia hortoni King = *Coscinophora* sp.?

Marginifera reticulata angusta King = *Glyptosteges* sp.?

M.? whitei King = *Oncosarina* sp.?

Prorichthofenia teguliferoides King = *Acritosia* sp.?

Uncinuloides guadalupensis (Shumard) = *Torynechus caelatus* Cooper and Grant

208. SKINNER RANCH FORMATION = USNM 705a

Composita subtilita (Hall)

Geyerella americana Girty = *G. hessi* Cooper and Grant

Hustedia hessensis King

Marginifera? whitei King = *Elliottella varicostata* Cooper and Grant

Meekella hessensis King

Prorichthofenia teguliferoides King = *Acritosia teguliferoides* (King)

Pugnoides texanus (Shumard) [doubtful]

Scacchinella gigantea Schellwien = *S. titan* Cooper and Grant

Spiriferina hilli Girty = *Metriolepis* sp.?

Squamularia guadalupensis (Shumard) = *Neophricadothyris catatona* Cooper and Grant

209. SKINNER RANCH FORMATION

Meekella hessensis King

Scacchinella gigantea Schellwien = *S. titan* Cooper and Grant

210. SKINNER RANCH FORMATION

Enteletes liumbonus King

211. SKINNER RANCH FORMATION = approximately USNM 720e

Composita subtilita (Hall)

Hustedia hessensis King

Meekella grandis King [doubtful]

M. hessensis King

Productus ivesi Newberry [doubtful]

Prorichthofenia likharewi King = *Hercosia?* sp.?

Scacchinella gigantea Schellwien = *S. titan* Cooper and Grant

Spiriferina angulata King = *Crenispirifer angulatus* (King)

Streptorhynchus lamellatum King = *Diplanus lamellatus* (King)

S. undulatum King = *Tropidelasma undulatum* (King)

212. HESS FORMATION (TAYLOR RANCH MEMBER)

Hustedia hessensis King

Pugnoides transversus King = *Antronaria transversa* (King)

215. HESS FORMATION (TAYLOR RANCH MEMBER)

Meekella attenuata Girty

222. HESS FORMATION (TAYLOR RANCH MEMBER) = USNM 716n

Aulosteges medlicottianus Waagen = *Edriosteges* sp.?

Camarophoria venusta Girty = *Stenoscisma pyraustoides* Cooper and Grant

Enteletes dumblei Girty = *E. subcircularis* Cooper and Grant

Hustedia hessensis King

Linoproductus cora angustus King = *L. undatus* Cooper and Grant

Lyttonia hortoni King = *Coscinophora* sp.?

L. nobilis americanus (Girty)

Marginifera? whitei King = *Oncosarina whitei* (King)

Meekella hessensis King

Productus hessensis King = *Thamnosia silicica* Cooper and Grant

P. ivesi Newberry = *Peniculauris imitata* Cooper and Grant

Prorichthofenia teguliferoides King = *Acritosia teguliferoides* (King)

Pugnoides transversus King = *Antronaria transversa* (King)

Rhipidomella hessensis King

223. HESS FORMATION (UPPER) = USNM 726n

Composita mexicana (Hall) = *C. bucculenta* Cooper and Grant

C. subtilita (Hall)

Dielasmina guadalupensis Girty = *Plectelasma kingi* Cooper and Grant

Hustedia meekana (Shumard)

Marginifera manzanica Girty = *Oncosarina* sp.?

Meekella attenuata Girty

Productus ivesi Newberry = *Peniculauris imitata* Cooper and Grant

Prorichthofenia likharewi King = *Acritosia peculiaris* Cooper and Grant

Pugnoides texanus (Shumard) = *Pontisia ventricola* Cooper and Grant

Spiriferina hilli Girty = *Reticulariina pusilla* Cooper and Grant

Uncinuloides guadalupensis (Shumard) [doubtful]

224. SKINNER RANCH FORMATION (SULLIVAN PEAK MEMBER)

Spiriferina hilli Girty = *Reticulariina* sp.?

226. SKINNER RANCH FORMATION (SULLIVAN PEAK MEMBER)

Aulosteges medlicottianus Waagen = *Limbella* sp.?

Camarophoria venusta Girty

Marginifera reticulata King = *Spyridiophora reticulata* (King)

Meekella attenuata Girty

M. difficilis Girty

Prorichthofenia likharewi King = ?

227. SKINNER RANCH FORMATION (DUGOUT MOUNTAIN MEMBER)

Camarophoria venusta Girty

Chonetes subliratus Girty

Marginifera reticulata King = *Glyptosteges* sp.?

228. SKINNER RANCH FORMATION (SULLIVAN PEAK MEMBER)

Aulosteges magnicostatus Girty

Marginifera cristobalensis Girty

M. reticulata King = *Spyridiophora reticulata* (King)

Meekella difficilis Girty

Prorichthofenia likharewi King = *Acritosia* sp.?

Streptorhynchus lamellatum King = *Diplanus* sp.?

231. SKINNER RANCH FORMATION AND CATHEDRAL MOUNTAIN FORMATION [mixed]

Aulosteges triagonalis King = *Agelesia triagonalis* (King) [see note Part III, page 894]

Chonetes subliratus Girty

Enteletes plummeri King

Productus leonardensis King = *Institella leonardensis* (King)

Prorichthofenia likharewi King = *Hercosia uddeni* (Böse)

Squamularia guadalupensis (Shumard) = *Neophricadothyris* sp.?

Uncinuloides guadalupensis (Shumard) = *Torynechus caelatus* Cooper and Grant

232. SKINNER RANCH FORMATION AND CATHEDRAL MOUNTAIN FORMATION [mixed]

Aulosteges triagonalis King = *Agelesia triagonalis* (King)

Composita subtilita (Hall)

Enteletes plummeri King

Hustedia meekana (Shumard)

Linoproductus waagenianus (Girty) = *Megousia* sp.?

Marginifera cristobalensis Girty

M. reticulata King = *Spyridiophora reticulata* (King)

Martinia rhomboidalis Girty

Meekella attenuata Girty

Productus leonardensis King = *Institella leonardensis* (King)

P. occidentalis Newberry = *Rugatia paraindica* (McKee)

P. schucherti King = *Xestosia schucherti* (King)

Prorichthofenia likharewi King = *Hercosia uddeni* (Böse)

P. permiana (Shumard) [doubtful]

Rhipidomella leonardensis King = *Acosarina mesoplatys* (King)

Squamularia guadalupensis (Shumard) = *Neophricadothyris* sp.?

233. CATHEDRAL MOUNTAIN FORMATION

Aulosteges triagonalis King = *Agelesia triagonalis* (King)

Composita mexicana (Hall) [doubtful]

Hustedia mormoni papillata (Shumard) [doubtful]

234. SKINNER RANCH FORMATION [top] OR CATHEDRAL MOUNTAIN FORMATION [base]

Hustedia meekana (Shumard)

235. CATHEDRAL MOUNTAIN FORMATION

Meekella difficilis Girty

Pugnoides texanus (Shumard) [doubtful]

236. CATHEDRAL MOUNTAIN FORMATION

Hustedia meekana (Shumard)

237. CATHEDRAL MOUNTAIN FORMATION

Aulosteges magnicostatus Girty

A. triagonalis King = *Agelesia triagonalis* (King)

Hustedia meekana (Shumard)

238. CATHEDRAL MOUNTAIN FORMATION [probable]

Chonetes subliratus Girty

Hustedia mormoni papillata (Shumard) [doubtful]

Lyttonia nobilis americanus (Girty)

Meekella attenuata Girty

239. WORD FORMATION (WILLIS RANCH MEMBER)

Aulosteges guadalupensis Shumard = *Rhamnaria kingorum* Muir-Wood and Cooper

**A. triagonalis* King = not this species = ?

A. tuberculatus King = *Echinosteges tuberculatus* (King)

Avonia walcottiana (Girty) = *Costispinifera* sp.?

Chonetes subliratus Girty

Dielasma spatulatum Girty [doubtful]

D. schucherti minor King = *Pseudodielasma minor* (King)

Hustedia mormoni papillata (Shumard) [doubtful]

Leiorhynchus weeksi nobilis (Girty) = *Leiorhynchoidea* sp.

Lyttonia nobilis americanus (Girty) = *Collemataria elongata* Cooper and Grant

Marginifera opima (Girty) = *Liosotella* sp.?

M.? wordensis King = *Liosotella wordensis* (King)

Meekella attenuata Girty

M. skenoides Girty

Neospirifer pseudocameratus (Girty) = *N. amphigyus* Cooper and Grant

240. WORD FORMATION (WILLIS RANCH MEMBER)

Aulosteges guadalupensis Shumard = *Rhamnaria kingorum* Muir-Wood and Cooper

Avonia subhorrida rugatula (Girty) = *Echinauris lateralis* Muir-Wood and Cooper

A. walcottiana (Girty) = *Costispinifera costata* (King)

Composita emarginata affinis Girty [doubtful]

Linoproductus nasutus King

L. waagenianus (Girty) = *Megousia definita* Cooper and Grant

Marginifera? wordensis King = *Liosotella wordensis* (King)

Meekella skenoides Girty

Streptorhynchus pygmaeum Girty [doubtful]

Waagenoconcha montpelierensis Girty = *W. magnifica* Cooper and Grant

241. ROAD CANYON FORMATION

Aulosteges guadalupensis Shumard = *Rhamnaria tenuispinosa* Cooper and Grant

A. tuberculatus King = *Echinosteges tuberculatus* (King)

Avonia latidorsata (Girty) [doubtful]

A. subhorrida rugatula (Girty) = *Echinauris* sp.

A. walcottiana (Girty) = *Costispinifera costata* (King)

A. w. costata King = *Costispinifera costata* (King)

Camarophoria deloi King = *Stenoscisma maniculum* Cooper and Grant

Chonetes subliratus Girty = *Dyoros* (*Tetragonetes*) sp.?

Composita persinuata Meek [doubtful]

Derbyia? crenulata Girty [doubtful]

Elivina sulcifer (Shumard) = *Spiriferella* sp.?

Enteletes dumblei Girty = *E. subnudus* Cooper and Grant

E. wordensis King [doubtful]

Hustedia meekana (Shumard)

H. pusilla (Girty) [doubtful]

Linoproductus nasutus King

L. waagenianus (Girty) = *Megousia auriculata* Muir-Wood and Cooper

Marginifera sublaevis King [doubtful]

Martinia rhomboidalis Girty

Neospirifer pseudocameratus (Girty) = *N. bakeri* King

Productus occidentalis Newberry = *Rugatia* sp.?

Prorichthofenia permiana (Shumard) = ?

Pugnoides swallovianus (Shumard) [doubtful]

Punctospirifer billingsi (Shumard) = *Paraspiriferina setulosa* Cooper and Grant

212. WORD FORMATION (WILLIS RANCH MEMBER)

Marginifera popei (Shumard) = *Liosotella* sp.?

Meekella attenuata Girty

243. WORD FORMATION (WILLIS RANCH MEMBER)

Aulosteges guadalupensis Shumard = *Rhamnaria kingorum* Muir-Wood and Cooper

A. tuberculatus King = *Echinosteges tuberculatus* (King)

Avonia signata (Girty) = *Grandaurispina kingorum* Muir-Wood and Cooper

Buxtonia victorioensis King = *Kochiproductus* sp.?

Chonetes subliratus Girty = *Dyoros* (*Dyoros*) *extensus* Cooper and Grant

Composita emarginata affinis Girty [doubtful]
Dielasma spatulatum Girty [doubtful]
Elivina sulcifer (Shumard) = *Spiriferella gravis* Cooper and Grant
Hustedia meekana (Shumard)
H. mormoni papillata (Shumard) [doubtful]
Marginifera opima (Girty) = *Liosotella* sp.?
Meekella skenoides Girty
Prorichthofenia permiana (Shumard) = *Cyclacantharia kingorum* Cooper and Grant
Pugnoides swallovianus (Shumard) = *Wellerella girtyi* Cooper and Grant
Punctospirifer billingsi (Shumard) [doubtful]
Rhynchopora taylori Girty = *R. palumbula* Cooper and Grant

244. WORD FORMATION (APPEL RANCH MEMBER)

Lyttonia nobilis americanus

245. SKINNER RANCH FORMATION [top] OR CATHEDRAL MOUNTAIN FORMATION [base]

Aulosteges magnicostatus Girty
Enteletes liumbonus King [doubtful]
Hustedia meekana (Shumard)
Martinia rhomboidalis Girty
Prorichthofenia permiana (Shumard) [doubtful]
Streptorhynchus lamellatum = *Diplanus lamellatus* (King)

246. WORD FORMATION (APPEL RANCH MEMBER) = USNM 715i?

Avonia signata (Girty) = *Grandaurispina crassa* Cooper and Grant
Camarophoria venusta Girty = *Stenoscisma renode* Cooper and Grant
Chonetes quadratus King = *Dyoros* (*Tetragonetes*) *quadrangulatus* Cooper and Grant
Composita emarginata affinis Girty [doubtful]
Derbyia? crenulata Girty [doubtful]
Elivina sulcifer (Shumard) = *Spiriferella* sp.?
Hustedia meekana (Shumard)
Linoproductus nasutus King
L. (*Cancrinella*) *phosphaticus* (Girty) = *Cancrinella distorta* Cooper and Grant
Marginifera opima (Girty) = *Paucispinifera* sp.?
M. popei (Shumard) = *Liosotella irregularis* Cooper and Grant
M.? texana (Girty) = *Bothrionia transversa* Cooper and Grant
Neospirifer pseudocameratus (Girty)
Productus arcticus Whitfield = *Thamnosia phragmophora* Cooper and Grant
P. guadalupensis Girty = *Yakovlevia indentata* Cooper and Grant
Squamularia guadalupensis (Shumard) = *Neophricadothyris* sp.?

247. WORD FORMATION (APPEL RANCH MEMBER)

Aulosteges guadalupensis Shumard = *Rhamnaria kingorum* Muir-Wood and Cooper

A. tuberculatus King = *Echinosteges tuberculatus* (King)
Avonia signata (Girty) = *Grandaurispina crassa* Cooper and Grant
Camarophoria venusta Girty
Chonetes quadratus King = *Dyoros* (*Tetragonetes*) *quadrangulatus* Cooper and Grant
Composita emarginata affinis Girty [doubtful]
Elivina sulcifer (Shumard) = *Spiriferella clypeata* Cooper and Grant
Hustedia meekana (Shumard)
Linoproductus nasutus King
L. (*Cancrinella*) *phosphaticus* (Girty) = *Cancrinella distorta* Cooper and Grant
Lyttonia nobilis americanus (Girty)
Marginifera opima (Girty) = *Paucispinifera* sp.?
M. popei (Shumard) = *Liosotella irregularis* Cooper and Grant
M.? texana (Girty) = *Bothrionia transversa* Cooper and Grant
Meekella skenoides Girty
Productus arcticus Whitfield = *Thamnosia phragmophora* Cooper and Grant
P. guadalupensis (Girty) = *Yakovlevia indentata* Cooper and Grant
P. occidentalis Newberry [doubtful]
Prorichthofenia permiana (Shumard) = *Cyclacantharia* sp.?
Spiriferina laxa Girty = *Reticulariina cerina* Cooper and Grant
Squamularia guadalupensis (Shumard) = *Neophricadothyris conara* Cooper and Grant
Waagenoconcha montpelierensis (Girty) = *W. magnifica* Cooper and Grant

248. WORD FORMATION (APPEL RANCH MEMBER)

Aulosteges guadalupensis Shumard = *Rhamnaria kingorum* Muir-Wood and Cooper
Avonia signata (Girty) = *Grandaurispina crassa* Cooper and Grant
A. walcottiana (Girty) = *Echinauris* sp.?
Chonetes hillanus Girty [doubtful]
Composita emarginata affinis Girty [doubtful]
Derbyia? crenulata Girty [doubtful]
Elivina sulcifer (Shumard) = *Spiriferella clypeata* Cooper and Grant
Hustedia meekana (Shumard)
Linoproductus nasutus King
Marginifera opima (Girty) = *Paucispinifera* sp.?
M. popei (Shumard) = *Liosotella irregularis* Cooper and Grant
Meekella skenoides Girty

249. ROAD CANYON FORMATION

Lyttonia nobilis americanus (Girty)

250. WORD FORMATION (CHINA TANK MEMBER)

Chonetes subliratus Girty
Lyttonia nobilis americanus (Girty)

Meekella skenoides Girty
Neospirifer pseudocameratus (Girty)

251.   ROAD CANYON FORMATION

Enteletes wordensis King [doubtful]
Lyttonia nobilis americanus (Girty)

252.   WORD FORMATION (APPEL RANCH MEMBER)

Aulosteges guadalupensis Shumard = *Rhamnaria kingorum* Muir-Wood and Cooper
Elivina sulcifer (Shumard) = *Spiriferella clypeata* Cooper and Grant
Meekella attenuata Girty

253.   WORD FORMATION (APPEL RANCH MEMBER)

Avonia signata (Girty) = *Grandaurispina crassa* Cooper and Grant
Chonetes subliratus Girty
Hustedia meekana (Shumard)
Marginifera opima (Girty) = *Paucispinifera* sp.

256.   WORD FORMATION OR CATHEDRAL MOUNTAIN FORMATION

Chonetes quadratus King = *Dyoros* (*Tetragonetes*) *quadrangulatus* Cooper and Grant
Neospirifer pseudocameratus (Girty)
Productus ivesi Newberry = *Peniculauris* sp.?
Rhipidomella mesoplatys King = *Acosarina mesoplatys* (King)
Squamularia guadalupensis (Shumard) = *Neophricadothyris* sp.?

257.   WORD FORMATION

Composita emarginata affinis Girty [doubtful]
Neospirifer pseudocameratus (Girty)
Productus ivesi Newberry [doubtful]

264.   WORD FORMATION (CHINA TANK MEMBER)

Enteletes dumblei Girty [doubtful]
E. wordensis King
Hustedia mormoni papillata (Shumard) [doubtful]
Lyttonia nobilis americanus (Girty)
Meekella attenuata Girty
Spiriferina pyramidalis Girty = *Metriolepis* sp.?

265.   WORD FORMATION [0.8 mi NW of hill 5079, northwestern Hess Canyon quadrangle, float lying on the surface of the upper Vidrio]

Ambocoelia guadalupensis Girty = *Crurithyris tholiaphor* Cooper and Grant
Aulosteges guadalupensis Shumard = *Rhamnaria* sp.?
Camarophoria? indentata (Shumard) = ?
Chonetes subliratus Girty = *Dyoros* (*Dyoros*) sp.?
Derbyia elevata King
Elivina sulcifer (Shumard) = *Spiriferella* sp.?
Enteletes wordensis King
Hustedia meekana (Shumard) [doubtful]
Leiorhynchus weeksi nobilis (Girty) = *Leiorhynchoidea* sp.?
Lyttonia nobilis americanus (Girty)
Marginifera? wordensis King = *Liosotella wordensis* (King)
Meekella attenuata Girty
Productus schucherti King [doubtful]
Prorichthofenia permiana (Shumard) = *Cyclacantharia* sp.?
Spiriferina laxa Girty = *Reticulariina* sp.?

301.   CATHEDRAL MOUNTAIN FORMATION

Chonetes permianus Shumard [doubtful]
Productus ivesi Newberry = *Peniculauris* sp.?

United States Geological Survey Localities

Descriptions are given for those localities not included in the list presented in Part I, page 135.

664 (green). *Rugatia occidentalis parvauris* Cooper and Grant

2903 (green). Cherry Canyon Formation [about 700 ft above basal black limestone in Delaware Mountain Sandstone, escarpment on E side of road at entrance to Guadalupe Canyon, Guadalupe Peak Quadrangle]

   Costispinifera walcottiana (Girty)

2906 (green). *Rigbyella girtyi* Stehli

2919 (green). *Paucispinifera guadalupensis* (Girty)

2920 (green). *Bryorhynchus? nitidum* (Girty)

2926. *Ambocoelia planoconvexa* var. *guadalupensis* Girty = *Crurithyris guadalupensis* (Girty)
   Aulosteges medlicottianus var. *americanus* Girty = [brachial valve of *Ombonia*]
   Camarophoria venusta Girty = *Stenoscisma* sp.?

Chonetes hillanus Girty = *Dyoros* (*Dyoros*) sp.?
Composita emarginata Girty
Composita emarginata var. *affinis* Girty = *Composita affinis* Girty
Crania sp.
Dielasma cordatum Girty
Dielasma prolongatum Girty
Dielasma? scutulatum Girty = *Pseudodielasma scutulatum* (Girty)
Dielasma spatulatum Girty
Dielasma sulcatum Girty
Dielasmina guadalupensis Girty = *Plectelasma guadalupense* (Girty)
Eliva inflata Cooper and Grant
Geyerella americana Girty
Heterelasma shumardianum Girty
Heterelasma venustulum Girty
Hustedia meekana (Shumard) Girty = *Hustedia* sp.?
Hustedia meekana var. *trigonalis* Girty = *Thedusia trigonalis* (Girty)

Leptodus guadalupensis Girty = *Collemataria guadalupensis* (Girty)

Martinia rhomboidalis Girty

Martinia shumardiana Girty

Notothyris schuchertensis Girty = *Timorina schuchertensis* (Girty)

Notothyris schuchertensis var. *ovata* Girty = *Timorina ovata* (Girty)

Orthotetes distortus Girty = *Ombonia guadalupensis* (Girty)

Orthotetes distortus campanulatus Girty = *Ombonia guadalupensis* (Girty)

Orthotetes guadalupensis Girty = *Ombonia guadalupensis* (Girty)

Productus latidorsatus Girty = *Paucispinifera latidorsata* (Girty)

Productus occidentalis Girty [not Newberry] = *Paucispinifera* sp.?

Productus? pileolus Shumard = *Scapharina pileolus* (Shumard)

Productus pinniformis Girty = *Compressoproductus pinniformis* (Girty)

Productus semireticulatus var. *capitanensis* Girty = *Thamnosia capitanensis* (Girty)

Productus waagenianus Girty = *Megousia? waageniana* (Girty)

Pugnax? bisulcata var. *seminuloides* Girty = *Bryorhynchus gratiosum* (Girty)

Pugnax elegans Girty = *Tautosia elegans* (Girty)

Pugnax shumardiana Girty = *Tautosia shumardiana* (Girty)

Pugnax swalloviana (Shumard) Girty = *Anteridocus swalloviana* (Shumard) of Girty

Rhamnaria shumardi Cooper and Grant

Rhynchonella? indentata Shumard, Girty = *Strigirhynchia* sp.?

Rhynchonella? longaeva Girty = *Fascicosta* sp.?

Richthofenia permiana Girty [not Shumard] = ?

Spirifer mexicanus Shumard of Girty = *Cartorhium mexicanum* (Girty)

Spirifer sulcifer Shumard = *Spiriferella sulcifer* (Shumard)

Spiriferina billingsi Shumard Girty = *Paraspiriferina billingsi* (Shumard) of Girty

Spiriferina billingsi var. *retusa* Girty = *Paraspiriferina billingsi retusa* (Girty)

Spiriferina pyramidalis Girty = *Sarganostega pyramidalis* (Girty)

Spiriferina sulcata Girty = *Paraspiriferina evax* (Girty)

Spiriferina welleri Girty = *Reticulariina welleri* (Girty)

Squamularia guadalupensis Shumard of Girty = *Astegosia subquadrata* (Girty)

Squamularia guadalupensis var. *ovalis* Girty = *Astegosia subquadrata* (Girty)

Squamularia guadalupensis var. *subquadrata* Girty = *Astegosia subquadrata* (Girty)

Streptorhynchus gregarium Girty = *Tropidelasma gregarium* (Girty)

2930. *Bryorhynchus bisulcatum* (Shumard)
Bryorhynchus gratiosum (Girty)
Dyoros (Dyoros) subliratus (Girty)

2962. *Tropidelasma perattenuatum* (Girty)

2967 (green). *Petasmatherus pusillus* (Girty)

2969. *Craspedona newelli* Cooper and Grant

3763. *Camarophoria venusta* Girty = *Stenoscisma* sp.?
Enteletes globosus Girty
Hustedia bipartita Girty
Hustedia papillata (Shumard) of Girty = *Hustedia* sp.?
Lyttonia nobilis americanus (Girty) = *Collemataria* sp.?
Meekella difficilis Girty = *Meekella skenoides* Girty
Meekella skenoides Girty
Productus guadalupensis var. *comancheanus* Girty = *Paucispinifera comancheana* (Girty)
Productus meekanus Girty = *Grandaurispina* sp.?
Productus subhorridus var. *rugatulus* Girty = *Costispinifera rugatula* (Girty)
Richthofenia permiana Girty [not Shumard] = ?
Spiriferina hilli Girty = *Spiriferellina* sp.?
Streptorhynchus pygmaeum Girty = *Tropidelasma* sp.?
Strophalosia hystricula Girty = *Heteralosia* sp.?

3764 (green). ["The recorded locality is the vicinity of the Diablo Mtns., but this is probably a mistake. The material to which this label actually applies and with which the present lot is probably mixed appears to be that mentioned in Von Streerowitz's report and sent to the U.S. National Museum by E. T. Dumble, Jan. 18, 1892" Girty (1909:512).]

Collemataria americana (Girty)

3840 (green). *Chonosteges magnicostatus* (Girty)

6452 (blue). Delaware Mountain Formation [True Canyon, Delaware Mtns., 7 mi NW of 7-Heart Gap, Culberson Co., Texas]

Glossothyropsis robusta (Girty)

7404. *Anteridocus swallovianus* (Shumard)
Cartorhium sp.
Composita emarginata Girty
Dielasma prolongatum Girty
Dielasma sp.
Dielasma sp. 6
Echinosteges guadalupensis (Shumard)
Eliva inflata Cooper and Grant
Heterelasma sp.
Hustedia sp.
Liosotella opima (Girty)
Paraspiriferina billingsi (Shumard)
Pseudoleptodus guadalupensis Stehli
Ptilotorhynchus delicatum Cooper and Grant
Stenoscisma sp.
Strigirhynchia indentata (Shumard)
Thamnosia capitanensis (Girty)

7415 (blue). Carlsbad Limestone Formation [N rim of Pine Spring Canyon, 2.3 mi N 5° W of summit of El Capitan, between third and fourth hills NW of trail leading down into canyon, Guadalupe Peak Quadrangle, Culberson Co., Texas]

    Notothyris sp.

7416. *Plectelasma guadalupense* (Girty)

7417 (blue). *Eolyttonia* sp.
    Meekella skenoides Girty
    Pseudoleptodus guadalupensis Stehli

7612. *Pseudoleptodus guadalupensis* Stehli

7641 (blue). Middle Delaware Mountain Formation (Bed B B, upper part of South Wells Limestone Member) [just W of Long Point, between Delaware River and D Ranch South Wells, E of quadrangle, Guadalupe Peak Quadrangle, Culberson Co., Texas]

    Leiorhynchoidea sulcata Cooper and Grant

7649. *Glossothyropsis robusta* (Girty)
    Leiorhynchoidea sulcata Cooper and Grant
    Paranorella sp.

7666. *Acosarina* sp.
    Anemonaria sp.
    Cenorhynchia sp.

Chaeniorhynchus sp.
Chonosteges sp.
Composita sp.
Derbyia sp.
Dielasma sp.
Echinauris sp.
Edriosteges sp.
Institella leonardensis (R. E. King)
Lepidospirifer cf. *L. costellus* (R. E. King)
Martinia sp.
Meekella sp.
Megousia sp.
Neophricadothyris sp.
Neospirifer sp.
Niviconia globosa (R. E. King)
Peniculauris sp.
Rhipidomella sp.
Rugatia paraindica (McKee)
Stenoscisma triquetrum Cooper and Grant
Tautosia sp.
Thamnosia sp.
Waagenoconcha sp.
Xestosia sp.

9999. *Reticulariina hueconiana* Cooper and Grant
    Stenoscisma sp. 1

American Museum of Natural History, Kansas University, and National Museum of Natural History Localities

Descriptions for localities that appear in this list but not in Part I, pages 135–165, will be found herein in "Corrigenda" under "Additions to Localities." Abbreviations used in locality designations in this list are:

A = American Museum of Natural History [abbreviated elsewhere herein: AMNH]
M = Kansas University (R. C. Moore) [abbreviated elsewhere herein: Moore]
N = National Museum of Natural History, formerly United States National Museum [abbreviated elsewhere herein: USNM]

Following the species name of each listed form there appears a rarity code symbol indicating the abundance of the species in the collection:

VR = very rare (1–5 specimens)
  R = rare (6–25 specimens)

C = common (26–100 specimens)
A = abundant (101–300 specimens)
VA = very abundant (301–3000 specimens)
SA = super abundant (more than 3000 specimens)

The magnitude of occurrence in the collection indicated by the rarity code is a measure of the probable abundance of that species in the rocks of the Glass Mountains. A truly accurate measure of abundance is not possible due to the methods of recovery used. Also, evaluation of the actual numbers of specimens represented by dissociated valves and broken valves was not undertaken. Considering collecting bias and the factors mentioned, these rarity symbols are, nevertheless, indicative of the relative abundance of each species at the designated localities.

	Rarity code
LOCALITY A21 : Cherry Canyon Formation, Getaway Member	
Cartorhium retusum Cooper and Grant	VR
Cyclacantharia kingorum Cooper and Grant	R
Derbyia sp.	VR

	Rarity code
Dielasma pictile Cooper and Grant	VR
Dyoros (*Dyoros*) *convexus* Cooper and Grant	R
Dyoros (*Tetragonetes*) *complanatus* Cooper and Grant	VR
Echinauris productelloides Cooper and Grant	R
Echinosteges tuberculatus (R.E. King)	VR

Rarity code

LOCALITY A21 - Continued

Eolyttonia progressa Cooper and Grant	VR
Geyerella sp. 2	VR
Grandaurispina undulata Cooper and Grant	VR
Heteralosia magnispina Cooper and Grant	VR
Hustedia citeria Cooper and Grant	VR
Liosotella spinumbona Cooper and Grant	VR
Liosotella wordensis (R.E. King)	R
Micraphelia scitula Cooper and Grant	R
Paucispinifera tumida Cooper and Grant	VR
Petasmatherus opulus Cooper and Grant	VR
Pseudodielasma sp.	VR
Rhamnaria sulcata Cooper and Grant	R
Thedusia dischides Cooper and Grant	VR
Wellerella girtyi seorsa Cooper and Grant	VR
Xenosteges quadratus Cooper and Grant	VR

LOCALITY A25 : Bell Canyon Formation, Lamar Member

Arionthia lamaria Cooper and Grant	VR
Composita affinis Girty	VR
Crenispirifer myllus Cooper and Grant	R
Derbyia sp.	VR
Hustedia opsia Cooper and Grant	R
Martinia rhomboidalis Girty	R
Neophricadothyris sp.	VR
Ombonia guadalupensis (Girty)	R
Paraspiriferina billingsi (Shumard)	VR
Reticulariina sp.	VR
Sarganostega pressa Cooper and Grant	R
Spiriferellina nuda Cooper and Grant	VR
Thedusia trigonalis (Girty)	VR
Tropidelasma gregarium (Girty)	R

LOCALITY A28 : Cherry Canyon Formation, Getaway Member

Echinauris productelloides Cooper and Grant	VR
Hustedia citeria Cooper and Grant	VR
Meekella skenoides Girty	VR

LOCALITY A33 : Bell Canyon Formation, Pinery Member

Anteridocus swallovianus (Shumard)	VR
Bryorhynchus bisulcatum (Shumard)	A
Chonetinetes varians Cooper and Grant	VR
Composita pyriformis Cooper and Grant	VR
Crenispirifer jubatus Cooper and Grant	VR
Derbyia sp.	VR
Dyoros (Dyoros) intrepidus Cooper and Grant	VR
Fascicosta elongata Cooper and Grant	VR
Heterelasma shumardianum Girty	VR
Hustedia demissa Cooper and Grant	VR
Hustedia opsia Cooper and Grant	VR
Hustedia rupinata Cooper and Grant	R
Madarosia anterolamellata Cooper and Grant	VR
Micraphelia subalata Cooper and Grant	VR
Paraspiriferina sapinea Cooper and Grant	VR
Paucispinifera latidorsata (Girty)	VR
Plectelasma guadalupense (Girty)	VR
Reticulariina welleri (Girty)	VR
Spiriferella sp.	VR
Spiriferellina nuda Cooper and Grant	VR
Tautosia shumardiana (Girty)	VR
Thedusia sp.	VR
Thedusia ventricosa Cooper and Grant	VR
Timorina ovata (Girty)	VR

Rarity code

LOCALITY A37 : Bell Canyon Formation, Lamar Member

Allorhynchus sp.	VR
Anteridocus swallovianus (Shumard)	VR
Aphaurosia rotundata Cooper and Grant	VR
Arionthia lamaria Cooper and Grant	VR
Astegosia subquadrata (Girty)	R
Composita affinis Girty	R
Composita emarginata Girty	VR
Crenispirifer myllus Cooper and Grant	R
Crurithyris guadalupensis (Girty)	VR
Deltarina magnicostata Cooper and Grant	VR
Derbyia sp. 1	VR
Dielasma sp.	VR
Dielasma subcirculare Cooper and Grant	VR
Elivina detecta Cooper and Grant	VR
Heteralosia magnispina Cooper and Grant	VR
Hustedia opsia Cooper and Grant	R
Lirellaria costellata Cooper and Grant	VR
Martinia rhomboidalis Girty	R
Ombonia guadalupensis (Girty)	VR
Paraspiriferina billingsi (Shumard)	VR
Reticulariina sp.	R
Sarganostega pressa Cooper and Grant	R
Scapharina levis Cooper and Grant	VR
Sestropoma cribriferum Cooper and Grant	VR
Stenoscisma trabeatum Cooper and Grant	VR
Tautosia elegans (Girty)	VR
Tropidelasma gregarium (Girty)	C

LOCALITY A38 : Bell Canyon Formation, Lamar Member

Allorhynchus venustulum Cooper and Grant	VR
Arionthia lamaria Cooper and Grant	VR
Collemataria sp.	VR
Collemataria spatulata Cooper and Grant	VR
Composita affinis Girty	VR
Crenispirifer myllus Cooper and Grant	R
Crurithyris guadalupensis (Girty)	VR
Derbyia sp. 1	VR
Eolyttonia sp.	VR
Heteralosia paucispinosa Cooper and Grant	VR
Hustedia opsia Cooper and Grant	R
Lirellaria costellata Cooper and Grant	VR
Martinia rhomboidalis Girty	VR
Metriolepis sp.	VR
Ombonia guadalupensis (Girty)	R
Paraspiriferina billingsi (Shumard)	R
Reticulariina phoxa Cooper and Grant	VR
Reticulariina sp.	VR
Rigbyella girtyi (Wanner and Sieverts)	VR
Sarganostega pressa Cooper and Grant	R
Sarganostega transversalis Cooper and Grant	VR
Scapharina levis Cooper and Grant	R
Sestropoma cribriferum Cooper and Grant	VR
Tautosia elegans (Girty)	VR
Thedusia ventricosa Cooper and Grant	VR
Timorina ovata (Girty)	VR
Tropidelasma gregarium (Girty)	R

LOCALITY A39 : Bell Canyon Formation, Lamar Member

Astegosia subquadrata (Girty)	VR
Composita affinis Girty	R
Hustedia opsia Cooper and Grant	VR
Martinia rhomboidalis Girty	VR

	Rarity code
LOCALITY A39 - Continued	
Meekella sp.	VR
Ombonia guadalupensis (Girty)	VR
Paraspiriferina billingsi (Shumard)	VR
Paucispinifera latidorsata (Girty)	VR
Sarganostega pressa Cooper and Grant	VR
Sestropoma cribriferum Cooper and Grant	VR
Thedusia ventricosa Cooper and Grant	VR
Tropidelasma gregarium (Girty)	VR
LOCALITY A40 : Bell Canyon Formation, Lamar Member	
Allorhynchus venustulum Cooper and Grant	R
Anomaloria anomala Cooper and Grant	R
Anteridocus bicostatus Cooper and Grant	VR
Anteridocus swallovianus (Shumard)	VR
Astegosia subquadrata (Girty)	C
Bryorhynchus bisulcatum (Shumard)	VR
Cleiothyridina pilularis Cooper and Grant	VR
Collemataria spatulata Cooper and Grant	VR
Composita affinis Girty	R
Crenispirifer myllus Cooper and Grant	R
Crurithyris guadalupensis (Girty)	R
Derbyia sp. 1	VR
Elivina detecta Cooper and Grant	VR
Hustedia opsia Cooper and Grant	C
Lirellaria costellata Cooper and Grant	VR
Martinia rhomboidalis Girty	C
Ombonia guadalupensis (Girty)	R
Paraspiriferina sapinea Cooper and Grant	R
Sestropoma cribriferum Cooper and Grant	VR
Stenoscisma trabeatum Cooper and Grant	VR
Tautosia elegans (Girty)	R
Timorina schuchertensis (Girty)	VR
Tropidelasma gregarium (Girty)	R
LOCALITY A46 : Bone Spring Formation	
Micraphelia pumilis Cooper and Grant	VA
Pseudoleptodus? sp. 1	VR
LOCALITY A B188-6 : San Andres Formation	
Composita sp.	C
Tropidelasma curtum Cooper and Grant	R
LOCALITY A B188-8 : San Andres Formation	
Altiplecus sp.	VR
Crurithyris sp.	VR
Derbyia sp.	VR
Derbyia texta Cooper and Grant	VR
Enteletes sp.	C
Enteletes subnudus Cooper and Grant	R
Heterelasma sp.	VR
Meekella skenoides Girty	VR
Metriolepis sp.	VR
Metriolepis ziczac Cooper and Grant	R
Paucispinifera costellata Cooper and Grant	VR
Rhynchopora sp.	VR
Wellerella girtyi girtyi Cooper and Grant	R
LOCALITY A347 : Bell Canyon Formation, Lamar Member	
Allorhynchus venustulum Cooper and Grant	VR
Anomaloria anomala Cooper and Grant	R
Anteridocus bicostatus Cooper and Grant	VR
Anteridocus swallovianus (Shumard)	VR
Aphaurosia rotundata Cooper and Grant	VR
Arionthia lamaria Cooper and Grant	R

	Rarity code
Astegosia subquadrata (Girty)	A
Collemataria spatulata Cooper and Grant	VR
Composita affinis Girty	C
Crenispirifer myllus Cooper and Grant	R
Crurithyris guadalupensis (Girty)	VR
Deltarina magnicostata Cooper and Grant	VR
Derbyia sp. 1	VR
Dielasma cordatum Girty	VR
Dielasma sulcatum Girty	VR
Elivina detecta Cooper and Grant	C
Geyerella americana Girty	VR
Hustedia opsia Cooper and Grant	R
Martinia rhomboidalis Girty	A
Ombonia guadalupensis (Girty)	R
Paranorella aquilonia Cooper and Grant	VR
Paraspiriferina billingsi (Shumard)	R
Reticulariina welleri (Girty)	VR
Rhynchopora sp. b	VR
Sarganostega pressa Cooper and Grant	R
Spiriferellina nuda Cooper and Grant	VR
Stenoscisma abbreviatum Cooper and Grant	VR
Stenoscisma trabeatum Cooper and Grant	VR
Tautosia shumardiana (Girty)	VR
Tropidelasma gregarium (Girty)	R
LOCALITY A348 : Bell Canyon Formation, Lamar Member	
Allorhynchus venustulum Cooper and Grant	VR
Arionthia lamaria Cooper and Grant	VR
Astegosia subquadrata (Girty)	VR
Collemataria spatulata Cooper and Grant	VR
Composita affinis Girty	VR
Crenispirifer myllus Cooper and Grant	VR
Hustedia opsia Cooper and Grant	VR
Martinia rhomboidalis Girty	VR
Ombonia guadalupensis (Girty)	VR
Sarganostega pressa Cooper and Grant	VR
Scapharina levis Cooper and Grant	VR
Spiriferellina nuda Cooper and Grant	VR
Tautosia shumardiana (Girty)	VR
Tropidelasma gregarium (Girty)	R
LOCALITY A351 : Bell Canyon Formation, Lamar Member	
Allorhynchus venustulum Cooper and Grant	VR
Astegosia subquadrata (Girty)	VR
Composita affinis Girty	R
Crenispirifer myllus Cooper and Grant	VR
Crurithyris guadalupensis (Girty)	R
Derbyia sp.	VR
Dyoros (Dyoros) hillanus (Girty)	VR
Heteralosia magnispina Cooper and Grant	VR
Hustedia opsia Cooper and Grant	R
Martinia rhomboidalis Girty	R
Ombonia guadalupensis (Girty)	VR
Paraspiriferina sp.	VR
Reticulariina laxa (Girty)	VR
Reticulariina sp.	VR
Sarganostega pressa Cooper and Grant	VR
Thedusia trigonalis (Girty)	VR
Tropidelasma gregarium (Girty)	R
LOCALITY A369 : Bone Spring Formation	
Composita cracens Cooper and Grant	VR
Composita sp.	VR
Crenispirifer sagus Cooper and Grant	R

	Rarity code
LOCALITY A369 - Continued	
Cyclacantharia sp.	VR
Derbyia sp.	VR
Dielasma sp.	VR
Dyoros (*Tetragonetes*) *rectangulatus* Cooper and Grant	C
Echinauris sp.	R
Elivina sp.	VR
Hustedia decollatensis Cooper and Grant	C
Hustedia sp.	R
Kochiproductus sp.	VR
Meekella hessensis R.E. King	C
Megousia auriculata Muir-Wood and Cooper	C
Paraspiriferina sp.	VR
Paucispinifera sp.	VR
Pseudodielasma sp.	VR
Quadrochonetes girtyi Stehli	VR
Reticulariina sp.	VR
Reticulariina tetrica Cooper and Grant	VR
Rugatia paraindica (McKee)	VR
Sarganostega prisca Cooper and Grant	R
Scapharina sp.	VR

	Rarity code
LOCALITY A373 : Bell Canyon Formation, Lamar Member	
Deltarina magnicostata Cooper and Grant	VR
Derbyia sp. 1	VR
Hustedia opsia Cooper and Grant	C
Sarganostega pressa Cooper and Grant	VR
Sestropoma cribriferum Cooper and Grant	VR
Spiriferellina nuda Cooper and Grant	VR
Thedusia ventricosa Cooper and Grant	VR

	Rarity code
LOCALITY A375 : Bell Canyon Formation, Pinery Member	
Dyoros (*Dyoros*) *intrepidus* Cooper and Grant	VR
Heteralosia magnispina Cooper and Grant	VR
Paucispinifera sp.	VR
Scapharina levis Cooper and Grant	VR

	Rarity code
LOCALITY A384 : Bell Canyon Formation, Lamar Member	
Anomaloria anomala Cooper and Grant	VR
Astegosia subquadrata (Girty)	C
Composita affinis Girty	R
Geyerella americana Girty	VR
Martinia rhomboidalis Girty	R
Stenoscisma trabeatum Cooper and Grant	VR

	Rarity code
LOCALITY A385 : Bell Canyon Formation, McCombs Member	
Crenispirifer sp.	R
Cyclacantharia sp.	VR
Derbyia sp. 1	VR
Heteralosia magnispina Cooper and Grant	VR
Metriolepis sp.	VR
Paraspiriferina sp.	VR
Reticulariina sp.	VR
Sarganostega pressa Cooper and Grant	VR
Scapharina rugosa Cooper and Grant	VR

	Rarity code
LOCALITY A388 : Bell Canyon Formation, Rader Member	
Arionthia lamaria Cooper and Grant	VR
Astegosia subquadrata (Girty)	VR
Bryorhynchus bisulcatum (Shumard)	R
Composita affinis Girty	VR
Composita emarginata Girty	VR

	Rarity code
Composita pyriformis Cooper and Grant	VR
Crenispirifer sp.	VR
Derbyia sp.	VR
Dyoros (*Dyoros*) *intrepidus* Cooper and Grant	VR
Glossothyropsis sp. 1 (Girty)	VR
Hustedia rupinata Cooper and Grant	R
Micraphelia subalata Cooper and Grant	R
Paraspiriferina sp.	VR
Plectelasma guadalupense (Girty)	VR
Reticulariina phoxa Cooper and Grant	VR
Spiriferella sp.	VR
Thedusia trigonalis (Girty)	VR

	Rarity code
LOCALITY A389 : Bell Canyon Formation, Rader Member	
Astegosia subquadrata (Girty)	VR
Martinia rhomboidalis Girty	VR
Ombonia guadalupensis (Girty)	VR

	Rarity code
LOCALITY A390 : Hueco Formation	
Composita cracens Cooper and Grant	C

	Rarity code
LOCALITY A397 : Bell Canyon Formation, Pinery Member	
Bryorhynchus bisulcatum (Shumard)	VR
Crenispirifer sp.	VR
Cyclacantharia sp.	VR
Derbyia sp.	VR
Echinosteges guadalupensis (Shumard)	VR
Heteralosia sp.	VR
Hustedia rupinata Cooper and Grant	R
Metriolepis pedicosa Cooper and Grant	VR
Micraphelia scitula Cooper and Grant	VR
Micraphelia subalata Cooper and Grant	C
Paraspiriferina sp.	R
Reticulariina echinata Cooper and Grant	VR
Reticulariina sp.	VR
Scapharina levis Cooper and Grant	VR
Scapharina rugosa Cooper and Grant	VR
Sestropoma cribriferum Cooper and Grant	VR
Spiriferella sulcifer (Shumard)	R
Thedusia trigonalis (Girty)	VR
Thedusia ventricosa Cooper and Grant	R
Tropidelasma gregarium (Girty)	VR

	Rarity code
LOCALITY A398 : Bell Canyon Formation, Pinery Member	
Altiplecus? deltosus Cooper and Grant	R
Altiplecus trapezoidalis Cooper and Grant	R
Anteridocus swallovianus (Shumard)	VR
Arionthia lamaria Cooper and Grant	VR
Chonetinetes varians Cooper and Grant	VR
Composita emarginata Girty	R
Craspedona newelli Cooper and Grant	VR
Crenispirifer jubatus Cooper and Grant	R
Crurithyris guadalupensis (Girty)	R
Deltarina magnicostata Cooper and Grant	VR
Derbyia sp.	VR
Derbyia sp. 1	VR
Dielasma sp.	VR
Dyoros (*Dyoros*) *intrepidus* Cooper and Grant	R
Elivina? annectans Cooper and Grant	VR
Hustedia opsia Cooper and Grant	R
Hustedia rupinata Cooper and Grant	C
Hustedia sp.	VR
Meekella skenoides Girty	VR

	Rarity code
LOCALITY A398 - Continued	
Metriolepis nabis Cooper and Grant	VR
Micraphelia scitula Cooper and Grant	VR
Neophricadothyris sp.	VR
Ombonia guadalupensis (Girty)	VR
Paraspiriferina sapinea Cooper and Grant	R
Paucispinifera latidorsata (Girty)	VR
Paucispinifera spinosa Cooper and Grant	C
Reticulariina echinata Cooper and Grant	VR
Sarganostega transversalis Cooper and Grant	VR
Sestropoma cribriferum Cooper and Grant	C
Spiriferella sulcifer (Shumard)	VR
Tautosia shumardiana (Girty)	VR
Thamnosia capitanensis (Girty)	VR
Thedusia trigonalis (Girty)	VR
LOCALITY A401 : Bell Canyon Formation, Pinery Member	
Anteridocus bicostatus Cooper and Grant	VR
Anteridocus swallovianus (Shumard)	VR
Collemataria spatulata Cooper and Grant	VR
Composita emarginata Girty	VR
Deltarina magnicostata Cooper and Grant	VR
Elivina detecta Cooper and Grant	VR
Heteralosia paucispinosa Cooper and Grant	VR
Holosia regularis Cooper and Grant	VR
Hustedia rupinata Cooper and Grant	VR
Paucispinifera latidorsata (Girty)	VR
Rhamnaria shumardi Cooper and Grant	VR
Scapharina rugosa Cooper and Grant	R
Spiriferella sp.	VR
Tautosia elegans (Girty)	VR
Tautosia shumardiana (Girty)	VR
Thamnosia capitanensis (Girty)	VR
Thedusia ventricosa Cooper and Grant	R
LOCALITY A402 : Cherry Canyon Formation, Manzanita Member	
Composita sp.	R
Derbyia sp.	VR
Heterelasma shumardianum Girty	VR
LOCALITY A403 : Bell Canyon Formation, Rader Member	
Aphaurosia rotundata Cooper and Grant	VR
Arionthia lamaria Cooper and Grant	VR
Bryorhynchus bisulcatum (Shumard)	C
Composita emarginata Girty	VR
Craspedona newelli Cooper and Grant	VR
Crenispirifer jubatus Cooper and Grant	R
Derbyia sp.	VR
Derbyia texta Cooper and Grant	VR
Dyoros (Dyoros) intrepidus Cooper and Grant	R
Echinosteges guadalupensis (Shumard)	VR
Elivina? annectans Cooper and Grant	VR
Hustedia demissa Cooper and Grant	VR
Hustedia rupinata Cooper and Grant	C
Metriolepis nabis Cooper and Grant	VR
Micraphelia scitula Cooper and Grant	R
Micraphelia subalata Cooper and Grant	C
Paraspiriferina billingsi (Shumard)	R
Paraspiriferina sapinea Cooper and Grant	VR
Paucispinifera latidorsata (Girty)	VR
Phrenophoria perplexa Cooper and Grant	VR
Reticulariina laxa (Girty)	VR
Reticulariina sp.	VR

	Rarity code
Sarganostega pressa Cooper and Grant	VR
Sarganostega transversalis Cooper and Grant	VR
Scapharina rugosa Cooper and Grant	VR
Sestropoma cribriferum Cooper and Grant	VR
Spiriferella sulcifer (Shumard)	R
Spiriferellina nuda Cooper and Grant	VR
Tautosia elegans (Girty)	VR
Thamnosia capitanensis (Girty)	VR
Thedusia trigonalis (Girty)	VR
Thedusia ventricosa Cooper and Grant	R
LOCALITY A404 : Bell Canyon Formation, Rader Member	
Acanthocrania sp.	VR
Altiplecus? deltosus Cooper and Grant	R
Altiplecus trapezoidalis Cooper and Grant	VR
Arionthia lamaria Cooper and Grant	VR
Chonetinetes varians Cooper and Grant	VR
Cyclacantharia sp. 5	VR
Derbyia sp.	VR
Heteralosia magnispina Cooper and Grant	VR
Hustedia rupinata Cooper and Grant	R
Micraphelia subalata Cooper and Grant	R
Paraspiriferina sapinea Cooper and Grant	R
Plectelasma guadalupense (Girty)	VR
Scapharina rugosa Cooper and Grant	VR
Sestropoma cribriferum Cooper and Grant	VR
Spiriferella sulcifer (Shumard)	VR
Thedusia ventricosa Cooper and Grant	R
LOCALITY A409 : Bell Canyon Formation, McCombs Member	
Acanthocrania sp.	VR
Collemataria spatulata Cooper and Grant	VR
Ctenalosia fixata Cooper and Stehli	VR
Derbyia sp.	VR
Eolyttonia sp.	VR
Hustedia opsia Cooper and Grant	R
Hustedia sp.	VR
Meekella skenoides Girty	VR
Paucispinifera sp.	VR
Pseudodielasma pinyonense Cooper and Grant	VR
Rhamnaria shumardi Cooper and Grant	VR
Thedusia ventricosa Cooper and Grant	VR
Xenosteges quadratus Cooper and Grant	VR
LOCALITY A410 : Bell Canyon Formation, Rader Member	
Altiplecus? deltosus Cooper and Grant	R
Arionthia lamaria Cooper and Grant	VR
Bryorhynchus bisulcatum (Shumard)	R
Cartorhium sp.	VR
Chonetinetes varians Cooper and Grant	VR
Composita affinis Girty	VR
Composita emarginata Girty	VR
Composita pyriformis Cooper and Grant	VR
Crenispirifer jubatus Cooper and Grant	R
Derbyia sp.	R
Deltarina magnicostata Cooper and Grant	VR
Dielasma sulcatum Girty	VR
Dyoros (Dyoros) intrepidus Cooper and Grant	VR
Echinosteges guadalupensis (Shumard)	VR
Eliva shumardi Cooper and Grant	VR
Elivina? annectans Cooper and Grant	VR
Fascicosta bella Cooper and Grant	VR
Fascicosta longaeva (Girty)	VR

	Rarity code
LOCALITY A410 - Continued	
Heteralosia magnispina Cooper and Grant	VR
Heteralosia sp. 6	VR
Hustedia demissa Cooper and Grant	VR
Hustedia opsia Cooper and Grant	VR
Hustedia rupinata Cooper and Grant	C
Metriolepis nabis Cooper and Grant	VR
Metriolepis sp.	VR
Micraphelia scitula Cooper and Grant	R
Micraphelia subalata Cooper and Grant	C
Paraspiriferina billingsi (Shumard)	R
Paucispinifera sp.	VR
Reticulariina echinata Cooper and Grant	VR
Reticulariina phoxa Cooper and Grant	VR
Reticulariina sp.	R
Sarganostega transversalis Cooper and Grant	VR
Scapharina rugosa Cooper and Grant	R
Sestropoma cribriferum Cooper and Grant	R
Spiriferella sulcifer (Shumard)	R
Thamnosia capitanensis (Girty)	VR
Thedusia ventricosa Cooper and Grant	R
Tropidelasma gregarium (Girty)	R
LOCALITY A414 : Cherry Canyon Formation, South Wells Member	
Glossothyropsis robusta (Girty)	VR
Leiorhynchoidea sulcata Cooper and Grant	R
LOCALITY A417 : Carlsbad Formation?	
Anteridocus bicostatus Cooper and Grant	VR
Arionthia lamaria Cooper and Grant	VR
Cyclacantharia sp. 6	R
Echinauris sp.	VR
Hustedia opsia Cooper and Grant	C
Meekella skenoides Girty	VR
Paraspiriferina sp.	R
Paucispinifera sp.	VR
LOCALITY A430 : Bell Canyon Formation, Lamar Member	
Allorhynchus venustulum Cooper and Grant	VR
Anomaloria anomala Cooper and Grant	VR
Aphaurosia rotundata Cooper and Grant	VR
Aphaurosia scutata Cooper and Grant	VR
Arionthia lamaria Cooper and Grant	VR
Astegosia subquadrata (Girty)	R
Collemataria spatulata Cooper and Grant	R
Composita affinis Girty	R
Crurithyris guadalupensis (Girty)	R
Deltarina magnicostata Cooper and Grant	VR
Derbyia sp. 1	R
Dielasma sp.	VR
Dielasma sulcatum Girty	VR
Dyoros (*Dyoros*) *hillanus* (Girty)	VR
Fascicosta elongata Cooper and Grant	VR
Heteralosia magnispina Cooper and Grant	VR
Hustedia opsia Cooper and Grant	R
Martinia rhomboidalis Girty	VR
Ombonia guadalupensis (Girty)	C
Paraspiriferina billingsi (Shumard)	R
Ptilotorhynchus delicatum Cooper and Grant	VR
Reticulariina sp.	VR
Rigbyella girtyi (Wanner and Sieverts)	VR
Sarganostega pressa Cooper and Grant	VR
Scapharina levis Cooper and Grant	VR
Stenoscisma trabeatum Cooper and Grant	VR

	Rarity code
Tautosia elegans (Girty)	VR
Tautosia shumardiana (Girty)	VR
Tropidelasma gregarium (Girty)	R
LOCALITY A435 : Bell Canyon Formation, Pinery Member	
Bryorhynchus bisulcatum (Shumard)	VR
Composita sp.	VR
Crenispirifer jubatus Cooper and Grant	VR
Derbyia sp.	VR
Dyoros (*Dyoros*) *intrepidus* Cooper and Grant	VR
Hustedia rupinata Cooper and Grant	R
Hustedia sp.	VR
Micraphelia scitula Cooper and Grant	VR
Paraspiriferina sapinea Cooper and Grant	VR
Reticulariina sp.	VR
Sarganostega transversalis Cooper and Grant	VR
Sestropoma cribriferum Cooper and Grant	VR
Spiriferellina nuda Cooper and Grant	VR
Thamnosia capitanensis (Girty)	VR
Thedusia trigonalis (Girty)	VR
Tropidelasma gregarium (Girty)	VR
LOCALITY A437 : Bell Canyon Formation, Pinery Member	
Altiplecus trapezoidalis Cooper and Grant	VR
Arionthia lamaria Cooper and Grant	VR
Composita pyriformis Cooper and Grant	VR
Crenispirifer jubatus Cooper and Grant	R
Derbyia sp.	R
Dielasma sp.	VR
Elivina? annectans Cooper and Grant	R
Hustedia demissa Cooper and Grant	R
Hustedia opsia Cooper and Grant	VR
Hustedia rupinata Cooper and Grant	C
Micraphelia scitula Cooper and Grant	VR
Paraspiriferina sapinea Cooper and Grant	C
Reticulariina welleri (Girty)	VR
Sestropoma cribriferum Cooper and Grant	VR
Spiriferellina nuda Cooper and Grant	VR
Thedusia trigonalis (Girty)	VR
Thedusia ventricosa Cooper and Grant	VR
LOCALITY A475 : Capitan Formation	
Cartorhium mexicanum (Shumard)	R
Composita emarginata Girty	VR
Eolyttonia sp.	VR
Liosotella popei (Shumard)	VR
Pseudoleptodus guadalupensis (Stehli)	R
Stenoscisma trabeatum Cooper and Grant	R
Thamnosia capitanensis (Girty)	VR
LOCALITY A492 : Bone Spring Formation	
Acosarina mesoplatys (R.E. King)	A
Antronaria dissona Cooper and Grant	C
Antronaria specialis Cooper and Grant	C
Antronaria spectabilis Cooper and Grant	C
Chonosteges limbatus Cooper and Grant	VR
Chonosteges variabilis Cooper and Grant	VR
Composita cracens Cooper and Grant	R
Composita sp.	R
Cyclacantharia sp.	VR
Derbyia sp.	VR
Diplanus lamellatus (R.E. King)	VR
Dyoros (*Lissosia*) *vagabundus* Cooper and Grant	VR
Echinauris sp.?	VR

LOCALITY A492 - Continued	Rarity code
Enteletes leonardensis R.E. King	R
Enteletes subcircularis Cooper and Grant	R
Glyptosteges insculptus Cooper and Grant	R
Gypospirifer infraplicus (R.E. King)	VR
Hercosia uddeni (Böse)	VR
Heterelasma sulciplicatum Cooper and Grant	R
Hustedia ampullacea Cooper and Grant	R
Hustedia decollatensis Cooper and Grant	R
Linoproductus sp.	VR
Meekella hessensis R.E. King	C
Neophricadothyris sp.	R
Nudauris sp.	VR
Peniculauris imitata Cooper and Grant	VR
Petasmatherus sp.	VR
Rhamnaria sp.	VR
Rhipidomella hessensis R.E. King	C
Rhipidomella hispidula Cooper and Grant	R
Spinifrons magna Cooper and Grant	VR
Spyridiophora reticulata (R.E. King)	VR
Stenoscisma levicostum Cooper and Grant	R
Stenoscisma sp.	R
Wellerella? nitidula Cooper and Grant	C

LOCALITY A496 : Cherry Canyon Formation, Getaway Member |
---|---
Allorhynchus permianum permianum Stehli | VR
Allorhynchus sp. | R
Bothrionia pulchra Cooper and Grant | VR
Cartorhium retusum Cooper and Grant | VR
Composita parasulcata Cooper and Grant | R
Composita prospera Cooper and Grant | VR
Crurithyris tholiaphor Cooper and Grant | R
Cyclacantharia kingorum Cooper and Grant | C
Cyclacantharia robusta Cooper and Grant | VR
Derbyia pannucia Cooper and Grant | VR
Dielasma sp. | VR
Dyoros (Dyoros) extensus Cooper and Grant | R
Dyoros (Tetragonetes) complanatus Cooper and Grant | R
Echinauris productelloides Cooper and Grant | C
Echinosteges tuberculatus (R.E. King) | VR
Eolyttonia progressa Cooper and Grant | R
Grandaurispina undulata Cooper and Grant | VR
Hustedia citeria Cooper and Grant | C
Hustedia hapala Cooper and Grant | R
Hustedia tomea Cooper and Grant | VR
Leiorhynchoidea scelesta Cooper and Grant | VR
Liosotella wordensis (R.E. King) | C
Meekella skenoides Girty | R
Metriolepis exserta Cooper and Grant | VR
Neophricadothyris conara Cooper and Grant | VR
Paraspiriferina paginata Cooper and Grant | VR
Paucispinifera tumida Cooper and Grant | VR
Petasmatherus opulus Cooper and Grant | VR
Pseudodielasma magnum Cooper and Grant | R
Pseudodielasma sp. | VR
Reticulariina girtyi Cooper and Grant | R
Rhamnaria sulcata Cooper and Grant | R
Rhynchopora palumbula Cooper and Grant | VR
Thedusia dischides Cooper and Grant | VR
Undulella guadalupensis Cooper and Grant | R
Wellerella girtyi seorsa Cooper and Grant | C

LOCALITY A497 : Bone Spring Formation |
---|---
Antronaria mesicostalis (Girty) | VR
Antronaria spectabilis Cooper and Grant | R

 | Rarity code
---|---
Antronaria voluminosa Cooper and Grant | VR
Composita cracens Cooper and Grant | R
Crenispirifer angulatus (R.E. King) | R
Derbyia sp. | VR
Eolyttonia pocillata Cooper and Grant | VR
Hustedia hessensis R.E. King | R
Isogramma sp. | VR
Kozlowskia kingi Stehli | VR
Kozlowskia sp. | VR
Meekella hessensis R.E. King | VR
Pseudoleptodus sp. | VR
Reticulariina sp. | VR
Rhipidomella hessensis R.E. King | R
Rhipidomella hispidula Cooper and Grant | R
Spinifrons magna Cooper and Grant | VR
Stenoscisma levicostum Cooper and Grant | VR
Wellerella? nitidula Cooper and Grant | VR

LOCALITY A500 : Cathedral Mountain Formation |
---|---
Acanthocrania sp. | VR
Acosarina mesoplatys (R.E. King) | A
Anteridocus erugatus Cooper and Grant | VR
Anteridocus gongylus Cooper and Grant | R
Antronaria speciosa Cooper and Grant | VR
Cartorhium latum (R.E. King) | C
Cenorhynchia mitigata Cooper and Grant | VR
Choanodus irregularis Cooper and Grant | R
Choanodus perfectus Cooper and Grant | VR
Chondronia bella Cooper and Grant | R
Chonosteges pulcher Cooper and Grant | R
Chonosteges variabilis Cooper and Grant | R
Collemataria gregaria Cooper and Grant | C
Composita bucculenta Cooper and Grant | VR
Composita imbricata Cooper and Grant | R
Composita sp. | R
Compressoproductus curtus Cooper and Grant | VR
Coscinophora nodosa (Cooper and Stehli) | R
Derbyia complicata Cooper and Grant | VR
Derbyia informis Cooper and Grant | R
Derbyia laqueata Cooper and Grant | C
Dielasma sp. | VR
Diplanus lamellatus (R.E. King) | R
Dyoros (Dyoros) extensiformis Cooper and Grant | VR
Dyoros (Lissosia) vagabundus Cooper and Grant | VR
Dyoros (Tetragonetes) rectangulatus Cooper and Grant | R
Echinauris irregularis Cooper and Grant | C
Edriosteges multispinosus Muir-Wood and Cooper | R
Enteletes leonardensis R.E. King | A
Enteletes plummeri R.E. King | VR
Eolyttonia circularis Cooper and Grant | R
Eolyttonia pocillata Cooper and Grant | C
Goniarina futilis Cooper and Grant | R
Hercosia uddeni (Böse) | C
Heterelasma gibbosum Cooper and Grant | VR
Hustedia ampullacea Cooper and Grant | VR
Hustedia lusca Cooper and Grant | A
Hustedia spicata Cooper and Grant | C
Institella leonardensis (R.E. King) | A
Lepidospirifer angulatus Cooper and Grant | VR
Lepidospirifer demissus Cooper and Grant | VR
Lepidospirifer inferus Cooper and Grant | VR
Linoproductus delicatus Cooper and Grant | VR
Loxophragmus ellipticus Cooper and Grant | C
Martinia miranda Cooper and Grant | R
Meekella calathica Cooper and Grant | A
Megousia auriculata Muir-Wood and Cooper | VR

LOCALITY A500 - Continued	Rarity code
Metriolepis carotica Cooper and Grant	R
Metriolepis tegulata Cooper and Grant	R
Neophricadothyris bullata Cooper and Grant	C
Neospirifer mansuetus Cooper and Grant	R
Niviconia globosa (R.E. King)	A
Peniculauris subcostata (R.E. King)	VR
Petasmaia expansa Cooper and Grant	R
Pontisia stehlii stehlii Cooper and Grant	VR
Pontisia stehlii tumidosa Cooper and Grant	VR
Rallacosta actina Cooper and Grant	VR
Reticulariina sp.	VR
Rhamnaria tenuispinosa Cooper and Grant	VR
Rhipidomella hispidula Cooper and Grant	A
Rugatia paraindica (McKee)	VR
Spiriferellina tricosa Cooper and Grant	VR
Stenoscisma doricranum Cooper and Grant	VR
Stenoscisma triquetrum Cooper and Grant	VR
Tautosia fastigiata Cooper and Grant	VR
Texarina wordensis (R.E. King)	VR
Thedusia bucrenata Cooper and Grant	VR
Torynechus caelatus Cooper and Grant	VR
Trophisina fenaria Cooper and Grant	VR
Xenosteges adherens Muir-Wood and Cooper	C

LOCALITY A501 : Road Canyon Formation	Rarity code
Acosarina mesoplatys (R.E. King)	C
Antronaria speciosa Cooper and Grant	VR
Composita bucculenta Cooper and Grant	R
Composita sp.	R
Cooperina subcuneata Cooper and Grant	VR
Derbyia laqueata Cooper and Grant	VR
Derbyia sp.	VR
Dyoros (Lissosia) vagabundus Cooper and Grant	VR
Echinauris irregularis Cooper and Grant	VR
Edriosteges multispinosus Muir-Wood and Cooper	VR
Hercosestria cribrosa Cooper and Grant	VR
Hercosia uddeni (Böse)	VR
Hustedia lusca Cooper and Grant	C
Hustedia spicata Cooper and Grant	VR
Institella leonardensis (R.E. King)	VR
Meekella calathica Cooper and Grant	R
Rhipidomella hispidula Cooper and Grant	VR
Spiriferellina tricosa Cooper and Grant	VR
Stenoscisma aptatum Cooper and Grant	VR
Xenosteges trivialis Cooper and Grant	VR

LOCALITY A503 : Road Canyon Formation	Rarity code
Acosarina mesoplatys (R.E. King)	R
Ametoria residua Cooper and Grant	VR
Collemataria sp.	R
Composita crassa Cooper and Grant	R
Cyclacantharia paucispinosa Cooper and Grant	R
Cyclacantharia transitoria Cooper and Grant	VR
Derbyia cincinnata Cooper and Grant	VR
Derbyia informis Cooper and Grant	VR
Dielasma ellipsoideum Cooper and Grant	VR
Dyoros (Dyoros) angulatus Cooper and Grant	VR
Dyoros (Dyoros) extensus Cooper and Grant	R
Dyoros (Dyoros) transversus Cooper and Grant	VR
Dyoros (Tetragonetes) solidus Cooper and Grant	R
Echinauris irregularis Cooper and Grant	VR
Echinauris lappacea Cooper and Grant	VR
Echinauris liumbona Cooper and Grant	VR
Echinauris parva Cooper and Grant	C
Edriosteges multispinosus Muir-Wood and Cooper	VR

| Rarity code
--- | ---
Edriosteges sp. | VR
Eolyttonia sp. | R
Hercosestria cribrosa Cooper and Grant | VR
Hustedia consuta Cooper and Grant | R
Hustedia narinosa Cooper and Grant | C
Hustedia sp. | VR
Isogramma sp. | VR
Meekella calathica Cooper and Grant | C
Megousia auriculata Muir-Wood and Cooper | R
Metriolepis tegulata Cooper and Grant | VR
Neophricadothyris bullata Cooper and Grant | VR
Neophricadothyris crassibecca Cooper and Grant | VR
Neospirifer bakeri bakeri R.E. King | R
Neospirifer formulosus Cooper and Grant | VR
Niviconia globosa (R.E. King) | VR
Paucispinifera sulcata Cooper and Grant | VR
Peniculauris costata Cooper and Grant | VR
Rhamnaria tenuispinosa Cooper and Grant | VR
Rhynchopora hebetata Cooper and Grant | VR
Rugatia mckeei Cooper and Grant | VR
Stenoscisma camurum Cooper and Grant | VR
Stenoscisma triquetrum Cooper and Grant | R
Thedusia mesocostata Cooper and Grant | R
Tropidelasma corniculum Cooper and Grant | VR
Waagenoconcha convexa Cooper and Grant | VR
Yakovlevia immatura Cooper and Grant | VR

LOCALITY A504 : Cathedral Mountain Formation	Rarity code
Anteridocus gongylus Cooper and Grant	VR
Cartorhium latum (R.E. King)	VR
Choanodus perfectus Cooper and Grant	VR
Chonosteges pulcher Cooper and Grant	VR
Chonosteges variabilis Cooper and Grant	VR
Collemataria gregaria Cooper and Grant	VR
Composita crassa Cooper and Grant	C
Derbyia sp.	VR
Dyoros (Lissosia) vagabundus Cooper and Grant	R
Eolyttonia circularis Cooper and Grant	VR
Hustedia lusca Cooper and Grant	R
Hustedia spicata Cooper and Grant	VR
Lepidospirifer demissus Cooper and Grant	VR
Martinia miranda Cooper and Grant	R
Meekella calathica Cooper and Grant	R
Meekella sp.	VR
Metriolepis tegulata Cooper and Grant	VR
Neophricadothyris bullata Cooper and Grant	R
Niviconia globosa (R.E. King)	VR
Rhamnaria tenuispinosa Cooper and Grant	VR
Rhipidomella hispidula Cooper and Grant	VR
Rugatia paraindica (McKee)	VR
Texarina wordensis (R.E. King)	VR
Torynechus caelatus Cooper and Grant	VR
Xenosteges adherens Muir-Wood and Cooper	R

LOCALITY A505 : Word Formation, Willis Ranch Member	Rarity code
Allorhynchus permianum wordense Cooper and Grant	R
Allorhynchus triangulatum Cooper and Grant	VR
Cactosteges anomalus Cooper and Grant	VR
Cancrinella subquadrata Cooper and Grant	VR
Collemataria elongata Cooper and Grant	C
Composita enormis Cooper and Grant	C
Cooperina inexpectata Termier, Termier and Pajaud	R
Cyclacantharia kingorum Cooper and Grant	A
Derbyia filosa Cooper and Grant	VR
Derbyia texta Cooper and Grant	C

Rarity code

LOCALITY A505 - Continued

Dielasma adamanteum Cooper and Grant	R
Dielasma zebratum Cooper and Grant	R
Dyoros (Dyoros) extensus Cooper and Grant	A
Dyoros (Lissosia) concavus Cooper and Grant	R
Echinauris lateralis Muir-Wood and Cooper	C
Echinosteges tuberculatus (R.E. King)	C
Glossothyropsis rectangulata Cooper and Grant	VR
Grandaurispina kingorum Muir-Wood and Cooper	C
Heteralosia hystricula (Girty)	C
Heterelasma concavum Cooper and Grant	VR
Hustedia pugilla pugilla Cooper and Grant	C
Lepidocrania sublamellosa Cooper and Grant	VR
Liosotella wordensis (R.E. King)	VA
Meekella skenoides Girty	A
Megousia definita Cooper and Grant	R
Paraspiriferina setulosa Cooper and Grant	C
Paucispinifera auriculata Muir-Wood and Cooper	A
Phrenophoria subcarinata Cooper and Grant	VR
Rhamnaria kingorum Muir-Wood and Cooper	A
Rhynchopora palumbula Cooper and Grant	VR
Spiriferella calcarata Cooper and Grant	R
Spiriferellina hilli (Girty)	R
Thedusia procera Cooper and Grant	C
Undulella undulata Cooper and Grant	C
Waagenoconcha magnifica Cooper and Grant	VR
Wellerella girtyi girtyi Cooper and Grant	A
Xenosteges quadratus Cooper and Grant	R
Yakovlevia hessorum Cooper and Grant	C

LOCALITY A506 : Word Formation, Willis Ranch Member

Acanthocrania intermedia Cooper and Grant	VR
Cactosteges anomalus Cooper and Grant	R
Collemataria elongata Cooper and Grant	C
Composita parasulcata Cooper and Grant	VR
Cooperina inexpectata Termier, Termier and Pajaud	R
Costispinifera costata (R.E. King)	C
Cyclacantharia kingorum Cooper and Grant	C
Derbyia filosa Cooper and Grant	VR
Derbyia pannucia Cooper and Grant	R
Derbyia texta Cooper and Grant	VR
Dielasma adamanteum Cooper and Grant	VR
Dielasma zebratum Cooper and Grant	VR
Dyoros (Dyoros) tenuis Cooper and Grant	R
Echinauris lateralis Muir-Wood and Cooper	VR
Echinosteges tuberculatus (R.E. King)	VR
Enteletes wordensis R.E. King	C
Grandaurispina kingorum Muir-Wood and Cooper	R
Heteralosia hystricula (Girty)	C
Heterelasma concavum Cooper and Grant	VR
Hustedia pugilla pugilla Cooper and Grant	R
Hustedia sculptilis Cooper and Grant	VR
Liosotella wordensis (R.E. King)	C
Meekella skenoides Girty	C
Megousia definita Cooper and Grant	VR
Megousia flexuosa Cooper and Grant	VR
Metriolepis pulvinata Cooper and Grant	R
Neospirifer amphigyus Cooper and Grant	VR
Paraspiriferina laqueata Cooper and Grant	R
Paucispinifera transversa Cooper and Grant	R
Rhamnaria kingorum Muir-Wood and Cooper	R
Rhynchopora palumbula Cooper and Grant	VR
Spiriferellina hilli (Girty)	C
Thedusia procera Cooper and Grant	R

Rarity code

Tropidelasma anthicum Cooper and Grant	VR
Xenosteges quadratus Cooper and Grant	VR

LOCALITY A507 : Road Canyon Formation

Acosarina mesoplatys (R.E. King)	C
Cenorhynchia mitigata Cooper and Grant	VR
Cenorhynchia parvula Cooper and Grant	VR
Composita stalagmium Cooper and Grant	C
Cyclacantharia paucispinosa Cooper and Grant	R
Derbyia cincinnata Cooper and Grant	VR
Derbyia laqueata Cooper and Grant	R
Dielasma ellipsoideum Cooper and Grant	R
Edriosteges multispinosus Muir-Wood and Cooper	VR
Hercosestria cribrosa Cooper and Grant	SA
Holotricharina hirsuta Cooper and Grant	C
Hustedia connorsi Cooper and Grant	A
Kutorginella umbonata (Muir-Wood and Cooper)	VR
Meekella calathica Cooper and Grant	C
Megousia auriculata Muir-Wood and Cooper	VR
Neophricadothyris bullata Cooper and Grant	C
Neospirifer thescelus Cooper and Grant	R
Paucispinifera sulcata Cooper and Grant	C
Petasmatherus nitidus Cooper and Grant	VR
Reticulariina craticula Cooper and Grant	C
Rhamnaria tenuispinosa Cooper and Grant	VR
Rhamnaria vinnula Cooper and Grant	VR
Rhynchopora hebetata Cooper and Grant	VR
Stenoscisma triquetrum Cooper and Grant	R
Texarina wordensis (R.E. King)	R
Tschernyschewia sp.	VR

LOCALITY A509 : Road Canyon Formation

Composita crassa Cooper and Grant	VR
Derbyia laqueata Cooper and Grant	VR
Dielasma emarginatum Cooper and Grant	VR
Dyoros (Dyoros) angulatus Cooper and Grant	R
Dyoros (Dyoros) extensus Cooper and Grant	VR
Dyoros (Lissosia) parvus Cooper and Grant	R
Echinauris bella Cooper and Grant	R
Heterelasma glansfagea Cooper and Grant	R
Hustedia consuta Cooper and Grant	C
Hustedia cuneata Cooper and Grant	R
Liosotella costata Cooper and Grant	VR
Megousia auriculata Muir-Wood and Cooper	R
Metriolepis ziczac Cooper and Grant	VR
Neospirifer bakeri bakeri R.E. King	R
Paucispinifera sulcata Cooper and Grant	VR
Rhynchopora sphenoides Cooper and Grant	VR
Spiriferella sp.	VR
Tautosia galbina Cooper and Grant	VR
Yakovlevia sulcata Cooper and Grant	R

LOCALITY A512 : Cherry Canyon Formation, Getaway Member

Acanthocrania conferta Cooper and Grant	VR
Allorhynchus permianum permianum Stehli	R
Bothrionia guadalupensis Cooper and Grant	C
Bryorhynchus gratiosum (Girty)	VR
Cancrinella sp.	VR
Cartorhium retusum Cooper and Grant	R
Cenorhynchia nasuta Cooper and Grant	R
Composita parasulcata Cooper and Grant	R
Composita prospera Cooper and Grant	A
Cooperina inexpectata Termier, Termier and Pajaud	VR
Craspedona newelli Cooper and Grant	VR
Crurithyris sp.	VR

	Rarity code
LOCALITY A512 - Continued	
Crurithyris tholiaphor Cooper and Grant	C
Ctenalosia fixata Cooper and Stehli	C
Cyclacantharia robusta Cooper and Grant	VA
Derbyia filosa Cooper and Grant	C
Derbyia pannucia Cooper and Grant	R
Derbyia texta Cooper and Grant	A
Dielasma ligonorum Cooper and Grant	R
Dielasma pictile Cooper and Grant	C
Dielasma sp.	C
Divaricosta squarrosa Cooper and Grant	R
Dyoros (*Dyoros*) *convexus* Cooper and Grant	VA
Dyoros (*Tetragonetes*) *auriculatus* Cooper and Grant	VR
Dyoros (*Tetragonetes*) *subquadratus* Cooper and Grant	C
Echinauris productelloides Cooper and Grant	C
Echinosteges tuberculatus (R.E. King)	VR
Eolyttonia progressa Cooper and Grant	C
Glossothyropsis sp. (Girty)	VR
Grandaurispina rudis Cooper and Grant	C
Heteralosia magnispina Cooper and Grant	C
Heterelasma concavum Cooper and Grant	VR
Hustedia citeria Cooper and Grant	VA
Hustedia hapala Cooper and Grant	A
Hustedia tomea Cooper and Grant	C
Leiorhynchoidea scelesta Cooper and Grant	C
Leurosina delicata Cooper and Grant	C
Liosotella spinumbona Cooper and Grant	A
Liosotella wordensis (R.E. King)	C
Madarosia pentagona Cooper and Grant	VR
Meekella skenoides Girty	A
Megousia definita Cooper and Grant	VR
Metriolepis exserta Cooper and Grant	C
Metriolepis sp.	VR
Paranorella sp. 3	VR
Paraspiriferina paginata Cooper and Grant	C
Paucispinifera sp.	VR
Paucispinifera tumida Cooper and Grant	C
Petasmatherus recticardinatus Cooper and Grant	VR
Petrocrania teretis Cooper and Grant	VR
Phrenophoria irregularis Cooper and Grant	R
Phrenophoria pinguiformis Cooper and Grant	R
Polymorpharia polymorpha Cooper and Grant	R
Pseudodielasma magnum Cooper and Grant	VR
Pseudodielasma sp.	R
Ptygmactrum sp.	VR
Ptygmactrum spiculatum Cooper and Grant	VR
Reticulariina roscida Cooper and Grant	A
Rhamnaria sulcata Cooper and Grant	C
Rhynchopora guadalupensis Cooper and Grant	VR
Sestropoma cribriferum Cooper and Grant	R
Spiriferella gloverae Cooper and Grant	R
Stenoscisma sp.	R
Strophalosia inexpectans Cooper and Grant	VR
Tautosia transenna Cooper and Grant	C
Thedusia dischides Cooper and Grant	VA
Tropidelasma furcillatum Cooper and Grant	R
Waagenoconcha magnifica Cooper and Grant	R
Wellerella girtyi seorsa Cooper and Grant	VR
Xenosteges anomalus Cooper and Grant	C
Xenosteges quadratus Cooper and Grant	C
Yakovlevia costellata Cooper and Grant	VR
LOCALITY A519 : Cherry Canyon Formation, Getaway Member	
Acanthocrania sp.	VR

	Rarity code
Bothrionia pulchra Cooper and Grant	VR
Cartorhium retusum Cooper and Grant	VR
Composita parasulcata Cooper and Grant	VR
Composita prospera Cooper and Grant	VR
Cyclacantharia kingorum Cooper and Grant	R
Derbyia texta Cooper and Grant	R
Dielasma pictile Cooper and Grant	VR
Dyoros (*Dyoros*) *convexus* Cooper and Grant	C
Dyoros (*Tetragonetes*) *auriculatus* Cooper and Grant	VR
Dyoros (*Tetragonetes*) *complanatus* Cooper and Grant	VR
Echinauris productelloides Cooper and Grant	C
Eolyttonia progressa Cooper and Grant	R
Grandaurispina rudis Cooper and Grant	C
Heteralosia magnispina Cooper and Grant	VR
Hustedia citeria Cooper and Grant	C
Hustedia tomea Cooper and Grant	VR
Lepidocrania sublamellosa Cooper and Grant	VR
Liosotella wordensis (R.E. King)	C
Meekella skenoides Girty	VR
Megousia definita Cooper and Grant	VR
Metriolepis exserta Cooper and Grant	VR
Paraspiriferina paginata Cooper and Grant	VR
Paucispinifera tumida Cooper and Grant	R
Pseudoleptodus getawayensis Stehli	VR
Reticulariina roscida Cooper and Grant	R
Rhamnaria sulcata Cooper and Grant	R
Thedusia dischides Cooper and Grant	R
Xenosteges quadratus Cooper and Grant	VR
LOCALITY A520 : Skinner Ranch Formation	
Acosarina dorsisulcata Cooper and Grant	R
Acritosia peculiaris Cooper and Grant	VR
Acritosia teguliferoides (R.E. King)	R
Antronaria dissona Cooper and Grant	R
Composita apheles Cooper and Grant	R
Crenispirifer angulatus (R.E. King)	VR
Derbyia crenulata Girty	R
Echinauris sp.?	VR
Elliottella minima (Stehli)	VR
Enteletes sp.	R
Hustedia hessensis R.E. King	R
Kozlowskia sp.	VR
Linoproductus angustus R.E. King	VR
Meekella hessensis R.E. King	C
Micraphelia sp.	VR
Neophricadothyris bullata Cooper and Grant	VR
Oncosarina sp.	VR
Orthotichia newelli Cooper and Grant	VR
Rhipidomella hessensis R.E. King	VR
Scacchinella titan Cooper and Grant	VR
Stenoscisma sp.	VR
LOCALITY A524 : Bell Canyon Formation, Pinery Member	
Altiplecus? deltosus Cooper and Grant	VR
Anteridocus swallovianus (Shumard)	VR
Bryorhynchus bisulcatum (Shumard)	VR
Cartorhium sp.	VR
Chonetinetes varians Cooper and Grant	VR
Composita affinis Girty	VR
Composita emarginata Girty	R
Composita pyriformis Cooper and Grant	VR
Crenispirifer jubatus Cooper and Grant	R
Derbyia sp.	VR
Dielasma sulcatum Girty	VR

	Rarity code

LOCALITY A524 - Continued

Species	Rarity code
Dyoros (*Dyoros*) *intrepidus* Cooper and Grant	R
Elivina? *annectans* Cooper and Grant	VR
Fascicosta longaeva (Girty)	VR
Heteralosia magnispina Cooper and Grant	VR
Hustedia rupinata Cooper and Grant	R
Micraphelia scitula Cooper and Grant	VR
Paraspiriferina sapinea Cooper and Grant	VR
Paucispinifera rara Cooper and Grant	VR
Plectelasma guadalupense (Girty)	VR
Pseudodielasma pinyonense Cooper and Grant	VR
Rallacosta imporcata Cooper and Grant	VR
Reticulariina welleri (Girty)	VR
Sarganostega transversalis Cooper and Grant	VR
Sestropoma cribriferum Cooper and Grant	VR
Tautosia shumardiana (Girty)	VR
Thedusia emarginata Cooper and Grant	VR
Thedusia ventricosa Cooper and Grant	VR

LOCALITY A528 : Bell Canyon Formation, Pinery Member

Species	Rarity code
Arionthia lamaria Cooper and Grant	VR
Composita affinis Girty	VR
Crenispirifer jubatus Cooper and Grant	R
Dyoros (*Dyoros*) *intrepidus* Cooper and Grant	VR
Heteralosia magnispina Cooper and Grant	R
Hustedia opsia Cooper and Grant	VR
Hustedia rupinata Cooper and Grant	R
Paraspiriferina billingsi (Shumard)	VR
Reticulariina sp.	R
Reticulariina welleri (Girty)	VR
Sarganostega transversalis Cooper and Grant	VR
Scapharina rugosa Cooper and Grant	R
Sestropoma cribriferum Cooper and Grant	R
Tropidelasma gregarium (Girty)	VR

LOCALITY A537 : Bell Canyon Formation, Pinery Member

Species	Rarity code
Bryorhynchus bisulcatum (Shumard)	VR
Composita emarginata Girty	R
Composita pyriformis Cooper and Grant	VR
Craspedona newelli Cooper and Grant	VR
Crenispirifer jubatus Cooper and Grant	VR
Derbyia sp.	R
Dielasma sp.	VR
Dielasma sulcatum Girty	VR
Hustedia rupinata Cooper and Grant	R
Hustedia sp.	VR
Meekella skenoides Girty	VR
Metriolepis sp.	VR
Micraphelia scitula Cooper and Grant	R
Paraspiriferina sapinea Cooper and Grant	VR
Reticulariina sp.	VR
Rhamnaria shumardi Cooper and Grant	VR
Sestropoma cribriferum Cooper and Grant	VR
Spiriferella sulcifer (Shumard)	VR
Spiriferellina nuda Cooper and Grant	VR
Thamnosia capitanensis (Girty)	VR
Thedusia trigonalis (Girty)	VR
Tropidelasma gregarium (Girty)	VR

LOCALITY A547 : Cherry Canyon Formation, Getaway Member

Species	Rarity code
Allorhynchus permianum permianum Stehli	VR
Composita sp.	VR

Species	Rarity code
Hustedia citeria Cooper and Grant	VR
Thedusia dischides Cooper and Grant	VR

LOCALITY A585 : Cherry Canyon Formation, Getaway Member

Species	Rarity code
Allorhynchus formulosum Cooper and Grant	C
Cartorhium retusum Cooper and Grant	VR
Cenorhynchia nasuta Cooper and Grant	VR
Composita parasulcata Cooper and Grant	VR
Composita prospera Cooper and Grant	C
Dielasma compactum Cooper and Grant	VR
Dyoros (*Dyoros*) *extensus* Cooper and Grant	VR
Heterelasma concavum Cooper and Grant	VR
Hustedia citeria Cooper and Grant	C
Meekella skenoides Girty	VR
Metriolepis sp.	VR
Paraspiriferina paginata Cooper and Grant	VR
Reticulariina girtyi Cooper and Grant	R
Spiriferella sp.	VR
Stenoscisma camurum Cooper and Grant	C
Stenoscisma sp.	R

LOCALITY A591 : Bone Spring Formation

Species	Rarity code
Acosarina dorsisulcata Cooper and Grant	VR
Antronaria pluricosta Cooper and Grant	R
Antronaria specialis Cooper and Grant	VR
Antronaria spectabilis Cooper and Grant	R
Cartorhium latum (R.E. King)	VR
Choanodus perfectus Cooper and Grant	VR
Chondronia bella Cooper and Grant	R
Chonosteges variabilis Cooper and Grant	R
Composita cracens Cooper and Grant	C
Crurithyris longirostris Cooper and Grant	R
Derbyia sp.	VR
Dielasma sp.	VR
Echinauris irregularis Cooper and Grant	VR
Enteletes sp.	R
Eolyttonia circularis Cooper and Grant	VR
Eolyttonia pocillata Cooper and Grant	VR
Glyptosteges insculptus Cooper and Grant	C
Hercosia uddeni (Böse)	C
Hustedia decollatensis Cooper and Grant	C
Iotina minuta Cooper and Grant	R
Lirellaria diabloensis Cooper and Grant	VR
Meekella hessensis R.E. King	C
Meekella sp.	VR
Metriolepis diabloensis Cooper and Grant	R
Neophricadothyris bullata Cooper and Grant	R
Neophricadothyris sp.	C
Neospirifer neali Cooper and Grant	VR
Nudauris sp.	VR
Phrenophoria repugnans Cooper and Grant	R
Pseudoleptodus? sp. 2	VR
Reticulariina sp.	VR
Rhipidomella hessensis R.E. King	VR
Sceletonia crassa Cooper and Grant	VR
Spinifrons quadrata Stehli	VR
Spyridiophora reticulata (R.E. King)	C
Stenoscisma levicostum Cooper and Grant	C
Thedusia sp.	VR
Tschernyschewia americana Cooper and Grant	VR
Wellerella? *nitidula* Cooper and Grant	C

LOCALITY A592 : Bone Spring Formation

Species	Rarity code
Dyoros (*Lissosia*) *vagabundus* Cooper and Grant	VR
Wellerella? *nitidula* Cooper and Grant	VR

	Rarity code
LOCALITY A600 : Cherry Canyon Formation, Getaway Member	
Allorhynchus permianum permianum Stehli	R
Bothrionia pulchra Cooper and Grant	VR
Cancrinella sp.	VR
Cartorhium retusum Cooper and Grant	R
Composita parasulcata Cooper and Grant	C
Composita prospera Cooper and Grant	R
Composita sp.	R
Cooperina inexpectata Termier, Termier and Pajaud	VR
Crurithyris tholiaphor Cooper and Grant	R
Cyclacantharia kingorum Cooper and Grant	C
Cyclacantharia robusta Cooper and Grant	VR
Derbyia pannucia Cooper and Grant	VR
Derbyia texta Cooper and Grant	C
Dielasma pictile Cooper and Grant	R
Dielasma sp.	VR
Dyoros (Dyoros) convexus Cooper and Grant	VR
Dyoros (Dyoros) extensus Cooper and Grant	R
Dyoros (Tetragonetes) complanatus Cooper and Grant	C
Echinauris productelloides Cooper and Grant	C
Echinosteges tuberculatus (R.E. King)	R
Eolyttonia progressa Cooper and Grant	R
Eolyttonia sp.	VR
Grandaurispina sp. 6	VR
Grandaurispina undulata Cooper and Grant	VR
Heteralosia magnispina Cooper and Grant	VR
Hustedia citeria Cooper and Grant	R
Leiorhynchoidea scelesta Cooper and Grant	VR
Leurosina delicata Cooper and Grant	VR
Liosotella spinumbona Cooper and Grant	VR
Liosotella wordensis (R.E. King)	C
Meekella skenoides Girty	R
Metriolepis exserta Cooper and Grant	VR
Neophricadothyris conara Cooper and Grant	VR
Paranorella aquilonia Cooper and Grant	VR
Paraspiriferina paginata Cooper and Grant	R
Paucispinifera tumida Cooper and Grant	R
Petasmatherus opulus Cooper and Grant	R
Phrenophoria pinguiformis Cooper and Grant	VR
Pseudodielasma magnum Cooper and Grant	R
Pseudodielasma sp.	R
Reticulariina girtyi Cooper and Grant	R
Rhamnaria sulcata Cooper and Grant	C
Rhynchopora guadalupensis Cooper and Grant	VR
Spiriferella calcarata Cooper and Grant	VR
Spiriferella gloverae Cooper and Grant	VR
Tautosia transenna Cooper and Grant	VR
Thedusia dischides Cooper and Grant	VR
Undulella guadalupensis Cooper and Grant	C
Wellerella girtyi seorsa Cooper and Grant	R
Xenosteges quadratus Cooper and Grant	R
LOCALITY A624 : Bone Spring Formation	
Antronaria specialis Cooper and Grant	VR
Composita cracens Cooper and Grant	VR
Enteletes stehlii Cooper and Grant	R
Hustedia sp.	VR
Kochiproductus elongatus Cooper and Grant	VR
Meekella hessensis R.E. King	VR
Neophricadothyris catatona Cooper and Grant	R
Rhipidomella hessensis R.E. King	R
Wellerella? nitidula Cooper and Grant	VR
LOCALITY A625 : Bone Spring Formation	
Acosarina dorsisulcata Cooper and Grant	R

	Rarity code
Acritosia teguliferoides (R.E. King)	R
Altiplecus cooperi Stehli	VR
Antiquatonia planumbona Stehli	VR
Antronaria dissona Cooper and Grant	VR
Antronaria mesicostalis (Girty)	VR
Cartorhium zoyei Cooper and Grant	VR
Chonetinella biplicata (R.E. King)	VR
Collemataria americana (Girty)	VR
Collemataria marshalli (Stehli)	C
Composita cracens Cooper and Grant	R
Crenispirifer angulatus (R.E. King)	R
Derbyia crenulata Girty	C
Derbyia nasuta Girty	VR
Dielasma diabloense Stehli	R
Diplanus lamellatus (R.E. King)	VR
Elliottella minima (Stehli)	R
Enteletes stehlii Cooper and Grant	VR
Eolyttonia diabloensis (Stehli)	C
Goniarina permiana (Stehli)	VR
Hustedia hessensis R.E. King	C
Kozlowskia kingi Stehli	R
Leurosina sinesulca (Stehli)	R
Leurosina vulgarica Cooper and Grant	R
Linoproductus angustus R.E. King	VR
Liraria lirata Cooper and Grant	VR
Meekella attenuata Girty	C
Meekella intermedia Cooper and Grant	VR
Meekella sp.	VR
Nudauris diabloensis Stehli	R
Orthotichia irregularis Cooper and Grant	R
Petrocrania diabloensis Cooper and Grant	VR
Poikilosakos informis Cooper and Grant	VR
Pontisia nanas (Stehli)	VR
Quadrochonetes girtyi Stehli	VR
Ramavectus diabloensis Stehli	R
Reticulariina newelli (Stehli)	VR
Reticulariina tetrica Cooper and Grant	VR
Rhamnaria eximia Cooper and Grant	R
Rhipidomella hessensis R.E. King	VR
Scacchinella americana Stehli	VR
Spinifrons quadrata Stehli	C
Tautosia lenumbona (Stehli)	VR
Teguliferina conida (Stehli)	R
Thamnosia parvispinosa (Stehli)	VR
LOCALITY A626 : Hueco Formation	
Dasysaria undulata Cooper and Grant	VR
Derbyia sp.	VR
Kochiproductus sp.	VR
Meekella sp.	VR
LOCALITY A628 : Bone Spring Formation	
Acritosia teguliferoides (R.E. King)	R
Altiplecus cooperi Stehli	VR
Chonetinella victoriana (Girty)	VR
Collemataria americana (Girty)	VR
Collemataria marshalli (Stehli)	VR
Crenispirifer angulatus (R.E. King)	VR
Cyclacantharia sp.	VR
Derbyia crenulata Girty	VR
Derbyia nasuta Girty	VR
Diplanus lamellatus (R.E. King)	VR
Dyoros (Dyoros) consanguineus (Girty)	VR
Dyoros (Dyoros) magnus Stehli	VR
Elliottella transversalis (Stehli)	R
Fimbrinia ovata Cooper and Grant	VR

	Rarity code
LOCALITY A628 - Continued	
Goniarina permiana (Stehli)	R
Heteralosia sp. 4	VR
Hustedia glomerosa Cooper and Grant	R
Hustedia hessensis R.E. King	VR
Kozlowskia kingi Stehli	VR
Meekella hessensis R.E. King	VR
Meekella intermedia Cooper and Grant	VR
Orthotetella wolfcampensis R.E. King	VR
Orthotichia irregularis Cooper and Grant	R
Poikilosakos informis Cooper and Grant	VR
Quadrochonetes girtyi Stehli	VR
Reticulariina tetrica Cooper and Grant	VR
Rhipidomella hessensis R.E. King	VR
Scacchinella americana Stehli	VR
Spinifrons magna Cooper and Grant	R
LOCALITY A629 : Bone Spring Formation	
Acritosia teguliferoides (R.E. King)	VR
Antiquatonia planumbona Stehli	VR
Antronaria spectabilis Cooper and Grant	VR
Cancrinella sparsispinosa Cooper and Grant	VR
Chonetinella victoriana (Girty)	R
Collemataria americana (Girty)	VR
Crurithyris sulcata Stehli	R
Cyclacantharia sp.	VR
Derbyia nasuta Girty	VR
Dielasma diabloense Stehli	VR
Dyoros (*Dyoros*) *consanguineus* (Girty)	R
Elliottella transversalis (Stehli)	R
Eolyttonia diabloensis (Stehli)	VR
Goniarina permiana (Stehli)	R
Hustedia glomerosa Cooper and Grant	VR
Kozlowskia kingi Stehli	R
Limbella victorioensis Stehli	VR
Linoproductus angustus R.E. King	VR
Meekella attenuata Girty	R
Meekella intermedia Cooper and Grant	VR
Nudauris diabloensis Stehli	VR
Poikilosakos informis Cooper and Grant	VR
Quadrochonetes girtyi Stehli	R
Rallacosta sp. 2	VR
Rhipidomella hessensis R.E. King	VR
Spinifrons magna Cooper and Grant	C
Spinifrons quadrata Stehli	VR
Stenoscisma kalum Stehli	R
Stenoscisma multicostum Stehli	R
Tautosia lenumbona (Stehli)	VR
Tautosia magnisepta (Stehli)	VR
Teguliferina conida (Stehli)	VR
Thamnosia parvispinosa (Stehli)	VR
LOCALITY A631 : Bone Spring Formation	
Acosarina dorsisulcata Cooper and Grant	C
Acritosia teguliferoides (R.E. King)	C
Altiplecus cooperi Stehli	VR
Anomalesia perplexa Cooper and Grant	VR
Antiquatonia planumbona Stehli	VR
Chonetinella biplicata (R.E. King)	C
Collemataria americana (Girty)	VR
Composita cracens Cooper and Grant	VR
Crenispirifer angulatus (R.E. King)	VR
Crurithyris sulcata Stehli	VR
Cyclacantharia sp.	VR
Derbyia crenulata Girty	C
Derbyia nasuta Girty	VR

	Rarity code
Derbyia sp.	R
Dielasma sp.	VR
Diplanus lamellatus (R.E. King)	C
Dyoros (*Dyoros*) *consanguineus* (Girty)	R
Dyoros (*Dyoros*) *magnus* Stehli	VR
Elliottella minima (Stehli)	C
Enteletes stehlii Cooper and Grant	R
Eolyttonia diabloensis (Stehli)	R
Goniarina permiana (Stehli)	VR
Heteralosia sp.	VR
Hustedia glomerosa Cooper and Grant	VR
Hustedia hessensis R.E. King	C
Kozlowskia kingi Stehli	C
Leurosina sinesulca (Stehli)	R
Leurosina vulgarica Cooper and Grant	A
Linoproductus angustus R.E. King	VR
Meekella attenuata Girty	C
Meekella intermedia Cooper and Grant	R
Orthotichia irregularis Cooper and Grant	C
Poikilosakos informis Cooper and Grant	VR
Pontisia nanas (Stehli)	VR
Quadrochonetes praecursor Cooper and Grant	C
Reticulariina newelli (Stehli)	VR
Reticulariina tetrica Cooper and Grant	R
Rhamnaria eximia Cooper and Grant	VR
Rhipidomella hessensis R.E. King	C
Spinifrons quadrata Stehli	C
Teguliferina conida (Stehli)	R
LOCALITY A632 : Bone Spring Formation	
Antronaria mesicostalis (Girty)	VR
Collemataria americana (Girty)	VR
Composita cracens Cooper and Grant	VR
Enteletes stehlii Cooper and Grant	R
Hustedia hessensis R.E. King	VR
Leiorhynchoidea sp.	VR
Meekella attenuata Girty	VR
Neophricadothyris catatona Cooper and Grant	VR
Rhipidomella hessensis R.E. King	VR
Spinifrons quadrata Stehli	VR
Stenoscisma sp.	VR
Teguliferina conida (Stehli)	VR
LOCALITY A633 : Bone Spring Formation	
Echinauris sp.	R
LOCALITY A634 : Bone Spring Formation	
Acosarina dorsisulcata Cooper and Grant	VR
Chonosteges limbatus Cooper and Grant	VR
Composita cracens Cooper and Grant	VR
Echinauris sp.	R
Enteletes stehlii Cooper and Grant	VR
Leurosina vulgarica Cooper and Grant	R
Martinia fucina Cooper and Grant	VR
Neophricadothyris catatona Cooper and Grant	R
Pontisia nanas (Stehli)	VR
LOCALITY A635 : Bell Canyon Formation, Hegler Member	
Acanthocrania minutispinosa Cooper and Grant	VR
Altiplecus? deltosus Cooper and Grant	R
Arionthia polypleura (Girty)	R
Cartorhium sp.	VR
Chonetinetes varians Cooper and Grant	C
Composita pyriformis Cooper and Grant	VR
Cooperina inexpectata Termier, Termier and Pajaud	VR
Craspedona newelli Cooper and Grant	VR

Rarity code   Rarity code

LOCALITY A635 - Continued

Crenispirifer jubatus Cooper and Grant	R
Ctenalosia rotunda Cooper and Grant	VR
Derbyia sp.	C
Dielasma sp.	R
Dielasma sulcatum Girty	VR
Dyoros (Dyoros) attenuatus Cooper and Grant	VR
Dyoros (Dyoros) intrepidus Cooper and Grant	VR
Echinauris sp.	VR
Elivina? annectans Cooper and Grant	R
Glossothyropsis robusta (Girty)	VR
Heteralosia magnispina Cooper and Grant	R
Heterelasma venustulum Girty	VR
Hustedia rupinata Cooper and Grant	C
Hustedia samiata Cooper and Grant	VR
Hustedia sp.	VR
Liosotella opima (Girty)	R
Meekella skenoides Girty	VR
Metriolepis nabis Cooper and Grant	VR
Metriolepis pedicosa Cooper and Grant	R
Metriolepis sp.	VR
Micraphelia scitula Cooper and Grant	A
Micraphelia subalata Cooper and Grant	R
Paraspiriferina sapinea Cooper and Grant	C
Paraspiriferina sp.	VR
Paucispinifera latidorsata (Girty)	VR
Plectelasma guadalupense (Girty)	VR
Pseudodielasma pinyonense Cooper and Grant	VR
Pseudoleptodus guadalupensis (Stehli)	VR
Reticulariina echinata Cooper and Grant	VR
Reticulariina sp. 2	R
Reticulariina welleri (Girty)	VR
Rhamnaria shumardi Cooper and Grant	VR
Sarganostega transversalis Cooper and Grant	R
Scapharina levis Cooper and Grant	VR
Scapharina rugosa Cooper and Grant	R
Sestropoma cribriferum Cooper and Grant	R
Spiriferella sulcifer (Shumard)	R
Spiriferellina nuda Cooper and Grant	VR
Thamnosia capitanensis (Girty)	VR
Thedusia trigonalis (Girty)	VR
Thedusia ventricosa Cooper and Grant	VR
Xenosteges umbonatus Cooper and Grant	C

LOCALITY A636 : Bell Canyon Formation, Pinery Member

Arionthia lamaria Cooper and Grant	VR
Cartorhium sp.	R
Crenispirifer jubatus Cooper and Grant	R
Derbyia sp.	VR
Hustedia demissa Cooper and Grant	VR
Hustedia rupinata Cooper and Grant	C
Paraspiriferina sapinea Cooper and Grant	R
Reticulariina sp.	VR
Sarganostega transversalis Cooper and Grant	VR
Spiriferellina nuda Cooper and Grant	R
Thedusia trigonalis (Girty)	VR
Thedusia ventricosa Cooper and Grant	R

LOCALITY A652 : Cherry Canyon Formation, Getaway Member

Ctenalosia fixata Cooper and Stehli	VR
Hustedia citeria Cooper and Grant	VR
Meekella skenoides Girty	VR
Rhamnaria sulcata Cooper and Grant	VR
Thedusia dischides Cooper and Grant	VR

LOCALITY A653 : Hueco Formation

Composita mexicana (Hall)	C

LOCALITY A655 : Bone Spring Formation

Scacchinella americana Stehli	VR

LOCALITY A658 : Bone Spring Formation

Acosarina mesoplatys (R.E. King)	C
Agelesia triagonalis (R.E. King)	R
Choanodus irregularis Cooper and Grant	VR
Dielasma sp. 4	VR
Diplanus lamellatus (R.E. King)	C
Echinauris sp.	VR
Enteletes plummeri R.E. King	C
Heterelasma sp.	VR
Hustedia ampullacea Cooper and Grant	R
Hustedia sp.	R
Institella leonardensis (R.E. King)	VR
Meekella hessensis R.E. King	C
Megousia auriculata Muir-Wood and Cooper	VR
Metriolepis tegulata Cooper and Grant	R
Neophricadothyris sp.	R
Rhipidomella hispidula Cooper and Grant	C

LOCALITY A660 : Bone Spring Formation

Acritosia teguliferoides (R.E. King)	VR
Chonosteges pulcher Cooper and Grant	VR
Composita nucella Cooper and Grant	R
Diplanus lamellatus (R.E. King)	VR
Hustedia decollatensis Cooper and Grant	VR
Meekella hessensis R.E. King	R
Xenosteges adherens Muir-Wood and Cooper	VR

LOCALITY A661 : Bone Spring Formation

Cartorhium latum (R.E. King)	VR
Neophricadothyris sp.	VR

LOCALITY A663 : Bone Spring Formation

Neospirifer mansuetus Cooper and Grant	VR

LOCALITY A678 : Bone Spring Formation, Cutoff Member

Allorhynchus sp.	VR
Anemonaria sublaevis (R.E. King)	VR
Anteridocus bicostatus Cooper and Grant	VR
Anteridocus eximius Cooper and Grant	C
Chonetinella sp. 5	VR
Composita nucella Cooper and Grant	VA
Crurithyris sp.	VR
Cyclacantharia sp.	VR
Derbyia sp.	VR
Echinauris irregularis Cooper and Grant	C
Glossothyropsis sp. 1 (Girty)	VR
Grandaurispina sp.	VR
Heterelasma sp.	VR
Hustedia decollatensis Cooper and Grant	C
Meekella sp.	VR
Metriolepis sp.	VR
Paraspiriferina sp.	R
Paucispinifera sp.	VR
Phrenophoria corpulenta Cooper and Grant	VR
Phrenophoria incomitata Cooper and Grant	VR
Pseudodielasma sp.	R
Rhynchopora sp.	R
Rhynchopora sp. a	VR
Stenoscisma sp.	R

LOCALITY A696 : Bone Spring Formation

Antronaria indentata Cooper and Grant	R

	Rarity code
LOCALITY A696 - Continued	
Chonetinella magna Cooper and Grant	C
Chonosteges variabilis Cooper and Grant	VR
Crurithyris inflata Stehli	R
Derbyia crenulata Girty	VR
Derbyia nasuta Girty	VR
Dyoros (Dyoros) consanguineus (Girty)	VR
Elliottella transversalis (Stehli)	VR
Enteletes stehlii Cooper and Grant	R
Eolyttonia diabloensis (Stehli)	VR
Fimbrinia ovata Cooper and Grant	VR
Goniarina permiana (Stehli)	C
Hustedia glomerosa Cooper and Grant	VR
Meekella angustiplicata Cooper and Grant	C
Neophricadothyris catatona Cooper and Grant	VR
Rhipidomella hessensis R.E. King	R
Scacchinella americana Stehli	VR
Spinifrons magna Cooper and Grant	VR
Teguliferina conida (Stehli)	R
LOCALITY A697 : Bone Spring Formation	
Acosarina dorsisulcata Cooper and Grant	VR
Antiquatonia planumbona Stehli	VR
Antronaria mesicostalis (Girty)	VR
Composita cracens Cooper and Grant	R
Crenispirifer angulatus (R.E. King)	R
Crurithyris inflata Stehli	VR
Dasysaria undulata? Cooper and Grant	VR
Derbyia sp.	VR
Enteletes stehlii Cooper and Grant	R
Hustedia hessensis R.E. King	R
Kozlowskia sp.	R
Meekella angustiplicata Cooper and Grant	VR
Meekella hessensis R.E. King	VR
Meekella intermedia Cooper and Grant	VR
Rhipidomella hessensis R.E. King	R
LOCALITY A699 : Bone Spring Formation	
Acosarina dorsisulcata Cooper and Grant	R
Antronaria mesicostalis (Girty)	VR
Derbyia crenulata Girty	VR
Derbyia nasuta Girty	VR
Meekella attenuata Girty	VR
Scacchinella americana Stehli	VR
LOCALITY A700 : Hueco Formation	
Acritosia silicica Cooper and Grant	R
Beecheria sp.	VR
Composita mexicana (Hall)	R
Composita strongyle Cooper and Grant	VR
Crurithyris sp.	R
Dielasma sp.	VR
Kozlowskia sp.	VR
Lowenstamia sp.	VR
Meekella circularis Cooper and Grant	R
Orthotichia kozlowskii R.E. King	C
Scacchinella exasperata Cooper and Grant	VR
LOCALITY A703 : Cibolo Formation, Breccia Zone	
Acosarina mesoplatys (R.E. King)	C
Acritosia silicica Cooper and Grant	R
Chonetinella ciboloensis Cooper and Grant	R
Collemataria americana (Girty)	VR
Composita crassa Cooper and Grant	VR
Crenispirifer sp.	VR
Derbyia nasuta Girty	VR
Derbyia sp.	VR

	Rarity code
Diplanus rarus Cooper and Grant	R
Dyoros (Dyoros) magnus Stehli	VR
Enteletes wolfcampensis R.E. King	VR
Kozlowskia sp.	VR
Meekella magnifica Cooper and Grant	R
Neophricadothyris sp.	VR
Scacchinella titan Cooper and Grant	C
LOCALITY A725 : Capitan Formation	
Aneuthelasma amygdalinum Cooper and Grant	VR
Astegosia subquadrata (Girty)	C
Geyerella americana Girty	VR
Martinia rhomboidalis Girty	R
LOCALITY A774 : Capitan Formation	
Aneuthelasma amygdalinum Cooper and Grant	R
Grandaurispina sp.	VR
Stenoscisma sp.	VR
Thamnosia capitanensis (Girty)	VR
LOCALITY A799 : Capitan Formation	
Strigirhynchia indentata (Shumard)	VR
LOCALITY A801 : Capitan Formation	
Anteridocus swallovianus (Shumard)	VR
Dielasma prolongatum Girty	VR
LOCALITY A803 : Capitan Formation	
Composita emarginata Girty	VR
LOCALITY A804 : Capitan Formation	
Anteridocus swallovianus (Shumard)	VR
Hustedia opsia Cooper and Grant	VR
Paraspiriferina billingsi (Shumard)	VR
Stenoscisma sp.	VR
Tautosia shumardiana (Girty)	VR
LOCALITY A806 : Capitan Formation	
Composita emarginata Girty	VR
Strigirhynchia indentata (Shumard)	VR
LOCALITY A817 : Capitan Formation	
Astegosia subquadrata (Girty)	VR
Composita affinis Girty	VR
Martinia rhomboidalis Girty	VR
LOCALITY A820 : Capitan Formation	
Derbyia sp.	VR
Martinia rhomboidalis Girty	VR
LOCALITY A830 : Capitan Formation	
Astegosia subquadrata (Girty)	VR
Eliva inflata Cooper and Grant	VR
Paraspiriferina billingsi (Shumard)	VR
LOCALITY A837 : Capitan Formation	
Dielasma prolongatum Girty	VR
Liosotella popei (Shumard)	VR
Pleurelasma costatum Cooper and Grant	VR
LOCALITY A840 : Capitan Formation	
Anteridocus swallovianus (Shumard)	VR
Astegosia subquadrata (Girty)	VR
Martinia rhomboidalis Girty	VR
LOCALITY A843 : Capitan Formation	
Astegosia subquadrata (Girty)	VR
LOCALITY A847 : Capitan Formation	
Anteridocus swallovianus (Shumard)	R
Dyoros (Dyoros) hillanus (Girty)	VR

	Rarity code
LOCALITY A847 - Continued	
Eliva inflata Cooper and Grant	VR
Heterelasma shumardianum Girty	VR
Liosotella popei (Shumard)	VR
Martinia rhomboidalis Girty	VR
Paraspiriferina billingsi (Shumard)	VR
Plectelasma guadalupense (Girty)	VR
Stenoscisma trabeatum Cooper and Grant	VR
Strigirhynchia indentata (Shumard)	VR
Tautosia shumardiana (Girty)	VR
Thamnosia capitanensis (Girty)	VR
LOCALITY A853 : Capitan Formation	
Composita affinis Girty	VR
Strigirhynchia indentata (Shumard)	VR
LOCALITY M23 : Cathedral Mountain Formation	
Chonosteges pulcher Cooper and Grant	VR
Compressoproductus thomasi Cooper and Grant	VR
Hustedia spicata Cooper and Grant	VR
Rhipidomella hispidula Cooper and Grant	R
LOCALITY M30 : Bell Canyon Formation, Pinery Member	
Hustedia rupinata Cooper and Grant	VR
Sarganostega transversalis Cooper and Grant	VR
Thedusia trigonalis (Girty)	VR
LOCALITY M31 : Cherry Canyon Formation, Getaway Member	
Bryorhynchus bisulcatum (Shumard)	R
Cyclacantharia kingorum Cooper and Grant	VR
Derbyia texta Cooper and Grant	VR
Dielasma pictile Cooper and Grant	VR
Dyoros (*Lissosia*) *concavus* Cooper and Grant	R
Dyoros (*Tetragonetes*) *complanatus* Cooper and Grant	R
Echinauris productelloides Cooper and Grant	VR
Echinosteges tuberculatus (R.E. King)	VR
Eolyttonia progressa Cooper and Grant	VR
Grandaurispina sp.	VR
Hustedia citeria Cooper and Grant	R
Liosotella wordensis (R.E. King)	R
Meekella skenoides Girty	VR
Megousia definita Cooper and Grant	VR
Metriolepis exserta Cooper and Grant	VR
Paraspiriferina paginata Cooper and Grant	VR
Paucispinifera sp.	VR
Reticulariina girtyi Cooper and Grant	R
Rhamnaria sulcata Cooper and Grant	VR
Spiriferella sp.	VR
Thedusia dischides Cooper and Grant	VR
Xenosteges quadratus Cooper and Grant	VR
LOCALITY M9804 : Putnam Formation	
Lowenstamia texana Stehli	R
LOCALITY M9818 : Putnam Formation	
Lowenstamia texana Stehli	R
LOCALITY M9880 : Pueblo Formation	
Nudauris reticulata Cooper and Grant	C
LOCALITY N45 : Graham Formation	
Waagenoconcha prophetica Cooper and Grant	VR
Cleiothyridina sp.	R
Dasysaria wolfcampensis (R.E. King)	R
Echinauris cf. *boulei* (Kozlowski)	VR
Enteletes costellatus Cooper and Grant	R
Hustedia huecoensis R.E. King	C

	Rarity code
Kochiproductus quadratus Cooper and Grant	VR
Nudauris transversa Cooper and Grant	R
Pontisia sp.	C
Reticulariina powwowensis Cooper and Grant	VR
Waagenoconcha sulcata Cooper and Grant	VR
LOCALITY N510 : Graham Formation	
Nudauris presplendens Cooper and Grant	R
LOCALITY N510a : Graham Formation	
Sulcataria rostrata (Dunbar and Condra)	A
LOCALITY N510g : Graham Formation	
Martinia renfroae Cooper and Grant	VR
LOCALITY N511r : Graham Formation	
Waagenoconcha prophetica Cooper and Grant	VR
LOCALITY N512h : Graham Formation	
Nudauris presplendens Cooper and Grant	R
LOCALITY N513c : Graham Formation	
Nudauris presplendens Cooper and Grant	VR
LOCALITY N518v : Gunsight Formation	
Sulcataria rostrata (Dunbar and Condra)	C
LOCALITY N519 : Shale Below Cass Formation	
Derbyoides nebrascensis Dunbar and Condra	VR
Diplanus redactus Cooper and Grant	VR
Meekella sp.	R
Rhynchopora dossena Cooper and Grant	R
Teguliferina armata Cooper and Grant	C
LOCALITY N700a : Gaptank Formation	
Diplanus redactus Cooper and Grant	VR
Kozlowskia sp.	VR
Meekella prionota Cooper and Grant	VR
Parenteletes cooperi R.E. King	C
Rhynchopora dossena Cooper and Grant	R
Teguliferina armata Cooper and Grant	R
LOCALITY N700b : Gaptank Formation	
Parenteletes cooperi R.E. King	VR
LOCALITY N700e : Gaptank Formation	
Hystriculina sp.	VR
Juresania sp. 1	VR
Linoproductus sp.	VR
LOCALITY N700f : Gaptank Formation	
Antiquatonia inflativentra Cooper and Grant	VR
Chonetinella sp.	VR
Enteletes wolfcampensis R.E. King	VR
Eridmatus marathonensis Cooper and Grant	VR
Hustedia sp.	VR
Juresania sp. 1	VR
Kutorginella sp.	VR
Linoproductus sp.	VR
Teguliferina armata Cooper and Grant	R
LOCALITY N700g : Gaptank Formation	
Antiquatonia sp.	VR
Beecheria sp.	VR
Derbyia sp.	VR
Echinaria cf. *moorei* (Dunbar and Condra)	VR
Eridmatus marathonensis Cooper and Grant	VR
Kochiproductus primitivus Cooper and Grant	VR
Kozlowskia sp.	R
Limbella costellata Cooper and Grant	R
Linoproductus sp.	VR
Meekella prionota Cooper and Grant	VR

Rarity code (right of each entry)

LOCALITY N700g - Continued

	Rarity code
Meekella texana R.E. King	VR
Neophricadothyris sp.	VR
Reticulatia sp.	VR
Scacchinella primitiva Cooper and Grant	C
Teguliferina boesei R.E. King	C

LOCALITY N700i : Gaptank Formation, Uddenites Member

Teguliferina boesei R.E. King	VR

LOCALITY N700-1 : Cathedral Mountain Formation, Wedin Member

Acosarina mesoplatys (R.E. King)	C
Agelesia triagonalis (R.E. King)	A
Cartorhium coristum Cooper and Grant	VR
Choanodus perfectus Cooper and Grant	VR
Chonosteges pulcher Cooper and Grant	R
Collemataria irregularis Cooper and Grant	R
Compressoproductus thomasi Cooper and Grant	VR
Crurithyris sp.	VR
Derbyia complicata Cooper and Grant	R
Diplanus lamellatus (R.E. King)	C
Echinauris irregularis Cooper and Grant	R
Enteletes plummeri R.E. King	C
Eolyttonia sp.	VR
Hercosia uddeni (Böse)	R
Hustedia lusca Cooper and Grant	VR
Institella leonardensis (R.E. King)	R
Kochiproductus sp.	VR
Lepidospirifer demissus Cooper and Grant	VR
Meekella calathica Cooper and Grant	R
Neophricadothyris bullata Cooper and Grant	VR
Nudauris linospina Cooper and Grant	VR
Rhamnaria tenuispinosa Cooper and Grant	VR
Rhipidomella hispidula Cooper and Grant	R
Rugatia paraindica (McKee)	VR
Stenoscisma triquetrum Cooper and Grant	VR
Torynechus caelatus Cooper and Grant	VR
Xenosteges adherens Muir-Wood and Cooper	VR

LOCALITY N700o : Skinner Ranch Formation, Dugout Mtn Member

Chonosteges variabilis Cooper and Grant	VR
Glyptosteges intricatus Cooper and Grant	VR
Peniculauris sp. 1	VR
Rhamnaria grandis Cooper and Grant	VR

LOCALITY N700p : Skinner Ranch Formation, Dugout Mtn Member

Glyptosteges intricatus Cooper and Grant	VR
Torynechus alectorius Cooper and Grant	VR

LOCALITY N700r : Skinner Ranch Formation, Dugout Mtn Member

Glyptosteges intricatus Cooper and Grant	VR
Nudauris sp.	VR
Peniculauris sp. 1	VR

LOCALITY N700s : Skinner Ranch Formation, Dugout Mtn Member

Echinauris sp.	VR
Glyptosteges intricatus Cooper and Grant	VR

LOCALITY N700t : Skinner Ranch Formation, Dugout Mtn Member

Chonosteges variabilis Cooper and Grant	VR
Spyridiophora reticulata (R.E. King)	VR

LOCALITY N700v : Road Canyon Formation

	Rarity code
Collumatus solitarius Cooper and Grant	R
Composita enormis Cooper and Grant	VR
Composita sp.	R
Cyclacantharia transitoria Cooper and Grant	VR
Derbyia laqueata Cooper and Grant	VR
Echinauris sp.	VR
Enteletes sp.	R
Eolyttonia sp.	VR
Hustedia connorsi Cooper and Grant	C
Liosotella wordensis (R.E. King)	VR
Meekella calathica Cooper and Grant	R
Megousia mucronata Cooper and Grant	R
Neophricadothyris sp.	VR
Paraspiriferina sp.	R
Paucispinifera sulcata Cooper and Grant	R
Rhynchopora hebetata Cooper and Grant	VR
Spiriferellina sp.	VR
Stenoscisma sp.	VR
Tropidelasma corniculum Cooper and Grant	VR

LOCALITY N700x : Cathedral Mountain Formation, Wedin Member

Agelesia triagonalis (R.E. King)	A
Cartorhium coristum Cooper and Grant	VR
Cenorhynchia mitigata Cooper and Grant	VR
Choanodus perfectus Cooper and Grant	R
Chonosteges pulcher Cooper and Grant	C
Compressoproductus thomasi Cooper and Grant	R
Cooperina parva Cooper and Grant	VR
Derbyia complicata Cooper and Grant	VR
Diplanus lamellatus (R.E. King)	R
Echinauris irregularis Cooper and Grant	VR
Enteletes leonardensis R.E. King	R
Enteletes plummeri R.E. King	C
Hercosia uddeni (Böse)	R
Hustedia spicata Cooper and Grant	VR
Institella leonardensis (R.E. King)	C
Meekella calathica Cooper and Grant	R
Metriolepis larina Cooper and Grant	VR
Neophricadothyris bullata Cooper and Grant	VR
Stenoscisma triquetrum Cooper and Grant	VR
Texarina wordensis (R.E. King)	VR
Torynechus caelatus Cooper and Grant	VR
Xenosteges adherens Muir-Wood and Cooper	VR

LOCALITY N700y : Skinner Ranch Formation, Sullivan Peak Member

Acosarina dorsisulcata Cooper and Grant	VR

LOCALITY N701 : Neal Ranch Formation

Acanthocrania sp.	VR
Acosarina rectimarginata Cooper and Grant	C
Altiplecus argutus Cooper and Grant	VR
Antiquatonia inflativentra Cooper and Grant	VR
Atelestegastus marginatus Cooper and Grant	R
Beecheria elliptica Cooper and Grant	R
Camarelasma neali Cooper and Grant	VR
Cancrinella parva Cooper and Grant	R
Cenorhynchia hebata Cooper and Grant	VR
Chelononia neali Cooper and Grant	R
Chondronia rectimarginata Cooper and Grant	R
Chonetinella costellata Cooper and Grant	C
Chonetinella crassiparva Cooper and Grant	C
Chonetinella sp. 2	VR
Chonetinella sp.	VR

	Rarity code
LOCALITY N701 - Continued	
Cleiothyridina rectimarginata Cooper and Grant	VR
Composita strongyle Cooper and Grant	C
Cooperina triangulata Cooper and Grant	VR
Crurithyris tumibilis Cooper and Grant	C
Ctenalosia primitiva Cooper and Grant	VR
Derbyia bella Cooper and Grant	C
Derbyia carteri Cooper and Grant	R
Derbyia profunda Cooper and Grant	R
Derbyia scitula Cooper and Grant	A
Derbyia sp.	C
Derbyoides dunbari Cooper and Grant	VR
Derbyoides marathonensis Cooper and Grant	R
Diplanus catatonus Cooper and Grant	C
Diplanus redactus Cooper and Grant	VR
Echinaria sp. 1	VR
Echinauris interrupta Cooper and Grant	VR
Echinosteges? sp.	VR
Enteletes wolfcampensis R.E. King	A
Eolyttonia fredericksi (R.E. King)	VR
Eolyttonia phialiforma Cooper and Grant	VR
Eridmatus sp.	VR
Fimbrinia plummeri (R.H. King)	VR
Geyerella kingorum Cooper and Grant	VR
Goniarina sp.	VR
Hustedia crepax Cooper and Grant	R
Hustedia culcitula Cooper and Grant	A
Hypopsia versuta Cooper and Grant	R
Hystriculina convexa Cooper and Grant	C
Hystriculina minima Cooper and Grant	VR
Hystriculina sulcata Cooper and Grant	A
Hystriculina ventroplana Cooper and Grant	VR
Juresania sp. 1	VR
Juresania sp. 3	VR
Kochiproductus sp. 3	R
Kozlowskia sp.	VR
Kutorginella uddeni Cooper and Grant	R
Lepidocrania sparsispinosa Cooper and Grant	R
Limbella wolfcampensis (R.E. King)	C
Linoproductus sp.	R
Meekella magnifica Cooper and Grant	VR
Meekella prionota Cooper and Grant	A
Meekella sp.	R
Neochonetes liratus Cooper and Grant	C
Neophricadothyris transversa Cooper and Grant	VR
Neospirifer apothescelus Cooper and Grant	R
Nudauris splendens Cooper and Grant	C
Orthotetella wolfcampensis R.E. King	R
Orthotichia kozlowskii R.E. King	A
Paraspiriferina amoena Cooper and Grant	R
Paraspiriferina sp.	R
Parenteletes superbus Cooper and Grant	VR
Pontisia kingi Cooper and Grant	R
Pseudoleptodus conicus Cooper and Grant	VR
Pseudoleptodus primitivus Cooper and Grant	VR
Reticulariina strigosa Cooper and Grant	VR
Reticulatia robusta Cooper and Grant	C
Schuchertella? subvexa Cooper and Grant	R
Spiriferellina nasuta Cooper and Grant	R
Spuriosa circularis Cooper and Grant	VR
Spyridiophora distincta Cooper and Stehli	VR
Striatifera linoproductiformis Cooper and Grant	VR
Sulcataria? compacta Cooper and Grant	R
Sulcataria latisulcata Cooper and Grant	VR
Teguliferina boesei R.E. King	A

	Rarity code
Tropidelasma culmenatum Cooper and Grant	R
Waagenoconcha prophetica Cooper and Grant	VR
LOCALITY N701a : Neal Ranch Formation	
Camarelasma neali Cooper and Grant	VR
Chondronia rectimarginata Cooper and Grant	VR
Cleiothyridina rectimarginata Cooper and Grant	R
Composita strongyle Cooper and Grant	VR
Crurithyris tumibilis Cooper and Grant	VR
Derbyia carteri Cooper and Grant	VA
Derbyia profunda Cooper and Grant	VR
Diplanus catatonus Cooper and Grant	R
Enteletes wolfcampensis R.E. King	VR
Eolyttonia fredericksi (R.E. King)	C
Geyerella kingorum Cooper and Grant	C
Hustedia trita leptyca Cooper and Grant	VR
Hystriculina minima Cooper and Grant	VR
Hystriculina ventroplana Cooper and Grant	VR
Kozlowskia nasuta Cooper and Grant	VR
Limbella wolfcampensis (R.E. King)	R
Linoproductus sp.	R
Meekella magnifica Cooper and Grant	R
Meekella prionota Cooper and Grant	VR
Neophricadothyris transversa Cooper and Grant	R
Nothopindax egregius Cooper and Grant	VR
Orthotetella wolfcampensis R.E. King	VR
Orthotichia kozlowskii R.E. King	R
Stenoscisma sp.	VR
Striatifera linoproductiformis Cooper and Grant	VR
Teguliferina boesei R.E. King	A
Tropidelasma culmenatum Cooper and Grant	R
LOCALITY N701a[1] : Neal Ranch Formation	
Cancrinella parva Cooper and Grant	VR
Composita strongyle Cooper and Grant	VR
Derbyia carteri Cooper and Grant	VR
Derbyia profunda Cooper and Grant	VR
Enteletes wolfcampensis R.E. King	VR
Hustedia culcitula Cooper and Grant	VR
Hystriculina minima Cooper and Grant	VR
Limbella wolfcampensis (R.E. King)	VR
Meekella magnifica Cooper and Grant	R
Nudauris tribulosa Cooper and Grant	VR
Reticulatia sp. 1	VR
LOCALITY N701a[2] : Neal Ranch Formation	
Geyerella sp. 3	VR
LOCALITY N701a[3] : Neal Ranch Formation	
Acanthocrania sp.	R
Atelestegastus marginatus Cooper and Grant	VR
Cenorhynchia hebata Cooper and Grant	VR
Chelononia straminea Cooper and Grant	R
Composita strongyle Cooper and Grant	R
Cooperina triangulata Cooper and Grant	C
Crurithyris tumibilis Cooper and Grant	R
Derbyia profunda Cooper and Grant	VR
Diplanus catatonus Cooper and Grant	R
Enteletes wolfcampensis R.E. King	R
Eolyttonia fredericksi (R.E. King)	VR
Fimbrinia plummeri (R.H. King)	VR
Goniarina pyelodes Cooper and Grant	R
Hustedia trita leptyca Cooper and Grant	C
Hystriculina minima Cooper and Grant	VR
Lepidocrania sparsispinosa Cooper and Grant	C

	Rarity code
LOCALITY N701a[1] - Continued	
Limbella wolfcampensis (R.E. King)	R
Linoproductus sp.	VR
Meekella prionota Cooper and Grant	VR
Neochonetes liratus Cooper and Grant	C
Neophricadothyris transversa Cooper and Grant	C
Nudauris splendens Cooper and Grant	VR
Orthotichia kozlowskii R.E. King	C
Paraspiriferina amoena Cooper and Grant	C
Pontisia kingi Cooper and Grant	C
Psilocamara hesperia Cooper and Grant	R
Rhipidomella miscella Cooper and Grant	VR
Rhynchopora molina Cooper and Grant	VR
Teguliferina boesei R.E. King	VR
LOCALITY N701b : Neal Ranch Formation	
Paraspiriferina amoena Cooper and Grant	VR
Reticulariina strigosa Cooper and Grant	VR
Reticulatia huecoensis (R.E. King)	VR
LOCALITY N701c : Neal Ranch Formation	
Acosarina rectimarginata Cooper and Grant	R
Acritosia magna Cooper and Grant	VR
Atelestegastus marginatus Cooper and Grant	VR
Camarelasma neali Cooper and Grant	C
Cancrinella parva Cooper and Grant	VR
Cenorhynchia hebata Cooper and Grant	R
Chonetinella costellata Cooper and Grant	VR
Cleiothyridina rectimarginata Cooper and Grant	R
Composita strongyle Cooper and Grant	R
Crurithyris tumibilis Cooper and Grant	C
Derbyia carteri Cooper and Grant	R
Derbyia profunda Cooper and Grant	VR
Derbyia scitula Cooper and Grant	R
Derbyia sp.	C
Diplanus catatonus Cooper and Grant	C
Echinaria sp. 1	VR
Echinauris interrupta Cooper and Grant	VR
Echinauris subquadrata Cooper and Grant	VR
Enteletes wolfcampensis R.E. King	C
Eolyttonia catilla Cooper and Grant	VR
Eolyttonia fredericksi (R.E. King)	C
Geyerella kingorum Cooper and Grant	C
Hemileurus runcinatus Cooper and Grant	R
Hustedia crepax Cooper and Grant	VR
Hustedia sp.	VR
Hustedia trita leptyca Cooper and Grant	C
Hystriculina minima Cooper and Grant	R
Hystriculina sulcata Cooper and Grant	R
Kochiproductus sp. 3	VR
Kutorginella uddeni Cooper and Grant	VR
Lepidocrania sparsispinosa Cooper and Grant	VR
Limbella wolfcampensis (R.E. King)	C
Linoproductus semisulcatus Cooper and Grant	VR
Linoproductus sp.	VR
Meekella magnifica Cooper and Grant	R
Meekella prionota Cooper and Grant	R
Neochonetes liratus Cooper and Grant	VR
Neochonetes parvus Cooper and Grant	R
Neophricadothyris transversa Cooper and Grant	R
Neospirifer apothescelus Cooper and Grant	VR
Nudauris splendens Cooper and Grant	VR
Orthotetella wolfcampensis R.E. King	VR
Orthotichia kozlowskii R.E. King	C
Parenteletes superbus Cooper and Grant	R
Pontisia kingi Cooper and Grant	R
Pseudoleptodus conicus Cooper and Grant	VR

	Rarity code
Reticulariina strigosa Cooper and Grant	VR
Reticulatia robusta Cooper and Grant	VR
Reticulatia sp. 1	VR
Rhipidomella miscella Cooper and Grant	R
Rhynchopora molina Cooper and Grant	VR
Spiriferellina nasuta Cooper and Grant	VR
Striatifera linoproductiformis Cooper and Grant	VR
Teguliferina boesei R.E. King	VA
Teguliferina solidispinosa Cooper and Grant	R
Tropidelasma culmenatum Cooper and Grant	R
LOCALITY N701d : Neal Ranch Formation	
Acosarina rectimarginata Cooper and Grant	SA
Altiplecus argutus Cooper and Grant	C
Atelestegastus marginatus Cooper and Grant	C
Beecheria elliptica Cooper and Grant	R
Calliprotonia sp.	VR
Cancrinella parva Cooper and Grant	R
Cenorhynchia hebata Cooper and Grant	C
Cenorhynchia ventricosa Cooper and Grant	VR
Chelononia straminea Cooper and Grant	VR
Chondronia rectimarginata Cooper and Grant	R
Chonetinella sp.	VR
Cleiothyridina rectimarginata Cooper and Grant	C
Composita strongyle Cooper and Grant	C
Cooperina triangulata Cooper and Grant	A
Crurithyris tumibilis Cooper and Grant	A
Ctenalosia primitiva Cooper and Grant	VR
Derbyia carteri Cooper and Grant	VA
Derbyia profunda Cooper and Grant	C
Derbyia scitula Cooper and Grant	A
Derbyia sp.	R
Dielasma pygmaeum Cooper and Grant	VR
Diplanus catatonus Cooper and Grant	VA
Echinauris interrupta Cooper and Grant	C
Echinauris subquadrata Cooper and Grant	VR
Enteletes wolfcampensis R.E. King	C
Eolyttonia fredericksi (R.E. King)	R
Eridmatus sp.	R
Fimbrinia plummeri (R.H. King)	VR
Geyerella kingorum Cooper and Grant	VR
Goniarina sp.	VR
Hemileurus runcinatus Cooper and Grant	R
Hustedia crepax Cooper and Grant	VR
Hustedia trita leptyca Cooper and Grant	VA
Hystriculina convexa Cooper and Grant	C
Hystriculina minima Cooper and Grant	C
Hystriculina sulcata Cooper and Grant	VR
Juresania sp. 2	R
Kochiproductus sp. 3	VR
Lepidocrania sparsispinosa Cooper and Grant	VR
Limbella wolfcampensis (R.E. King)	R
Linoproductus semisulcatus Cooper and Grant	VR
Linoproductus sp.	VR
Meekella prionota Cooper and Grant	A
Neochonetes liratus Cooper and Grant	VR
Neochonetes parvus Cooper and Grant	R
Neochonetes sp.	VR
Neophricadothyris transversa Cooper and Grant	R
Neospirifer apothescelus Cooper and Grant	R
Pontisia kingi Cooper and Grant	C
Pseudoleptodus conicus Cooper and Grant	C
Reticulariina strigosa Cooper and Grant	VR
Reticulatia robusta Cooper and Grant	R
Rhipidomella miscella Cooper and Grant	C
Rhynchopora molina Cooper and Grant	C

Rarity code

LOCALITY N701d - Continued

	Rarity code
Spyridiophora distincta Cooper and Stehli	VR
Stenoscisma sp.	VR
Striatifera linoproductiformis Cooper and Grant	A
Sulcataria latisulcata Cooper and Grant	VR
Teguliferina boesei R.E. King	VA
Tropidelasma culmenatum Cooper and Grant	VR

LOCALITY N701e : Gaptank Formation, Uddenites Member

Antiquatonia inflativentra Cooper and Grant	R
Cancrinella sp.	VR
Chonetinella costellata Cooper and Grant	R
Chonetinella parva Cooper and Grant	VR
Composita strongyle Cooper and Grant	VR
Crurithyris tumibilis Cooper and Grant	VR
Derbyia sp.	VR
Diplanus redactus Cooper and Grant	VR
Enteletes wolfcampensis R.E. King	VR
Eridmatus marathonensis Cooper and Grant	VR
Gypospirifer anancites Cooper and Grant	R
Hystriculina sulcata Cooper and Grant	C
Hystriculina ventroplana Cooper and Grant	R
Juresania sp. 1	VR
Kochiproductus primitivus Cooper and Grant	VR
Kutorginella uddeni Cooper and Grant	VR
Linoproductus sp.	VR
Meekella texana R.E. King	VR
Neochonetes liratus Cooper and Grant	VR
Neochonetes sp.	VR
Neophricadothyris transversa Cooper and Grant	VR
Nudauris splendens Cooper and Grant	R
Nudauris tribulosa Cooper and Grant	VR
Orthotichia kozlowskii R.E. King	C
Pontisia kingi Cooper and Grant	VR
Reticulariina sp.	VR
Reticulatia sp. 2	VR
Rhynchopora molina Cooper and Grant	VR
Teguliferina boesei R.E. King	R
Waagenoconcha prophetica Cooper and Grant	VR

LOCALITY N701f : Gaptank Formation, Uddenites Member

Composita sp.	VR
Derbyia carteri Cooper and Grant	VR
Echinaria cf. *moorei* (Dunbar and Condra)	VR
Echinauris subquadrata Cooper and Grant	VR
Hystriculina sulcata Cooper and Grant	VR
Juresania sp. 1	VR
Linoproductus sp.	VR
Meekella texana R.E. King	VR
Neophricadothyris transversa Cooper and Grant	VR
Neospirifer apothescelus Cooper and Grant	VR
Nudauris splendens Cooper and Grant	VR
Parenteletes cooperi R.E. King	C
Reticulatia sp. 2	VR
Scacchinella triangulata Cooper and Grant	VR
Teguliferina boesei R.E. King	VR

LOCALITY N701g : Neal Ranch Formation

Acritosia magna Cooper and Grant	C
Chondronia rectimarginata Cooper and Grant	R
Derbyia profunda Cooper and Grant	C
Enteletes wolfcampensis R.E. King	VR
Hustedia trita leptyca Cooper and Grant	VR
Limbella wolfcampensis (R.E. King)	VR

	Rarity code
Lowenstamia sp. 1	VR
Meekella magnifica Cooper and Grant	VA
Orthotichia kozlowskii R.E. King	SA
Pontisia kingi Cooper and Grant	VR
Tropidelasma culmenatum Cooper and Grant	VR

LOCALITY N701h : Neal Ranch Formation

Acosarina rectimarginata Cooper and Grant	R
Acritosia magna Cooper and Grant	C
Atelestegastus marginatus Cooper and Grant	A
Camarelasma neali Cooper and Grant	VA
Chelononia straminea Cooper and Grant	VR
Chondronia rectimarginata Cooper and Grant	A
Cleiothyridina rectimarginata Cooper and Grant	A
Composita strongyle Cooper and Grant	VR
Crurithyris tumibilis Cooper and Grant	C
Derbyia carteri Cooper and Grant	R
Derbyia profunda Cooper and Grant	C
Diplanus catatonus Cooper and Grant	C
Eolyttonia fredericksi (R.E. King)	C
Geyerella kingorum Cooper and Grant	VA
Hemileurus runcinatus Cooper and Grant	C
Hustedia trita leptyca Cooper and Grant	R
Hystriculina minima Cooper and Grant	VR
Limbella wolfcampensis (R.E. King)	A
Lowenstamia sp. 1	VR
Meekella prionota Cooper and Grant	C
Neochonetes liratus Cooper and Grant	VR
Neophricadothyris transversa Cooper and Grant	VR
Nothopindax egregius Cooper and Grant	R
Orthotetella wolfcampensis R.E. King	VR
Parenteletes superbus Cooper and Grant	A
Rhipidomella miscella Cooper and Grant	R
Spyridiophora distincta Cooper and Stehli	R
Stenoscisma sp.	VR
Teguliferina boesei R.E. King	VA
Tropidelasma culmenatum Cooper and Grant	VA

LOCALITY N701j : Neal Ranch Formation

Orthotetella wolfcampensis R.E. King	VR

LOCALITY N701k : Neal Ranch Formation

Acanthocrania sp.	VR
Acosarina rectimarginata Cooper and Grant	SA
Acritosia magna Cooper and Grant	C
Atelestegastus marginatus Cooper and Grant	C
Camarelasma neali Cooper and Grant	VA
Cenorhynchia hebata Cooper and Grant	R
Chondronia rectimarginata Cooper and Grant	A
Cleiothyridina rectimarginata Cooper and Grant	A
Composita strongyle Cooper and Grant	R
Crurithyris tumibilis Cooper and Grant	A
Derbyia carteri Cooper and Grant	VR
Derbyia profunda Cooper and Grant	A
Dielasma pygmaeum Cooper and Grant	R
Diplanus catatonus Cooper and Grant	VA
Enteletes wolfcampensis R.E. King	A
Eolyttonia fredericksi (R.E. King)	R
Geyerella kingorum Cooper and Grant	VA
Goniarina pyelodes Cooper and Grant	A
Hemileurus runcinatus Cooper and Grant	VA
Hustedia trita leptyca Cooper and Grant	C
Hustedia trita trita Cooper and Grant	A
Hystriculina convexa Cooper and Grant	VR
Hystriculina sulcata Cooper and Grant	VR
Limbella wolfcampensis (R.E. King)	A

Rarity code

LOCALITY N701k - Continued

Meekella prionota Cooper and Grant	C
Neochonetes parvus Cooper and Grant	R
Neochonetes sp.	VR
Neophricadothyris transversa Cooper and Grant	R
Neospirifer apothescelus Cooper and Grant	VR
Nothopindax egregius Cooper and Grant	VR
Orthotetella wolfcampensis R.E. King	VR
Paraspiriferina amoena Cooper and Grant	VR
Parenteletes superbus Cooper and Grant	C
Pontisia kingi Cooper and Grant	R
Rhipidomella miscella Cooper and Grant	C
Rhynchopora molina Cooper and Grant	VR
Spyridiophora distincta Cooper and Stehli	R
Teguliferina boesei R.E. King	VA
Tropidelasma culmenatum Cooper and Grant	A

LOCALITY N701-l : Neal Ranch Formation

Beecheria expansa Cooper and Grant	VR
Cleiothyridina rectimarginata Cooper and Grant	R
Composita strongyle Cooper and Grant	C
Crurithyris tumibilis Cooper and Grant	C
Derbyia bella Cooper and Grant	VA
Derbyia strophomenoidea Cooper and Grant	C
Derbyoides dunbari Cooper and Grant	VR
Dielasma pygmaeum Cooper and Grant	R
Diplanus catatonus Cooper and Grant	R
Diplanus redactus Cooper and Grant	VR
Enteletes wolfcampensis R.E. King	R
Eolyttonia fredericksi (R.E. King)	VR
Geyerella kingorum Cooper and Grant	VR
Goniarina sp.	VR
Hustedia trita leptyca Cooper and Grant	C
Hystriculina sulcata Cooper and Grant	R
Limbella wolfcampensis (R.E. King)	R
Lowenstamia ampla Cooper and Grant	R
Lowenstamia sp.	R
Meekella prionota Cooper and Grant	VA
Meekella sp.	VR
Neophricadothyris transversa Cooper and Grant	VR
Neospirifer placidus Cooper and Grant	VR
Orthotichia kozlowskii R.E. King	C
Paraspiriferina sp.	VR
Parenteletes cooperi R.E. King	R
Parenteletes superbus Cooper and Grant	R
Pontisia kingi Cooper and Grant	R
Pseudoleptodus conicus Cooper and Grant	VR
Psilocamara hesperia Cooper and Grant	VR
Reticulariina strigosa Cooper and Grant	VR
Reticulatia robusta Cooper and Grant	VR
Rhipidomella miscella Cooper and Grant	VR
Rhynchopora molina Cooper and Grant	VR
Teguliferina boesei R.E. King	C

LOCALITY N701p : Gaptank Formation, Uddenites Member

Acosarina sp.	VR
Beecheria sp.	VR
Chonetinella costellata Cooper and Grant	VR
Composita sp.	VR
Crurithyris tumibilis Cooper and Grant	VR
Echinaria cf. *moorei* (Dunbar and Condra)	VR
Enteletes wolfcampensis R.E. King	VR
Eridmatus marathonensis Cooper and Grant	VR
Gypospirifer anancites Cooper and Grant	VR
Hustedia sp.	R

Rarity code

Hystriculina sulcata Cooper and Grant	R
Hystriculina ventroplana Cooper and Grant	VR
Juresania sp. 1	VR
Kutorginella uddeni Cooper and Grant	VR
Leiorhynchoidea sp.	VR
Linoproductus sp.	VR
Lissochonetes parvisulcatus Cooper and Grant	R
Meekella prionota Cooper and Grant	VR
Neochonetes liratus Cooper and Grant	VR
Neochonetes sp.	VR
Neophricadothyris transversa Cooper and Grant	VR
Nudauris splendens Cooper and Grant	VR
Nudauris tribulosa Cooper and Grant	VR
Orthotetella wolfcampensis R.E. King	VR
Parenteletes cooperi R.E. King	VR
Reticulariina sp.	VR
Reticulatia sp. 2	VR
Sulcataria sp. 1	VR
Teguliferina boesei R.E. King	R

LOCALITY N701q : Gaptank Formation, Uddenites Member

Antiquatonia inflativentra Cooper and Grant	VR
Cancrinella sp.	VR
Chonetinella parva Cooper and Grant	VR
Composita strongyle Cooper and Grant	VR
Crurithyris tumibilis Cooper and Grant	VR
Derbyia carteri Cooper and Grant	VR
Derbyia sp.	VR
Eridmatus marathonensis Cooper and Grant	VR
Eridmatus sp.	VR
Hystriculina sulcata Cooper and Grant	C
Hystriculina ventroplana Cooper and Grant	C
Juresania sp. 1	VR
Kochiproductus sp.	VR
Kutorginella uddeni Cooper and Grant	R
Linoproductus sp. 1	R
Meekella texana R.E. King	R
Neochonetes liratus Cooper and Grant	VR
Neophricadothyris transversa Cooper and Grant	VR
Orthotichia kozlowskii R.E. King	R
Parenteletes cooperi R.E. King	R
Pontisia kingi Cooper and Grant	VR
Reticulatia sp. 2	VR
Rhynchopora molina Cooper and Grant	R
Scacchinella triangulata Cooper and Grant	VR
Teguliferina boesei R.E. King	VR
Waagenoconcha prophetica Cooper and Grant	VR

LOCALITY N701r : Gaptank Formation, Uddenites Member

Antiquatonia inflativentra Cooper and Grant	VR
Eridmatus marathonensis Cooper and Grant	VR
Hystriculina sulcata Cooper and Grant	VR
Juresania sp. 1	VR
Linoproductus sp.	VR

LOCALITY N701t : Gaptank Formation, Uddenites Member

Beecheria sp.	VR
Eridmatus marathonensis Cooper and Grant	VR
Hustedia sp.	VR
Hystriculina sulcata Cooper and Grant	VR
Kutorginella uddeni Cooper and Grant	VR
Linoproductus sp.	VR
Neochonetes liratus Cooper and Grant	VR

	Rarity code
LOCALITY N701t - Continued	
Neochonetes sp.	VR
Neospirifer apothescelus Cooper and Grant	VR
Parenteletes cooperi R.E. King	VR
Teguliferina boesei R.E. King	VR
LOCALITY N701u : Gaptank Formation, Uddenites Member	
Derbyia profunda Cooper and Grant	VR
Echinaria sp. 2	VR
Echinauris subquadrata Cooper and Grant	VR
Rhynchopora molina Cooper and Grant	VR
LOCALITY N701v : Gaptank Formation, Uddenites Member	
Acosarina sp.	VR
Antiquatonia inflativentra Cooper and Grant	VR
Cancrinella sp.	VR
Chonetinella costellata Cooper and Grant	VR
Composita sp.	VR
Diplanus redactus Cooper and Grant	VR
Eridmatus marathonensis Cooper and Grant	R
Gypospirifer anancites Cooper and Grant	VR
Hystriculina sulcata Cooper and Grant	R
Hystriculina ventroplana Cooper and Grant	R
Kochiproductus primitivus Cooper and Grant	VR
Kutorginella uddeni Cooper and Grant	R
Limbella wolfcampensis (R.E. King)	VR
Linoproductus meniscus Dunbar and Condra	VR
Meekella prionota Cooper and Grant	VR
Neochonetes liratus Cooper and Grant	VR
Nudauris splendens Cooper and Grant	VR
Parenteletes cooperi R.E. King	VR
Pontisia kingi Cooper and Grant	VR
Reticulatia sp. 2	VR
Rhipidomella sp.	VR
Rhynchopora molina Cooper and Grant	VR
Scacchinella triangulata Cooper and Grant	VR
Teguliferina boesei R.E. King	R
Tropidelasma culmenatum Cooper and Grant	VR
Waagenoconcha prophetica Cooper and Grant	VR
LOCALITY N701x : Gaptank Formation, Uddenites Member	
Composita strongyle Cooper and Grant	VR
Goniarina sp. 4	VR
Juresania sp. 1	VR
Kochiproductus primitivus Cooper and Grant	VR
Linoproductus sp.	VR
Meekella magnifica Cooper and Grant	VR
Neophricadothyris transversa Cooper and Grant	VR
Neospirifer apothescelus Cooper and Grant	VR
Nudauris splendens Cooper and Grant	VR
Orthotetella wolfcampensis R.E. King	VR
Parenteletes cooperi R.E. King	VR
Scacchinella triangulata Cooper and Grant	VR
Teguliferina boesei R.E. King	VR
LOCALITY N701y : Gaptank Formation	
Derbyoides sp. 1	VR
Echinauris subquadrata Cooper and Grant	VR
Hystriculina ventroplana Cooper and Grant	VR
Kutorginella uddeni Cooper and Grant	R
Linoproductus meniscus Dunbar and Condra,	VR
Nudauris splendens Cooper and Grant	C
Reticulatia sp.	VR
Rhynchopora sp.	VR

	Rarity code
Teguliferina boesei R.E. King	VR
LOCALITY N702 : Cathedral Mountain Formation	
Acanthocrania densispina Cooper and Grant	R
Acosarina mesoplatys (R.E. King)	VA
Amphipella arcaria Cooper and Grant	R
Anemonaria sublaevis (R.E. King)	R
Anteridocus erugatus Cooper and Grant	VR
Anteridocus gongylus Cooper and Grant	C
Antronaria speciosa Cooper and Grant	VR
Beecheria sp.	VR
Cartorhium latum (R.E. King)	C
Cenorhynchia mitigata Cooper and Grant	C
Cenorhynchia saginata Cooper and Grant	VR
Chaeniorhynchus inauris Cooper and Grant	R
Choanodus irregularis Cooper and Grant	C
Choanodus perfectus Cooper and Grant	R
Chondronia bella Cooper and Grant	C
Chonosteges costellatus Cooper and Grant	VR
Chonosteges pulcher Cooper and Grant	VR
Chonosteges variabilis Cooper and Grant	A
Collemataria gregaria Cooper and Grant	A
Composita bucculenta Cooper and Grant	C
Composita imbricata Cooper and Grant	A
Composita sp.	C
Compressoproductus thomasi Cooper and Grant	VR
Cooperina parva Cooper and Grant	VR
Derbyia complicata Cooper and Grant	R
Derbyia informis Cooper and Grant	C
Derbyia laqueata Cooper and Grant	A
Derbyia sp.	VR
Dielasma anterolatum Cooper and Grant	VR
Dielasma obesum Cooper and Grant	VR
Dielasma perplexum Cooper and Grant	R
Dielasma sp. 7	VR
Diplanus lamellatus (R.E. King)	C
Dyoros (Lissosia) vagabundus Cooper and Grant	A
Dyoros (Tetragonetes) giganteus Cooper and Grant	VR
Dyoros (Tetragonetes) rectangulatus Cooper and Grant	R
Echinauris crassa Cooper and Grant	C
Echinauris irregularis Cooper and Grant	VA
Edriosteges beedei (R.E. King)	VR
Edriosteges multispinosus Muir-Wood and Cooper	C
Elassonia petila Cooper and Grant	R
Enteletes leonardensis R.E. King	C
Enteletes plummeri R.E. King	R
Eolyttonia chaotica Cooper and Grant	VR
Eolyttonia circularis Cooper and Grant	C
Eolyttonia pocillata Cooper and Grant	C
Goniarina futilis Cooper and Grant	A
Grandaurispina? vaga Cooper and Grant	R
Hercosestria cribrosa Cooper and Grant	VR
Hercosestria sp.	VR
Hercosia uddeni (Böse)	VA
Heteralosia sp. 1	VR
Heterelasma contortum Cooper and Grant	VR
Heterelasma gibbosum Cooper and Grant	R
Hustedia ampullacea Cooper and Grant	R
Hustedia lusca Cooper and Grant	VA
Hustedia sp.	R
Hustedia spicata Cooper and Grant	VA
Institella leonardensis (R.E. King)	A
Isogramma lobatum Cooper and Grant	VR
Lepidocrania tardispinosa Cooper and Grant	VR
Lepidospirifer angulatus Cooper and Grant	R

	Rarity code
LOCALITY N702 - Continued	
Lepidospirifer demissus Cooper and Grant	C
Linoproductus delicatus Cooper and Grant	VR
Loxophragmus ellipticus Cooper and Grant	C
Martinia miranda Cooper and Grant	A
Meekella calathica Cooper and Grant	VA
Meekella occidentalis (Newberry)	VR
Megousia auriculata Muir-Wood and Cooper	C
Megousia umbonata Cooper and Grant	VR
Metriolepis carotica Cooper and Grant	C
Metriolepis tegulata Cooper and Grant	C
Neophricadothyris bullata Cooper and Grant	A
Neophricadothyris sp. 1	VR
Neophricadothyris sp. 2	VR
Neophricadothyris sp.	VR
Neospirifer mansuetus Cooper and Grant	C
Niviconia globosa (R.E. King)	VA
Nudauris linospina Cooper and Grant	C
Paucispinifera sp.	VR
Peniculauris subcostata (R.E. King)	C
Petasmaia expansa Cooper and Grant	VR
Phrenophoria nesiotes Cooper and Grant	VR
Phrenophoria vetula Cooper and Grant	VR
Pontisia stehlii stehlii Cooper and Grant	VR
Pontisia stehlii tumidosa Cooper and Grant	C
Pseudoleptodus sp.	VR
Ptygmactrum mordicum Cooper and Grant	VR
Rallacosta actina Cooper and Grant	R
Reticulariina craticula Cooper and Grant	C
Reticulariina venustula Cooper and Grant	VR
Rhamnaria tenuispinosa Cooper and Grant	C
Rhipidomella hispidula Cooper and Grant	A
Rhynchopora hebetata Cooper and Grant	VR
Rugatia occidentalis parvauris (Newberry)	R
Rugatia paraindica (McKee)	C
Spiriferellina tricosa Cooper and Grant	VR
Stenoscisma aptatum Cooper and Grant	VR
Stenoscisma calvatum Cooper and Grant	VR
Stenoscisma doricranum Cooper and Grant	R
Stenoscisma exutum Cooper and Grant	C
Stenoscisma fabarium Cooper and Grant	VR
Stenoscisma triquetrum Cooper and Grant	C
Tautosia fastigiata Cooper and Grant	R
Tautosia pulchra Cooper and Grant	VR
Texarina paucula Cooper and Grant	VR
Texarina wordensis (R.E. King)	C
Thamnosia anterospinosa Cooper and Grant	R
Torynechus caelatus Cooper and Grant	VR
Trophisina fenaria Cooper and Grant	C
Xenosteges adherens Muir-Wood and Cooper	A
Xestosia obsolescens Cooper and Grant	VR
LOCALITY N702a : Cathedral Mountain Formation	
Acanthocrania sp.	VR
Acosarina mesoplatys (R.E. King)	VA
Anteridocus erugatus Cooper and Grant	VR
Anteridocus gongylus Cooper and Grant	VA
Cartorhium latum (R.E. King)	C
Cenorhynchia mitigata Cooper and Grant	C
Choanodus irregularis Cooper and Grant	VR
Chondronia bella Cooper and Grant	VA
Chonosteges variabilis Cooper and Grant	C
Composita crassa Cooper and Grant	VR
Composita sp.	C
Derbyia laqueata Cooper and Grant	R

	Rarity code
Dielasma anterolatum Cooper and Grant	VR
Dielasma perplexum Cooper and Grant	VR
Diplanus lamellatus (R.E. King)	VR
Dyoros (*Lissosia*) *vagabundus* Cooper and Grant	R
Dyoros (*Tetragonetes*) *rectangulatus* Cooper and Grant	R
Echinauris irregularis Cooper and Grant	R
Edriosteges multispinosus Muir-Wood and Cooper	R
Elassonia petila Cooper and Grant	VR
Eolyttonia circularis Cooper and Grant	C
Eolyttonia pocillata Cooper and Grant	R
Glossothyropsis sp. 1 (Girty)	VR
Hercosia uddeni (Böse)	C
Heterelasma gibbosum Cooper and Grant	R
Hustedia lusca Cooper and Grant	C
Hustedia spicata Cooper and Grant	SA
Lepidospirifer angulatus Cooper and Grant	VR
Lepidospirifer demissus Cooper and Grant	C
Martinia miranda Cooper and Grant	VR
Meekella calathica Cooper and Grant	A
Megousia auriculata Muir-Wood and Cooper	VR
Metriolepis tegulata Cooper and Grant	VR
Neophricadothyris bullata Cooper and Grant	R
Neophricadothyris sp.	VR
Neospirifer mansuetus Cooper and Grant	C
Niviconia abrupta Cooper and Grant	VR
Niviconia globosa (R.E. King)	VA
Nudauris linospina Cooper and Grant	VR
Peniculauris subcostata (R.E. King)	VR
Pontisia stehlii stehlii Cooper and Grant	VR
Pontisia stehlii tumidosa Cooper and Grant	C
Pseudoleptodus sp.	VR
Reticulariina craticula Cooper and Grant	R
Reticulariina venustula Cooper and Grant	C
Rhamnaria tenuispinosa Cooper and Grant	C
Rhipidomella hispidula Cooper and Grant	C
Rhynchopora hebetata Cooper and Grant	VR
Rugatia paraindica (McKee)	VR
Spiriferellina tricosa Cooper and Grant	VR
Stenoscisma doricranum Cooper and Grant	VA
Stenoscisma sp.	VR
Stenoscisma triquetrum Cooper and Grant	VR
Tautosia pulchra Cooper and Grant	VR
Texarina wordensis (R.E. King)	C
Xenosteges adherens Muir-Wood and Cooper	C
LOCALITY N702a[1] : Cathedral Mountain Formation	
Cartorhium latum (R.E. King)	R
Choanodus irregularis Cooper and Grant	VR
Collemataria gregaria Cooper and Grant	A
Eolyttonia circularis Cooper and Grant	C
Megousia auriculata Muir-Wood and Cooper	VR
Neospirifer mansuetus Cooper and Grant	R
LOCALITY N702b : Cathedral Mountain Formation	
Acanthocrania sp.	VR
Acosarina mesoplatys (R.E. King)	VA
Anemonaria sublaevis (R.E. King)	R
Anteridocus gongylus Cooper and Grant	R
Cancrinella sp. 1	R
Cartorhium latum (R.E. King)	C
Cenorhynchia mitigata Cooper and Grant	VR
Choanodus irregularis Cooper and Grant	VR
Choanodus perfectus Cooper and Grant	C
Chondronia bella Cooper and Grant	VR
Chonosteges variabilis Cooper and Grant	C
Collemataria gregaria Cooper and Grant	R

Rarity code

LOCALITY N702b - Continued

Composita bucculenta Cooper and Grant	R
Composita imbricata Cooper and Grant	C
Compressoproductus curtus Cooper and Grant	C
Derbyia informis Cooper and Grant	R
Derbyia laqueata Cooper and Grant	A
Derbyia sp.	VR
Dielasma ellipsoideum Cooper and Grant	VR
Dielasma sp.	VR
Dyoros (Dyoros) extensiformis Cooper and Grant	VR
Dyoros (Lissosia) vagabundus Cooper and Grant	A
Dyoros (Tetragonetes) giganteus Cooper and Grant	VR
Dyoros (Tetragonetes) rectangulatus Cooper and Grant	C
Echinauris irregularis Cooper and Grant	C
Echinauris sp.	C
Edriosteges multispinosus Muir-Wood and Cooper	VR
Eolyttonia chaotica Cooper and Grant	VR
Eolyttonia circularis Cooper and Grant	VR
Eolyttonia pocillata Cooper and Grant	C
Glossothyropsis sp. 1 (Girty)	VR
Goniarina sp. 2	VR
Grandaurispina sp. 3	VR
Grandaurispina? vaga Cooper and Grant	VR
Hercosia uddeni (Böse)	VA
Heterelasma gibbosum Cooper and Grant	VR
Hustedia ampullacea Cooper and Grant	R
Hustedia compressa Cooper and Grant	VR
Hustedia lusca Cooper and Grant	A
Hustedia sp.	R
Hustedia spicata Cooper and Grant	VA
Hustedia trisecta Cooper and Grant	C
Institella leonardensis (R.E. King)	VA
Isogramma lobatum Cooper and Grant	VR
Kochiproductus sp. 6	VR
Lepidospirifer inferus Cooper and Grant	C
Loxophragmus ellipticus Cooper and Grant	A
Martinia miranda Cooper and Grant	VA
Meekella calathica Cooper and Grant	VA
Megousia auriculata Muir-Wood and Cooper	C
Metriolepis carotica Cooper and Grant	R
Metriolepis larina Cooper and Grant	VR
Metriolepis tegulata Cooper and Grant	C
Neophricadothyris bullata Cooper and Grant	A
Neospirifer mansuetus Cooper and Grant	C
Niviconia globosa (R.E. King)	VA
Nudauris linospina Cooper and Grant	VR
Paucispinifera sp.	VR
Peniculauris subcostata (R.E. King)	VR
Petasmaia expansa Cooper and Grant	C
Phrenophoria planifrons Cooper and Grant	VR
Phrenophoria vetula Cooper and Grant	VR
Pontisia stehlii tumidosa Cooper and Grant	R
Ptygmactrum angulatum Cooper and Grant	R
Ptygmactrum mordicum Cooper and Grant	VR
Rallacosta actina Cooper and Grant	R
Reticulariina sp.	VR
Reticulariina venustula Cooper and Grant	VR
Rhamnaria tenuispinosa Cooper and Grant	C
Rhipidomella hispidula Cooper and Grant	A
Rugatia paraindica (McKee)	VR
Stenoscisma exutum Cooper and Grant	R
Stenoscisma triquetrum Cooper and Grant	A
Tautosia fastigiata Cooper and Grant	A
Tautosia sp.	VR
Texarina wordensis (R.E. King)	R

Rarity code

Thedusia bucrenata Cooper and Grant	R
Xenosteges adherens Muir-Wood and Cooper	A

LOCALITY N702c : Road Canyon Formation

Acanthocrania densispina Cooper and Grant	C
Acosarina mesoplatys (R.E. King)	SA
Acritosia? vestibula Cooper and Grant	C
Anteridocus erugatus Cooper and Grant	A
Cenorhynchia atmeta Cooper and Grant	C
Cenorhynchia mitigata Cooper and Grant	R
Cenorhynchia parvula Cooper and Grant	R
Cenorhynchia saginata Cooper and Grant	C
Chondronia ovalis Cooper and Grant	C
Chonosteges costellatus Cooper and Grant	R
Collemataria gregaria Cooper and Grant	R
Composita stalagmium Cooper and Grant	VA
Cooperina parva Cooper and Grant	R
Cooperina subcuneata Cooper and Grant	VR
Crurithyris minutalis Cooper and Grant	VA
Cyclacantharia paucispinosa Cooper and Grant	VA
Derbyia cincinnata Cooper and Grant	R
Derbyia informis Cooper and Grant	C
Derbyia laqueata Cooper and Grant	A
Dielasma ellipsoideum Cooper and Grant	A
Dielasma sp.	VR
Dyoros (Dyoros) extensiformis Cooper and Grant	C
Dyoros (Tetragonetes) rectangulatus Cooper and Grant	VR
Echinauris bella Cooper and Grant	C
Echinauris crassa Cooper and Grant	VR
Echinauris irregularis Cooper and Grant	VA
Edriosteges multispinosus Muir-Wood and Cooper	A
Elassonia micraria Cooper and Grant	VA
Eolyttonia chaotica Cooper and Grant	C
Hercosestria cribrosa Cooper and Grant	SA
Heterelasma glansfagea Cooper and Grant	A
Holotricharina hirsuta Cooper and Grant	VA
Hustedia ampullacea Cooper and Grant	VR
Hustedia connorsi Cooper and Grant	SA
Hustedia narinosa Cooper and Grant	VA
Kutorginella sullivanensis (R.E. King)	R
Kutorginella umbonata (Muir-Wood and Cooper)	A
Lepidocrania tardispinosa Cooper and Grant	A
Meekella calathica Cooper and Grant	VA
Megousia auriculata Muir-Wood and Cooper	C
Metriolepis sp.	VR
Neophricadothyris bullata Cooper and Grant	VA
Neospirifer thescelus Cooper and Grant	C
Paucispinifera sp.	VR
Paucispinifera sulcata Cooper and Grant	VA
Peniculauris peniculifera Cooper and Grant	VR
Peniculauris subcostata (R.E. King)	VR
Peniculauris transversa Cooper and Grant	C
Petasmatherus nitidus Cooper and Grant	VR
Pontisia stehlii stehlii Cooper and Grant	A
Pontisia stehlii tumidosa Cooper and Grant	C
Reticulariina craticula Cooper and Grant	VA
Reticulariina venustula Cooper and Grant	VR
Rhamnaria sp.	VR
Rhamnaria tenuispinosa Cooper and Grant	C
Rhamnaria vinnula Cooper and Grant	R
Rhynchopora hebetata Cooper and Grant	R
Rhynchopora sphenoides Cooper and Grant	VR
Rugatia convexa Cooper and Grant	R
Rugatia incurvata (R.E. King)	C
Spinarella paulula Cooper and Grant	R

	Rarity code
LOCALITY N702c - Continued	
Spinarella perfecta Cooper and Grant	R
Spiriferellina tricosa Cooper and Grant	A
Stenoscisma aptatum Cooper and Grant	C
Stenoscisma calvatum Cooper and Grant	R
Stenoscisma camurum Cooper and Grant	VR
Stenoscisma sp.	VR
Stenoscisma triquetrum Cooper and Grant	A
Texarina wordensis (R.E. King)	A
Tschernyschewia sp.	VR
Waagenoconcha convexa Cooper and Grant	C
Waagenoconcha platys Cooper and Grant	VR

LOCALITY N702d : Hess Formation, Taylor Ranch Member

Acolosia elliptica Cooper and Grant	R
Acosarina dorsisulcata Cooper and Grant	R
Acritosia peculiaris Cooper and Grant	VR
Acritosia solida Cooper and Grant	C
Antronaria speciosa Cooper and Grant	C
Antronaria transversa (R.E. King)	C
Chondronia ningula Cooper and Grant	R
Chonosteges limbatus Cooper and Grant	R
Collemataria sp.	R
Composita apsidata Cooper and Grant	R
Composita sp.	R
Compressoproductus sp. 5	VR
Cooperina parva Cooper and Grant	R
Crurithyris sp. b	VR
Cyclacantharia sp. 4	VR
Derbyia crenulata Girty	R
Dielasma longisulcatum Cooper and Grant	VR
Diplanus lamellatus (R.E. King)	A
Edriosteges sp. 1	R
Elassonia sobrina Cooper and Grant	R
Enteletes subcircularis Cooper and Grant	R
Eolyttonia sp. 1	R
Goniarina appeli Cooper and Grant	VR
Goniarina futilis Cooper and Grant	R
Hustedia cepacea Cooper and Grant	C
Limbella sp. 1	VR
Linoproductus undatus Cooper and Grant	R
Meekella hessensis R.E. King	R
Neophricadothyris bullata Cooper and Grant	VR
Neospirifer neali Cooper and Grant	R
Neospirifer notialis Cooper and Grant	R
Oncosarina whitei (R.E. King)	R
Peniculauris imitata Cooper and Grant	C
Pontisia nanas (Stehli)	VR
Rhipidomella hessensis R.E. King	R
Rugaria hessensis (R.E. King)	R
Scacchinella titan Cooper and Grant	VR
Spyridiophora reticulata (R.E. King)	R
Stenoscisma hadrum Cooper and Grant	R
Teguliferina compacta Cooper and Grant	VR
Thamnosia silicica Cooper and Grant	R
Tropidelasma costellatum Cooper and Grant	R
Tschernyschewia inexpectans Cooper and Grant	VR

LOCALITY N702e : Hess Formation, Taylor Ranch Member

Acosarina dorsisulcata Cooper and Grant	A
Antronaria speciosa Cooper and Grant	R
Antronaria transversa (R.E. King)	A
Chondronia ningula Cooper and Grant	C
Chonosteges limbatus Cooper and Grant	C

	Rarity code
Composita apsidata Cooper and Grant	A
Compressoproductus sp. 1	VR
Crurithyris sp. c	C
Derbyia crenulata Girty	VR
Dielasma longisulcatum Cooper and Grant	VR
Diplanus lamellatus (R.E. King)	VR
Enteletes subcircularis Cooper and Grant	C
Goniarina futilis Cooper and Grant	VR
Heterelasma sp. 4	VR
Hustedia cepacea Cooper and Grant	A
Limbella sp. 1	VR
Linoproductus undatus Cooper and Grant	R
Meekella hessensis R.E. King	R
Neospirifer notialis Cooper and Grant	C
Oncosarina whitei (R.E. King)	C
Peniculauris imitata Cooper and Grant	C
Rhipidomella hessensis R.E. King	VA
Rugaria hessensis (R.E. King)	A
Spyridiophora reticulata (R.E. King)	R
Stenoscisma doricranum Cooper and Grant	VR
Stenoscisma hadrum Cooper and Grant	C
Stenoscisma sp.	VR
Teguliferina compacta Cooper and Grant	VR
Thamnosia silicica Cooper and Grant	C

LOCALITY N702ent : Cathedral Mountain Formation

Acosarina mesoplatys (R.E. King)	C
Anemonaria sublaevis (R.E. King)	VR
Anteridocus erugatus Cooper and Grant	R
Anteridocus gongylus Cooper and Grant	VR
Antronaria speciosa Cooper and Grant	VR
Cartorhium latum (R.E. King)	VR
Chondronia bella Cooper and Grant	C
Chonosteges variabilis Cooper and Grant	VR
Collemataria gregaria Cooper and Grant	C
Composita bucculenta Cooper and Grant	C
Composita sp.	C
Compressoproductus curtus Cooper and Grant	VR
Derbyia laqueata Cooper and Grant	VR
Dielasma perplexum Cooper and Grant	VR
Dyoros (*Lissosia*) *vagabundus* Cooper and Grant	VR
Echinauris irregularis Cooper and Grant	C
Enteletes leonardensis R.E. King	C
Eolyttonia circularis Cooper and Grant	VR
Eolyttonia pocillata Cooper and Grant	VR
Grandaurispina? vaga Cooper and Grant	VR
Hercosia uddeni (Böse)	VR
Hustedia spicata Cooper and Grant	A
Institella leonardensis (R.E. King)	VR
Loxophragmus ellipticus Cooper and Grant	VR
Meekella calathica Cooper and Grant	R
Metriolepis carotica Cooper and Grant	VR
Neophricadothyris bullata Cooper and Grant	C
Neospirifer mansuetus Cooper and Grant	VR
Niviconia globosa (R.E. King)	C
Rhipidomella hispidula Cooper and Grant	R
Rhynchopora hebetata Cooper and Grant	VR
Stenoscisma doricranum Cooper and Grant	C
Stenoscisma triquetrum Cooper and Grant	VR
Tautosia pulchra Cooper and Grant	C
Texarina wordensis (R.E. King)	VR
Thamnosia anterospinosa Cooper and Grant	VR

LOCALITY N702f : Hess Formation, Taylor Ranch Member

Antronaria speciosa Cooper and Grant	VR

	Rarity code
LOCALITY N702f - Continued	
Antronaria transversa (R.E. King)	VR
Composita bucculenta Cooper and Grant	VR
Dielasma longisulcatum Cooper and Grant	VR
Echinauris sp.	VR
Enteletes subcircularis Cooper and Grant	R
Eolyttonia sp.	VR
Limbella sp. 1	VR
Linoproductus undatus Cooper and Grant	R
Meekella hessensis R.E. King	VR
Oncosarina whitei (R.E. King)	R
Peniculauris imitata Cooper and Grant	R
Rhipidomella hessensis R.E. King	VR
Thamnosia silicica Cooper and Grant	VR
Tschernyschewia inexpectans Cooper and Grant	VR
LOCALITY N702h : Neal Ranch Formation	
Linoproductus semisulcatus Cooper and Grant	VR
LOCALITY N702inst : Cathedral Mountain Formation	
Cartorhium latum (R.E. King)	VR
Composita stalagmium Cooper and Grant	C
Derbyia informis Cooper and Grant	VR
Derbyia laqueata Cooper and Grant	VR
Edriosteges multispinosus Muir-Wood and Cooper	VR
Institella leonardensis (R.E. King)	VR
Meekella calathica Cooper and Grant	VR
Neospirifer mansuetus Cooper and Grant	VR
Niviconia globosa (R.E. King)	R
Nudauris linospina Cooper and Grant..................	VR
Phrenophoria vetula Cooper and Grant	VR
Pontisia stehlii tumidosa Cooper and Grant	VR
Rallacosta actina Cooper and Grant	VR
Rhipidomella hispidula Cooper and Grant	R
Xenosteges adherens Muir-Wood and Cooper...........	VR
LOCALITY N702j : Gaptank Formation, Uddenites Member	
Meekella texana R.E. King	R
Neochonetes liratus Cooper and Grant	VR
Parenteletes cooperi R.E. King..........................	VR
Teguliferina boesei R.E. King	VR
LOCALITY N702k : Gaptank Formation, Uddenites Member	
Meekella texana R.E. King	VR
Parenteletes cooperi R.E. King..........................	VR
LOCALITY N702-low : Cathedral Mountain Formation	
Acosarina mesoplatys (R.E. King)	C
Anteridocus gongylus Cooper and Grant................	R
Antronaria speciosa Cooper and Grant	VR
Cenorhynchia mitigata Cooper and Grant	VR
Cenorhynchia saginata Cooper and Grant	VR
Chaeniorhynchus inauris Cooper and Grant	VR
Choanodus irregularis Cooper and Grant	VR
Chondronia bella Cooper and Grant	A
Chonosteges variabilis Cooper and Grant...............	R
Collemataria gregaria Cooper and Grant	A
Composita bucculenta Cooper and Grant	C
Composita sp.	C
Composita stalagmium Cooper and Grant	C
Compressoproductus curtus Cooper and Grant	VR
Derbyia complicata Cooper and Grant	VR
Derbyia informis Cooper and Grant.....................	R
Derbyia laqueata Cooper and Grant	C
Dielasma obesum Cooper and Grant.....................	VR

	Rarity code
Dielasma perplexum Cooper and Grant	R
Diplanus lamellatus (R.E. King)	R
Dyoros (*Tetragonetes*) *rectangulatus* Cooper and Grant.....	VR
Echinauris irregularis Cooper and Grant	VR
Edriosteges multispinosus Muir-Wood and Cooper.....	VR
Enteletes leonardensis R.E. King	C
Eolyttonia circularis Cooper and Grant	C
Eolyttonia pocillata Cooper and Grant.................	C
Hercosia uddeni (Böse)	A
Hustedia ampullacea Cooper and Grant...............	VR
Hustedia lusca Cooper and Grant	A
Hustedia spicata Cooper and Grant	VA
Institella leonardensis (R.E. King).....................	A
Lepidocrania tardispinosa Cooper and Grant	VR
Lepidospirifer angulatus Cooper and Grant	VR
Lepidospirifer demissus Cooper and Grant.............	VR
Linoproductus delicatus Cooper and Grant	VR
Loxophragmus ellipticus Cooper and Grant	VR
Martinia miranda Cooper and Grant	R
Meekella calathica Cooper and Grant	C
Megousia auriculata Muir-Wood and Cooper..........	VR
Megousia umbonata Cooper and Grant	VR
Neophricadothyris bullata Cooper and Grant	C
Neospirifer mansuetus Cooper and Grant	R
Niviconia globosa (R.E. King)..........................	VA
Nudauris linospina Cooper and Grant.................	R
Peniculauris subcostata (R.E. King)	VR
Petasmaia expansa Cooper and Grant	R
Petasmatherus mundus Cooper and Grant..............	R
Phrenophoria vetula Cooper and Grant	VR
Pontisia stehlii tumidosa Cooper and Grant	R
Rhipidomella hispidula Cooper and Grant	C
Rhynchopora hebetata Cooper and Grant	VR
Rugatia paraindica (McKee)	R
Stenoscisma doricranum Cooper and Grant	C
Stenoscisma exutum Cooper and Grant	R
Stenoscisma fabarium Cooper and Grant...............	R
Stenoscisma triquetrum Cooper and Grant	C
Taphrosestria? sp.	VR
Tautosia pulchra Cooper and Grant....................	VR
Texarina wordensis (R.E. King)	R
Thamnosia anterospinosa Cooper and Grant	R
Trophisina fenaria Cooper and Grant	C
Xenosteges adherens Muir-Wood and Cooper...........	R
LOCALITY N702m : Hess Formation, Taylor Ranch Member	
Acosarina dorsisulcata Cooper and Grant	VR
Antronaria speciosa Cooper and Grant	VR
Chondronia ningula Cooper and Grant	VR
Composita bucculenta Cooper and Grant...............	VR
Echinauris sp.	VR
Enteletes subcircularis Cooper and Grant	R
Eolyttonia sp.	VR
Limbella sp. 1	VR
Linoproductus undatus Cooper and Grant	VR
Oncosarina whitei (R.E. King)	VR
Peniculauris imitata Cooper and Grant.................	C
Thamnosia silicica Cooper and Grant	VR
Tschernyschewia inexpectans Cooper and Grant	VR
LOCALITY N702n : Gaptank Formation, Uddenites Member	
Echinaria cf. *moorei* (Dunbar and Condra).............	VR

	Rarity code
LOCALITY N702n - Continued	
Eridmatus sp.	VR
Hystriculina sp.	VR
Isogramma sp.	VR
Kochiproductus primitivus Cooper and Grant	VR
Kutorginella uddeni Cooper and Grant	VR
Limbella costellata Cooper and Grant	VR
Meekella prionota Cooper and Grant	VR
Meekella texana R.E. King	VR
Neospirifer apothescelus Cooper and Grant	VR
Nudauris splendens Cooper and Grant	VR
Pareneteletes cooperi R.E. King	VR
Scacchinella triangulata Cooper and Grant	VR
Teguliferina boesei R.E. King	R
LOCALITY N702q : Gaptank Formation, Uddenites Member	
Derbyia sp.	VR
Echinaria cf. *moorei* (Dunbar and Condra)	VR
Gypospirifer anancites Cooper and Grant	VR
Hystriculina sulcata Cooper and Grant	VR
Kochiproductus primitivus Cooper and Grant	VR
Kochiproductus sp.	VR
Linoproductus sp.	VR
Meekella texana R.E. King	VR
Pareneteletes cooperi R.E. King	R
Scacchinella triangulata Cooper and Grant	R
Teguliferina boesei R.E. King	VR
Tropidelasma sp. 2	VR
LOCALITY N702r : Gaptank Formation, Uddenites Member	
Juresania sp. 1	VR
Pareneteletes cooperi R.E. King	VR
Pareneteletes superbus Cooper and Grant	VR
Scacchinella triangulata Cooper and Grant	VR
Teguliferina boesei R.E. King	VR
LOCALITY N702t : Neal Ranch Formation	
Nudauris tribulosa Cooper and Grant	VR
LOCALITY N702un : Cathedral Mountain Formation	
Acosarina mesoplatys (R.E. King)	VA
Anemonaria sublaevis (R.E. King)	VR
Anteridocus gongylus Cooper and Grant	C
Antronaria speciosa Cooper and Grant	VR
Cartorhium latum (R.E. King)	C
Cenorhynchia mitigata Cooper and Grant	R
Choanodus irregularis Cooper and Grant	R
Choanodus perfectus Cooper and Grant	A
Chondronia bella Cooper and Grant	R
Chonosteges costellatus Cooper and Grant	R
Chonosteges variabilis Cooper and Grant	A
Collemataria gregaria Cooper and Grant	C
Composita bucculenta Cooper and Grant	C
Composita imbricata Cooper and Grant	R
Composita sp.	A
Compressoproductus thomasi Cooper and Grant	VR
Derbyia complicata Cooper and Grant	VR
Derbyia informis Cooper and Grant	R
Derbyia laqueata Cooper and Grant	C
Derbyia sp.	R
Dielasma perplexum Cooper and Grant	VR
Dielasma sp.	VR
Diplanus lamellatus (R.E. King)	VR

	Rarity code
Dyoros (*Dyoros*) *extensiformis* Cooper and Grant	R
Dyoros (*Lissosia*) *vagabundus* Cooper and Grant	C
Dyoros (*Tetragonetes*) *rectangulatus* Cooper and Grant	R
Echinauris irregularis Cooper and Grant	C
Edriosteges multispinosus Muir-Wood and Cooper	VR
Elassonia petila Cooper and Grant	VR
Enteletes leonardensis R.E. King	R
Eolyttonia chaotica Cooper and Grant	R
Eolyttonia circularis Cooper and Grant	C
Eolyttonia pocillata Cooper and Grant	C
Eolyttonia sp. 2	VR
Grandaurispina? vaga Cooper and Grant	C
Hercosia uddeni (Böse)	VA
Heterelasma gibbosum Cooper and Grant	R
Hustedia ampullacea Cooper and Grant	VR
Hustedia lusca Cooper and Grant	VA
Hustedia sp.	VR
Hustedia spicata Cooper and Grant	C
Institella leonardensis (R.E. King)	A
Kochiproductus sp. 6	VR
Lepidospirifer angulatus Cooper and Grant	VR
Lepidospirifer demissus Cooper and Grant	C
Loxophragmus ellipticus Cooper and Grant	R
Martinia miranda Cooper and Grant	C
Meekella calathica Cooper and Grant	VA
Megousia auriculata Muir-Wood and Cooper	VR
Metriolepis carotica Cooper and Grant	C
Metriolepis tegulata Cooper and Grant	R
Neophricadothyris bullata Cooper and Grant	A
Neospirifer mansuetus Cooper and Grant	C
Niviconia globosa (R.E. King)	VA
Nudauris linospina Cooper and Grant	R
Peniculauris subcostata (R.E. King)	VR
Petasmaia expansa Cooper and Grant	C
Petrocrania sp.	VR
Pontisia stehlii tumidosa Cooper and Grant	R
Rallacosta actina Cooper and Grant	VR
Reticulariina venustula Cooper and Grant	VR
Rhamnaria tenuispinosa Cooper and Grant	C
Rhipidomella hispidula Cooper and Grant	A
Rhynchopora hebetata Cooper and Grant	R
Rugatia paraindica (McKee)	C
Stenoscisma aptatum Cooper and Grant	VR
Stenoscisma calvatum Cooper and Grant	C
Stenoscisma doricranum Cooper and Grant	C
Stenoscisma triquetrum Cooper and Grant	VR
Tautosia fastigiata Cooper and Grant	VR
Texarina wordensis (R.E. King)	R
Thamnosia anterospinosa Cooper and Grant	R
Thedusia bucrenata Cooper and Grant	VR
Torynechus caelatus Cooper and Grant	C
Trophisina fenaria Cooper and Grant	A
Xenosteges adherens Muir-Wood and Cooper	C
Xestosia obsolescens Cooper and Grant	C
LOCALITY N703 : Road Canyon Formation	
Acosarina mesoplatys (R.E. King)	C
Ametoria residua Cooper and Grant	VR
Chonetinetes angustisulcatus Cooper and Grant	VR
Collemataria sp.	VR
Composita crassa Cooper and Grant	VR
Crurithyris minutalis Cooper and Grant	R
Cyclacantharia paucispinosa Cooper and Grant	VR
Derbyia cincinnata Cooper and Grant	VR
Derbyia complicata Cooper and Grant	VR

	Rarity code
LOCALITY N703 - Continued	
Derbyia informis Cooper and Grant	R
Derbyia laqueata Cooper and Grant	VR
Dielasma ellipsoideum Cooper and Grant	VR
Dyoros (Dyoros) extensus Cooper and Grant	VR
Dyoros (Tetragonetes) solidus Cooper and Grant	C
Echinauris bella Cooper and Grant	R
Echinauris lappacea Cooper and Grant	R
Echinauris liumbona Cooper and Grant	C
Echinauris parva Cooper and Grant	R
Echinauris sp.	A
Eolyttonia sp.	VR
Goniarina sp.	VR
Grandaurispina sp. 1	VR
Hercosestria cribrosa Cooper and Grant	VR
Holotricharina hirsuta Cooper and Grant	VR
Hustedia consuta Cooper and Grant	R
Hustedia narinosa Cooper and Grant	VR
Hustedia sp.	R
Kutorginella umbonata (Muir-Wood and Cooper)	VR
Meekella calathica Cooper and Grant	VR
Megousia auriculata Muir-Wood and Cooper	R
Metriolepis tegulata Cooper and Grant	VR
Neophricadothyris bullata Cooper and Grant	R
Neospirifer bakeri bakeri R.E. King	R
Paucispinifera costellata Cooper and Grant	VR
Peniculauris costata Cooper and Grant	VR
Phrenophoria planiventra Cooper and Grant	VR
Pseudoleptodus? giganteus Cooper and Grant	VR
Rhamnaria tenuispinosa Cooper and Grant	R
Roemerella gigantissima Cooper and Grant	VR
Rugatia incurvata (R.E. King)	VR
Stenoscisma sp.	VR
Stenoscisma triquetrum Cooper and Grant	VR
Tautosia galbina Cooper and Grant	VR
Thedusia mesocostata Cooper and Grant	VR
Thedusia sp.	VR
Waagenoconcha convexa Cooper and Grant	C
Xenosteges trivialis Cooper and Grant	VR
LOCALITY N703a : Road Canyon Formation	
Acanthocrania densispina Cooper and Grant	R
Acosarina mesoplatys (R.E. King)	VA
Amphipella attenuata Cooper and Grant	VR
Bothrostegium sp.	VR
Cenorhynchia atmeta Cooper and Grant	VR
Cenorhynchia parvula Cooper and Grant	C
Chaeniorhynchus salutare Cooper and Grant	R
Chondronia ovalis Cooper and Grant	C
Chonetinetes angustisulcatus Cooper and Grant	VR
Chonosteges costellatus Cooper and Grant	VR
Collemataria gregaria Cooper and Grant	C
Composita crassa Cooper and Grant	A
Composita sp.	R
Composita stalagmium Cooper and Grant	VR
Compressoproductus sp. 3	VR
Cyclacantharia paucispinosa Cooper and Grant	VA
Derbyia complicata Cooper and Grant	VR
Derbyia informis Cooper and Grant	C
Derbyia laqueata Cooper and Grant	A
Derbyia sp.	VR
Dielasma ellipsoideum Cooper and Grant	VR
Dielasma sp.	VR
Dyoros (Tetragonetes) rectangulatus Cooper and Grant	VR
Dyoros (Tetragonetes) solidus Cooper and Grant	VR
Echinauris bella Cooper and Grant	VR

	Rarity code
Echinauris crassa Cooper and Grant	R
Echinauris irregularis Cooper and Grant	A
Echinauris sp.	VR
Edriosteges multispinosus Muir-Wood and Cooper	A
Elassonia micraria Cooper and Grant	R
Eolyttonia chaotica Cooper and Grant	R
Hercosestria cribrosa Cooper and Grant	VA
Holotricharina hirsuta Cooper and Grant	R
Holotricharina? sp. 1	VR
Hustedia connorsi Cooper and Grant	C
Hustedia consuta Cooper and Grant	A
Hustedia narinosa Cooper and Grant	C
Hustedia sp.	VR
Kutorginella umbonata (Muir-Wood and Cooper)	VR
Meekella calathica Cooper and Grant	VA
Megousia auriculata Muir-Wood and Cooper	R
Mesolobus? permianus Cooper and Grant	VR
Metriolepis larina Cooper and Grant	R
Metriolepis tegulata Cooper and Grant	VR
Neophricadothyris bullata Cooper and Grant	A
Neophricadothyris crassibecca Cooper and Grant	VR
Neospirifer bakeri bakeri R.E. King	R
Neospirifer thescelus Cooper and Grant	R
Paraspiriferina sp.	VR
Paucispinifera sulcata Cooper and Grant	C
Peniculauris peniculifera Cooper and Grant	VR
Petasmatherus sp.	VR
Pontisia stehlii stehlii Cooper and Grant	R
Pontisia stehlii tumidosa Cooper and Grant	R
Reticulariina craticula Cooper and Grant	C
Reticulariina venustula Cooper and Grant	R
Rhamnaria tenuispinosa Cooper and Grant	VR
Rhynchopora hebetata Cooper and Grant	R
Rugatia incurvata (R.E. King)	R
Rugatia paraindica (McKee)	VR
Spiriferellina tricosa Cooper and Grant	A
Stenoscisma calvatum Cooper and Grant	VR
Stenoscisma sp.	VR
Stenoscisma triquetrum Cooper and Grant	R
Texarina wordensis (R.E. King)	C
Thedusia mesocostata Cooper and Grant	VR
Tropidelasma corniculum Cooper and Grant	VR
Waagenoconcha convexa Cooper and Grant	R
Xenosteges magnus Cooper and Grant	C
LOCALITY N703a[1] : Cathedral Mountain Formation	
Acosarina mesoplatys (R.E. King)	A
Anteridocus gongylus Cooper and Grant	C
Cartorhium latum (R.E. King)	C
Cenorhynchia parvula Cooper and Grant	VR
Choanodus irregularis Cooper and Grant	C
Choanodus perfectus Cooper and Grant	VR
Chondronia bella Cooper and Grant	R
Chonosteges costellatus Cooper and Grant	A
Collemataria gregaria Cooper and Grant	A
Composita crassa Cooper and Grant	R
Compressoproductus sp.	VR
Cooperina parva Cooper and Grant	VR
Derbyia laqueata Cooper and Grant	R
Dielasma perplexum Cooper and Grant	VR
Dyoros (Dyoros) extensiformis Cooper and Grant	VR
Dyoros (Lissosia) vagabundus Cooper and Grant	C
Dyoros (Tetragonetes) rectangulatus Cooper and Grant	VR
Echinauris irregularis Cooper and Grant	C
Edriosteges multispinosus Muir-Wood and Cooper	A

	Rarity code

LOCALITY N703a[1] - Continued

	Rarity code
Edriosteges tenuispinosus Cooper and Grant	VR
Eolyttonia circularis Cooper and Grant	VR
Hercosia uddeni (Bose)	A
Hustedia connorsi Cooper and Grant	VR
Hustedia lusca Cooper and Grant	C
Hustedia spicata Cooper and Grant	C
Lepidocrania sp.	VR
Lepidospirifer angulatus Cooper and Grant	C
Martinia miranda Cooper and Grant	VR
Meekella calathica Cooper and Grant	C
Megousia auriculata Muir-Wood and Cooper	VR
Metriolepis tegulata Cooper and Grant	VR
Neophricadothyris bullata Cooper and Grant	VR
Nudauris linospina Cooper and Grant	VR
Peniculauris subcostata (R.E. King)	R
Pontisia stehlii tumidosa Cooper and Grant	R
Pseudoleptodus sp. 5	VR
Rhamnaria tenuispinosa Cooper and Grant	C
Rhipidomella hispidula Cooper and Grant	VR
Rugatia occidentalis parvauris (Newberry)	VR
Rugatia paraindica (McKee)	R
Spiriferellina tricosa Cooper and Grant	VR
Stenoscisma sp.	VR
Texarina wordensis (R.E. King)	VR
Xenosteges adherens Muir-Wood and Cooper	C

LOCALITY N703b : Cathedral Mountain Formation

Acosarina mesoplatys (R.E. King)	C
Agelesia triagonalis (R.E. King)	R
Anemonaria sublaevis (R.E. King)	R
Anteridocus gongylus Cooper and Grant	VR
Antronaria speciosa Cooper and Grant	VR
Cartorhium latum (R.E. King)	R
Cenorhynchia parvula Cooper and Grant	VR
Chaeniorhynchus transversum Cooper and Grant	VR
Choanodus irregularis Cooper and Grant	C
Choanodus perfectus Cooper and Grant	VR
Chonosteges costellatus Cooper and Grant	VR
Chonosteges variabilis Cooper and Grant	R
Collemataria gregaria Cooper and Grant	A
Collemataria irregularis Cooper and Grant	VR
Composita bucculenta Cooper and Grant	VR
Composita imbricata Cooper and Grant	C
Composita sp.	R
Compressoproductus curtus Cooper and Grant	VR
Compressoproductus thomasi Cooper and Grant	VR
Cyclacantharia paucispinosa Cooper and Grant	VR
Derbyia complicata Cooper and Grant	R
Derbyia informis Cooper and Grant	R
Derbyia laqueata Cooper and Grant	C
Derbyia sp.	R
Dielasma ellipsoideum Cooper and Grant	VR
Dielasma obesum Cooper and Grant	VR
Dielasma sp.	VR
Dyoros (*Lissosia*) *vagabundus* Cooper and Grant	C
Echinauris irregularis Cooper and Grant	A
Echinauris sp.	R
Edriosteges multispinosus Muir-Wood and Cooper	C
Enteletes leonardensis R.E. King	VR
Eolyttonia circularis Cooper and Grant	C
Eolyttonia pocillata Cooper and Grant	R
Goniarina sp. 2	VR
Grandaurispina? vaga Cooper and Grant	VR
Hercosia uddeni (Böse)	C

	Rarity code
Heterelasma gibbosum Cooper and Grant	VR
Heterelasma sp.	VR
Hustedia ampullacea Cooper and Grant	R
Hustedia lusca Cooper and Grant	A
Hustedia spicata Cooper and Grant	C
Institella leonardensis (R.E. King)	C
Kochiproductus sp. 6	VR
Kutorginella umbonata (Muir-Wood and Cooper)	VR
Lepidospirifer angulatus Cooper and Grant	R
Lepidospirifer costellus (R.E. King)	VR
Lepidospirifer demissus Cooper and Grant	VR
Loxophragmus ellipticus Cooper and Grant	R
Martinia miranda Cooper and Grant	R
Meekella calathica Cooper and Grant	A
Meekella sp.	VR
Megousia auriculata Muir-Wood and Cooper	R
Metriolepis carotica Cooper and Grant	C
Metriolepis tegulata Cooper and Grant	R
Neophricadothyris bullata Cooper and Grant	VR
Neospirifer mansuetus Cooper and Grant	R
Niviconia globosa (R.E. King)	A
Nudauris linospina Cooper and Grant	R
Peniculauris subcostata (R.E. King)	C
Petasmaia expansa Cooper and Grant	VR
Pontisia stehlii tumidosa Cooper and Grant	VR
Pseudoleptodus sp.	VR
Rallacosta xystica Cooper and Grant	R
Reticulariina venustula Cooper and Grant	VR
Rhamnaria tenuispinosa Cooper and Grant	R
Rhipidomella hispidula Cooper and Grant	R
Rhynchopora hebetata Cooper and Grant	VR
Rugatia paraindica (McKee)	R
Spiriferellina tricosa Cooper and Grant	R
Stenoscisma aptatum Cooper and Grant	VR
Stenoscisma doricranum Cooper and Grant	VR
Stenoscisma exutum Cooper and Grant	R
Stenoscisma triquetrum Cooper and Grant	C
Tautosia fastigiata Cooper and Grant	VR
Texarina wordensis (R.E. King)	VR
Thamnosia anterospinosa Cooper and Grant	VR
Thedusia bucrenata Cooper and Grant	VR
Torynechus caelatus Cooper and Grant	R
Trophisina fenaria Cooper and Grant	C
Xenosteges adherens Muir-Wood and Cooper	A

LOCALITY N703bs : Cathedral Mountain Formation

Acosarina mesoplatys (R.E. King)	C
Agelesia triagonalis (R.E. King)	VA
Anteridocus gongylus Cooper and Grant	VR
Cancrinella sp. 1	VR
Cartorhium latum (R.E. King)	R
Cenorhynchia parvula Cooper and Grant	VR
Choanodus irregularis Cooper and Grant	VR
Chondronia bella Cooper and Grant	R
Chonosteges multicostatus Cooper and Grant	C
Composita imbricata Cooper and Grant	R
Composita sp.	VR
Compressoproductus curtus Cooper and Grant	VR
Compressoproductus thomasi Cooper and Grant	VR
Derbyia informis Cooper and Grant	VR
Derbyia laqueata Cooper and Grant	R
Diplanus lamellatus (R.E. King)	R
Dyoros (*Lissosia*) *vagabundus* Cooper and Grant	VR
Echinauris irregularis Cooper and Grant	C
Edriosteges multispinosus Muir-Wood and Cooper	VR
Enteletes plummeri R.E. King	C

	Rarity code
LOCALITY N703bs - Continued	
Eolyttonia circularis Cooper and Grant	VR
Eolyttonia pocillata Cooper and Grant	VR
Goniarina futilis Cooper and Grant	VR
Hercosia uddeni (Böse)	C
Heterelasma gibbosum Cooper and Grant	VR
Hustedia lusca Cooper and Grant	A
Hustedia spicata Cooper and Grant	R
Institella leonardensis (R.E. King)	C
Linoproductus delicatus Cooper and Grant	VR
Loxophragmus ellipticus Cooper and Grant	R
Meekella calathica Cooper and Grant	A
Metriolepis carotica Cooper and Grant	C
Metriolepis larina Cooper and Grant	VR
Metriolepis tegulata Cooper and Grant	R
Neophricadothyris bullata Cooper and Grant	R
Neospirifer mansuetus Cooper and Grant	R
Peniculauris subcostata (R.E. King)	VR
Pontisia stehlii tumidosa Cooper and Grant	VR
Ptygmactrum angulatum Cooper and Grant	VR
Rhamnaria tenuispinosa Cooper and Grant	VR
Rhipidomella hispidula Cooper and Grant	A
Rhynchopora hebetata Cooper and Grant	VR
Stenoscisma aptatum Cooper and Grant	VR
Texarina wordensis (R.E. King)	VR
Thedusia bucrenata Cooper and Grant	VR
Xenosteges adherens Muir-Wood and Cooper	R

	Rarity code
LOCALITY N703c : Road Canyon Formation	
Acosarina mesoplatys (R.E. King)	A
Anemonaria sublaevis (R.E. King)	R
Bothrostegium compactum Cooper and Grant	C
Collemataria sp.	R
Composita crassa Cooper and Grant	R
Crurithyris minutalis Cooper and Grant	R
Cyclacantharia paucispinosa Cooper and Grant	C
Derbyia cincinnata Cooper and Grant	R
Derbyia complicata Cooper and Grant	R
Derbyia informis Cooper and Grant	VR
Derbyia laqueata Cooper and Grant	R
Dielasma expansum Cooper and Grant	VR
Dyoros (*Dyoros*) *angulatus* Cooper and Grant	R
Dyoros (*Dyoros*) *extensus* Cooper and Grant	R
Dyoros (*Dyoros*) *transversus* Cooper and Grant	C
Dyoros (*Tetragonetes*) *rectangulatus* Cooper and Grant	C
Dyoros (*Tetragonetes*) *solidus* Cooper and Grant	C
Echinauris bella Cooper and Grant	VR
Echinauris irregularis Cooper and Grant	R
Echinauris liumbona Cooper and Grant	C
Echinauris parva Cooper and Grant	R
Echinauris sp.	C
Edriosteges multispinosus Muir-Wood and Cooper	R
Glossothyropsis superba Cooper and Grant	VR
Grandaurispina sp. 1	VR
Hercosestria cribrosa Cooper and Grant	C
Heteralosia hystricula (Girty)	VR
Holotricharina hirsuta Cooper and Grant	R
Horridonia texana R.E. King	VR
Hustedia ampullacea Cooper and Grant	VR
Hustedia connorsi Cooper and Grant	C
Hustedia consuta Cooper and Grant	C
Hustedia cuneata Cooper and Grant	R
Kutorginella sullivanensis (R.E. King)	VR
Lepidocrania tardispinosa Cooper and Grant	VR
Meekella calathica Cooper and Grant	A
Megousia auriculata Muir-Wood and Cooper	C

	Rarity code
Metriolepis tegulata Cooper and Grant	C
Neophricadothyris crassibecca Cooper and Grant	R
Neospirifer bakeri bakeri R.E. King	R
Niviconia globosa (R.E. King)	VR
Paucispinifera sp.	VR
Paucispinifera sulcata Cooper and Grant	R
Peniculauris costata Cooper and Grant	VR
Petasmatherus pumilus Cooper and Grant	VR
Pontisia stehlii stehlii Cooper and Grant	VR
Pontisia stehlii tumidosa Cooper and Grant	VR
Pseudodielasma sp.	VR
Ptygmactrum extensum Cooper and Grant	VR
Reticulariina pristina Cooper and Grant	VR
Rhamnaria tenuispinosa Cooper and Grant	VR
Rhamnaria vinnula Cooper and Grant	VR
Rhynchopora hebetata Cooper and Grant	VR
Rugatia incurvata (R.E. King)	VR
Rugatia mckeei Cooper and Grant	VR
Spiriferellina tricosa Cooper and Grant	VR
Stenoscisma calvatum Cooper and Grant	VR
Texarina wordensis (R.E. King)	VR
Thedusia mesocostata Cooper and Grant	C
Waagenoconcha convexa Cooper and Grant	C
Xenosteges magnus Cooper and Grant	VR
Yakovlevia immatura Cooper and Grant	VR

	Rarity code
LOCALITY N703d : Road Canyon Formation	
Acosarina mesoplatys (R.E. King)	C
Allorhynchus sp.	VR
Ametoria residua Cooper and Grant	R
Cartorhium sp.	VR
Cenorhynchia saginata Cooper and Grant	VR
Composita crassa Cooper and Grant	C
Composita sp.	VR
Crurithyris minutalis Cooper and Grant	VR
Cyclacantharia paucispinosa Cooper and Grant	VR
Derbyia cincinnata Cooper and Grant	VR
Derbyia complicata Cooper and Grant	C
Derbyia filosa Cooper and Grant	VR
Derbyia informis Cooper and Grant	VR
Derbyia laqueata Cooper and Grant	VR
Derbyia sp. 2	VR
Dielasma ellipsoideum Cooper and Grant	VR
Dyoros (*Dyoros*) *angulatus* Cooper and Grant	C
Dyoros (*Dyoros*) *extensus* Cooper and Grant	VR
Dyoros (*Dyoros*) *transversus* Cooper and Grant	C
Dyoros (*Lissosia*) *parvus* Cooper and Grant	R
Dyoros (*Tetragonetes*) *solidus* Cooper and Grant	A
Dyoros (*Tetragonetes*) *strigosus* Cooper and Grant	VR
Echinauris bella Cooper and Grant	R
Echinauris irregularis Cooper and Grant	R
Echinauris lappacea Cooper and Grant	C
Echinauris liumbona Cooper and Grant	C
Echinauris sp.	VR
Edriosteges multispinosus Muir-Wood and Cooper	R
Eolyttonia chaotica Cooper and Grant	R
Glossothyropsis superba Cooper and Grant	VR
Heterelasma glansfagea Cooper and Grant	R
Holotricharina hirsuta Cooper and Grant	R
Hustedia consuta Cooper and Grant	A
Hustedia cuneata Cooper and Grant	R
Hustedia sp.	VR
Kutorginella umbonata (Muir-Wood and Cooper)	R
Meekella calathica Cooper and Grant	C

	Rarity code
LOCALITY N703d - Continued	
Meekella sp.	VR
Megousia auriculata Muir-Wood and Cooper	VA
Metriolepis tegulata Cooper and Grant	VR
Neophricadothyris cordata Cooper and Grant	A
Neospirifer bakeri columbarius Cooper and Grant	A
Paucispinifera sulcata Cooper and Grant	VR
Peniculauris costata Cooper and Grant	R
Petasmatherus nitidus Cooper and Grant	VR
Petasmatherus cf. *opulus* Cooper and Grant	VR
Petasmatherus pumilus Cooper and Grant	VR
Phrenophoria? nudumbona Cooper and Grant	VR
Phrenophoria pentagonalis Cooper and Grant	VR
Phrenophoria ventricosa Cooper and Grant	R
Pontisia stehlii stehlii Cooper and Grant	VR
Ptygmactrum extensum Cooper and Grant	R
Reticulariina pristina Cooper and Grant	C
Rhamnaria rectangulata Cooper and Grant	VR
Rhamnaria tenuispinosa Cooper and Grant	R
Rhynchopora hebetata Cooper and Grant	R
Rugatia incurvata (R.E. King)	VR
Rugatia mckeei Cooper and Grant	VR
Spinarella costellata Cooper and Grant	VR
Spiriferellina tricosa Cooper and Grant	VR
Stenoscisma camurum Cooper and Grant	R
Thedusia mesocostata Cooper and Grant	C
Waagenoconcha convexa Cooper and Grant	R
Yakovlevia immatura Cooper and Grant	R
LOCALITY N703e : Word Formation, China Tank Member	
Allorhynchus permianum wordense Cooper and Grant	VR
Cyclacantharia kingorum Cooper and Grant	VR
Echinauris lateralis Muir-Wood and Cooper	VR
Heteralosia hystricula (Girty)	VR
Hustedia pugilla nasiterna Cooper and Grant	VR
Liosotella wordensis (R.E. King)	VR
Phrenophoria subcarinata Cooper and Grant	VR
Rhamnaria kingorum Muir-Wood and Cooper	C
Wellerella girtyi girtyi Cooper and Grant	VR
LOCALITY N703-l : Gaptank Formation, Uddenites Member	
Antiquatonia inflativentra Cooper and Grant	VR
Composita sp.	R
Derbyia sp.	VR
Echinaria cf. *moorei* (Dunbar and Condra)	VR
Hystriculina sp.	VR
Juresania sp. 1	VR
Kutorginella uddeni Cooper and Grant	VR
Linoproductus sp.	VR
Meekella texana R.E. King	VR
Neospirifer apothescelus Cooper and Grant	VR
LOCALITY N703o : Gaptank Formation, Uddenites Member	
Echinaria cf. *moorei* (Dunbar and Condra)	VR
Echinauris subquadrata Cooper and Grant	VR
Eridmatus marathonensis Cooper and Grant	VR
Meekella texana R.E. King	VR
Scacchinella triangulata Cooper and Grant	R
LOCALITY N703p : Gaptank Formation, Uddenites Member	
Chonetinella costellata Cooper and Grant	VR
Enteletes wolfcampensis R.E. King	VR

	Rarity code
Gypospirifer anancites Cooper and Grant	VR
Hystriculina sulcata Cooper and Grant	VR
Orthotetella wolfcampensis R.E. King	VR
Pareneletes cooperi R.E. King	VR
Teguliferina boesei R.E. King	VR
LOCALITY N703x : Gaptank Formation, Uddenites Member	
Limbella wolfcampensis (R.E. King)	VR
Meekella prionota Cooper and Grant	VR
Scacchinella triangulata Cooper and Grant	VR
Teguliferina boesei R.E. King	VR
LOCALITY N703y : Skinner Ranch Formation, Poplar Tank Member	
Nudauris enigmatica Cooper and Grant	VR
LOCALITY N704 : Word Formation, Appel Ranch Member	
Arionthia germana Cooper and Grant	VR
Composita enormis Cooper and Grant	R
Costispinifera costata (R.E. King)	VR
Cyclacantharia kingorum Cooper and Grant	R
Derbyia filosa Cooper and Grant	VR
Derbyia texta Cooper and Grant	VR
Dielasma compactum Cooper and Grant	VR
Dyoros (*Dyoros*) *extensus* Cooper and Grant	R
Dyoros (*Tetragonetes*) *quadrangulatus* Cooper and Grant	VR
Echinauris lateralis Muir-Wood and Cooper	VR
Eolyttonia progressa Cooper and Grant	VR
Heteralosia hystricula (Girty)	R
Hustedia pugilla hebetata Cooper and Grant	VR
Liosotella irregularis Cooper and Grant	VR
Liosotella wordensis (R.E. King)	VR
Meekella skenoides Girty	VR
Paraspiriferina rotundata Cooper and Grant	VR
Paucispinifera auriculata Muir-Wood and Cooper	VR
Petasmatherus opulus Cooper and Grant	VR
Phrenophoria subcarinata Cooper and Grant	VR
Rhamnaria kingorum Muir-Wood and Cooper	R
Stenoscisma renode Cooper and Grant	VR
Waagenoconcha magnifica Cooper and Grant	VR
LOCALITY N704d : Gaptank Formation	
Reticulatia huecoensis (R.E. King)	VR
LOCALITY N704f : Lenox Hills Formation	
Hystriculina sulcata Cooper and Grant	VR
LOCALITY N704q : Lenox Hills Formation	
Limbella wolfcampensis (R.E. King)	VR
LOCALITY N704r : Lenox Hills Formation	
Dasysaria wolfcampensis (R.E. King)	VR
Hystriculina sulcata? Cooper and Grant	VR
Kochiproductus primitivus Cooper and Grant	VR
Linoproductus sp.	VR
LOCALITY N704y : Skinner Ranch Formation, Sullivan Peak Member	
Geyerella hessi Cooper and Grant	VR
LOCALITY N704z : Cathedral Mountain Formation	
Echinauris sp.	VR
LOCALITY N705 : Lenox Hills Formation	
Composita discina Cooper and Grant	VR
Composita sp.	VR
Derbyia profunda Cooper and Grant	VR

Rarity code

LOCALITY N705 - Continued

Echinauris subquadrata Cooper and Grant	VR
Enteletes wolfcampensis R.E. King	VR
Geyerella kingorum Cooper and Grant	R
Kochiproductus sp.	VR
Limbella wolfcampensis (R.E. King)	R
Meekella magnifica Cooper and Grant	R
Meekella prionota Cooper and Grant	VR
Nudauris convexa Cooper and Grant	VR
Parenteletes superbus Cooper and Grant	C
Rhynchopora molina Cooper and Grant	VR
Spyridiophora sp. 2	VR
Striatifera linoproductiformis Cooper and Grant	VR
Teguliferina boesei R.E. King	VR
Tropidelasma strobilum Cooper and Grant	R

LOCALITY N705a : Skinner Ranch Formation

Acanthocrania sp.	VR
Acosarina dorsisulcata Cooper and Grant	C
Acritosia teguliferoides (R.E. King)	C
Altiplecus glebosus Cooper and Grant	A
Anomalesia perplexa Cooper and Grant	VR
Antiquatonia hessensis (R.E. King)	VR
Antronaria dissona Cooper and Grant	A
Antronaria titania Cooper and Grant	R
Chonetinella biplicata (R.E. King)	C
Cleiothyridina mulsa Cooper and Grant	C
Collemataria platys Cooper and Grant	C
Composita apheles Cooper and Grant	VA
Cooperina sp.	VR
Crenispirifer angulatus (R.E. King)	A
Crurithyris sp.	VR
Derbyia crenulata Girty	C
Derbyia nasuta Girty	C
Derbyia sp.	VR
Dielasma sp. 1	R
Dielasma sp. 2	R
Diplanus lamellatus (R.E. King)	C
Diplanus rarus Cooper and Grant	R
Elliottella varicostata Cooper and Grant	A
Enteletes stehlii Cooper and Grant	C
Fimbrinia ovata Cooper and Grant	R
Geyerella hessi Cooper and Grant	VR
Goniarina magniextensa Cooper and Grant	VR
Gypospirifer infraplicus (R.E. King)	R
Heteralosia sp.	VR
Hustedia catella Cooper and Grant	C
Hustedia hessensis R.E. King	C
Hustedia sp.	R
Isogramma sp.	VR
Kozlowskia alata Cooper and Grant	A
Kozlowskia subsphaeroidalis Cooper and Grant	VR
Leurosina vulgarica Cooper and Grant	C
Limbella limbata Cooper and Grant	VR
Linoproductus angustus R.E. King	VR
Martinia sp. 2	VR
Meekella caperata Cooper and Grant	C
Meekella enormis Cooper and Grant	C
Meekella hessensis R.E. King	R
Metriolepis scrupea Cooper and Grant	C
Neophricadothyris catatona Cooper and Grant	C
Nudauris enigmatica Cooper and Grant	R
Orthotichia newelli Cooper and Grant	C
Poikilosakos informis Cooper and Grant	VR
Pontisia costata Cooper and Grant	C

Rarity code

Reticulariina tetrica Cooper and Grant	C
Rhamnaria grandis Cooper and Grant	VR
Rhipidomella hessensis R.E. King	A
Scacchinella titan Cooper and Grant	A
?Stenoscisma doricranum Cooper and Grant	VR
Stenoscisma myioides Cooper and Grant	C
Stenoscisma pyraustoides Cooper and Grant	C
Teguliferina conida (Stehli)	C
Tricoria hirpex Cooper and Grant	A

LOCALITY N705b : Skinner Ranch Formation

Altiplecus glebosus Cooper and Grant	VR
Antiquatonia hessensis (R.E. King)	VR
Composita apheles Cooper and Grant	VR
Derbyia sp.	VR
Enteletes rotundobesus Cooper and Grant	VR
Eolyttonia gigantea Cooper and Grant	VR
Orthotichia newelli Cooper and Grant	VR
Scacchinella titan Cooper and Grant	VR
Stenoscisma pyraustoides Cooper and Grant	VR

LOCALITY N705ca : Gaptank Formation

Chonetinella costellata Cooper and Grant	R
Chonetinella parva Cooper and Grant	VR
Chonetinella sp.	VR
Eridmatus marathonensis Cooper and Grant	VR
Hustedia sp.	VR
Rhipidomella sp.	R

LOCALITY N705f : Gaptank Formation

Composita sp.	VR

LOCALITY N705h : Gaptank Formation, Uddenites Member

Echinauris subquadrata Cooper and Grant	VR
Hystriculina sulcata Cooper and Grant	VR
Linoproductus sp.	VR
Neospirifer apothescelus Cooper and Grant	VR
Nudauris splendens Cooper and Grant	R

LOCALITY N705i : Gaptank Formation

Kutorginella sp.	VR

LOCALITY N705k : Lenox Hills Formation

Composita discina Cooper and Grant	R
Derbyia sp.	VR
Echinauris sp.	VR
Enteletes wolfcampensis R.E. King	R
Eolyttonia fredericksi (R.E. King)	VR
Hustedia trita trita Cooper and Grant	VR
Hystriculina sp.	VR
Limbella wolfcampensis (R.E. King)	C
Meekella prionota Cooper and Grant	VR
Orthotichia kozlowskii R.E. King	VR
Parenteletes superbus Cooper and Grant	R
?Rhipidomella miscella Cooper and Grant	VR
Scacchinella exasperata Cooper and Grant	C
?Stenoscisma problematicum Cooper and Grant	VR
Teguliferina boesei R.E. King	VR
Tropidelasma strobilum Cooper and Grant	A

LOCALITY N705-l : Skinner Ranch Formation

Scacchinella titan Cooper and Grant	VR

LOCALITY N705m : Lenox Hills Formation

Acritosia peculiaris Cooper and Grant	VR
Cancrinella sp.	VR
Composita strongyle Cooper and Grant	VR

	Rarity code
LOCALITY N705m - Continued	
Enteletes wolfcampensis R.E. King	VR
Eolyttonia fredericksi (R.E. King)	VR
Geyerella sp. 1	VR
Limbella wolfcampensis (R.E. King)	R
Orthotichia kozlowskii R.E. King	VR
Pontisia kingi Cooper and Grant	VR
Scacchinella exasperata Cooper and Grant	C
Teguliferina boesei R.E. King	VR
Tropidelasma strobilum Cooper and Grant	VR
LOCALITY N705n : Skinner Ranch Formation	
Acritosia peculiaris Cooper and Grant	VR
Antronaria voluminosa Cooper and Grant	VR
Beecheria sp.	VR
Elliottella varicostata Cooper and Grant	VR
Glyptosteges intricatus Cooper and Grant	VR
Limbella limbata Cooper and Grant	VR
Linoproductus sp.	VR
Stenoscisma hadrum Cooper and Grant	VR
Teguliferina boesei R.E. King	VR
LOCALITY N705o : Skinner Ranch Formation	
Acosarina dorsisulcata Cooper and Grant	R
Acritosia teguliferoides (R.E. King)	VR
Chonosteges limbatus Cooper and Grant	VR
Glyptosteges intricatus Cooper and Grant	VR
Hustedia sp.	VR
Limbella limbata Cooper and Grant	VR
Meekella hessensis R.E. King	VR
Oncosarina spinicostata Cooper and Grant	VR
Spyridiophora reticulata (R.E. King)	VR
LOCALITY N705q : Gaptank Formation	
Limbella costellata Cooper and Grant	VR
Meekella texana R.E. King	VR
Tropidelasma strobilum Cooper and Grant	VR
LOCALITY N705r : Skinner Ranch Formation	
Acritosia peculiaris Cooper and Grant	VR
Antronaria transversa (R.E. King)	VR
Chonosteges variabilis Cooper and Grant	R
Derbyia crenulata Girty	VR
Diplanus lamellatus (R.E. King)	R
Glyptosteges intricatus Cooper and Grant	VR
Hustedia sp.	VR
Limbella sp. 1	VR
Meekella hessensis R.E. King	VR
Neophricadothyris sp.	VR
Rhipidomella hessensis R.E. King	VR
Spyridiophora reticulata (R.E. King)	R
Stenoscisma hadrum Cooper and Grant	VR
Teguliferina compacta Cooper and Grant	R
Tropidelasma costellatum Cooper and Grant	VR
Tropidelasma sp. 5	VR
LOCALITY N705s : Lenox Hills Formation	
Composita strongyle Cooper and Grant	R
Enteletes wolfcampensis R.E. King	VR
Limbella wolfcampensis (R.E. King)	R
Meekella magnifica Cooper and Grant	VR
Orthotichia kozlowskii R.E. King	VR
Parenteletes superbus Cooper and Grant	VR
Pontisia kingi Cooper and Grant	VR
Scacchinella exasperata Cooper and Grant	C
Teguliferina boesei R.E. King	R
Tropidelasma strobilum Cooper and Grant	R

	Rarity code
LOCALITY N705v : Gaptank Formation	
Composita sp.	VR
Linoproductus sp.	VR
Nudauris splendens Cooper and Grant	VR
LOCALITY N706 : Word Formation, Willis Ranch Member	
Acanthocrania intermedia Cooper and Grant	C
Allorhynchus permianum wordense Cooper and Grant	A
Allorhynchus sp.	VR
Allorhynchus triangulatum Cooper and Grant	R
Allorhynchus variabile Cooper and Grant	VR
Arionthia blothrhachis Cooper and Grant	VR
Bothrionia nasuta Cooper and Grant	R
Cactosteges anomalus Cooper and Grant	A
Cancrinella subquadrata Cooper and Grant	VR
Cartorhium chelomatum Cooper and Grant	C
Cartorhium vidriense Cooper and Grant	VR
Cenorhynchia triangulata Cooper and Grant	VR
Collemataria elongata Cooper and Grant	VA
Composita enormis Cooper and Grant	A
Composita parasulcata Cooper and Grant	A
Cooperina inexpectata Termier, Termier and Pajaud	A
Costispinifera costata (R.E. King)	VA
Crurithyris tholiaphor Cooper and Grant	C
Cyclacantharia kingorum Cooper and Grant	VA
Derbyia filosa Cooper and Grant	A
Derbyia pannucia Cooper and Grant	A
Dielasma adamanteum Cooper and Grant	C
Dielasma compactum Cooper and Grant	A
Dielasma planidorsatum Cooper and Grant	VR
Dielasma zebratum Cooper and Grant	C
Dyoros (Dyoros) extensus Cooper and Grant	VA
Dyoros (Dyoros) tenuis Cooper and Grant	A
Dyoros (Lissosia) concavus Cooper and Grant	A
Dyoros (Tetragonetes) wordensis Cooper and Grant	R
Echinauris lateralis Muir-Wood and Cooper	C
Echinosteges tuberculatus (R.E. King)	C
Ectoposia wildei Cooper and Grant	VR
Enteletes wordensis R.E. King	VA
Glossothyropsis rectangulata Cooper and Grant	R
Grandaurispina bella Cooper and Grant	C
Grandaurispina kingorum Muir-Wood and Cooper	C
Heteralosia hystricula (Girty)	A
Heterelasma concavum Cooper and Grant	C
Heterelasma pentagonum Cooper and Grant	R
Heterelasma solidum Cooper and Grant	C
Heterelasma sp.	VR
Hustedia pugilla nasiterna Cooper and Grant	VR
Hustedia pugilla pugilla Cooper and Grant	VA
Hustedia sculptilis Cooper and Grant	R
Hustedia sp.	VR
Leiorhynchoidea amygdaloidea Cooper and Grant	C
Lepidocrania sublamellosa Cooper and Grant	R
Leurosina lata Cooper and Grant	C
Liosotella parva Cooper and Grant	VR
Liosotella wordensis (R.E. King)	A
Meekella skenoides Girty	VA
Megousia definita Cooper and Grant	VR
Megousia flexuosa Cooper and Grant	C
Megousia mucronata Cooper and Grant	R
Metriolepis pulvinata Cooper and Grant	C
Neochonetes sp.	R
Neophricadothyris conara Cooper and Grant	VR
Neospirifer amphigyus Cooper and Grant	C
Notothyris venusta Cooper and Grant	VR

	Rarity code
LOCALITY N706 - Continued	
Paraspiriferina laqueata Cooper and Grant	A
Paucispinifera auriculata Muir-Wood and Cooper	C
Paucispinifera intermedia Cooper and Grant	R
Paucispinifera quadrata Cooper and Grant	R
Paucispinifera sp.	VR
Paucispinifera transversa Cooper and Grant	C
Petasmatherus opulus Cooper and Grant	A
Petrocrania teretis Cooper and Grant	VR
Phrenophoria subcarinata Cooper and Grant	R
Polymorpharia polymorpha Cooper and Grant	VR
Pseudodielasma gibberum Cooper and Grant	VA
Pseudodielasma minor (R.E. King)	A
Pseudodielasma ovatum Cooper and Grant	A
Pseudodielasma pingue Cooper and Grant	VR
Pseudodielasma plicatum Cooper and Grant	C
Pseudodielasma sp.	SA
Pseudodielasma sulcatum Cooper and Grant	C
Pseudoleptodus annosus Cooper and Grant	VR
Reticulariina cerina Cooper and Grant	C
Reticulariina senticosa Cooper and Grant	C
Reticulariina sp.	R
Rhamnaria kingorum Muir-Wood and Cooper	A
Rhynchopora palumbula Cooper and Grant	A
Spiriferella calcarata Cooper and Grant	C
Spiriferellina hilli (Girty)	A
Spiriferellina sp.	VR '
Spiriferinaella scalpata Cooper and Grant	VR
Stenoscisma renode Cooper and Grant	R
Tautosia transenna Cooper and Grant	C
Texarina elongata Cooper and Grant	VR
Texarina oblongata Cooper and Grant	C
Thedusia procera Cooper and Grant	C
Tropidelasma anthicum Cooper and Grant	R
Undulella undulata Cooper and Grant	A
Waagenoconcha magnifica Cooper and Grant	C
Wellerella girtyi girtyi Cooper and Grant	A
Xenosteges quadratus Cooper and Grant	C
Yakovlevia hessorum Cooper and Grant	C
LOCALITY N706a : Word Formation, China Tank Member	
Cyclacantharia kingorum Cooper and Grant	VR
Dielasma planidorsatum Cooper and Grant	VR
Enteletes wordensis R.E. King	VR
Heteralosia hystricula (Girty)	C
Hustedia pugilla nasiterna Cooper and Grant	VR
Meekella skenoides Girty	VR
Megousia definita Cooper and Grant	VR
LOCALITY N706b : Word Formation, Lens	
Allorhynchus permianum wordense Cooper and Grant	R
Bothrionia nasuta Cooper and Grant	C
Bothrionia transversa Cooper and Grant	R
Cancrinella expansa Cooper and Grant	VR
Cartorhium chelomatum Cooper and Grant	C
Cenorhynchia fracida Cooper and Grant	R
Collemataria elongata Cooper and Grant	A
Composita enormis Cooper and Grant	A
Composita parasulcata Cooper and Grant	A
Composita sp.	R
Compressoproductus rarus Cooper and Grant	VR
Compressoproductus sp. 2	VR
Cooperina inexpectata Termier, Termier and Pajaud	C
Costispinifera costata (R.E. King)	C
Costispinifera rugatula (Girty)	VR

	Rarity code
Crurithyris tholiaphor Cooper and Grant	C
Ctenalosia fixata Cooper and Stehli	VR
Cyclacantharia kingorum Cooper and Grant	VA
Cyclacantharia kingorum agaricoidea Cooper and Grant	VR
Derbyia filosa Cooper and Grant	A
Derbyia pannucia Cooper and Grant	A
Derbyia sp.	VR
Derbyia texta Cooper and Grant	C
Dielasma adamanteum Cooper and Grant	R
Dielasma compactum Cooper and Grant	R
Dielasma gracile Cooper and Grant	C
Dielasma sp.	R
Dielasma zebratum Cooper and Grant	VR
Dyoros (*Dyoros*) *extensus* Cooper and Grant	VA
Dyoros (*Dyoros*) *planiextensus* Cooper and Grant	VA
Dyoros (*Lissosia*) *concavus* Cooper and Grant	R
Dyoros (*Tetragonetes*) *wordensis* Cooper and Grant	VR
Echinauris lateralis Muir-Wood and Cooper	VA
Echinauris sp.	R
Echinosteges tuberculatus (R.E. King)	C
Ectoposia wildei Cooper and Grant	VR
Eolyttonia progressa Cooper and Grant	R
Glossothyropsis rectangulata Cooper and Grant	VR
Grandaurispina gibbosa Cooper and Grant	A
Heteralosia hystricula (Girty)	VA
Heterelasma concavum Cooper and Grant	R
Heterelasma pentagonum Cooper and Grant	VR
Heterelasma solidum Cooper and Grant	VR
Heterelasma sp.	VR
Hustedia pugilla pluscula Cooper and Grant	VA
Hustedia sculptilis Cooper and Grant	VR
Hustedia sp.	R
Leiorhynchoidea amygdaloidea Cooper and Grant	VR
Lepidocrania sublamellosa Cooper and Grant	VR
Leurosina lata Cooper and Grant	R
Liosotella parva Cooper and Grant	VR
Liosotella tetragonalis Cooper and Grant	A
Liosotella wordensis (R.E. King)	A
Meekella skenoides Girty	A
Megousia definita Cooper and Grant	VR
Metriolepis pulvinata Cooper and Grant	R
Neophricadothyris conara Cooper and Grant	C
Neospirifer amphigyus Cooper and Grant	VR
Notothyris venusta Cooper and Grant	VR
Paranorella sp. 1	R
Paraspiriferina laqueata Cooper and Grant	R
Paraspiriferina rotundata Cooper and Grant	C
Paucispinifera auriculata Muir-Wood and Cooper	C
Paucispinifera quadrata Cooper and Grant	VA
Paucispinifera sp.	VR
Paucispinifera transversa Cooper and Grant	VR
Petasmatherus opulus Cooper and Grant	A
Petrocrania teretis Cooper and Grant	VR
Phrenophoria subcarinata Cooper and Grant	C
Pseudodielasma ovatum Cooper and Grant	C
Pseudodielasma sp.	VR
Ptygmactrum spiculatum Cooper and Grant	VR
Reticulariina cerina Cooper and Grant	A
Reticulariina sp. 1	R
Rhamnaria kingorum Muir-Wood and Cooper	VA
Rhynchopora palumbula Cooper and Grant	C
Spiriferella gravis Cooper and Grant	VA
Spiriferella levis Cooper and Grant	C
Spiriferellina hilli (Girty)	C
Spiriferellina paucicostata Cooper and Grant	VR

	Rarity code
LOCALITY N706b - Continued	
Spiriferinaella scalpata Cooper and Grant	R
Stenoscisma renode Cooper and Grant	VA
Tautosia transenna Cooper and Grant	C
Texarina elongata Cooper and Grant	R
Thedusia procera Cooper and Grant	C
Tropidelasma anthicum Cooper and Grant	R
Undulella undulata Cooper and Grant	R
Waagenoconcha magnifica Cooper and Grant	VR
Wellerella girtyi girtyi Cooper and Grant	R
Xenosteges quadratus Cooper and Grant	A

LOCALITY N706c : Word Formation, China Tank Member

	Rarity code
Acanthocrania intermedia Cooper and Grant	R
Acolosia glabra Cooper and Grant	R
Allorhynchus permianum wordense Cooper and Grant	VR
Allorhynchus triangulatum Cooper and Grant	C
Allorhynchus variabile Cooper and Grant	C
Arionthia blothrhachis Cooper and Grant	C
Bothrionia nasuta Cooper and Grant	VR
Cactosteges anomalus Cooper and Grant	C
Cancrinella planumbona Cooper and Grant	VR
Cartorhium chelomatum Cooper and Grant	R
Cartorhium vidriense Cooper and Grant	VR
Cenorhynchia fracida Cooper and Grant	VR
Cenorhynchia pentagonalis Cooper and Grant	R
Collemataria elongata Cooper and Grant	VA
Composita enormis Cooper and Grant	A
Composita parasulcata Cooper and Grant	A
Compressoproductus rarus Cooper and Grant	R
Cooperina inexpectata Termier, Termier and Pajaud	C
Costispinifera rugatula (Girty)	VA
Crenispirifer sp.	VR
Crurithyris tholiaphor Cooper and Grant	A
Ctenalosia fixata Cooper and Stehli	C
Ctenalosia sp.	R
Cyclacantharia kingorum Cooper and Grant	VA
Derbyia filosa Cooper and Grant	A
Derbyia pannucia Cooper and Grant	A
Derbyia texta Cooper and Grant	C
Dielasma adamanteum angulatum Cooper and Grant	VR
Dielasma compactum Cooper and Grant	C
Dielasma planidorsatum Cooper and Grant	C
Dielasma sp.	R
Dielasma zebratum Cooper and Grant	VR
Dyoros (Dyoros) extensus Cooper and Grant	A
Dyoros (Lissosia) concavus Cooper and Grant	A
Echinauris lateralis Muir-Wood and Cooper	VR
Echinosteges tuberculatus (R.E. King)	C
Ectoposia grandis Cooper and Grant	VR
Enteletes wordensis R.E. King	VA
Grandaurispina kingorum Muir-Wood and Cooper	C
Heteralosia hystricula (Girty)	A
Heterelasma concavum Cooper and Grant	VR
Heterelasma solidum Cooper and Grant	VR
Holosia sp. 1	VR
Hustedia bipartita Girty	C
Hustedia pugilla nasiterna Cooper and Grant	SA
Hustedia sculptilis Cooper and Grant	VR
Leiorhynchoidea sp.	VR
Lepidocrania sublamellosa Cooper and Grant	VR
Leurosina lata Cooper and Grant	C
Liosotella parva Cooper and Grant	C
Liosotella wordensis (R.E. King)	A

	Rarity code
Meekella skenoides Girty	VA
Megousia definita Cooper and Grant	VR
Megousia flexuosa Cooper and Grant	VR
Megousia mucronata Cooper and Grant	A
Metriolepis pulvinata Cooper and Grant	R
Neophricadothyris conara Cooper and Grant	VR
Neospirifer amphigyus Cooper and Grant	A
Notothyris venusta Cooper and Grant	R
Paranorella comptula Cooper and Grant	R
Paraspiriferina laqueata Cooper and Grant	A
Paucispinifera auriculata Muir-Wood and Cooper	C
Paucispinifera intermedia Cooper and Grant	C
Paucispinifera magnispina Cooper and Grant	R
Paucispinifera transversa Cooper and Grant	C
Petasmatherus opulus Cooper and Grant	A
Phrenophoria subcarinata Cooper and Grant	R
Pseudodielasma minor (R.E. King)	R
Pseudodielasma sp.	VR
Pseudodielasma subcirculare Cooper and Grant	VR
Ptygmactrum sp.	VR
Reticulariina cerina Cooper and Grant	R
Reticulariina senticosa Cooper and Grant	C
Reticulariina sp.	VR
Rhamnaria kingorum delicata Muir-Wood and Cooper	A
Rhynchopora palumbula Cooper and Grant	C
Spiriferella calcarata Cooper and Grant	R
Spiriferella embrithes Cooper and Grant	C
Spiriferellina hilli (Girty)	A
Spiriferellina sp.	R
Spiriferinaella limata Cooper and Grant	R
Stenoscisma renode Cooper and Grant	C
Stenoscisma repigratum Cooper and Grant	VR
Stenoscisma sp.	VR
Tautosia transenna Cooper and Grant	R
Texarina elongata Cooper and Grant	VR
Texarina oblongata Cooper and Grant	R
Thamnosia sp.	VR
Thedusia procera Cooper and Grant	C
Tropidelasma anthicum Cooper and Grant	VR
Undulella undulata Cooper and Grant	C
Waagenoconcha magnifica Cooper and Grant	R
Wellerella girtyi girtyi Cooper and Grant	C
Xenosteges quadratus Cooper and Grant	C
Yakovlevia intermedia Cooper and Grant	R

LOCALITY N706d : Word Formation, Appel Ranch Member

	Rarity code
Arionthia germana Cooper and Grant	A
Cartorhium orbiculatum Cooper and Grant	C
Composita enormis Cooper and Grant	C
Composita parasulcata Cooper and Grant	VR
Ctenalosia fixata Cooper and Stehli	A
Ctenalosia sp.	VR
Cyclacantharia kingorum Cooper and Grant	C
Derbyia filosa Cooper and Grant	A
Derbyia pannucia Cooper and Grant	VR
Derbyia texta Cooper and Grant	C
Dielasma sp.	VR
Dyoros (Dyoros) extensus Cooper and Grant	A
Dyoros (Tetragonetes) quadrangulatus Cooper and Grant	VR
Echinauris lateralis Muir-Wood and Cooper	VR
Grandaurispina crassa Cooper and Grant	C
Heteralosia hystricula (Girty)	C
Heteralosia sp.	R
Hustedia pugilla hebetata Cooper and Grant	A

	Rarity code
LOCALITY N706d - Continued	
Hustedia pugilla nasiterna Cooper and Grant	VR
Hustedia pugilla pluscula Cooper and Grant	VR
Liosotella irregularis Cooper and Grant	VA
Meekella skenoides Girty	A
Paucispinifera auriculata Muir-Wood and Cooper	R
Rhamnaria kingorum Muir-Wood and Cooper	C
Rhynchopora tenera Cooper and Grant	VR
Spiriferella propria Cooper and Grant	A
Spiriferinaella scalpata Cooper and Grant	VR
Tautosia transenna Cooper and Grant	VR
Thamnosia phragmophora Cooper and Grant	R
Waagenoconcha magnifica Cooper and Grant	VR
Xenosteges quadratus Cooper and Grant	VR
LOCALITY N706e : Word Formation, Willis Ranch Member	
Acanthocrania intermedia Cooper and Grant	C
Acolosia? anomala Cooper and Grant	VR
Allorhynchus permianum wordense Cooper and Grant	C
Allorhynchus triangulatum Cooper and Grant	VR
Bothrionia transversa Cooper and Grant	VR
Cactosteges anomalus Cooper and Grant	R
Cancrinella subquadrata Cooper and Grant	R
Cenorhynchia fracida Cooper and Grant	R
Cleiothyridina rara Cooper and Grant	VR
Collemataria elongata Cooper and Grant	VA
Composita enormis Cooper and Grant	A
Composita parasulcata Cooper and Grant	VA
Cooperina inexpectata Termier, Termier and Pajaud	VA
Costispinifera costata (R.E. King)	R
Crurithyris tholiaphor Cooper and Grant	C
Cyclacantharia kingorum Cooper and Grant	VA
Derbyia filosa Cooper and Grant	A
Derbyia pannucia Cooper and Grant	A
Derbyia sp.	R
Derbyia texta Cooper and Grant	A
Dielasma adamanteum Cooper and Grant	A
Dielasma adamanteum angulatum Cooper and Grant	VR
Dielasma compactum Cooper and Grant	R
Dielasma sp.	VR
Dielasma zebratum Cooper and Grant	A
Dyoros (Dyoros) extensus Cooper and Grant	VA
Dyoros (Lissosia) concavus Cooper and Grant	A
Dyoros (Tetragonetes) wordensis Cooper and Grant	A
Echinauris lateralis Muir-Wood and Cooper	VA
Echinosteges tuberculatus (R.E. King)	VA
Ectoposia wildei Cooper and Grant	VR
Glossothyropsis rectangulata Cooper and Grant	C
Grandaurispina bella Cooper and Grant	R
Grandaurispina elongata Cooper and Grant	C
Grandaurispina kingorum Muir-Wood and Cooper	VA
Heteralosia hystricula (Girty)	VA
Heterelasma concavum Cooper and Grant	C
Heterelasma pentagonum Cooper and Grant	R
Heterelasma solidum Cooper and Grant	R
Hustedia pugilla pugilla Cooper and Grant	VA
Hustedia sp.	C
Leiorhynchoidea amygdaloidea Cooper and Grant	R
Leiorhynchoidea sp.	VR
Lepidocrania sublamellosa Cooper and Grant	A
Leurosina lata Cooper and Grant	C
Liosotella parva Cooper and Grant	VR
Liosotella wordensis (R.E. King)	VA
Lirellaria? sp. 1	VR

	Rarity code
Meekella skenoides Girty	VA
Megousia definita Cooper and Grant	C
Megousia flexuosa Cooper and Grant	VR
Metriolepis pulvinata Cooper and Grant	R
Neospirifer amphigyus Cooper and Grant	VR
Paranorella sp. 1	VR
Paraspiriferina laqueata Cooper and Grant	R
Paraspiriferina setulosa Cooper and Grant	A
Paraspiriferina sp.	VR
Paucispinifera auriculata Muir-Wood and Cooper	VA
Paucispinifera magnispina Cooper and Grant	VR
Petasmatherus opulus Cooper and Grant	R
Petrocrania teretis Cooper and Grant	VR
Phrenophoria subcarinata Cooper and Grant	C
Pseudodielasma gibberum Cooper and Grant	C
Pseudodielasma lobatum Cooper and Grant	VA
Pseudodielasma minor (R.E. King)	VA
Pseudodielasma ovatum Cooper and Grant	VA
Pseudodielasma pingue Cooper and Grant	A
Pseudodielasma sp.	SA
Pseudodielasma subcirculare Cooper and Grant	A
Pseudodielasma sulcatum Cooper and Grant	A
Pseudoleptodus sp.	VR
Reticulariina senticosa Cooper and Grant	R
Reticulariina sp.	VR
Rhamnaria kingorum Muir-Wood and Cooper	VA
Rhynchopora palumbula Cooper and Grant	C
Spiriferella calcarata Cooper and Grant	C
Spiriferella gravis Cooper and Grant	C
Spiriferellina hilli (Girty)	VA
Stenoscisma renode Cooper and Grant	R
Stenoscisma sp.	VR
Tautosia transenna Cooper and Grant	A
Texarina elongata Cooper and Grant	VR
Texarina oblongata Cooper and Grant	C
Thedusia procera Cooper and Grant	A
Tropidelasma anthicum Cooper and Grant	VR
Undulella undulata Cooper and Grant	VA
Waagenoconcha magnifica Cooper and Grant	C
Wellerella girtyi girtyi Cooper and Grant	VA
Xenosteges quadratus Cooper and Grant	C
Yakovlevia hessorum Cooper and Grant	VA
LOCALITY N706f : Road Canyon Formation	
Acosarina mesoplatys (R.E. King)	R
Altiplecus sp. 2	VR
Cenorhynchia saginata Cooper and Grant	R
Composita crassa Cooper and Grant	R
Composita enormis Cooper and Grant	VR
Composita pilula Cooper and Grant	VR
Composita sp.	VR
Coscinophora magnifica Cooper and Grant	VR
Costispinifera rugatula (Girty)	VR
Crurithyris minutalis Cooper and Grant	R
Cyclacantharia transitoria Cooper and Grant	VR
Derbyia filosa Cooper and Grant	R
Dielasma ellipsoideum Cooper and Grant	VR
Dielasma sp.	VR
Echinauris bella Cooper and Grant	VR
Echinauris irregularis Cooper and Grant	VR
Echinauris lappacea Cooper and Grant	R
Elassonia micraria Cooper and Grant	VR
Enteletes densus Cooper and Grant	VR
Enteletes sp.	R
Heterelasma glansfagea Cooper and Grant	C

	Rarity code
LOCALITY N706f - Continued	
Hustedia consuta Cooper and Grant	C
Hustedia cuneata Cooper and Grant	R
Lepidocrania tardispinosa Cooper and Grant	VR
Meekella calathica Cooper and Grant	R
Metriolepis ziczac Cooper and Grant	R
Neophricadothyris crassibecca Cooper and Grant	VR
Neospirifer bakeri bakeri R.E. King	VR
Paraspiriferina cellulana Cooper and Grant	R
Paucispinifera sp.	VR
Paucispinifera sulcata Cooper and Grant	VR
Petasmatherus nitidus Cooper and Grant	R
Petasmatherus pumilus Cooper and Grant	C
Phrenophoria? compressa Cooper and Grant	VR
Phrenophoria sp.	VR
Reticulariina sp.	VR
Rhamnaria vinnula Cooper and Grant	VR
Rhynchopora hebetata Cooper and Grant	C
Rhytisia rugosa Cooper and Grant	R
Spiriferella sp.	VR
Stenoscisma calvatum Cooper and Grant	VR
Stenoscisma camurum Cooper and Grant	R
Stenoscisma maniculum Cooper and Grant	VR
Stenoscisma sp.	VR
Stenoscisma triquetrum Cooper and Grant	VR
Texarina wordensis (R.E. King)	VR
Tropidelasma corniculum Cooper and Grant	R
LOCALITY N706g : Lenox Hills Formation	
Enteletes wolfcampensis R.E. King	VR
Limbella wolfcampensis (R.E. King)	VR
Parenteletes superbus Cooper and Grant	R
Rhynchopora molina Cooper and Grant	VR
LOCALITY N706x : Neal Ranch Formation	
Chelononia straminea Cooper and Grant	VR
Chonetinella costellata Cooper and Grant	VR
Chonetinella sp. 1	VR
Diplanus catatonus Cooper and Grant	VR
Eolyttonia fredericksi (R.E. King)	VR
Hustedia trita trita Cooper and Grant	VR
Juresania sp. 2	VR
Limbella wolfcampensis (R.E. King)	VR
Linoproductus semisulcatus Cooper and Grant	R
Nudauris splendens Cooper and Grant	VR
Nudauris tribulosa Cooper and Grant	VR
Reticulatia robusta Cooper and Grant	VR
Rhynchopora molina Cooper and Grant	VR
LOCALITY N706z : Word Formation, China Tank Member	
Acanthocrania conferta Cooper and Grant	VR
Allorhynchus permianum wordense Cooper and Grant	VR
Cartorhium chelomatum Cooper and Grant	VR
Collemataria elongata Cooper and Grant	R
Cooperina inexpectata Termier, Termier and Pajaud	R
Cyclacantharia kingorum Cooper and Grant	R
Dyoros (Dyoros) extensus Cooper and Grant	R
Echinauris lateralis Muir-Wood and Cooper	R
Grandaurispina kingorum Muir-Wood and Cooper	VR
Heteralosia hystricula (Girty)	R
Hustedia pugilla nasiterna Cooper and Grant	VR
Liosotella wordensis (R.E. King)	R
Meekella skenoides Girty	VR
Paraspiriferina laqueata Cooper and Grant	VR
Paucispinifera auriculata Muir-Wood and Cooper	R

	Rarity code
Petasmatherus opulus Cooper and Grant	VR
Rhamnaria kingorum Muir-Wood and Cooper	VR
Rhynchopora palumbula Cooper and Grant	VR
Spiriferella calcarata Cooper and Grant	VR
Thedusia procera Cooper and Grant	VR
Yakovlevia hessorum Cooper and Grant	VR
LOCALITY N707 : Skinner Ranch Formation, Sullivan Peak Member	
Antronaria emarginata Cooper and Grant	VR
Antronaria transversa (R.E. King)	VR
Antronaria voluminosa Cooper and Grant	R
Cartorhium zoyei Cooper and Grant	VR
Chonosteges limbatus Cooper and Grant	VR
Composita apheles Cooper and Grant	C
Derbyia nasuta Girty	R
Enteletes rotundobesus Cooper and Grant	R
Enteletes sp.	VR
Eolyttonia gigantea Cooper and Grant	VR
Geyerella hessi Cooper and Grant	C
Limbella limbata Cooper and Grant	R
Meekella caperata Cooper and Grant	R
Meekella hessensis R.E. King	VR
Oncosarina spinicostata Cooper and Grant	R
Rhipidomella hessensis R.E. King	VR
Scacchinella titan Cooper and Grant	C
Spyridiophora reticulata (R.E. King)	VR
Stenoscisma hadrum Cooper and Grant	VR
LOCALITY N707a : Skinner Ranch Formation, Decie Ranch Member	
Acosarina dorsisulcata Cooper and Grant	C
Acritosia peculiaris Cooper and Grant	R
Acritosia teguliferoides (R.E. King)	VR
Antronaria dissona Cooper and Grant	VR
Antronaria emarginata Cooper and Grant	VR
Antronaria titania Cooper and Grant	C
Antronaria voluminosa Cooper and Grant	VR
Cancrinella sp.	VR
Cartorhium zoyei Cooper and Grant	R
Chonosteges matutinus Cooper and Grant	R
Chonosteges variabilis Cooper and Grant	VR
Composita apheles Cooper and Grant	C
Composita discina Cooper and Grant	C
Compressoproductus concentricus Cooper and Grant	VR
Coscinophora monilifera Cooper and Grant	C
Crurithyris sp. a	VR
Cyclacantharia gigantea Cooper and Grant	VR
Derbyia nasuta Girty	A
Dielasma hessense Cooper and Grant	VR
Dielasma sp.	VR
Diplanus apochordus Cooper and Grant	R
Diplanus lamellatus (R.E. King)	C
Diplanus rarus Cooper and Grant	VR
Enteletes rotundobesus Cooper and Grant	A
Eolyttonia gigantea Cooper and Grant	C
Geyerella hessi Cooper and Grant	A
Goniarina futilis Cooper and Grant	VR
Hustedia cepacea Cooper and Grant	C
Limbella limbata Cooper and Grant	R
Linoproductus angustus R.E. King	VR
Meekella caperata Cooper and Grant	VR
Meekella enormis Cooper and Grant	C
Meekella hessensis R.E. King	R
Nudauris enigmatica Cooper and Grant	VR
Oncosarina rotunda Cooper and Grant	C

LOCALITY N707a - Continued

	Rarity code
Peniculauris sp. 1	VR
Reticulariina tetrica Cooper and Grant	VR
Rhamnaria grandis Cooper and Grant	VR
Rhipidomella hessensis R.E. King	R
Rhynchopora patula Cooper and Grant	VR
Rhynchopora sp. 1	VR
Rugaria crassa Cooper and Grant	R
Scacchinella titan Cooper and Grant	A
Spyridiophora reticulata (R.E. King)	R
Stenoscisma problematicum Cooper and Grant	C
Thamnosia parvispinosa (Stehli)	R
Tropidelasma rhamphodes Cooper and Grant	VA

LOCALITY N707b : Skinner Ranch Formation, Sullivan Peak Member

	Rarity code
Acosarina dorsisulcata Cooper and Grant	R
Acritosia sp.	R
Agelesia triagonalis (R.E. King)	VR
Chondronia sp.	VR
Chonosteges variabilis Cooper and Grant	VR
Composita apheles Cooper and Grant	R
Composita sp.	R
Derbyia crenulata Girty	VR
Derbyia sp.	VR
Diplanus lamellatus (R.E. King)	VR
Echinauris sp.	VR
Enteletes sp.	VR
Eolyttonia sp.	VR
Geyerella hessi Cooper and Grant	VR
Glyptosteges angustus (R.E. King)	R
Glyptosteges intricatus Cooper and Grant	R
Goniarina sp.	VR
Hercosia uddeni (Böse)	VR
Hustedia cepacea Cooper and Grant	VR
Hustedia sp.	VR
Isogramma sp.	VR
Lepidospirifer sp.	VR
Limbella limbata Cooper and Grant	VR
Linoproductus sp.	VR
Meekella hessensis R.E. King	R
Meekella sp.	R
Metriolepis sp.	VR
Neophricadothyris sp.	VR
Peniculauris sp. 1	VR
Reticulariina impressa Cooper and Grant	VR
Rhipidomella hessensis R.E. King	VR
Scacchinella titan Cooper and Grant	VR
Sceletonia crassa Cooper and Grant	VR
Spyridiophora reticulata (R.E. King)	R
Stenoscisma hadrum Cooper and Grant	VR
Stenoscisma sp.	VR
Teguliferina cf. *conida* (Stehli)	VR
Torynechus alectorius Cooper and Grant	VR

LOCALITY N707c : Skinner Ranch Formation, Sullivan Peak Member

Acosarina dorsisulcata Cooper and Grant	VR
Antronaria dissona Cooper and Grant	VR
Composita apheles Cooper and Grant	R
Enteletes sp.	VR
Hustedia sp.	VR
Meekella hessensis R.E. King	R
Metriolepis sp.	VR
Rhipidomella hessensis R.E. King	VR

LOCALITY N707d : Skinner Ranch Formation, Sullivan Peak Member

	Rarity code
Acosarina dorsisulcata Cooper and Grant	R
Acritosia peculiaris Cooper and Grant	R
Allorhynchus sp.	VR
Antronaria voluminosa Cooper and Grant	R
Cartorhium zoyei Cooper and Grant	VR
Chonosteges variabilis Cooper and Grant	VR
Composita apheles Cooper and Grant	R
Composita bucculenta Cooper and Grant	R
Compressoproductus parvus Cooper and Grant	VR
Coscinophora monilifera Cooper and Grant	VR
Crurithyris sp. b	VR
Derbyia crenulata Girty	VR
Derbyia nasuta Girty	VR
Derbyia sp.	VR
Diplanus lamellatus (R.E. King)	C
Echinauris sp.	VR
Enteletes sp.	R
Eolyttonia sp.	VR
Glyptosteges angustus (R.E. King)	R
Glyptosteges intricatus Cooper and Grant	VR
Goniarina sp.	VR
Hustedia catella Cooper and Grant	R
Kochiproductus sp. 5	VR
Limbella limbata Cooper and Grant	VR
Meekella hessensis R.E. King	C
Micraphelia sp.	VR
Neophricadothyris catatona Cooper and Grant	C
Neophricadothyris sp.	R
Oncosarina sp.	VR
Phrenophoria depressa Cooper and Grant	R
Phrenophoria sp. 1	VR
Pontisia nanas (Stehli)	VR
Pseudodielasma sp.	VR
Reticulariina impressa Cooper and Grant	VR
Reticulariina tetrica Cooper and Grant	VR
Rhamnaria grandis Cooper and Grant	VR
Rhipidomella hessensis R.E. King	R
Spyridiophora reticulata (R.E. King)	R
Stenoscisma hadrum Cooper and Grant	VR
Stenoscisma sp.	VR
Wellerella sp. 1	R

LOCALITY N707e : Road Canyon Formation

Acosarina mesoplatys (R.E. King)	VA
Cenorhynchia saginata Cooper and Grant	C
Chondronia ovalis Cooper and Grant	VR
Chonetinetes reversus Cooper and Grant	C
Collemataria sp.	R
Composita crassa Cooper and Grant	C
Crenispirifer sp.	VR
Crurithyris minutalis Cooper and Grant	VR
Cyclacantharia transitoria Cooper and Grant	C
Derbyia cincinnata Cooper and Grant	VR
Derbyia complicata Cooper and Grant	C
Derbyia informis Cooper and Grant	VR
Derbyia laqueata Cooper and Grant	C
Derbyia texta Cooper and Grant	R
Dielasma emarginatum Cooper and Grant	C
Dielasma expansum Cooper and Grant	C
Dyoros (*Dyoros*) *angulatus* Cooper and Grant	A
Dyoros (*Dyoros*) *endospinus* Cooper and Grant	C
Dyoros (*Dyoros*) *extensus* Cooper and Grant	C
Dyoros (*Dyoros*) *transversus* Cooper and Grant	A

Rarity code

LOCALITY N707e - Continued

Dyoros (*Lissosia*) *concavus* Cooper and Grant	VR
Dyoros (*Lissosia*) *parvus* Cooper and Grant	A
Echinauris bella Cooper and Grant	VA
Echinauris irregularis Cooper and Grant	VR
Echinauris lappacea Cooper and Grant	C
Edriosteges multispinosus Muir-Wood and Cooper	R
Eolyttonia chaotica Cooper and Grant	C
Geyerella inexpectata Cooper and Grant	VR
Glossothyropsis superba Cooper and Grant	VR
Grandaurispina sp. 2	VR
Heteralosia sp. 2	VR
Heterelasma glansfagea Cooper and Grant	A
Holosia ovalis Cooper and Grant	VR
Holotricharina sparsa Cooper and Grant	R
Hustedia consuta Cooper and Grant	VA
Hustedia cuneata Cooper and Grant	C
Hustedia sp.	VR
Kutorginella sullivanensis (R.E. King)	C
Lepidocrania tardispinosa Cooper and Grant	VR
Liosotella costata Cooper and Grant	VA
Liosotella wordensis (R.E. King)	C
Meekella calathica Cooper and Grant	R
Megousia auriculata Muir-Wood and Cooper	VA
Metriolepis ziczac Cooper and Grant	VR
Neophricadothyris cordata Cooper and Grant	C
Neospirifer bakeri bakeri R.E. King	A
Paraspiriferina cellulana Cooper and Grant	C
Paucispinifera costellata Cooper and Grant	R
Paucispinifera sulcata Cooper and Grant	R
Peniculauris costata Cooper and Grant	R
Petasmatherus pumilus Cooper and Grant	C
Phrenophoria planiventra Cooper and Grant	VR
Phrenophoria sp. 2	VR
Reticulariina sp.	VR
Reticulariina subulata Cooper and Grant	C
Reticulariina venustula Cooper and Grant	VR
Rhamnaria tenuispinosa Cooper and Grant	R
Rhynchopora sphenoides Cooper and Grant	A
Rugatia mckeei Cooper and Grant	R
Spinarella lobata Cooper and Grant	R
Stenoscisma bonum Cooper and Grant	VR
Stenoscisma camurum Cooper and Grant	C
Stenoscisma sp.	VR
Taphrosestria peculiaris Cooper and Grant	R
Tautosia galbina Cooper and Grant	R
Tropidelasma corniculum Cooper and Grant	VR
Waagenoconcha convexa Cooper and Grant	VR
Waagenoconcha platys Cooper and Grant	C
Yakovlevia sulcata Cooper and Grant	A

LOCALITY N707g : Skinner Ranch Formation, Decie Ranch Member

Acosarina dorsisulcata Cooper and Grant	R
Acritosia peculiaris Cooper and Grant	C
Antronaria voluminosa Cooper and Grant	VR
Chonosteges variabilis Cooper and Grant	VR
Composita apheles Cooper and Grant	R
Compressoproductus parvus Cooper and Grant	VR
Coscinophora monilifera Cooper and Grant	VR
Derbyia crenulata Girty	VR
Diplanus lamellatus (R.E. King)	R
Eolyttonia gigantea Cooper and Grant	R
Glyptosteges intricatus Cooper and Grant	VR
Hustedia catella Cooper and Grant	R

Rarity code

Leurosina vulgarica Cooper and Grant	R
Limbella limbata Cooper and Grant	VR
Meekella hessensis R.E. King	VR
Metriolepis sp.	R
Oncosarina spinicostata Cooper and Grant	C
Rhamnaria grandis Cooper and Grant	VR
Rhipidomella hessensis R.E. King	R
Spyridiophora reticulata (R.E. King)	VR

LOCALITY N707h : Skinner Ranch Formation

Acolosia recepta Cooper and Grant	R
Acosarina dorsisulcata Cooper and Grant	C
Acritosia peculiaris Cooper and Grant	VR
Anteridocus paucicostatus Cooper and Grant	R
Chondronia ningula Cooper and Grant	C
Composita sp.	R
Coscinophora monilifera Cooper and Grant	A
Derbyia sp.	VR
Enteletes rotundobesus Cooper and Grant	R
Enteletes sp.	VR
Geyerella hessi Cooper and Grant	VR
Hustedia sp.	VR
Meekella caperata Cooper and Grant	VR
Meekella enormis Cooper and Grant	VR
Rhipidomella hessensis R.E. King	VR
Stenoscisma sp.	VR
Tropidelasma rhamphodes Cooper and Grant	VR

LOCALITY N707ha : Skinner Ranch Formation, Poplar Tank Member

Acosarina dorsisulcata Cooper and Grant	C
Acritosia peculiaris Cooper and Grant	R
Chonosteges variabilis Cooper and Grant	R
Composita sp.	R
Compressoproductus sp. 4	R
Coscinophora monilifera Cooper and Grant	VR
Cryptacanthia sp. 1	VR
Derbyia crenulata Girty	VR
Diplanus lamellatus (R.E. King)	VR
Diplanus rarus Cooper and Grant	VR
Dyoros (*Dyoros*) *consanguineus* (Girty)	R
Geyerella sp.	VR
Hustedia catella Cooper and Grant	R
Hustedia cepacea Cooper and Grant	R
Lepidospirifer sp.	VR
Limbella limbata Cooper and Grant	VR
Linoproductus angustus R.E. King	VR
Meekella hessensis R.E. King	R
Metriolepis sp.	VR
Micraphelia sp.	R
Nudauris enigmatica Cooper and Grant	VR
Oncosarina spinicostata Cooper and Grant	A
Plectelasma sp. 1	VR
Reticulariina sp.	VR
Rhamnaria grandis Cooper and Grant	VR
Rhipidomella hessensis R.E. King	R
Spinifrons sp.	VR
Spyridiophora reticulata (R.E. King)	R

LOCALITY N707i : Skinner Ranch Formation, Poplar Tank Member

Spyridiophora reticulata (R.E. King)	VR

LOCALITY N707j : Lenox Hills Formation

Antiquatonia regularis Cooper and Grant	VR
Beecheria expansa Cooper and Grant	VR

	Rarity code
LOCALITY N707j - Continued	
Derbyia profunda Cooper and Grant	VR
Derbyia sp.	VR
Enteletes wolfcampensis R.E. King	VR
Fimbrinia sp. 1	VR
Hustedia trita trita Cooper and Grant	VR
Kozlowskia anterosulcata Cooper and Grant	VR
Limbella wolfcampensis (R.E. King)	VR
Meekella magnifica Cooper and Grant	VR
Neochonetes sp.	R
Nudauris splendens Cooper and Grant	VR
Rhynchopora molina Cooper and Grant	VR
Teguliferina boesei R.E. King	R
Tropidelasma strobilum Cooper and Grant	VR
LOCALITY N707ja : Lenox Hills Formation	
Eolyttonia fredericksi (R.E. King)	VR
LOCALITY N707-1 : Skinner Ranch Formation, Decie Ranch Member	
Acosarina dorsisulcata Cooper and Grant	R
Acritosia peculiaris Cooper and Grant	VR
Antronaria voluminosa Cooper and Grant	R
Cartorhium zoyei Cooper and Grant	VR
Collemataria platys Cooper and Grant	VR
Composita apheles Cooper and Grant	R
Derbyia sp.	VR
Dielasma sp.	VR
Diplanus lamellatus (R.E. King)	R
Echinauris sp.	VR
Hustedia catella Cooper and Grant	R
Meekella hessensis R.E. King	VR
Neophricadothyris sp.	VR
Oncosarina spinicostata Cooper and Grant	C
Peniculauris sp. 1	VR
Rhipidomella hessensis R.E. King	R
Spyridiophora reticulata (R.E. King)	VR
Tautosia podistra Cooper and Grant	C
LOCALITY N707m : Lenox Hills Formation	
Antiquatonia regularis Cooper and Grant	VR
Echinauris interrupta Cooper and Grant	R
Echinauris subquadrata Cooper and Grant	VR
Hystriculina sulcata Cooper and Grant	VR
Kutorginella uddeni Cooper and Grant	VR
Limbella wolfcampensis (R.E. King)	VR
Meekella prionota Cooper and Grant	VR
Neophricadothyris transversa Cooper and Grant	VR
LOCALITY N707n : Lenox Hills Formation	
Echinauris interrupta Cooper and Grant	VR
Hystriculina sp.	VR
?Stenoscisma problematicum Cooper and Grant	VR
LOCALITY N707o : Lenox Hills Formation	
Antiquatonia regularis Cooper and Grant	VR
Hystriculina sp.	VR
Nudauris splendens Cooper and Grant	VR
LOCALITY N707q : Cathedral Mountain Formation	
Anemonaria sublaevis (R.E. King)	R
Dyoros (*Lissosia*) *vagabundus* Cooper and Grant	R
Dyoros (*Tetragonetes*) *lateralis* Cooper and Grant	VR
Hercosia uddeni (Böse)	VR
Hustedia sp.	R
Institella leonardensis (R.E. King)	VR
Megousia umbonata Cooper and Grant	A
Neophricadothyris bullata Cooper and Grant	VR

	Rarity code
Neospirifer mansuetus Cooper and Grant	R
Nudauris linospina Cooper and Grant	R
Peniculauris subcostata (R.E. King)	R
Thamnosia anterospinosa Cooper and Grant	VR
Xestosia schucherti (R.E. King)	VR
LOCALITY N707s : Lenox Hills Formation	
Scacchinella exasperata Cooper and Grant	VR
LOCALITY N707t : Skinner Ranch Formation, Sullivan Peak Member	
Scacchinella titan Cooper and Grant	VR
LOCALITY N707u : Skinner Ranch Formation	
Tropidelasma rhamphodes Cooper and Grant	VR
LOCALITY N707v : Skinner Ranch Formation, Decie Ranch Member	
Antronaria voluminosa Cooper and Grant	VR
Composita discina Cooper and Grant	VR
Dielasma sp. 1	VR
Meekella enormis Cooper and Grant	VR
Scacchinella titan Cooper and Grant	R
Stenoscisma hadrum Cooper and Grant	VR
LOCALITY N707w : Skinner Ranch Formation, Decie Ranch Member	
Acosarina dorsisulcata Cooper and Grant	C
Acritosia teguliferoides (R.E. King)	C
Antronaria dissona Cooper and Grant	VR
Antronaria titania Cooper and Grant	VR
Beecheria sp.	VR
Cartorhium zoyei Cooper and Grant	VR
Chondronia parva Cooper and Grant	C
Composita discina Cooper and Grant	C
Derbyia crenulata Girty	VR
Derbyia nasuta Girty	R
Enteletes stehlii Cooper and Grant	C
Geyerella hessi Cooper and Grant	VR
Hustedia catella Cooper and Grant	R
Hystriculina pumila Cooper and Grant	VR
Kochiproductus sp. 1	VR
Limbella limbata Cooper and Grant	VR
Meekella caperata Cooper and Grant	A
Meekella enormis Cooper and Grant	R
Orthotichia newelli Cooper and Grant	C
Scacchinella titan Cooper and Grant	VA
Spyridiophora reticulata (R.E. King)	VR
Stenoscisma hadrum Cooper and Grant	R
Stenoscisma pansum Cooper and Grant	VR
LOCALITY N707x : Skinner Ranch Formation, Decie Ranch Member	
Acritosia peculiaris Cooper and Grant	VR
Composita apheles Cooper and Grant	VR
Geyerella hessi Cooper and Grant	VR
Limbella limbata Cooper and Grant	VR
Scacchinella titan Cooper and Grant	R
LOCALITY N707z : Skinner Ranch Formation	
Derbyia nasuta Girty	VR
Enteletes rotundobesus Cooper and Grant	VR
Limbella wolfcampensis (R.E. King)	R
Scacchinella titan Cooper and Grant	C
Tropidelasma rhamphodes Cooper and Grant	R
LOCALITY N708 : Cathedral Mountain Formation	
Acosarina mesoplatys (R.E. King)	C

	Rarity code
LOCALITY N708 - Continued	
Agelesia triagonalis (R.E. King)	C
Anteridocus erugatus Cooper and Grant	VR
Anteridocus gongylus Cooper and Grant	VR
Cartorhium coristum Cooper and Grant	R
Cenorhynchia mitigata Cooper and Grant	VR
Choanodus irregularis Cooper and Grant	C
Choanodus perfectus Cooper and Grant	R
Chonosteges pulcher Cooper and Grant	R
Composita bucculenta Cooper and Grant	VR
Composita imbricata Cooper and Grant	R
Composita sp.	VR
Compressoproductus thomasi Cooper and Grant	C
Derbyia complicata Cooper and Grant	R
Derbyia laqueata Cooper and Grant	VR
Derbyia sp.	VR
Dielasma perplexum Cooper and Grant	VR
Diplanus lamellatus (R.E. King)	C
Dyoros (*Lissosia*) *vagabundus* Cooper and Grant	VR
Echinauris irregularis Cooper and Grant	VR
Echinauris sp.	VR
Enteletes plummeri R.E. King	A
Eolyttonia pocillata Cooper and Grant	VR
Hercosia uddeni (Böse)	VR
Heterelasma gibbosum Cooper and Grant	R
Hustedia ampullacea Cooper and Grant	VR
Hustedia lusca Cooper and Grant	C
Institella leonardensis (R.E. King)	C
Lepidospirifer demissus Cooper and Grant	VR
Meekella calathica Cooper and Grant	C
Megousia auriculata Muir-Wood and Cooper	VR
Metriolepis larina Cooper and Grant	C
Neophricadothyris bullata Cooper and Grant	R
Pontisia stehlii stehlii Cooper and Grant	R
Pontisia stehlii tumidosa Cooper and Grant	VR
Reticulariina sp.	VR
Rhipidomella hispidula Cooper and Grant	A
Rugatia paraindica (McKee)	VR
Stenoscisma triquetrum Cooper and Grant	R
Tautosia pulchra Cooper and Grant	C
Texarina wordensis (R.E. King)	R
Torynechus caelatus Cooper and Grant	VR
Xenosteges adherens Muir-Wood and Cooper	R
LOCALITY N708a : Skinner Ranch Formation, Poplar Tank Member	
Coscinophora monilifera Cooper and Grant	VR
LOCALITY N708b : Neal Ranch Formation	
Eridmatus marathonensis Cooper and Grant	VR
Linoproductus sp.	VR
LOCALITY N708c : Cathedral Mountain Formation	
Cenorhynchia parvula Cooper and Grant	VR
Composita imbricata Cooper and Grant	R
Cyclacantharia paucispinosa Cooper and Grant	VR
Derbyia informis Cooper and Grant	VR
Edriosteges multispinosus Muir-Wood and Cooper	C
Neophricadothyris bullata Cooper and Grant	VR
LOCALITY N708e : Skinner Ranch Formation, Poplar Tank Member	
Acosarina dorsisulcata Cooper and Grant	VR
Acritosia peculiaris Cooper and Grant	C
Antronaria voluminosa Cooper and Grant	A
Cartorhium zoyei Cooper and Grant	VR
Chonosteges variabilis Cooper and Grant	VR

	Rarity code
Composita apheles Cooper and Grant	C
Compressoproductus parvus Cooper and Grant	C
Eolyttonia sp.	R
Glyptosteges angustus (R.E. King)	VR
Hustedia cepacea Cooper and Grant	C
Limbella limbata Cooper and Grant	VR
Meekella hessensis R.E. King	R
Nudauris enigmatica Cooper and Grant	C
Oncosarina spinicostata Cooper and Grant	A
Peniculauris sp. 1	VR
Plectelasma kingi Cooper and Grant	VR
Rhamnaria grandis Cooper and Grant	VR
Scacchinella titan Cooper and Grant	VR
Spyridiophora reticulata (R.E. King)	R
Stenoscisma hadrum Cooper and Grant	VR
Stenoscisma pansum Cooper and Grant	VR
LOCALITY N708p : Gaptank Formation	
Composita discina Cooper and Grant	VR
Meekella texana R.E. King	VR
LOCALITY N708q : Skinner Ranch Formation, Decie Ranch Member	
Acritosia peculiaris Cooper and Grant	VR
Acritosia teguliferoides (R.E. King)	R
Antiquatonia hessensis (R.E. King)	VR
Antiquatonia sp.	VR
Antronaria titania Cooper and Grant	VR
Composita discina Cooper and Grant	R
Derbyia nasuta Girty	VR
Enteletes stehlii Cooper and Grant	VR
Eolyttonia gigantea Cooper and Grant	VR
Geyerella hessi Cooper and Grant	VR
Glyptosteges angustus (R.E. King)	VR
Limbella limbata Cooper and Grant	R
Martinia sp. 1	VR
Meekella sp.	R
Orthotichia newelli Cooper and Grant	VR
Scacchinella titan Cooper and Grant	A
Stenoscisma amoenum Cooper and Grant	R
Stenoscisma hadrum Cooper and Grant	VR
LOCALITY N708u : Cathedral Mountain Formation	
Amphipella arcaria Cooper and Grant	VA
Cenorhynchia sp.	R
Choanodus perfectus Cooper and Grant	VR
Composita sp.	R
Dyoros (*Lissosia*) *vagabundus* Cooper and Grant	VR
Dyoros (*Tetragonetes*) *giganteus* Cooper and Grant	VR
Elassonia scitula Cooper and Grant	R
Glossothyropsis immatura Cooper and Grant	R
Goniarina sp. 1	R
Hustedia sp.	VR
Hustedia stataria Cooper and Grant	A
Hustedia trisecta Cooper and Grant	C
Lepidospirifer demissus Cooper and Grant	VR
Martinia miranda Cooper and Grant	C
Metriolepis tegulata Cooper and Grant	VR
Neophricadothyris bullata Cooper and Grant	R
Niviconia globosa (R.E. King)	VR
Nucleospira cunctata Cooper and Grant	VA
Petrocrania sp.	VR
Phrenophoria nesiotes Cooper and Grant	A
Pseudoleptodus? sp. 4	VR
Ptygmactrum angulatum Cooper and Grant	VR
Rallacosta laminata Cooper and Grant	C

	Rarity code
LOCALITY N708u - Continued	
Scenesia extensa Cooper and Grant	C
Stenoscisma fabarium Cooper and Grant	A
Stenoscisma triquetrum Cooper and Grant	VR
Thedusia discissa Cooper and Grant	VA
LOCALITY N708v : Skinner Ranch Formation, Sullivan Peak Member	
Enteletes sp.	VR
LOCALITY N708w : Neal Ranch Formation	
Parenteletes superbus Cooper and Grant	VR
LOCALITY N708x : Cathedral Mountain Formation	
Enteletes plummeri R.E. King	VR
LOCALITY N708y : Neal Ranch Formation	
Diplanus catatonus Cooper and Grant	VR
LOCALITY N708z : Skinner Ranch Formation, Decie Ranch Member	
Tropidelasma rhamphodes Cooper and Grant	R
LOCALITY N709 : Cathedral Mountain Formation	
Cartorhium latum (R.E. King)	VR
Chonosteges variabilis Cooper and Grant	VR
Enteletes plummeri R.E. King	VR
Institella leonardensis (R.E. King)	R
Megousia auriculata Muir-Wood and Cooper	VR
Torynechus caelatus Cooper and Grant	VR
Xestosia schucherti (R.E. King)	VR
LOCALITY N709a : Skinner Ranch Formation	
Chonosteges variabilis Cooper and Grant	VR
Heterelasma gibbosum Cooper and Grant	VR
Spyridiophora reticulata (R.E. King)	VR
Stenoscisma pyraustoides Cooper and Grant	VR
LOCALITY N709b : Moran Formation	
Cleiothyridina rectimarginata Cooper and Grant	R
LOCALITY N709c : Road Canyon Formation	
Acosarina mesoplatys (R.E. King)	C
Acritosia? vestibula Cooper and Grant	R
Anteridocus erugatus Cooper and Grant	C
Anteridocus seminudus Cooper and Grant	C
Cenorhynchia atmeta Cooper and Grant	R
Chondronia ovalis Cooper and Grant	C
Cleiothyridina nana Cooper and Grant	R
Composita crassa Cooper and Grant	C
Coscinophora magnifica Cooper and Grant	A
Crurithyris minutalis Cooper and Grant	VR
Derbyia cincinnata Cooper and Grant	VR
Derbyia informis Cooper and Grant	VR
Derbyia laqueata Cooper and Grant	C
Echinauris irregularis Cooper and Grant	VR
Echinauris lappacea Cooper and Grant	R
Edriosteges compactus Cooper and Grant	C
Elassonia micraria Cooper and Grant	VR
Hustedia consuta Cooper and Grant	R
Meekella calathica Cooper and Grant	A
Megousia auriculata Muir-Wood and Cooper	VR
Neospirifer thescelus Cooper and Grant	R
Rhamnaria tenuispinosa Cooper and Grant	VR
Spiriferellina tricosa Cooper and Grant	VR
Stenoscisma calvatum Cooper and Grant	R
Stenoscisma sp.	VR
Taphrosestria peculiaris Cooper and Grant	C

	Rarity code
LOCALITY N709g : Hess Formation	
Oncosarina spinicostata Cooper and Grant	C
Spyridiophora reticulata (R.E. King)	VR
LOCALITY N709h : Hess Formation	
Petasmatherus mundus Cooper and Grant	VR
LOCALITY N709-1 : Skinner Ranch Formation, Sullivan Peak Member	
Glyptosteges angustus (R.E. King)	VR
Limbella limbata Cooper and Grant	VR
LOCALITY N709o : Cathedral Mountain Formation	
Institella leonardensis (R.E. King)	VR
Limbella sp.	R
Texarina wordensis (R.E. King)	VR
Xestosia schucherti (R.E. King)	VR
LOCALITY N709t : Lenox Hills Formation	
Antiquatonia sp.	VR
Beecheria sp.	VR
Composita sp.	VR
Composita strongyle Cooper and Grant	R
Enteletes wolfcampensis R.E. King	R
Hystriculina sulcata Cooper and Grant	VR
Limbella wolfcampensis (R.E. King)	VR
Meekella magnifica Cooper and Grant	VR
Neophricadothyris catatona Cooper and Grant	VR
Parenteletes superbus Cooper and Grant	VR
Rhynchopora molina Cooper and Grant	VR
Stenoscisma peneleve Cooper and Grant	VR
Teguliferina boesei R.E. King	VR
LOCALITY N709u : Skinner Ranch Formation	
Acritosia teguliferoides (R.E. King)	VR
Cartorhium zoyei Cooper and Grant	VR
Chonetinella biplicata (R.E. King)	VR
Derbyia sp.	VR
Enteletes stehlii Cooper and Grant	VR
Meekella enormis Cooper and Grant	VR
Oncosarina sp.	VR
Pontisia stehlii stehlii Cooper and Grant	VR
Reticulatia sp.	VR
Scacchinella titan Cooper and Grant	C
Stenoscisma hadrum Cooper and Grant	VR
LOCALITY N709v : Skinner Ranch Formation	
Acosarina dorsisulcata Cooper and Grant	VR
Antronaria dissona Cooper and Grant	VR
Derbyia sp.	VR
Dielasma sp.	VR
Elliottella varicostata Cooper and Grant	VR
Enteletes stehlii Cooper and Grant	VR
Meekella hessensis R.E. King	VR
Orthotichia newelli Cooper and Grant	VR
Rhipidomella hessensis R.E. King	VR
Scacchinella titan Cooper and Grant	VR
Teguliferina conida (Stehli)	R
LOCALITY N709w : Lenox Hills Formation	
Derbyia nasuta Girty	VR
Enteletes wolfcampensis R.E. King	VR
Meekella magnifica Cooper and Grant	VR
Parenteletes superbus Cooper and Grant	VR
Tropidelasma strobilum Cooper and Grant	R
LOCALITY N709z : Skinner Ranch Formation	
Acosarina dorsisulcata Cooper and Grant	VR

	Rarity code
LOCALITY N709z - Continued	
Chonosteges variabilis Cooper and Grant	VR
Scacchinella titan Cooper and Grant	R
Spyridiophora reticulata (R.E. King)	VR
LOCALITY N710b : Cathedral Mountain Formation	
Enteletes leonardensis R.E. King	VR
LOCALITY N710d : Cathedral Mountain Formation, Wedin Member	
Agelesia triagonalis (R.E. King)	C
Chonosteges variabilis Cooper and Grant	VR
Derbyia crenulata Girty	VR
Diplanus lamellatus (R.E. King)	VR
Echinauris sp.	VR
Enteletes sp.	VR
Eolyttonia sp.	VR
Institella leonardensis (R.E. King)	VR
Meekella hessensis R.E. King	VR
Rhipidomella sp.	VR
LOCALITY N710h : Road Canyon Formation	
Chonetinetes reversus Cooper and Grant	A
Hustedia consuta Cooper and Grant	VR
Megousia auriculata Muir-Wood and Cooper	VR
LOCALITY N710i : Road Canyon Formation	
Chonetinetes reversus Cooper and Grant	VR
Megousia auriculata Muir-Wood and Cooper	R
Peniculauris costata Cooper and Grant	VR
LOCALITY N710r : Skinner Ranch Formation, Sullivan Peak Member	
Acosarina dorsisulcata Cooper and Grant	VR
Acritosia peculiaris Cooper and Grant	VR
Antronaria voluminosa Cooper and Grant	VR
Cancrinella fragosa Cooper and Grant	VR
Cartorhium zoyei Cooper and Grant	VR
Chonosteges variabilis Cooper and Grant	R
Composita apheles Cooper and Grant	R
Dielasma hessense Cooper and Grant	VR
Enteletes sp.	VR
Eolyttonia gigantea Cooper and Grant	VR
Geyerella hessi Cooper and Grant	VR
Glyptosteges intricatus Cooper and Grant	R
Hustedia hessensis R.E. King	VR
Kochiproductus elongatus Cooper and Grant	VR
Kochiproductus sp. 4	VR
Limbella limbata Cooper and Grant	VR
Megousia sp.	VR
Nudauris enigmatica Cooper and Grant	VR
Oncosarina spinicostata Cooper and Grant	C
Rhamnaria grandis Cooper and Grant	VR
Spyridiophora reticulata (R.E. King)	VR
Stenoscisma hadrum Cooper and Grant	R
Tautosia podistra Cooper and Grant	R
Torynechus alectorius Cooper and Grant	R
LOCALITY N710u : Road Canyon Formation	
Acosarina mesoplatys (R.E. King)	A
Acritosia? vestibula Cooper and Grant	R
Anteridocus erugatus Cooper and Grant	A
Bothrostegium derbyoideum Cooper and Grant	R
Cenorhynchia atmeta Cooper and Grant	C
Chondronia ovalis Cooper and Grant	A
Cleiothyridina nana Cooper and Grant	R
Collemataria sp.	VR

	Rarity code
Composita crassa Cooper and Grant	C
Composita sp.	R
Cooperina subcuneata Cooper and Grant	VR
Coscinophora magnifica Cooper and Grant	A
Cyclacantharia sp.	R
Cyclacantharia transitoria Cooper and Grant	C
Derbyia cincinnata Cooper and Grant	C
Derbyia laqueata Cooper and Grant	C
Dielasma sp.	VR
Dyoros (Dyoros) transversus Cooper and Grant	R
Echinauris bella Cooper and Grant	VR
Echinauris lappacea Cooper and Grant	C
Edriosteges compactus Cooper and Grant	C
Goniarina striata Cooper and Grant	VR
Heterelasma glansfagea Cooper and Grant	VR
Hustedia consuta Cooper and Grant	C
Kutorginella sullivanensis (R.E. King)	VR
Meekella calathica Cooper and Grant	A
Megousia auriculata Muir-Wood and Cooper	VA
Neophricadothyris cordata Cooper and Grant	VR
Neospirifer bakeri bakeri R.E. King	C
Paucispinifera sulcata Cooper and Grant	VR
Peniculauris costata Cooper and Grant	VR
Petasmatherus pumilus Cooper and Grant	VR
Reticulariina venustula Cooper and Grant	C
Stenoscisma calvatum Cooper and Grant	VR
Stenoscisma sp.	VR
Taphrosestria peculiaris Cooper and Grant	A
Texarina wordensis (R.E. King)	VR
LOCALITY N710w : Lenox Hills Formation	
Limbella wolfcampensis (R.E. King)	VR
LOCALITY N710x : Skinner Ranch Formation, Poplar Tank Member	
Acritosia peculiaris Cooper and Grant	VR
Scacchinella titan Cooper and Grant	VR
LOCALITY N710y : Skinner Ranch Formation, Sullivan Peak Member	
Peniculauris sp. 1	VR
LOCALITY N710z : Road Canyon Formation	
Composita crassa Cooper and Grant	R
Dielasma bellulum Cooper and Grant	VR
Dyoros (Dyoros) angulatus Cooper and Grant	R
Dyoros (Dyoros) transversus Cooper and Grant	R
Echinauris bella Cooper and Grant	R
Echinauris sp.	VR
Heterelasma glansfagea Cooper and Grant	VR
Holotricharina sparsa Cooper and Grant	VR
Hustedia connorsi Cooper and Grant	R
Kutorginella sullivanensis (R.E. King)	VR
Meekella calathica Cooper and Grant	VR
Megousia auriculata Muir-Wood and Cooper	A
Neophricadothyris crassibecca Cooper and Grant	VR
Neospirifer bakeri bakeri R.E. King	VR
Petasmatherus pumilus Cooper and Grant	VR
Reticulariina pristina Cooper and Grant	VR
Rhamnaria vinnula Cooper and Grant	VR
Rhynchopora sphenoides Cooper and Grant	VR
Spiriferella sp.	VR
Stenoscisma camurum Cooper and Grant	VR
Waagenoconcha platys Cooper and Grant	R
LOCALITY N711d : Skinner Ranch Formation	
Acritosia peculiaris Cooper and Grant	R

	Rarity code
LOCALITY N711d - Continued	
Allorhynchus sp.	VR
Antronaria titania Cooper and Grant	VR
Cartorhium zoyei Cooper and Grant	VR
Chonosteges variabilis Cooper and Grant	VR
Composita discina Cooper and Grant	VR
Compressoproductus concentricus Cooper and Grant	VR
Coscinophora monilifera Cooper and Grant	VR
Dielasma hessense Cooper and Grant	VR
Enteletes stehlii Cooper and Grant	VR
Eolyttonia gigantea Cooper and Grant	VR
Eolyttonia sp.	VR
Geyerella hessi Cooper and Grant	VR
Hustedia sp.	VR
Limbella limbata Cooper and Grant	VR
Martinia sp. 1	R
Nudauris enigmatica Cooper and Grant	VR
Oncosarina rotunda Cooper and Grant	R
Peniculauris sp. 1	VR
Spyridiophora reticulata (R.E. King)	VR
Stenoscisma pansum Cooper and Grant	R
LOCALITY N711i : Skinner Ranch Formation	
Acritosia teguliferoides (R.E. King)	VR
Scacchinella titan Cooper and Grant	R
LOCALITY N711k : Skinner Ranch Formation	
Enteletes sp.	VR
Stenoscisma hadrum Cooper and Grant	VR
LOCALITY N711o : Skinner Ranch Formation	
Neophricadothyris catatona Cooper and Grant	VR
Stenoscisma pyraustoides Cooper and Grant	VR
LOCALITY N711p : Skinner Ranch Formation	
Acosarina dorsisulcata Cooper and Grant	C
Acritosia teguliferoides (R.E. King)	R
Antronaria dissona Cooper and Grant	C
Composita discina Cooper and Grant	VR
Crurithyris sp. a	VR
Derbyia crenulata Girty	C
Dielasma sp.	VR
Elliottella varicostata Cooper and Grant	VR
Enteletes stehlii Cooper and Grant	A
Hustedia sp.	VR
Hystriculina pumila Cooper and Grant	A
Kozlowskia subsphaeroidalis Cooper and Grant	A
Meekella hessensis R.E. King	C
Orthotichia newelli Cooper and Grant	R
Peniculauris sp. 1	VR
Rhamnaria sp.	VR
Rhipidomella hessensis R.E. King	C
Rugaria crassa Cooper and Grant	VR
Scacchinella titan Cooper and Grant	R
Spinifrons delicatula Cooper and Grant	R
LOCALITY N711q : Cathedral Mountain Formation	
Acosarina mesoplatys (R.E. King)	R
Anemonaria sublaevis (R.E. King)	R
Cartorhium latum (R.E. King)	VR
Chonosteges variabilis Cooper and Grant	VR
Collemataria gregaria Cooper and Grant	VR
Crurithyris sp.	VR
Dyoros (Lissosia) vagabundus Cooper and Grant	VR
Dyoros (Tetragonetes) giganteus Cooper and Grant	VR
Dyoros (Tetragonetes) lateralis Cooper and Grant	R
Dyoros (Tetragonetes) planus Cooper and Grant	A

	Rarity code
Echinauris crassa Cooper and Grant	VR
Echinauris irregularis Cooper and Grant	R
Echinauris sp.	VR
Edriosteges multispinosus Muir-Wood and Cooper	VR
Hercosia uddeni (Böse)	C
Hustedia sp.	VR
Hustedia spicata Cooper and Grant	R
Meekella calathica Cooper and Grant	VR
Megousia auriculata Muir-Wood and Cooper	R
Micraphelia sp.	VR
Neospirifer mansuetus Cooper and Grant	VR
Niviconia globosa (R.E. King)	VR
Nudauris linospina Cooper and Grant	R
Peniculauris subcostata (R.E. King)	R
Reticulariina craticula Cooper and Grant	VR
Rhamnaria tenuispinosa Cooper and Grant	VR
Rugatia occidentalis parvauris (Newberry)	VR
Rugatia paraindica (McKee)	VR
Stenoscisma triquetrum Cooper and Grant	VR
Xenosteges adherens Muir-Wood and Cooper	VR
Xestosia schucherti (R.E. King)	R
LOCALITY N711r : Cathedral Mountain Formation	
Dyoros (Tetragonetes) planus Cooper and Grant	R
Nudauris linospina Cooper and Grant	VR
LOCALITY N711w : Cathedral Mountain Formation	
Anemonaria sublaevis (R.E. King)	VR
Composita crassa Cooper and Grant	VR
LOCALITY N711z : Skinner Ranch Formation	
Chonosteges variabilis Cooper and Grant	VR
Composita discina Cooper and Grant	VR
Enteletes sp.	VR
Heterelasma sp. 1	VR
Stenoscisma pyraustoides Cooper and Grant	VR
LOCALITY N712d : Hueco Formation	
Composita sp.	R
Crurithyris sp.	C
Dielasma sp.	VR
Heteralosia sp.	R
Reticulatia sp.	VR
LOCALITY N712e : Hueco Formation	
Composita cracens Cooper and Grant	R
Hustedia sp.	VR
Kozlowskia sp.	VR
Pontisia franklinensis Cooper and Grant	VA
Reticulariina hueconiana Cooper and Grant	VR
Stenoscisma hueconianum (Girty)	R
LOCALITY N712m : Hueco Formation	
Pontisia franklinensis Cooper and Grant	VA
Stenoscisma hueconianum (Girty)	C
Stenoscisma sp.	VR
LOCALITY N712n : Skinner Ranch Formation	
Scacchinella titan Cooper and Grant	VR
LOCALITY N712o : Cathedral Mountain Formation	
Acosarina mesoplatys (R.E. King)	A
Agelesia triagonalis (R.E. King)	VR
Cancrinella sp.	VR
Cartorhium latum (R.E. King)	VR
Choanodus irregularis Cooper and Grant	R
Chonosteges costellatus Cooper and Grant	VR
Chonosteges pulcher Cooper and Grant	VR

	Rarity code
LOCALITY N712o - Continued	
Collemataria gregaria Cooper and Grant	VR
Composita sp.	VR
Composita stalagmium Cooper and Grant	VR
Compressoproductus flabellatus Cooper and Grant	R
Compressoproductus thomasi Cooper and Grant	VR
Derbyia laqueata Cooper and Grant	VR
Derbyia sp.	R
Diplanus lamellatus (R.E. King)	VR
Dyoros (Lissosia) vagabundus Cooper and Grant	VR
Echinauris irregularis Cooper and Grant	C
Enteletes plummeri R.E. King	VR
Enteletes sp.	VR
Eolyttonia chaotica Cooper and Grant	R
Goniarina futilis Cooper and Grant	VR
Hercosestria laevis Cooper and Grant	R
Hercosia uddeni (Böse)	VR
Hustedia compressa Cooper and Grant	VR
Hustedia sp.	VR
Hustedia spicata Cooper and Grant	R
Institella leonardensis (R.E. King)	R
Linoproductus sp.	VR
Meekella calathica Cooper and Grant	R
Meekella sp.	R
Megousia auriculata Muir-Wood and Cooper	R
Metriolepis tegulata Cooper and Grant	VR
Neophricadothyris bullata Cooper and Grant	VR
Neophricadothyris sp.	VR
Peniculauris subcostata (R.E. King)	VR
Rallacosta actina Cooper and Grant	VR
Rhamnaria tenuispinosa Cooper and Grant	VR
Rhipidomella hispidula Cooper and Grant	R
Torynechus caelatus Cooper and Grant	VR
Waagenoconcha convexa Cooper and Grant	VR
Xenosteges adherens Muir-Wood and Cooper	R
Xestosia schucherti (R.E. King)	R
LOCALITY N712p : Skinner Ranch Formation	
Acosarina dorsisulcata Cooper and Grant	R
Acritosia peculiaris Cooper and Grant	VR
Antronaria titania Cooper and Grant	R
Cancrinella fragosa Cooper and Grant	C
Cartorhium zoyei Cooper and Grant	VR
Chonosteges variabilis Cooper and Grant	VR
Composita discina Cooper and Grant	VR
Coscinophora monilifera Cooper and Grant	R
Dielasma hessense Cooper and Grant	VR
Geyerella hessi Cooper and Grant	VR
Heterelasma sp.	VR
Hustedia sp.	VR
Hystriculina pumila Cooper and Grant	R
Limbella limbata Cooper and Grant	VR
Linoproductus sp.	R
Meekella hessensis R.E. King	R
Oncosarina spinicostata Cooper and Grant	R
Rhamnaria grandis Cooper and Grant	VR
Spyridiophora reticulata (R.E. King)	VR
Stenoscisma pansum Cooper and Grant	R
Tautosia podistra Cooper and Grant	R
Tropidelasma rhamphodes Cooper and Grant	VR
LOCALITY N712q : Road Canyon Formation	
Chonetinetes reversus Cooper and Grant	VR
LOCALITY N712t : Road Canyon Formation	
Derbyia sp.	VR

	Rarity code
Echinauris bella Cooper and Grant	R
Echinauris sp.	VR
Hustedia sp.	VR
Kutorginella umbonata (Muir-Wood and Cooper)	VR
Megousia auriculata Muir-Wood and Cooper	C
Petasmatherus pumilus Cooper and Grant	R
Texarina wordensis (R.E. King)	VR
LOCALITY N712w : Neal Ranch Formation	
Acosarina rectimarginata Cooper and Grant	SA
Cenorhynchia hebata Cooper and Grant	R
Chondronia rectimarginata Cooper and Grant	C
Derbyia profunda Cooper and Grant	A
Hemileurus runcinatus Cooper and Grant	C
Hystriculina convexa Cooper and Grant	VR
Reticulatia robusta Cooper and Grant	VR
Teguliferina boesei R.E. King	A
LOCALITY N712z : Neal Ranch Formation	
Diplanus catatonus Cooper and Grant	VR
Kozlowskia anterosulcata Cooper and Grant	VR
Linoproductus semisulcatus Cooper and Grant	VR
Neophricadothyris transversa Cooper and Grant	VR
Reticulatia robusta Cooper and Grant	VR
Spyridiophora distincta Cooper and Stehli	VR
LOCALITY N713 : Word Formation, China Tank Member	
Allorhynchus permianum wordense Cooper and Grant	VR
Arionthia blothrhachis Cooper and Grant	VR
Bothrionia nasuta Cooper and Grant	VR
Cactosteges anomalus Cooper and Grant	R
Cartorhium chelomatum Cooper and Grant	VR
Collemataria elongata Cooper and Grant	R
Composita enormis Cooper and Grant	VR
Composita parasulcata Cooper and Grant	VR
Costispinifera rugatula (Girty)	R
Cyclacantharia transitoria Cooper and Grant	R
Derbyia filosa Cooper and Grant	R
Derbyia pannucia Cooper and Grant	R
Derbyia texta Cooper and Grant	VR
Dielasma adamanteum Cooper and Grant	R
Dielasma compactum Cooper and Grant	R
Dielasma sp.	VR
Dielasma zebratum Cooper and Grant	R
Dyoros (Dyoros) extensus Cooper and Grant	R
Echinauris lateralis Muir-Wood and Cooper	VR
Echinosteges tuberculatus (R.E. King)	VR
Enteletes wordensis R.E. King	C
Glossothyropsis rectangulata Cooper and Grant	VR
Grandaurispina kingorum Muir-Wood and Cooper	VR
Heteralosia hystricula (Girty)	VR
Heterelasma concavum Cooper and Grant	R
Hustedia pugilla nasiterna Cooper and Grant	C
Hustedia sculptilis Cooper and Grant	R
Liosotella wordensis (R.E. King)	VR
Meekella skenoides Girty	C
Megousia mucronata Cooper and Grant	VR
Neospirifer amphigyus Cooper and Grant	VR
Paraspiriferina laqueata Cooper and Grant	C
Paucispinifera transversa Cooper and Grant	R
Pseudodielasma lobatum Cooper and Grant	R
Pseudodielasma minor (R.E. King)	C
Pseudodielasma pingue Cooper and Grant	VR
Pseudodielasma plicatum Cooper and Grant	R
Pseudodielasma sp.	A

	Rarity code
LOCALITY N713 - Continued	
Pseudoleptodus nodosus Cooper and Grant	VR
Rhamnaria kingorum Muir-Wood and Cooper	VR
Rhynchopora palumbula Cooper and Grant	VR
Spiriferellina hilli (Girty)	C
Tautosia transenna Cooper and Grant	VR
Texarina elongata Cooper and Grant	VR
Thedusia procera Cooper and Grant	R
Tropidelasma anthicum Cooper and Grant	VR
Xenosteges quadratus Cooper and Grant	VR
Yakovlevia hessorum Cooper and Grant	VR
LOCALITY N713a : Gaptank Formation, Uddenites Member	
Composita discina Cooper and Grant	VR
Hystriculina sulcata Cooper and Grant	VR
Reticulatia sp. 2	VR
Rhynchopora molina Cooper and Grant	VR
LOCALITY N713b : Gaptank Formation, Uddenites Member	
Meekella texana R.E. King	VR
Scacchinella triangulata Cooper and Grant	VR
Teguliferina boesei R.E. King	VR
LOCALITY N713c : Skinner Ranch Formation, Sullivan Peak Member	
Diplanus lamellatus (R.E. King)	VR
Reticulariina sp.	VR
Rhamnaria grandis Cooper and Grant	VR
Scacchinella titan Cooper and Grant	VR
Spyridiophora reticulata (R.E. King)	VR
LOCALITY N713d : Skinner Ranch Formation, Sullivan Peak Member	
Echinauris sp.	VR
Glyptosteges intricatus Cooper and Grant	VR
Spyridiophora reticulata (R.E. King)	VR
Stenoscisma hadrum Cooper and Grant	VR
LOCALITY N713e : Gaptank Formation	
Composita sp.	VR
Echinauris subquadrata Cooper and Grant	VR
Kozlowskia sp.	VR
Limbella costellata Cooper and Grant	VR
Reticulatia sp.	VR
LOCALITY N713g : Gaptank Formation, Uddenites Member	
Derbyoides sp. 2	VR
LOCALITY N713h : Neal Ranch Formation	
Chonetinella sp.	VR
Hustedia trita leptyca Cooper and Grant	VR
Meekella prionota Cooper and Grant	VR
Neospirifer apothescelus Cooper and Grant	VR
Pseudoleptodus conicus Cooper and Grant	VR
Reticulatia americana (Dunbar and Condra)	VR
Spyridiophora distincta Cooper and Stehli	VR
Teguliferina boesei R.E. King	VR
LOCALITY N713i : Skinner Ranch Formation, Sullivan Peak Member	
Composita sp.	VR
Scacchinella titan Cooper and Grant	VR
LOCALITY N713j : Lenox Hills Formation	
Linoproductus sp.	VR
LOCALITY N713k : Neal Ranch Formation	
Echinaria cf. *moorei* (Dunbar and Condra)	VR
Hystriculina sp.	VR
Nudauris splendens Cooper and Grant	VR
Rhynchopora molina Cooper and Grant	VR
LOCALITY N713-l : Neal Ranch Formation	
Derbyia profunda Cooper and Grant	VR
Parenteletes superbus Cooper and Grant	VR
LOCALITY N713m : Skinner Ranch Formation, Sullivan Peak Member	
Echinauris sp.?	VR
Limbella limbata Cooper and Grant	VR
Stenoscisma hadrum Cooper and Grant	VR
LOCALITY N713n : Skinner Ranch Formation	
Spyridiophora reticulata (R.E. King)	VR
LOCALITY N713o : Gaptank Formation, Uddenites Member	
Composita sp.	VR
Meekella prionota Cooper and Grant	VR
Parenteletes cooperi R.E. King	VR
Teguliferina boesei R.E. King	VR
LOCALITY N713p : Cathedral Mountain Formation	
Hustedia spicata Cooper and Grant	VR
LOCALITY N713q : Lenox Hills Formation	
Composita discina Cooper and Grant	VR
Limbella wolfcampensis (R.E. King)	VR
Parenteletes superbus Cooper and Grant	VR
LOCALITY N713r : Skinner Ranch Formation, Poplar Tank Member	
Oncosarina spinicostata Cooper and Grant	VR
Spyridiophora reticulata (R.E. King)	VR
LOCALITY N713s : Skinner Ranch Formation, Decie Ranch Member	
Spyridiophora reticulata (R.E. King)	VR
LOCALITY N713t : Cathedral Mountain Formation	
Enteletes plummeri R.E. King	VR
Institella leonardensis (R.E. King)	VR
Neophricadothyris bullata Cooper and Grant	VR
Stenoscisma triquetrum Cooper and Grant	VR
LOCALITY N713u : Gaptank Formation, Uddenites Member	
Derbyia profunda Cooper and Grant	VR
Derbyia sp.	VR
LOCALITY N713v : Cathedral Mountain Formation	
Enteletes sp.	VR
Glyptosteges intricatus Cooper and Grant	VR
LOCALITY N713w : Cathedral Mountain Formation	
Enteletes plummeri R.E. King	VR
Stenoscisma triquetrum Cooper and Grant	VR
LOCALITY N713x : Hess Formation	
Acosarina dorsisulcata Cooper and Grant	VR
Antronaria transversa (R.E. King)	VR
Dielasma longisulcatum Cooper and Grant	VR
Enteletes subcircularis Cooper and Grant	R
Limbella sp. 1	VR
Oncosarina whitei (R.E. King)	R
Peniculauris imitata Cooper and Grant	VR

	Rarity code
LOCALITY N713x - Continued	
Rhipidomella hessensis R.E. King	VR
Thamnosia silicica Cooper and Grant	VR
Tschernyschewia inexpectans Cooper and Grant	VR
LOCALITY N713y : Lenox Hills Formation	
Chonetinella sp.	VR
Composita discina Cooper and Grant	R
Echinauris interrupta Cooper and Grant	VR
Hustedia trita leptyca Cooper and Grant	R
Hystriculina convexa Cooper and Grant	VR
Kutorginella uddeni Cooper and Grant	VR
Rhipidomella miscella Cooper and Grant	R
Stenoscisma sp. 2	R
LOCALITY N713z : Skinner Ranch Formation, Sullivan Peak Member	
Rhipidomella hessensis R.E. King	VR
LOCALITY N714e : Skinner Ranch Formation, Decie Ranch Member	
Antiquatonia hessensis (R.E. King)	VR
Elliottella varicostata Cooper and Grant	VR
Scacchinella titan Cooper and Grant	R
LOCALITY N714o : Word Formation, Appel Ranch Member	
Allorhynchus triangulatum Cooper and Grant	VR
Arionthia germana Cooper and Grant	R
Cartorhium orbiculatum Cooper and Grant	R
Cartorhium retusum Cooper and Grant	VR
Composita enormis Cooper and Grant	R
Ctenalosia fixata Cooper and Stehli	VR
Cyclacantharia kingorum Cooper and Grant	C
Derbyia filosa Cooper and Grant	VR
Derbyia pannucia Cooper and Grant	VR
Derbyia texta Cooper and Grant	R
Dielasma zebratum Cooper and Grant	VR
Dyoros (*Dyoros*) *convexus* Cooper and Grant	C
Dyoros (*Dyoros*) *extensus* Cooper and Grant	C
Echinauris lateralis Muir-Wood and Cooper	VR
Echinosteges tuberculatus (R.E. King)	R
Eolyttonia progressa Cooper and Grant	C
Grandaurispina bella Cooper and Grant	VR
Grandaurispina crassa Cooper and Grant	VR
Heteralosia hystricula (Girty)	R
Hustedia pugilla hebetata Cooper and Grant	C
Liosotella irregularis Cooper and Grant	R
Liosotella tetragonalis Cooper and Grant	VR
Liosotella wordensis (R.E. King)	VR
Meekella skenoides Girty	R
Paraspiriferina rotundata Cooper and Grant	R
Paucispinifera auriculata Muir-Wood and Cooper	R
Rhamnaria kingorum Muir-Wood and Cooper	VR
Thamnosia phragmophora Cooper and Grant	VR
Thedusia procera Cooper and Grant	VR
Xenosteges quadratus Cooper and Grant	C
LOCALITY N714p : Skinner Ranch Formation	
Acosarina dorsisulcata Cooper and Grant	VR
Antronaria transversa (R.E. King)	VR
Composita discina Cooper and Grant	R
Derbyia nasuta Girty	VR
Derbyia sp.	VR
Diplanus rarus Cooper and Grant	VR
Eolyttonia gigantea Cooper and Grant	C

	Rarity code
Geyerella hessi Cooper and Grant	VR
Hustedia catella Cooper and Grant	VR
Hustedia sp.	VR
Meekella hessensis R.E. King	VR
Rhipidomella hessensis R.E. King	VR
Scacchinella titan Cooper and Grant	R
Teguliferina conida (Stehli)	C
LOCALITY N714q : Skinner Ranch Formation	
Meekella enormis Cooper and Grant	VR
Scacchinella titan Cooper and Grant	C
LOCALITY N714t : Skinner Ranch Formation, Decie Ranch Member	
Acolosia magna Cooper and Grant	VR
Acosarina dorsisulcata Cooper and Grant	VR
Acritosia peculiaris Cooper and Grant	R
Cartorhium zoyei Cooper and Grant	C
Composita apheles Cooper and Grant	VR
Compressoproductus concentricus Cooper and Grant	R
Coscinophora monilifera Cooper and Grant	R
Cyclacantharia gigantea Cooper and Grant	VR
Derbyia nasuta Girty	C
Enteletes rotundobesus Cooper and Grant	A
Eolyttonia gigantea Cooper and Grant	C
Geyerella hessi Cooper and Grant	C
Limbella limbata Cooper and Grant	C
Linoproductus angustus R.E. King	VR
Meekella enormis Cooper and Grant	VR
Nudauris enigmatica Cooper and Grant	VR
Oncosarina rotunda Cooper and Grant	C
Peniculauris sp. 1	VR
Reticulatia sp.	VR
Scacchinella titan Cooper and Grant	A
Tropidelasma rhamphodes Cooper and Grant	VA
LOCALITY N714v : Cathedral Mountain Formation, Wedin Member	
Acosarina mesoplatys (R.E. King)	C
Composita sp.	VR
Echinauris irregularis Cooper and Grant	VR
Echinauris sp.	VR
Meekella calathica Cooper and Grant	VR
Neophricadothyris sp.	VR
Reticulariina subulata Cooper and Grant	VR
Rugatia paraindica (McKee)	VR
LOCALITY N714w : Cathedral Mountain Formation, Wedin Member	
Acosarina mesoplatys (R.E. King)	R
Agelesia triagonalis (R.E. King)	VA
Cartorhium coristum Cooper and Grant	C
Choanodus irregularis Cooper and Grant	R
Choanodus perfectus Cooper and Grant	C
Chondronia bella Cooper and Grant	R
Chonosteges pulcher Cooper and Grant	C
Chonosteges variabilis Cooper and Grant	VR
Collemataria irregularis Cooper and Grant	C
Composita bucculenta Cooper and Grant	VR
Composita sp.	R
Compressoproductus thomasi Cooper and Grant	R
Coscinophora hortoni (R.E. King)	C
Derbyia complicata Cooper and Grant	C
Derbyia informis Cooper and Grant	VR
Derbyia laqueata Cooper and Grant	VR
Dielasma obesum Cooper and Grant	VR

Rarity code

LOCALITY N714w - Continued

Dielasma perplexum Cooper and Grant	VR
Diplanus lamellatus (R.E. King)	C
Dyoros (Lissosia) vagabundus Cooper and Grant	R
Echinauris crassa Cooper and Grant	R
Echinauris irregularis Cooper and Grant	R
Echinauris sp.	VR
Edriosteges multispinosus Muir-Wood and Cooper	VR
Enteletes plummeri R.E. King	A
Goniarina futilis Cooper and Grant	VR
Hercosia uddeni (Böse)	A
Heterelasma angulatum Cooper and Grant	VR
Heterelasma gibbosum Cooper and Grant	VR
Hustedia ampullacea Cooper and Grant	R
Hustedia spicata Cooper and Grant	C
Institella leonardensis (R.E. King)	VA
Meekella calathica Cooper and Grant	A
Metriolepis larina Cooper and Grant	R
Neophricadothyris bullata Cooper and Grant	R
Neospirifer mansuetus Cooper and Grant	VR
Petrocrania sp.	VR
Pseudoleptodus? sp. 6	VR
Reticulariina craticula Cooper and Grant	VR
Rhamnaria tenuispinosa Cooper and Grant	VR
Rhipidomella hispidula Cooper and Grant	A
Rhynchopora hebetata Cooper and Grant	VR
Spiriferellina tricosa Cooper and Grant	VR
Stenoscisma doricranum Cooper and Grant	VR
Texarina wordensis (R.E. King)	VR
Xenosteges adherens Muir-Wood and Cooper	R
Xestosia schucherti (R.E. King)	VR

LOCALITY N714wa : Cathedral Mountain Formation, Wedin Member

Acosarina mesoplatys (R.E. King)	R
Chondronia bella Cooper and Grant	R
Composita sp.	C
Derbyia complicata Cooper and Grant	VR
Stenoscisma sp.	VR

LOCALITY N714y : Skinner Ranch Formation, Sullivan Peak Member

Acosarina dorsisulcata Cooper and Grant	C
Acritosia peculiaris Cooper and Grant	VR
Anteridocus paucicostatus Cooper and Grant	C
Composita sp.	C
Coscinophora monilifera Cooper and Grant	VR
Diplanus lamellatus (R.E. King)	VR
Echinauris sp.	VR
Geyerella hessi Cooper and Grant	C
Hustedia inconspicua Cooper and Grant	C
Meekella hessensis R.E. King	R
Neophricadothyris sp.	R
Oncosarina spinicostata Cooper and Grant	R
Rhipidomella hessensis R.E. King	VR
Tropidelasma rhamphodes Cooper and Grant	VR
Tropidelasma sp. 1	VR

LOCALITY N714z : Skinner Ranch Formation

Scacchinella titan Cooper and Grant	R

LOCALITY N715 : Lenox Hills Formation

Acosarina sp.	VR
Antiquatonia regularis Cooper and Grant	R
Chonetinella sp. 3	VR

Rarity code

Composita sp.	VR
Derbyia profunda Cooper and Grant	VR
Derbyia sp. 3	VR
Echinaria sp. 1	VR
Echinauris interrupta Cooper and Grant	C
Enteletes sp.	VR
Fimbrinia sp. 1	VR
Hustedia trita trita Cooper and Grant	VR
Hystriculina dugoutensis (R.E. King)	R
Kochiproductus sp. 2	VR
Kozlowskia anterosulcata Cooper and Grant	R
Kutorginella uddeni Cooper and Grant	VR
Limbella wolfcampensis (R.E. King)	VR
Neochonetes sp.	VR
Neophricadothyris transversa Cooper and Grant	VR
Neospirifer apothescelus Cooper and Grant	VR
Teguliferina boesei R.E. King	VR
Tropidelasma strobilum Cooper and Grant	VR

LOCALITY N715a : Skinner Ranch Formation, Decie Ranch Member

Antronaria titania Cooper and Grant	VR
Antronaria voluminosa Cooper and Grant	VR
Composita discina Cooper and Grant	VR
Enteletes rotundobesus Cooper and Grant	VR
Limbella limbata Cooper and Grant	VR
Scacchinella titan Cooper and Grant	VR
Spyridiophora reticulata (R.E. King)	VR
Stenoscisma hadrum Cooper and Grant	VR
Stenoscisma problematicum Cooper and Grant	VR

LOCALITY N715b : Lenox Hills Formation

Antiquatonia costella Cooper and Grant	VR
Beecheria sp.	VR
Composita strongyle Cooper and Grant	R
Crurithyris tumibilis Cooper and Grant	R
Derbyia sp.	VR
Echinauris interrupta Cooper and Grant	VR
Hustedia sp.	VR
Hystriculina sp.	VR
Hystriculina ventroplana Cooper and Grant	R
Kutorginella uddeni Cooper and Grant	VR
Limbella wolfcampensis (R.E. King)	R
Linoproductus semisulcatus Cooper and Grant	R
Meekella texana R.E. King	VR
Neochonetes sp.	VR
Neophricadothyris transversa Cooper and Grant	R
Neospirifer apothescelus Cooper and Grant	VR
Nudauris convexa Cooper and Grant	VR
Orthotichia kozlowskii R.E. King	R
Reticulatia huecoensis (R.E. King)	VR
Spyridiophora compacta Cooper and Grant	R
Stenoscisma bellatulum Cooper and Grant	VR
Stenoscisma peneleve Cooper and Grant	R
Stenoscisma sp.	VR
Striatifera linoproductiformis Cooper and Grant	VR
Teguliferina boesei R.E. King	VR

LOCALITY N715c : Skinner Ranch Formation, Decie Ranch Member

Antronaria dissona Cooper and Grant	VR
Composita apheles Cooper and Grant	VR
Enteletes rotundobesus Cooper and Grant	VR
Neophricadothyris catatona Cooper and Grant	VR
Scacchinella titan Cooper and Grant	VR
Stenoscisma pyraustoides Cooper and Grant	VR

LOCALITY N715e : Neal Ranch Formation

	Rarity code
Derbyia profunda Cooper and Grant	VR
Echinaria sp. 1	VR
Eridmatus sp.	VR
Hystriculina convexa Cooper and Grant	VR
Juresania sp. 2	VR
Kozlowskia sp.	VR
Martinia sp.	VR
Meekella magnifica Cooper and Grant	VR
Rhynchopora molina Cooper and Grant	VR
Teguliferina boesei R.E. King	VR

LOCALITY N715f : Skinner Ranch Formation, Sullivan Peak Member

Antronaria titania Cooper and Grant	VR
Antronaria voluminosa Cooper and Grant	VR
Composita apheles Cooper and Grant	VR
Compressoproductus parvus Cooper and Grant	VR
Enteletes sp.	VR
Geyerella hessi Cooper and Grant	C
Glyptosteges intricatus Cooper and Grant	VR
Linoproductus sp.	VR
Oncosarina spinicostata Cooper and Grant	VR
Scacchinella titan Cooper and Grant	R
Spyridiophora reticulata (R.E. King)	VR
Stenoscisma problematicum Cooper and Grant	R

LOCALITY N715h : Skinner Ranch Formation, Sullivan Peak Member

Eolyttonia sp.	VR
Geyerella hessi Cooper and Grant	VR
Scacchinella titan Cooper and Grant	VR

LOCALITY N715i : Word Formation, Appel Ranch Member

Allorhynchus permianum wordense Cooper and Grant	VR
Bothrionia transversa Cooper and Grant	C
Cancrinella distorta Cooper and Grant	VR
Cancrinella subquadrata Cooper and Grant	VR
Cartorhium orbiculatum Cooper and Grant	VR
Cartorhium retusum Cooper and Grant	R
Composita enormis Cooper and Grant	R
Composita parasulcata Cooper and Grant	R
Crurithyris major Cooper and Grant	C
Ctenalosia fixata Cooper and Stehli	A
Ctenalosia sp.	VR
Cyclacantharia kingorum Cooper and Grant	C
Derbyia filosa Cooper and Grant	R
Derbyia pannucia Cooper and Grant	C
Derbyia texta Cooper and Grant	C
Dielasma compactum Cooper and Grant	R
Dielasma sp.	VR
Dielasma zebratum Cooper and Grant	R
Dyoros (*Dyoros*) *extensus* Cooper and Grant	VA
Dyoros (*Tetragonetes*) *quadrangulatus* Cooper and Grant	VA
Echinauris lateralis Muir-Wood and Cooper	VR
Echinauris sp.	C
Eolyttonia progressa Cooper and Grant	C
Glossothyropsis rectangulata Cooper and Grant	C
Grandaurispina crassa Cooper and Grant	C
Grandaurispina rara Cooper and Grant	C
Heteralosia hystricula (Girty)	VR
Heterelasma concavum Cooper and Grant	VR
Hustedia pugilla hebetata Cooper and Grant	A
Kochiproductus sp.	VR

	Rarity code
Leiorhynchoidea scelesta Cooper and Grant	C
Lepidocrania sublamellosa Cooper and Grant	VR
Leurosina lata Cooper and Grant	R
Leurosina marginata Cooper and Grant	VA
Liosotella irregularis Cooper and Grant	A
Meekella skenoides Girty	A
Megousia definita Cooper and Grant	C
Metriolepis pulvinata Cooper and Grant	R
Neophricadothyris conara Cooper and Grant	VR
Paraspiriferina rotundata Cooper and Grant	C
Paucispinifera auriculata Muir-Wood and Cooper	R
Phrenophoria subcarinata Cooper and Grant	C
Plectelasma dubium Cooper and Grant	R
Pseudodielasma globulum Cooper and Grant	C
Pseudodielasma ovatum Cooper and Grant	C
Pseudodielasma sp.	C
Reticulariina cerina Cooper and Grant	C
Rhamnaria kingorum Muir-Wood and Cooper	C
Rhynchopora tenera Cooper and Grant	R
Spiriferella clypeata Cooper and Grant	C
Spiriferella gravis Cooper and Grant	R
Spiriferella sp.	VR
Spiriferellina hilli (Girty)	VR
Spiriferellina paucicostata Cooper and Grant	R
Spiriferinaella scalpata Cooper and Grant	VR
Stenoscisma renode Cooper and Grant	VR
Texarina elongata Cooper and Grant	R
Thamnosia phragmophora Cooper and Grant	R
Thedusia procera Cooper and Grant	VR
Tropidelasma anthicum Cooper and Grant	VR
Waagenoconcha magnifica Cooper and Grant	C
Wellerella girtyi girtyi Cooper and Grant	C
Xenosteges quadratus Cooper and Grant	VR
Yakovlevia indentata Cooper and Grant	C

LOCALITY N715j : Skinner Ranch Formation, Sullivan Peak Member

Acritosia peculiaris Cooper and Grant	VR
Cartorhium zoyei Cooper and Grant	VR
Composita apheles Cooper and Grant	VR
Compressoproductus parvus Cooper and Grant	VR
Coscinophora monilifera Cooper and Grant	VR
Geyerella hessi Cooper and Grant	VR
Scacchinella titan Cooper and Grant	VR
Spyridiophora reticulata (R.E. King)	VR

LOCALITY N715-1 : Lenox Hills Formation

Enteletes sp.	VR

LOCALITY N715m : Skinner Ranch Formation, Sullivan Peak Member

Scacchinella titan Cooper and Grant	VR

LOCALITY N715n : Skinner Ranch Formation

Acritosia peculiaris Cooper and Grant	VR
Antronaria voluminosa Cooper and Grant	VR
Cartorhium zoyei Cooper and Grant	VR
Limbella limbata Cooper and Grant	VR
Meekella hessensis R.E. King	VR
Scacchinella titan Cooper and Grant	VR

LOCALITY N715o : Skinner Ranch Formation, Sullivan Peak Member

Glyptosteges intricatus Cooper and Grant	VR
Lepidospirifer sp.	VR

	Rarity code

LOCALITY N715p : Skinner Ranch Formation, Sullivan Peak Member

Peniculauris sp. 1 .... VR

LOCALITY N715q : Hess Formation

Peniculauris imitata Cooper and Grant............................ VR

LOCALITY N715u : Skinner Ranch Formation, Sullivan Peak Member

Derbyia sp. .... VR
Enteletes sp. .... R
Limbella limbata Cooper and Grant .... VR

LOCALITY N715v : Skinner Ranch Formation, Decie Ranch Member

Acosarina dorsisulcata Cooper and Grant C
Acritosia teguliferoides (R.E. King).............................. VR
Altiplecus glebosus Cooper and Grant............................ VR
Antiquatonia hessensis (R.E. King) .... VR
Antronaria dissona Cooper and Grant............................ R
Antronaria transversa (R.E. King) .... VR
Chonetinella sp. 4 .... VR
Collemataria platys Cooper and Grant............................ VR
Composita sp. .... VR
Crenispirifer angulatus (R.E. King)................................ R
Derbyia crenulata Girty .... VR
Derbyia nasuta Girty .... VR
Derbyia sp. .... VR
Dielasma hessense Cooper and Grant .... VR
Dielasma sp. .... VR
Diplanus lamellatus (R.E. King) .... VR
Elliottella varicostata Cooper and Grant........................ VR
Enteletes stehlii Cooper and Grant .... R
Hustedia catella Cooper and Grant................................ C
Hustedia hessensis R.E. King.. R
Hustedia sp. .... R
Hystriculina pumila Cooper and Grant .... R
Kozlowskia sp. .... R
Lepidocrania sp. .... VR
Meekella hessensis R.E. King.. R
Metriolepis scrupea Cooper and Grant............................ VR
Orthotichia newelli Cooper and Grant .... R
Rhipidomella hessensis R.E. King.................................. R
Scacchinella titan Cooper and Grant .... R
Stenoscisma hadrum Cooper and Grant .... R
Stenoscisma sp. .... VR
Teguliferina conida (Stehli) .... R
Tricoria hirpex Cooper and Grant.................................. VR
Tropidelasma rhamphodes Cooper and Grant .... VR

LOCALITY N715z : Gaptank Formation

Hystriculina sulcata Cooper and Grant............................ R
Kochiproductus primitivus Cooper and Grant.................. VR
Linoproductus sp. .... VR

LOCALITY N716a : Hess Formation

Hustedia sp. .... VR

LOCALITY N716g : Hess Formation

Composita sp. .... VR
Meekella sp. .... VR

LOCALITY N716k : Gaptank Formation

Scacchinella primitiva Cooper and Grant........................ VR

LOCALITY N716n : Hess Formation, Taylor Ranch Member

Acosarina dorsisulcata Cooper and Grant .... VR

	Rarity code

Acosarina sp. .... VR
Acritosia peculiaris Cooper and Grant .... VR
Acritosia solida Cooper and Grant.................................. VR
Antronaria speciosa Cooper and Grant .... R
Antronaria transversa (R.E. King) C
Chonetinella biplicata (R.E. King)................................ VR
Composita apsidata Cooper and Grant .... R
Enteletes subcircularis Cooper and Grant C
Eolyttonia sp. .... R
Hustedia sp. .... VR
Limbella sp. 1 .... R
Linoproductus undatus Cooper and Grant C
Meekella hessensis R.E. King.. VR
Oncosarina sp. .... VR
Oncosarina whitei (R.E. King)...................................... C
Peniculauris imitata Cooper and Grant C
Rhipidomella hessensis R.E. King C
Thamnosia silicica Cooper and Grant .... R
Tschernyschewia inexpectans Cooper and Grant.............. R

LOCALITY N716o : Hess Formation, Taylor Ranch Member

Acosarina dorsisulcata Cooper and Grant .... VR
Acritosia peculiaris Cooper and Grant .... VR
Antronaria speciosa Cooper and Grant .... R
Antronaria transversa (R.E. King) .... VR
Composita sp. .... VR
Compressoproductus concentricus Cooper and Grant...... VR
Dielasma longisulcatum Cooper and Grant...................... VR
Echinauris sp. .... VR
Enteletes subcircularis Cooper and Grant .... R
Eolyttonia sp. .... R
Limbella sp. 1 .... R
Linoproductus undatus Cooper and Grant .... R
Oncosarina whitei (R.E. King)...................................... C
Peniculauris imitata Cooper and Grant C
Rhipidomella hessensis R.E. King .... VR
Rugaria hessensis (R.E. King)...................................... VR
Stenoscisma pyraustoides Cooper and Grant.................... VR
Thamnosia silicica Cooper and Grant .... R
Tschernyschewia inexpectans Cooper and Grant.............. VR

LOCALITY N716p : Skinner Ranch Formation, Decie Ranch Member

Acritosia peculiaris Cooper and Grant .... VR
Antronaria titania Cooper and Grant.............................. VR
Cartorhium zoyei Cooper and Grant................................ VR
Composita apheles Cooper and Grant.............................. VR
Elliottella varicostata Cooper and Grant........................ VR
Eolyttonia sp. .... VR
Kozlowskia kingi Stehli.. VR
Kozlowskia subsphaeroidalis Cooper and Grant .... VR
Limbella limbata Cooper and Grant .... VR
Linoproductus angustus R.E. King .... VR
Martinia sp. .... VR
Neophricadothyris catatona Cooper and Grant .... R
Neophricadothyris sp. .... VR
Rhamnaria grandis Cooper and Grant............................ VR
Scacchinella titan Cooper and Grant .... VR
Stenoscisma pyraustoides Cooper and Grant.................... VR

LOCALITY N716q : Skinner Ranch Formation

Composita discina Cooper and Grant .... VR
Scacchinella titan Cooper and Grant C
Stenoscisma myioides Cooper and Grant .... R

	Rarity code
LOCALITY N716r : Lenox Hills Formation	
Acosarina sp.	VR
Composita discina Cooper and Grant	VR
Enteletes wolfcampensis R.E. King	VR
Gypospirifer anancites Cooper and Grant	VR
Hustedia trita trita Cooper and Grant	R
Hystriculina sulcata Cooper and Grant	VR
Limbella wolfcampensis (R.E. King)	VR
Nudauris convexa Cooper and Grant	VR
Parenteletes superbus Cooper and Grant	VR
Rhipidomella miscella Cooper and Grant	VR
Stenoscisma sp. 2	R
Sulcataria sp. 2	VR
Teguliferina boesei R.E. King	VR

LOCALITY N716t : Skinner Ranch Formation

Derbyia nasuta Girty	VR
Meekella enormis Cooper and Grant	VR
Meekella hessensis R.E. King	VR
Scacchinella titan Cooper and Grant	R

LOCALITY N716v : Word Formation, Appel Ranch Member

Composita enormis Cooper and Grant	R
Cyclacantharia kingorum Cooper and Grant	R
Derbyia pannucia Cooper and Grant	VR
Dielasma zebratum Cooper and Grant	VR
Dyoros (Dyoros) extensus Cooper and Grant	R
Echinosteges tuberculatus (R.E. King)	VR
Eolyttonia progressa Cooper and Grant	R
Hustedia pugilla hebetata Cooper and Grant	VR
Meekella skenoides Girty	VR
Neospirifer amphigyus Cooper and Grant	VR
Paraspiriferina rotundata Cooper and Grant	VR
Paucispinifera quadrata Cooper and Grant	R
Reticulariina cerina Cooper and Grant	R
Reticulariina sp.	VR
Spiriferella propria Cooper and Grant	VR
Stenoscisma renode Cooper and Grant	VR
Xenosteges quadratus Cooper and Grant	VR

LOCALITY N716x : Road Canyon Formation

Acosarina mesoplatys (R.E. King)	C
Anteridocus erugatus Cooper and Grant	C
Cenorhynchia mitigata Cooper and Grant	VR
Chondronia ovalis Cooper and Grant	C
Collemataria sp.	VR
Composita crassa Cooper and Grant	C
Composita sp.	VR
Composita stalagmium Cooper and Grant	VR
Coscinophora magnifica Cooper and Grant	C
Crenispirifer sp.	R
Cyclacantharia paucispinosa Cooper and Grant	C
Derbyia filosa Cooper and Grant	VR
Derbyia laqueata Cooper and Grant	VR
Derbyia texta Cooper and Grant	VR
Dielasma sp.	VR
Dyoros (Tetragonetes) rectangulatus Cooper and Grant	VR
Echinauris parva Cooper and Grant	R
Edriosteges multispinosus Muir-Wood and Cooper	R
Enteletes subnudus Cooper and Grant	R
Hustedia pugilla nasiterna Cooper and Grant	VR
Liosotella costata Cooper and Grant	R
Meekella calathica Cooper and Grant	C
Megousia auriculata Muir-Wood and Cooper	VR

	Rarity code
Metriolepis sp.	VR
Metriolepis ziczac Cooper and Grant	VR
Neophricadothyris crassibecca Cooper and Grant	R
Neospirifer bakeri bakeri R.E. King	R
Neospirifer thescelus Cooper and Grant	VR
Paraspiriferina pulchra Cooper and Grant	VR
Paucispinifera sulcata Cooper and Grant	VR
Pontisia stehlii stehlii Cooper and Grant	R
Reticulariina craticula Cooper and Grant	C
Reticulariina senticosa Cooper and Grant	VR
Reticulariina sp.	C
Rhynchopora hebetata Cooper and Grant	VR
Spinarella paulula Cooper and Grant	VR
Stenoscisma aptatum Cooper and Grant	VR
Stenoscisma camurum Cooper and Grant	VR
Stenoscisma triquetrum Cooper and Grant	R
Xenosteges magnus Cooper and Grant	VR

LOCALITY N716xa : Road Canyon Formation

Cactosteges anomalus Cooper and Grant	R
Collemataria sp.	R
Composita crassa Cooper and Grant	R
Cooperina subcuneata Cooper and Grant	VR
Costispinifera rugatula (Girty)	C
Crurithyris sp.	VR
Cyclacantharia transitoria Cooper and Grant	C
Derbyia cincinnata Cooper and Grant	R
Derbyia laqueata Cooper and Grant	VR
Dielasma zebratum Cooper and Grant	R
Echinauris lateralis Muir-Wood and Cooper	VR
Echinauris sp.	VR
Echinosteges tuberculatus (R.E. King)	VR
Heteralosia hystricula (Girty)	VR
Heterelasma solidum Cooper and Grant	VR
Hustedia consuta Cooper and Grant	C
Hustedia sculptilis Cooper and Grant	R
Liosotella wordensis (R.E. King)	C
Meekella skenoides Girty	C
Neophricadothyris crassibecca Cooper and Grant	C
Neospirifer bakeri bakeri R.E. King	VR
Paraspiriferina sp.	C
Paucispinifera transversa Cooper and Grant	VR
Ptygmactrum depressum Cooper and Grant	VR
Reticulariina senticosa Cooper and Grant	VR
Reticulariina sp.	VR
Rhamnaria kingorum delicata Muir-Wood and Cooper	VR
Texarina elongata Cooper and Grant	VR
Xenosteges trivialis Cooper and Grant	VR
Yakovlevia sulcata Cooper and Grant	VR

LOCALITY N716z : Road Canyon Formation

Composita crassa Cooper and Grant	VR
Edriosteges compactus Cooper and Grant	VR
Neophricadothyris crassibecca Cooper and Grant	VR
Taphrosestria peculiaris Cooper and Grant	VR

LOCALITY N717a : Skinner Ranch Formation, Sullivan Peak Member

Antronaria dissona Cooper and Grant	VR
Compressoproductus parvus Cooper and Grant	VR
Enteletes sp.	VR

LOCALITY N717e : Cathedral Mountain Formation, Wedin Member

Acosarina mesoplatys (R.E. King)	VR
Agelesia triagonalis (R.E. King)	C

	Rarity code

LOCALITY N717e - Continued

Cartorhium coristum Cooper and Grant	VR
Cartorhium latum (R.E. King)	VR
Choanodus irregularis Cooper and Grant	VR
Chondronia bella Cooper and Grant	VR
Chonosteges pulcher Cooper and Grant	C
Collemataria irregularis Cooper and Grant	R
Composita bucculenta Cooper and Grant	VR
Compressoproductus thomasi Cooper and Grant	VR
Derbyia complicata Cooper and Grant	R
Derbyia laqueata Cooper and Grant	VR
Diplanus lamellatus (R.E. King)	C
Dyoros (*Lissosia*) *vagabundus* Cooper and Grant	VR
Echinauris irregularis Cooper and Grant	R
Enteletes plummeri R.E. King	C
Hercosia uddeni (Böse)	R
Hustedia spicata Cooper and Grant	C
Institella leonardensis (R.E. King)	R
Meekella calathica Cooper and Grant	C
Metriolepis larina Cooper and Grant	R
Neophricadothyris bullata Cooper and Grant	VR
Rhamnaria tenuispinosa Cooper and Grant	VR
Rhipidomella hispidula Cooper and Grant	C
Xenosteges adherens Muir-Wood and Cooper	VR

LOCALITY N717g : Cathedral Mountain Formation

Dyoros (*Tetragonetes*) *planus* Cooper and Grant	VR
Echinauris sp.	VR
Megousia umbonata Cooper and Grant	R
Peniculauris subcostata (R.E. King)	R

LOCALITY N717i : Skinner Ranch Formation, Decie Ranch Member

Enteletes rotundobesus Cooper and Grant	VR

LOCALITY N717v : Skinner Ranch Formation

Acosarina dorsisulcata Cooper and Grant	VR

LOCALITY N718d : Word Formation, Willis Ranch Member

Cactosteges anomalus Cooper and Grant	VR
Collemataria elongata Cooper and Grant	VR
Costispinifera costata (R.E. King)	R
Derbyia pannucia Cooper and Grant	VR
Derbyia sp.	VR
Dielasma compactum Cooper and Grant	R
Dyoros (*Lissosia*) *concavus* Cooper and Grant	VR
Echinauris lateralis Muir-Wood and Cooper	VR
Enteletes wordensis R.E. King	VR
Hustedia sp.	R
Meekella skenoides Girty	R
Megousia definita Cooper and Grant	VR
Paraspiriferina setulosa Cooper and Grant	R
Reticulariina senticosa Cooper and Grant	VR
Spiriferellina hilli (Girty)	VR
Wellerella girtyi girtyi Cooper and Grant	VR

LOCALITY N718e : Neal Ranch Formation

Poikilosakos petaloides Cooper and Grant	VR

LOCALITY N718v : Skinner Ranch Formation, Poplar Tank Member

Antronaria voluminosa Cooper and Grant	VR
Diplanus lamellatus (R.E. King)	VR

LOCALITY N718y : Lenox Hills Formation

Composita strongyle Cooper and Grant	R

LOCALITY N718z : Skinner Ranch Formation, Sullivan Peak Member

Chonosteges variabilis Cooper and Grant	VR
Diplanus lamellatus (R.E. King)	VR
Hercosia uddeni (Böse)	VR

LOCALITY N719 : Hueco Formation

Composita cracens Cooper and Grant	VR
Dasysaria undulata Cooper and Grant	C

LOCALITY N719a : Neal Ranch Formation

Reticulatia huecoensis (R.E. King)	VR

LOCALITY N719e : Word Formation

Crurithyris tholiaphor Cooper and Grant	R

LOCALITY N719q : Hess Formation

Antiquatonia hessensis (R.E. King)	VR
Cancrinella sp.	VR
Composita sp.	R
Fimbrinia sp.	VR
Hustedia sp.	VR
Hystriculina sulcata Cooper and Grant	VR
Kochiproductus sp.	VR
Kutorginella sp.	R
Martinia cruenta Cooper and Grant	C
Neospirifer sp.	R
Reticulatia sp.	VR
Rhynchopora sp.	VR
Stenoscisma cf. *bellatulum* Cooper and Grant	R
Stenoscisma aff. *multicostum* Cooper and Grant	VR

LOCALITY N719r : Lenox Hills Formation

Hystriculina ventroplana Cooper and Grant	VR

LOCALITY N719s : Skinner Ranch Formation, Decie Ranch Member

Reticulatia sp.	VR

LOCALITY N719w : Road Canyon Formation

Geyerella inexpectata Cooper and Grant	VR
Neospirifer thescelus Cooper and Grant	VR

LOCALITY N719x : Road Canyon Formation

Acanthocrania densispina Cooper and Grant	VR
Acosarina mesoplatys (R.E. King)	A
Anteridocus erugatus Cooper and Grant	C
Cenorhynchia atmeta Cooper and Grant	R
?*Cenorhynchia mitigata* Cooper and Grant	VR
Cenorhynchia saginata Cooper and Grant	R
Composita crassa Cooper and Grant	VA
Composita stalagmium Cooper and Grant	VA
Crurithyris minutalis Cooper and Grant	C
Cyclacantharia paucispinosa Cooper and Grant	VA
Derbyia cincinnata Cooper and Grant	C
Derbyia complicata Cooper and Grant	VR
Derbyia laqueata Cooper and Grant	C
Dielasma ellipsoideum Cooper and Grant	C
Echinauris irregularis Cooper and Grant	C
Echinauris sp.	VR
Edriosteges multispinosus Muir-Wood and Cooper	C
Elassonia micraria Cooper and Grant	C
Eolyttonia chaotica Cooper and Grant	A
Hercosestria cribrosa Cooper and Grant	VA
Holotricharina sparsa Cooper and Grant	VR
Hustedia connorsi Cooper and Grant	C
Hustedia consuta Cooper and Grant	VR
Hustedia cuneata Cooper and Grant	C

LOCALITY N719x - Continued

	Rarity code
Hustedia narinosa Cooper and Grant	VA
Hustedia pugilla nasiterna Cooper and Grant	VR
Hustedia sp.	R
Kutorginella robusta Cooper and Grant	C
Kutorginella umbonata (Muir-Wood and Cooper)	VR
Meekella calathica Cooper and Grant	A
Megousia auriculata Muir-Wood and Cooper	C
Metriolepis tegulata Cooper and Grant	VR
Neophricadothyris bullata Cooper and Grant	R
Neophricadothyris crassibecca Cooper and Grant	A
Neospirifer bakeri bakeri R.E. King	R
Neospirifer thescelus Cooper and Grant	C
Paucispinifera sulcata Cooper and Grant	C
Peniculauris costata Cooper and Grant	VR
Peniculauris transversa Cooper and Grant	VR
Pontisia stehlii stehlii Cooper and Grant	C
Pontisia stehlii tumidosa Cooper and Grant	R
Reticulariina craticula Cooper and Grant	A
Reticulariina sp.	VR
Reticulariina venustula Cooper and Grant	R
Rhamnaria tenuispinosa Cooper and Grant	C
Rhamnaria vinnula Cooper and Grant	VR
Rhynchopora hebetata Cooper and Grant	VR
Rugatia incurvata (R.E. King)	VR
Spinarella lobata Cooper and Grant	R
Spinarella paulula Cooper and Grant	R
Spiriferellina tricosa Cooper and Grant	R
Stenoscisma calvatum Cooper and Grant	VR
Stenoscisma camurum Cooper and Grant	R
Stenoscisma triquetrum Cooper and Grant	A
Texarina wordensis (R.E. King)	C
Tschernyschewia sp.	VR
Xenosteges magnus Cooper and Grant	C

LOCALITY N719y : Skinner Ranch Formation

	Rarity code
Antiquatonia hessensis (R.E. King)	VR
Antronaria titania Cooper and Grant	VR
Composita apheles Cooper and Grant	VR
Hystriculina pumila Cooper and Grant	R
Kozlowskia subsphaeroidalis Cooper and Grant	R
Nudauris enigmatica Cooper and Grant	VR
Scacchinella titan Cooper and Grant	VR
Stenoscisma problematicum Cooper and Grant	VR

LOCALITY N719z : Word Formation, Appel Ranch Member

	Rarity code
Allorhynchus permianum wordense Cooper and Grant	VR
Bothrionia transversa Cooper and Grant	C
Cancrinella distorta Cooper and Grant	VR
Cancrinella subquadrata Cooper and Grant	VR
Cartorhium chelomatum Cooper and Grant	R
Cartorhium retusum Cooper and Grant	R
Composita enormis Cooper and Grant	C
Composita parasulcata Cooper and Grant	R
Cooperina inexpectata Termier, Termier and Pajaud	VR
Crurithyris major Cooper and Grant	C
Ctenalosia fixata Cooper and Stehli	C
Ctenalosia sp.	R
Cyclacantharia kingorum Cooper and Grant	A
Derbyia filosa Cooper and Grant	VR
Derbyia pannucia Cooper and Grant	R
Derbyia sp.	VR
Derbyia texta Cooper and Grant	C
Dielasma compactum Cooper and Grant	R

	Rarity code
Dielasma zebratum Cooper and Grant	R
Divaricosta vagabunda Cooper and Grant	VR
Dyoros (*Dyoros*) *extensus* Cooper and Grant	A
Dyoros (*Lissosia*) *parvus* Cooper and Grant	R
Dyoros (*Tetragonetes*) *quadrangulatus* Cooper and Grant	C
Echinauris lateralis Muir-Wood and Cooper	VR
Eolyttonia progressa Cooper and Grant	C
Glossothyropsis rectangulata Cooper and Grant	C
Grandaurispina crassa Cooper and Grant	C
Grandaurispina rara Cooper and Grant	C
Grandaurispina sp.	VR
Heteralosia hystricula (Girty)	VR
Heterelasma concavum Cooper and Grant	VR
Heterelasma pentagonum Cooper and Grant	VR
Hustedia pugilla hebetata Cooper and Grant	A
Hustedia sp.	VR
Leiorhynchoidea scelesta Cooper and Grant	A
Leurosina marginata Cooper and Grant	VA
Liosotella irregularis Cooper and Grant	A
Liosotella wordensis (R.E. King)	VR
Meekella skenoides Girty	A
Megousia definita Cooper and Grant	C
Neophricadothyris conara Cooper and Grant	VR
Paraspiriferina rotundata Cooper and Grant	C
Paraspiriferina sp.	VR
Paucispinifera auriculata Muir-Wood and Cooper	R
Paucispinifera sp.	VR
Phrenophoria bicostata Cooper and Grant	C
Phrenophoria subcarinata Cooper and Grant	C
Plectelasma dubium Cooper and Grant	R
Pseudodielasma globulum Cooper and Grant	C
Pseudodielasma ovatum Cooper and Grant	A
Pseudodielasma sp.	A
Pseudoleptodus lepidus Cooper and Grant	VR
Reticulariina cerina Cooper and Grant	C
Reticulariina sp.	VR
Rhamnaria kingorum Muir-Wood and Cooper	C
Rhynchopora tenera Cooper and Grant	VR
Spiriferella clypeata Cooper and Grant	C
Spiriferella propria Cooper and Grant	R
Spiriferellina paucicostata Cooper and Grant	VR
Stenoscisma renode Cooper and Grant	VR
Tautosia transenna Cooper and Grant	VR
Texarina elongata Cooper and Grant	VR
Thamnosia phragmophora Cooper and Grant	VR
Waagenoconcha magnifica Cooper and Grant	R
Wellerella girtyi girtyi Cooper and Grant	C
Xenosteges quadratus Cooper and Grant	R
Yakovlevia indentata Cooper and Grant	C

LOCALITY N720a : Hueco Formation

	Rarity code
Composita cracens Cooper and Grant	R
Dasysaria undulata Cooper and Grant	R

LOCALITY N720b : Hueco Formation

	Rarity code
Chondronia obesa Cooper and Grant	C
Composita cracens Cooper and Grant	C
Crurithyris sp.	VR
Derbyia sp.	R
Hustedia sp.	VR
Kozlowskia sp.	R
Kutorginella sp.	VR
Micraphelia sp.	C
Neophricadothyris sp.	VR
Pontisia franklinensis Cooper and Grant	C
Reticulariina hueconiana Cooper and Grant	VR

Rarity code

LOCALITY N720b - Continued

Stenoscisma sp. 1	R

LOCALITY N720c : Hueco Formation

Composita cracens Cooper and Grant	C
Dasysaria undulata Cooper and Grant	C
Derbyia sp.	R
Dielasma sp.	VR
Kozlowskia sp.	VR
Kutorginella sp.	VR
Nudauris sp.	VR

LOCALITY N720d : Road Canyon Formation

Acanthocrania densispina Cooper and Grant	VR
Acosarina mesoplatys (R.E. King)	A
Altiplecus sp. 2	VR
Bothrostegium derbyoideum Cooper and Grant	C
Cactosteges anomalus Cooper and Grant	R
Cartorhium sp.	VR
Chonetinetes angustisulcatus Cooper and Grant	C
Collemataria sp.	C
Composita crassa Cooper and Grant	C
Composita pilula Cooper and Grant	A
Composita sp.	R
Compressoproductus sp.	VR
Cooperina subcuneata Cooper and Grant	VR
Coscinophora magnifica Cooper and Grant	VR
Cyclacantharia transitoria Cooper and Grant	R
Derbyia cincinnata Cooper and Grant	R
Derbyia laqueata Cooper and Grant	C
Derbyia sp.	R
Dielasma bellulum Cooper and Grant	R
Dielasma sp.	R
Dyoros (*Dyoros*) *angulatus* Cooper and Grant	R
Dyoros (*Dyoros*) *extensiformis* Cooper and Grant	VR
Dyoros (*Dyoros*) *transversus* Cooper and Grant	C
Dyoros (*Lissosia*) *parvus* Cooper and Grant	C
Dyoros (*Tetragonetes*) *rectangulatus* Cooper and Grant	R
Echinauris bella Cooper and Grant	VR
Echinauris lappacea Cooper and Grant	R
Echinauris sp.	C
Echinosteges tuberculatus (R.E. King)	VR
Edriosteges multispinosus Muir-Wood and Cooper	VR
Elassonia micraria Cooper and Grant	VR
Enteletes subnudus Cooper and Grant	A
Geyerella inexpectata Cooper and Grant	C
Goniarina sp.	VR
Goniarina striata Cooper and Grant	C
Heterelasma glansfagea Cooper and Grant	R
Heterelasma sp.	R
Holotricharina sparsa Cooper and Grant	VR
Hustedia consuta Cooper and Grant	A
Leiorhynchoidea sp.	VR
Lepidocrania tardispinosa Cooper and Grant	VR
Lowenstamia sp.	VR
Meekella calathica Cooper and Grant	C
Meekella sp.	R
Megousia auriculata Muir-Wood and Cooper	C
Metriolepis ziczac Cooper and Grant	R
Micraphelia sp.	R
Neophricadothyris crassibecca Cooper and Grant	VR
Neospirifer bakeri bakeri R.E. King	R
Neospirifer formulosus Cooper and Grant	C
Notothyris gillilandensis Cooper and Grant	R
Ombonia invecta Cooper and Grant	C
Paraspiriferina cellulana Cooper and Grant	VR

Rarity code

Paraspiriferina pulchra Cooper and Grant	R
Paucispinifera costellata Cooper and Grant	VR
Paucispinifera sulcata Cooper and Grant	R
Peniculauris costata Cooper and Grant	VR
Petasmaia sp. 1	VR
Petasmatherus nitidus Cooper and Grant	A
Pontisia stehlii stehlii Cooper and Grant	R
Ptygmactrum acutum Cooper and Grant	VR
Rhamnaria sp.	VR
Rhamnaria tenuispinosa Cooper and Grant	C
Rhamnaria vinnula Cooper and Grant	C
Rhynchopora hebetata Cooper and Grant	R
Rhytisia rugosa Cooper and Grant	C
Simplicarina incompta Cooper and Grant	R
Spiriferinaella sp.	VR
Stenoscisma bonum Cooper and Grant	VR
Stenoscisma sp.	VR
Texarina wordensis (R.E. King)	VR
Thedusia mesocostata Cooper and Grant	C
Tropidelasma corniculum Cooper and Grant	A
Waagenoconcha convexa Cooper and Grant	VR
Xenosteges trivialis Cooper and Grant	C

LOCALITY N720e : Skinner Ranch Formation

Acolosia? exasperata Cooper and Grant	VR
Acosarina dorsisulcata Cooper and Grant	SA
Acritosia teguliferoides (R.E. King)	VR
Altiplecus glebosus Cooper and Grant	C
Anomalesia perplexa Cooper and Grant	VR
Antiquatonia hessensis (R.E. King)	R
Antronaria dissona Cooper and Grant	R
Antronaria titania Cooper and Grant	R
Cancrinella sparsispinosa Cooper and Grant	VR
Chonetinella biplicata (R.E. King)	C
Collemataria marshalli (Stehli)	VR
Composita apheles Cooper and Grant	A
Composita discina Cooper and Grant	VR
Crenispirifer angulatus (R.E. King)	VR
Crurithyris sp.	VR
Cyclacantharia gigantea Cooper and Grant	C
Cyclacantharia sp. 1	C
Derbyia crenulata Girty	C
Derbyia nasuta Girty	A
Dielasma hessense Cooper and Grant	VR
Dielasma sp. 1	C
Elliottella varicostata Cooper and Grant	C
Enteletes stehlii Cooper and Grant	C
Eolyttonia cornucopia Cooper and Grant	C
Eolyttonia gigantea Cooper and Grant	C
Fimbrinia ovata Cooper and Grant	R
Goniarina magniextensa Cooper and Grant	VR
Gypospirifer infraplicus (R.E. King)	R
Hercosia uddeni (Böse)	R
Heterelasma sp. 2	VR
Hustedia catella Cooper and Grant	A
Hustedia hessensis R.E. King	C
Isogramma sp.	VR
Kochiproductus sp.	VR
Kozlowskia alata Cooper and Grant	C
Leurosina vulgarica Cooper and Grant	R
Linoproductus angustus R.E. King	VR
Martinia sp. 2	VR
Meekella caperata Cooper and Grant	R
Meekella enormis Cooper and Grant	A
Meekella hessensis R.E. King	VR

Rarity code

LOCALITY N720e - Continued

Metriolepis scrupea Cooper and Grant	R
Neophricadothyris catatona Cooper and Grant	C
Nudauris enigmatica Cooper and Grant	R
Orthotichia newelli Cooper and Grant	A
Pontisia nanas (Stehli)	VR
Reticulariina pusilla Cooper and Grant	VR
Reticulariina tetrica Cooper and Grant	C
Rhipidomella hessensis R.E. King	C
Scacchinella titan Cooper and Grant	VA.
Stenoscisma myioides Cooper and Grant	VR
Stenoscisma pyraustoides Cooper and Grant	R
Stenoscisma sp.	VR
Teguliferina conida (Stehli)	C
Thamnosia parvispinosa (Stehli)	VR
Tricoria hirpex Cooper and Grant	R

LOCALITY N720f : Skinner Ranch Formation

Acritosia peculiaris Cooper and Grant	VR
Chonosteges variabilis Cooper and Grant	VR
Derbyia crenulata Girty	VR
Enteletes stehlii Cooper and Grant	VR
Eolyttonia sp.	VR
Glyptosteges intricatus Cooper and Grant	R
Hustedia catella Cooper and Grant	R
Hustedia hessensis R.E. King	VR
Meekella hessensis R.E. King	R
Pontisia costata Cooper and Grant	VR
Reticulariina pusilla Cooper and Grant	VR
Rhipidomella hessensis R.E. King	C
Stenoscisma hadrum Cooper and Grant	VR

LOCALITY N720g : Skinner Ranch Formation

Acanthocrania alta Cooper and Grant	VR
Acosarina dorsisulcata Cooper and Grant	C
Acritosia peculiaris Cooper and Grant	R
Cartorhium zoyei Cooper and Grant	VR
Chonetinella biplicata (R.E. King)	C
Composita apheles Cooper and Grant	R
Crenispirifer angulatus (R.E. King)	VR
Derbyia crenulata Girty	R
Dielasma sp.	VR
Elliottella varicostata Cooper and Grant	C
Enteletes stehlii Cooper and Grant	R
Eolyttonia sp.	VR
Hustedia hessensis R.E. King	R
Isogramma sp.	VR
Kozlowskia alata Cooper and Grant	R
Leurosina vulgarica Cooper and Grant	VR
Linoproductus angustus R.E. King	VR
Meekella hessensis R.E. King	C
Rhamnaria grandis Cooper and Grant	VR
Rhipidomella hessensis R.E. King	VR
Scacchinella titan Cooper and Grant	R
Stenoscisma problematicum Cooper and Grant	VR
Tricoria hirpex Cooper and Grant	VR

LOCALITY N720j : Skinner Ranch Formation

Cartorhium zoyei Cooper and Grant	VR
Enteletes rotundobesus Cooper and Grant	VR
Stenoscisma hadrum Cooper and Grant	VR

LOCALITY N720z : Lenox Hills Formation

Kutorginella uddeni Cooper and Grant	VR

LOCALITY N721f : Cathedral Mountain Formation

Rhamnaria tenuispinosa Cooper and Grant	VR

Rarity code

LOCALITY N721g : Neal Ranch Formation

Acanthocrania sp.	VR
Atelestegastus marginatus Cooper and Grant	C
Beecheria elliptica Cooper and Grant	VR
Cenorhynchia hebata Cooper and Grant	C
Cleiothyridina rectimarginata Cooper and Grant	VR
Composita strongyle Cooper and Grant	C
Cooperina triangulata Cooper and Grant	A
Crurithyris tumibilis Cooper and Grant	A
Ctenalosia primitiva Cooper and Grant	VR
Derbyia carteri Cooper and Grant	C
Derbyia profunda Cooper and Grant	VR
Diplanus catatonus Cooper and Grant	A
Echinauris interrupta Cooper and Grant	C
Enteletes wolfcampensis R.E. King	A
Eolyttonia fredericksi (R.E. King)	VR
Hustedia trita leptyca Cooper and Grant	A
Hystriculina minima Cooper and Grant	R
Kochiproductus sp. 3	VR
Lepidocrania sparsispinosa Cooper and Grant	R
Meekella prionota Cooper and Grant	C
Neochonetes parvus Cooper and Grant	VR
Neophricadothyris transversa Cooper and Grant	VR
Neospirifer apothescelus Cooper and Grant	VR
Orthotichia kozlowskii R.E. King	C
Pontisia kingi Cooper and Grant	R
Pseudoleptodus conicus Cooper and Grant	C
Reticulariina strigosa Cooper and Grant	R
Reticulatia robusta Cooper and Grant	VR
Rhipidomella miscella Cooper and Grant	C
Rhynchopora molina Cooper and Grant	R
Stenoscisma sp.	R
Striatifera linoproductiformis Cooper and Grant	A
Teguliferina boesei R.E. King	R

LOCALITY N721h : Gaptank Formation, Uddenites Member

Kutorginella uddeni Cooper and Grant	VR

LOCALITY N721i : Gaptank Formation, Uddenites Member

Kutorginella uddeni Cooper and Grant	VR

LOCALITY N721j : Road Canyon Formation

Acanthocrania densispina Cooper and Grant	VR
Acosarina mesoplatys (R.E. King)	A
Allorhynchus sp.	VR
Cactosteges anomalus Cooper and Grant	VR
Cartorhium sp.	VR
Cenorhynchia saginata Cooper and Grant	R
Chondronia ovalis Cooper and Grant	R
Chonetinetes angustisulcatus Cooper and Grant	C
Chonetinetes reversus Cooper and Grant	VR
Collemataria batilliformis Cooper and Grant	VA
Collemataria sp.	C
Composita crassa Cooper and Grant	C
Composita enormis Cooper and Grant	C
Composita sp.	R
Compressoproductus sp. 6	C
Cooperina subcuneata Cooper and Grant	C
Coscinophora magnifica Cooper and Grant	C
Costispinifera rugatula (Girty)	C
Crurithyris minutalis Cooper and Grant	VR
Crurithyris sp.	R
Cyclacantharia transitoria Cooper and Grant	A
Derbyia cincinnata Cooper and Grant	C

	Rarity code
LOCALITY N721j - Continued	
Derbyia laqueata Cooper and Grant	C
Dielasma bellulum Cooper and Grant	R
Dielasma sp.	VR
Dyoros (Dyoros) angulatus Cooper and Grant	C
Dyoros (Dyoros) transversus Cooper and Grant	C
Dyoros (Lissosia) concavus Cooper and Grant	C
Dyoros (Lissosia) parvus Cooper and Grant	R
Echinauris irregularis Cooper and Grant	C
Echinauris lappacea Cooper and Grant	A
Echinauris liumbona Cooper and Grant	VR
Echinauris sp.	C
Echinosteges tuberculatus (R.E. King)	VR
Edriosteges compactus Cooper and Grant	R
Edriosteges multispinosus Muir-Wood and Cooper	C
Enteletes sp.	R
Enteletes subnudus Cooper and Grant	VR
Eolyttonia chaotica Cooper and Grant	VR
?Glossothyropsis superba Cooper and Grant	VR
Goniarina striata Cooper and Grant	R
Heteralosia hystricula (Girty)	C
Heterelasma glansfagea Cooper and Grant	VR
Heterelasma sp.	R
Holotricharina sparsa Cooper and Grant	VR
Hustedia connorsi Cooper and Grant	A
Hustedia pugilla nasiterna Cooper and Grant	R
Hustedia sp.	R
Leiorhynchoidea sp.	R
Lepidocrania tardispinosa Cooper and Grant	VR
Leurosina lata Cooper and Grant	VR
Leurosina sp.	VR
Liosotella costata Cooper and Grant	VR
Liosotella wordensis (R.E. King)	R
Meekella calathica Cooper and Grant	VA
Megousia auriculata Muir-Wood and Cooper	C
Megousia mucronata Cooper and Grant	R
Metriolepis ziczac Cooper and Grant	R
Neophricadothyris crassibecca Cooper and Grant	R
Neospirifer bakeri bakeri R.E. King	R
Neospirifer formulosus Cooper and Grant	VR
Paranorella sp. 5	VR
Paraspiriferina pulchra Cooper and Grant	R
Paucispinifera parasulcata Cooper and Grant	VR
Paucispinifera sp.	R
Paucispinifera sulcata Cooper and Grant	C
Paucispinifera transversa Cooper and Grant	VR
Peniculauris costata Cooper and Grant	VR
Petasmatherus depressus Cooper and Grant	VR
Petasmatherus nitidus Cooper and Grant	A
Petasmatherus pumilus Cooper and Grant	R
Phrenophoria sp. 3	VR
Pontisia stehlii stehlii Cooper and Grant	VR
Ptygmactrum depressum Cooper and Grant	VR
Ptygmactrum extensum Cooper and Grant	VR
Reticulariina sp.	VR
Rhamnaria tenuispinosa Cooper and Grant	VR
Rhamnaria vinnula Cooper and Grant	C
Rhynchopora hebetata Cooper and Grant	R
Rhytisia rugosa Cooper and Grant	C
Simplicarina incompta Cooper and Grant	R
Spiriferellina sp.	VR
Spiriferellina tricosa Cooper and Grant	R
Stenoscisma bonum Cooper and Grant	R
Taphrosestria peculiaris Cooper and Grant	VR
Texarina sp.	VR

	Rarity code
Texarina wordensis (R.E. King)	R
Thedusia mesocostata Cooper and Grant	C
Tropidelasma corniculum Cooper and Grant	C
Undulella matutina Cooper and Grant	R
Waagenoconcha convexa Cooper and Grant	VR
Xenosteges magnus Cooper and Grant	C
Yakovlevia sulcata Cooper and Grant	VR
LOCALITY N721k : Neal Ranch Formation	
Linoproductus meniscus Dunbar and Condra	VR
LOCALITY N721-l : Gaptank Formation, Uddenites Member	
Linoproductus meniscus Dunbar and Condra	VR
LOCALITY N721m : Gaptank Formation, Uddenites Member	
Kochiproductus primitivus Cooper and Grant	VR
LOCALITY N721n : Neal Ranch Formation	
Reticulatia americana (Dunbar and Condra)	VR
LOCALITY N721o : Road Canyon Formation	
Acosarina mesoplatys (R.E. King)	R
Cenorhynchia atmeta Cooper and Grant	C
Cenorhynchia mitigata Cooper and Grant	R
Composita crassa Cooper and Grant	C
Crurithyris minutalis Cooper and Grant	R
Derbyia cincinnata Cooper and Grant	VR
Derbyia informis Cooper and Grant	VR
Dielasma ellipsoideum Cooper and Grant	C
Dielasma sp.	VR
Dyoros (Dyoros) extensiformis Cooper and Grant	VR
Echinauris bella Cooper and Grant	R
Echinauris lappacea Cooper and Grant	R
Edriosteges multispinosus Muir-Wood and Cooper	VR
Elassonia micraria Cooper and Grant	C
Eolyttonia chaotica Cooper and Grant	C
Hercosestria cribrosa Cooper and Grant	C
Heterelasma glansfagea Cooper and Grant	C
Holotricharina hirsuta Cooper and Grant	R
Hustedia connorsi Cooper and Grant	C
Hustedia narinosa Cooper and Grant	C
Hustedia sp.	C
Kutorginella robusta Cooper and Grant	C
Lepidocrania tardispinosa Cooper and Grant	VR
Meekella calathica Cooper and Grant	R
Neophricadothyris bullata Cooper and Grant	VR
Neophricadothyris crassibecca Cooper and Grant	C
Neospirifer thescelus Cooper and Grant	R
Paucispinifera sulcata Cooper and Grant	R
Peniculauris transversa Cooper and Grant	R
Petrocrania sp.	VR
Pontisia stehlii stehlii Cooper and Grant	A
Pontisia stehlii tumidosa Cooper and Grant	VR
Stenoscisma bonum Cooper and Grant	VR
Stenoscisma triquetrum Cooper and Grant	C
Texarina wordensis (R.E. King)	C
Xenosteges magnus Cooper and Grant	C
LOCALITY N721p : Word Formation, China Tank Member	
Cactosteges anomalus Cooper and Grant	VR
Dielasma compactum Cooper and Grant	VR
Dielasma planidorsatum Cooper and Grant	VR
Dyoros (Dyoros) extensus Cooper and Grant	VR
Leiorhynchoidea amygdaloidea Cooper and Grant	VR

	Rarity code
LOCALITY N721r : Road Canyon Formation	
Acosarina mesoplatys (R.E. King)	A
Anemonaria sublaevis (R.E. King)	R
Chonosteges costellatus Cooper and Grant	R
Composita crassa Cooper and Grant	VR
Cyclacantharia transitoria Cooper and Grant	C
Derbyia laqueata Cooper and Grant	VR
Dyoros (Dyoros) extensiformis Cooper and Grant	C
Dyoros (Lissosia) parvus Cooper and Grant	C
Dyoros (Tetragonetes) lateralis Cooper and Grant	VR
Echinauris lappacea Cooper and Grant	C
Echinauris sp.	VR
Edriosteges multispinosus Muir-Wood and Cooper	VR
Holotricharina hirsuta Cooper and Grant	VR
Hustedia consuta Cooper and Grant	R
Kutorginella sullivanensis (R.E. King)	VR
Meekella calathica Cooper and Grant	C
Megousia auriculata Muir-Wood and Cooper	A
Micraphelia? sp.	VR
Neophricadothyris cordata Cooper and Grant	VA
Neophricadothyris crassibecca Cooper and Grant	C
Neospirifer bakeri bakeri R.E. King	C
Neospirifer mansuetus Cooper and Grant	VR
Neospirifer thescelus Cooper and Grant	VR
Peniculauris subcostata (R.E. King)	VR
Phrenophoria? nudumbona Cooper and Grant	VR
Reticulariina venustula Cooper and Grant	VR
Rhamnaria tenuispinosa Cooper and Grant	VR
Rugatia occidentalis parvauris (Newberry)	VR
Rugatia paraindica (McKee)	VR
Spinarella perfecta Cooper and Grant	R
Waagenoconcha convexa Cooper and Grant	R
LOCALITY N721s : Road Canyon Formation	
Acosarina mesoplatys (R.E. King)	C
Cenorhynchia parvula Cooper and Grant	VR
Composita crassa Cooper and Grant	A
Cooperina subcuneata Cooper and Grant	VR
Cyclacantharia paucispinosa Cooper and Grant	R
Derbyia cincinnata Cooper and Grant	C
Dielasma ellipsoideum Cooper and Grant	R
Dyoros (Dyoros) transversus Cooper and Grant	VR
Echinauris irregularis Cooper and Grant	C
Echinauris sp.	R
Edriosteges multispinosus Muir-Wood and Cooper	C
Eolyttonia chaotica Cooper and Grant	C
Hercosestria cribrosa Cooper and Grant	VA
Heterelasma glansfagea Cooper and Grant	VR
Holotricharina hirsuta Cooper and Grant	VR
Hustedia narinosa Cooper and Grant	A
Kutorginella robusta Cooper and Grant	VR
Lepidocrania tardispinosa Cooper and Grant	R
Meekella calathica Cooper and Grant	C
Megousia auriculata Muir-Wood and Cooper	R
Neophricadothyris crassibecca Cooper and Grant	A
Neospirifer thescelus Cooper and Grant	R
Paucispinifera sulcata Cooper and Grant	C
Peniculauris transversa Cooper and Grant	VR
Pontisia stehlii stehlii Cooper and Grant	A
Reticulariina craticula Cooper and Grant	C
Rhynchopora hebetata Cooper and Grant	R
Stenoscisma camurum Cooper and Grant	VR
Stenoscisma triquetrum Cooper and Grant	C
Texarina wordensis (R.E. King)	A
Waagenoconcha convexa Cooper and Grant	VR

	Rarity code
LOCALITY N721t : Road Canyon Formation	
Acosarina mesoplatys (R.E. King)	C
Anteridocus seminudus Cooper and Grant	VR
Bothrostegium derbyoideum Cooper and Grant	R
Cenorhynchia saginata Cooper and Grant	C
Chondronia ovalis Cooper and Grant	A
Composita crassa Cooper and Grant	A
Cooperina subcuneata Cooper and Grant	VR
Coscinophora magnifica Cooper and Grant	A
Cyclacantharia paucispinosa Cooper and Grant	R
Derbyia cincinnata Cooper and Grant	A
Derbyia informis Cooper and Grant	C
Derbyia laqueata Cooper and Grant	R
Derbyia sp.	VR
Echinauris sp.	VR
Edriosteges compactus Cooper and Grant	A
Hercosestria cribrosa Cooper and Grant	C
Heterelasma glansfagea Cooper and Grant	R
Hustedia connorsi Cooper and Grant	R
Hustedia sp.	R
Meekella calathica Cooper and Grant	VA
Megousia auriculata Muir-Wood and Cooper	VR
Neophricadothyris crassibecca Cooper and Grant	R
Neospirifer thescelus Cooper and Grant	R
Paucispinifera sulcata Cooper and Grant	C
Pontisia stehlii stehlii Cooper and Grant	VR
Reticulariina sp.	VR
Reticulariina venustula Cooper and Grant	C
Rhamnaria tenuispinosa Cooper and Grant	VR
Spiriferellina tricosa Cooper and Grant	VR
Stenoscisma bonum Cooper and Grant	VR
Stenoscisma calvatum Cooper and Grant	C
Stenoscisma sp.	R
Taphrosestria peculiaris Cooper and Grant	C
Texarina wordensis (R.E. King)	R
Tropidelasma corniculum Cooper and Grant	VR
LOCALITY N721u : Cathedral Mountain Formation	
Acosarina mesoplatys (R.E. King)	VA
Agelesia triagonalis (R.E. King)	R
Altiplecus sp.	VR
Anemonaria sublaevis (R.E. King)	C
Cancrinella sp.	VR
Cenorhynchia sp.	VR
Cenorhynchia unicostata Cooper and Grant	R
Choanodus anomalus Cooper and Grant	VR
Choanodus irregularis Cooper and Grant	C
Choanodus perfectus Cooper and Grant	VR
Chonosteges pulcher Cooper and Grant	C
Chonosteges variabilis Cooper and Grant	R
Collemataria irregularis Cooper and Grant	C
Composita bucculenta Cooper and Grant	C
Composita imbricata Cooper and Grant	A
Composita sp.	C
Compressoproductus flabellatus Cooper and Grant	C
Compressoproductus sp.	VR
Compressoproductus thomasi Cooper and Grant	R
Cooperina parva Cooper and Grant	VR
Coscinophora nodosa (Cooper and Stehli)	VR
Coscinophora sp.	VR
Crurithyris sp.	R
Crurithyris sp. d	VR
Derbyia cincinnata Cooper and Grant	C
Derbyia complicata Cooper and Grant	R
Derbyia informis Cooper and Grant	C

LOCALITY N721u - Continued	Rarity code
Derbyia laqueata Cooper and Grant	C
Derbyia sp.	R
Dielasma anterolatum Cooper and Grant	VR
Dielasma ellipsoideum Cooper and Grant	VR
Dielasma sp.	R
Diplanus lamellatus (R.E. King)	A
Dyoros (Lissosia) vagabundus Cooper and Grant	C
Dyoros (Tetragonetes) giganteus Cooper and Grant	VR
Dyoros (Tetragonetes) planus Cooper and Grant	R
Echinauris circularis Cooper and Grant	C
Echinauris irregularis Cooper and Grant	SA
Echinauris sp.	VR
Edriosteges multispinosus Muir-Wood and Cooper	R
Edriosteges sp.	VR
Enteletes plummeri R.E. King	A
Enteletes sp.	R
Glyptosteges sulcatus Cooper and Grant	R
Goniarina sp. 5	R
Grandaurispina sp. 7	VR
Hercosestria laevis Cooper and Grant	A
Hercosia uddeni (Böse)	C
Heteralosia sp. 5	VR
Heteralosia sp.	VR
Heteralosia vidriensis Cooper and Grant	C
Heteraria blakemorei Cooper and Grant	R
Heterelasma gibbosum Cooper and Grant	VR
Hustedia compressa Cooper and Grant	R
Hustedia lusca Cooper and Grant	VA
Hustedia sp.	C
Institella leonardensis (R.E. King)	VA
Isogramma cf. *lobatum* Cooper and Grant	R
Kochiproductus sp. 6	VR
Kutorginella umbonata (Muir-Wood and Cooper)	VR
Lepidocrania tardispinosa Cooper and Grant	VR
Lepidospirifer demissus Cooper and Grant	R
Lepidospirifer inferus Cooper and Grant	VR
Linoproductus sp.	R
Meekella calathica Cooper and Grant	VA
Megousia auriculata Muir-Wood and Cooper	VA
Metriolepis larina Cooper and Grant	R
Metriolepis sp.	VR
Metriolepis tegulata Cooper and Grant	R
Neophricadothyris bullata Cooper and Grant	A
Neophricadothyris sp.	C
Neospirifer mansuetus Cooper and Grant	C
Notothyris sp.	VR
Paranorella sp. 4	VR
Peniculauris subcostata (R.E. King)	R
Petrocrania sp.	VR
Phrenophoria anterocostata Cooper and Grant	VR
Phrenophoria vetula Cooper and Grant	R
Pontisia stehlii stehlii Cooper and Grant	VR
Pseudodielasma sp.	VR
Pseudoleptodus cucullatus Cooper and Grant	VR
Pseudoleptodus? sp. 5	VR
Rhamnaria tenuispinosa Cooper and Grant	C
Rhipidomella hispidula Cooper and Grant	A
Rhynchopora hebetata Cooper and Grant	R
Rhytisia rugosa Cooper and Grant	VR
Rugaria hessensis (R.E. King)	VR
Rugatia paraindica (McKee)	R
Scacchinella sp.	VR
Siphonosia alleni Cooper and Grant	C

	Rarity code
Spyridiophora reticulata (R.E. King)	R
Stenoscisma sp.	VR
Stenoscisma triquetrum Cooper and Grant	R
Tautosia pulchra Cooper and Grant	VR
Thamnosia anterospinosa Cooper and Grant	R
Thedusia paucicostata Cooper and Grant	R
Thedusia sp.	R
Torynechus caelatus Cooper and Grant	R
Tropidelasma sp. 4	R
Waagenoconcha convexa Cooper and Grant	C
Xenosteges adherens Muir-Wood and Cooper	C
Xestosia schucherti (R.E. King)	C

LOCALITY N721v : Cathedral Mountain Formation

Megousia umbonata Cooper and Grant	VR

LOCALITY N721w : Road Canyon Formation

Acosarina mesoplatys (R.E. King)	C
Bothrostegium derbyoideum Cooper and Grant	R
Cenorhynchia mitigata Cooper and Grant	VR
Chondronia ovalis Cooper and Grant	C
Composita crassa Cooper and Grant	C
Coscinophora magnifica Cooper and Grant	A
Cyclacantharia transitoria Cooper and Grant	VR
Derbyia laqueata Cooper and Grant	R
Echinauris lappacea Cooper and Grant	R
Edriosteges multispinosus Muir-Wood and Cooper	R
Hustedia sp.	VR
Meekella calathica Cooper and Grant	A
Neospirifer bakeri bakeri R.E. King	VR
Taphrosestria peculiaris Cooper and Grant	C

LOCALITY N721x : Road Canyon Formation

Acosarina mesoplatys (R.E. King)	A
Anteridocus seminudus Cooper and Grant	C
Chonetinetes angustisulcatus Cooper and Grant	VR
Chonosteges costellatus Cooper and Grant	VR
Composita crassa Cooper and Grant	C
Composita quantilla Cooper and Grant	VA
Cooperina subcuneata Cooper and Grant	VR
Crurithyris minutalis Cooper and Grant	VR
Cyclacantharia transitoria Cooper and Grant	C
Derbyia laqueata Cooper and Grant	C
Dielasma expansum Cooper and Grant	VR
Dyoros (Tetragonetes) solidus Cooper and Grant	VR
Echinauris lappacea Cooper and Grant	C
Echinauris sp.	VR
Edriosteges multispinosus Muir-Wood and Cooper	R
Eolyttonia chaotica Cooper and Grant	R
Heteralosia sp.	VR
Hustedia connorsi Cooper and Grant	A
Kochiproductus sp. 6	VR
Liosotella costata Cooper and Grant	R
Meekella calathica Cooper and Grant	A
Megousia auriculata Muir-Wood and Cooper	R
Metriolepis sp.	VR
Neophricadothyris crassibecca Cooper and Grant	C
Neospirifer thescelus Cooper and Grant	C
Paraspiriferina sp.	VR
Peniculauris costata Cooper and Grant	VR
Peniculauris transversa Cooper and Grant	VR
Petasmatherus nitidus Cooper and Grant	A
Reticulariina sp.	C
Rhamnaria tenuispinosa Cooper and Grant	C
Rhynchopora hebetata Cooper and Grant	VR

	Rarity code
LOCALITY N721x - Continued	
Rhytisia rugosa Cooper and Grant	C
Spiriferellina tricosa Cooper and Grant	VR
Stenoscisma calvatum Cooper and Grant	C
Stenoscisma camurum Cooper and Grant	VR
Stenoscisma sp.	VR
Taphrosestria peculiaris Cooper and Grant	R
Texarina wordensis (R.E. King)	R
Thedusia sp.	R
Waagenoconcha convexa Cooper and Grant	VR
Xenosteges magnus Cooper and Grant	R
LOCALITY N721y : Road Canyon Formation	
Acosarina mesoplatys (R.E. King)	A
Anteridocus seminudus Cooper and Grant	R
Bothrostegium derbyoideum Cooper and Grant	C
Composita crassa Cooper and Grant	C
Composita pilula Cooper and Grant	VR
Composita sp.	C
Cyclacantharia paucispinosa Cooper and Grant	R
Cyclacantharia transitoria Cooper and Grant	C
Derbyia cincinnata Cooper and Grant	R
Derbyia complicata Cooper and Grant	VR
Derbyia informis Cooper and Grant	VR
Derbyia laqueata Cooper and Grant	C
Derbyia sp.	R
Dielasma sp.	VR
Echinauris crassa Cooper and Grant	VR
Echinauris irregularis Cooper and Grant	C
Echinauris lappacea Cooper and Grant	VR
Edriosteges compactus Cooper and Grant	R
Edriosteges multispinosus Muir-Wood and Cooper	A
Eolyttonia chaotica Cooper and Grant	C
Hercosestria cribrosa Cooper and Grant	C
Heteralosia sp. 3	VR
Holotricharina hirsuta Cooper and Grant	VR
Hustedia consuta Cooper and Grant	C
Hustedia sp.	VR
Lepidocrania tardispinosa Cooper and Grant	VR
Liosotella costata Cooper and Grant	VR
Meekella calathica Cooper and Grant	C
Meekella sp.	R
Megousia auriculata Muir-Wood and Cooper	VR
Metriolepis ziczac Cooper and Grant	VR
Neophricadothyris sp.	VR
Neospirifer bakeri bakeri R.E. King	VR
Neospirifer thescelus Cooper and Grant	VR
Paucispinifera costellata Cooper and Grant	VR
Paucispinifera sulcata Cooper and Grant	C
Petasmatherus pumilus Cooper and Grant	C
Reticulariina craticula Cooper and Grant	C
Reticulariina sp.	VR
Rhamnaria tenuispinosa Cooper and Grant	VR
Rhytisia rugosa Cooper and Grant	R
Rugatia paraindica (McKee)	VR
Stenoscisma bonum Cooper and Grant	R
Stenoscisma calvatum Cooper and Grant	R
Stenoscisma camurum Cooper and Grant	VR
Taphrosestria expansa Cooper and Grant	VR
Taphrosestria peculiaris Cooper and Grant	A
Tautosia sp.	VR
Texarina wordensis (R.E. King)	R
Xenosteges magnus Cooper and Grant	C
Yakovlevia sulcata Cooper and Grant	VR

	Rarity code
LOCALITY N721z : Road Canyon Formation	
Acanthocrania densispina Cooper and Grant	VR
Acosarina mesoplatys (R.E. King)	A
Chonetinetes angustisulcatus Cooper and Grant	VR
Collemataria batilliformis Cooper and Grant	C
Collemataria sp.	C
Composita crassa Cooper and Grant	C
Cooperina subcuneata Cooper and Grant	VR
Coscinophora magnifica Cooper and Grant	R
Cyclacantharia transitoria Cooper and Grant	C
Derbyia cincinnata Cooper and Grant	R
Dielasma sp.	R
Dyoros (Dyoros) transversus Cooper and Grant	C
Echinauris lappacea Cooper and Grant	R
Echinauris liumbona Cooper and Grant	C
Echinauris sp.	VR
Edriosteges multispinosus Muir-Wood and Cooper	R
Enteletes subnudus Cooper and Grant	R
Goniarina striata Cooper and Grant	R
Heteralosia hystricula (Girty)	VR
Hustedia ampullacea Cooper and Grant	VR
Hustedia connorsi Cooper and Grant	C
Lepidocrania tardispinosa Cooper and Grant	R
Meekella calathica Cooper and Grant	C
Megousia auriculata Muir-Wood and Cooper	R
Metriolepis ziczac Cooper and Grant	R
Neophricadothyris cordata Cooper and Grant	R
Neospirifer formulosus Cooper and Grant	R
Paraspiriferina pulchra Cooper and Grant	VR
Paucispinifera sulcata Cooper and Grant	C
Petasmatherus nitidus Cooper and Grant	C
Petasmatherus pumilus Cooper and Grant	VR
Rhamnaria tenuispinosa Cooper and Grant	C
Rhamnaria vinnula Cooper and Grant	C
Rhytisia rugosa Cooper and Grant	C
Simplicarina incompta Cooper and Grant	VR
Stenoscisma camurum Cooper and Grant	VR
Texarina wordensis (R.E. King)	R
Thedusia mesocostata Cooper and Grant	R
Tropidelasma corniculum Cooper and Grant	C
Xenosteges trivialis Cooper and Grant	C
LOCALITY N722a : Phosphoria Formation	
Echinauris magna Cooper and Grant	VR
LOCALITY N722b : Phosphoria Formation	
Echinauris magna Cooper and Grant	VR
LOCALITY N722c : Park City Formation	
Echinauris magna Cooper and Grant	C
LOCALITY N722d : Phosphoria Formation	
Echinauris magna Cooper and Grant	VR
LOCALITY N722e : Road Canyon Formation	
Acanthocrania densispina Cooper and Grant	VR
Acosarina mesoplatys (R.E. King)	VA
Bothrostegium pusillum Cooper and Grant	C
Chonetinetes angustisulcatus Cooper and Grant	R
Collemataria batilliformis Cooper and Grant	R
Collemataria sp.	C
Composita crassa Cooper and Grant	C
Cooperina subcuneata Cooper and Grant	R
Coscinophora magnifica Cooper and Grant	VR
Cyclacantharia transitoria Cooper and Grant	C
Derbyia cincinnata Cooper and Grant	C
Dielasma bellulum Cooper and Grant	R

	Rarity code
LOCALITY N722e - Continued	
Dielasma labiatum Cooper and Grant	VR
Dyoros (Dyoros) transversus Cooper and Grant	R
Echinauris lappacea Cooper and Grant	A
Echinauris sp.	R
Edriosteges compactus Cooper and Grant	R
Heteralosia vidriensis Cooper and Grant	VR
Hustedia connorsi Cooper and Grant	A
Lepidocrania tardispinosa Cooper and Grant	R
Meekella calathica Cooper and Grant	A
Megousia auriculata Muir-Wood and Cooper	R
Metriolepis ziczac Cooper and Grant	R
Neophricadothyris crassibecca Cooper and Grant	R
Paraspiriferina cellulana Cooper and Grant	R
Paucispinifera sulcata Cooper and Grant	R
Peniculauris costata Cooper and Grant	VR
Petasmatherus pumilus Cooper and Grant	R
Pseudodielasma sp.	VR
Rhamnaria vinnula Cooper and Grant	C
Rhynchopora sphenoides Cooper and Grant	VR
Rhytisia rugosa Cooper and Grant	C
Simplicarina incompta Cooper and Grant	VR
Stenoscisma bonum Cooper and Grant	VR
Texarina sp.	VR
Waagenoconcha convexa Cooper and Grant	VR
Xenosteges trivialis Cooper and Grant	C
Yakovlevia sulcata Cooper and Grant	VR
LOCALITY N722f : Road Canyon Formation	
Acosarina mesoplatys (R.E. King)	C
Anteridocus seminudus Cooper and Grant	C
Chondronia ovalis Cooper and Grant	C
Cleiothyridina nana Cooper and Grant	R
Composita crassa Cooper and Grant	VR
Composita sp.	C
Derbyia laqueata Cooper and Grant	C
Echinauris? sp.	VR
Edriosteges compactus Cooper and Grant	R
Hustedia sp.	VR
Meekella calathica Cooper and Grant	C
Metriolepis ziczac Cooper and Grant	VR
Taphrosestria peculiaris Cooper and Grant	C
LOCALITY N722g : Road Canyon Formation	
Acosarina mesoplatys (R.E. King)	C
Composita crassa Cooper and Grant	C
Derbyia cincinnata Cooper and Grant	VR
Dielasma ellipsoideum Cooper and Grant	VR
Dyoros (Dyoros) angulatus Cooper and Grant	C
Dyoros (Dyoros) transversus Cooper and Grant	VR
Dyoros (Lissosia) parvus Cooper and Grant	C
Echinauris bella Cooper and Grant	C
Heterelasma glansfagea Cooper and Grant	C
Hustedia consuta Cooper and Grant	VA
Hustedia cuneata Cooper and Grant	C
Hustedia sp.	R
Liosotella costata Cooper and Grant	R
Meekella calathica Cooper and Grant	VR
Megousia auriculata Muir-Wood and Cooper	C
Neophricadothyris sp.	VR
Neospirifer bakeri bakeri R.E. King	C
Paucispinifera sp.	VR
Petasmatherus pumilus Cooper and Grant	VR
Phrenophoria sp.	VR

	Rarity code
Reticulariina sp.	R
Rhynchopora hebetata Cooper and Grant	VR
Rhynchopora sphenoides Cooper and Grant	R
Stenoscisma bonum Cooper and Grant	R
Stenoscisma camurum Cooper and Grant	R
Tautosia galbina Cooper and Grant	R
Yakovlevia sulcata Cooper and Grant	C
LOCALITY N722h : Skinner Ranch Formation, Sullivan Peak Member	
Acosarina dorsisulcata Cooper and Grant	C
Acosarina sp.	VR
Acritosia peculiaris Cooper and Grant	C
Cartorhium zoyei Cooper and Grant	VR
Chonosteges variabilis Cooper and Grant	R
Cleiothyridina sp.	VR
Composita apheles Cooper and Grant	R
Composita bucculenta Cooper and Grant	VR
Composita sp.	VR
Derbyia crenulata Girty	R
Dielasma sp.	VR
Diplanus lamellatus (R.E. King)	R
Echinauris sp.	R
Enteletes sp.	R
Eolyttonia sp.	R
Glyptosteges angustus (R.E. King)	C
Glyptosteges intricatus Cooper and Grant	R
Hustedia cepacea Cooper and Grant	R
Hustedia sp.	R
Limbella sp.	VR
Meekella hessensis R.E. King	C
Meekella sp.	R
Neophricadothyris sp.	R
Peniculauris sp. 1	VR
Phrenophoria sp. 1	VR
Reticulariina sp.	R
Rhipidomella hessensis R.E. King	VR
Spyridiophora reticulata (R.E. King)	R
Stenoscisma hadrum Cooper and Grant	VR
LOCALITY N722j : Skinner Ranch Formation, Sullivan Peak Member	
Echinauris sp.	R
Spyridiophora reticulata (R.E. King)	VR
LOCALITY N722k : Skinner Ranch Formation, Sullivan Peak Member	
Limbella limbata Cooper and Grant	VR
LOCALITY N722-l : Skinner Ranch Formation, Sullivan Peak Member	
Acosarina dorsisulcata Cooper and Grant	A
Acosarina sp.	VR
Acritosia peculiaris Cooper and Grant	R
Antronaria voluminosa Cooper and Grant	R
Cartorhium zoyei Cooper and Grant	VR
Chonosteges variabilis Cooper and Grant	C
Collemataria platys Cooper and Grant	VR
Composita apheles Cooper and Grant	C
Compressoproductus parvus Cooper and Grant	VR
Coscinophora monilifera Cooper and Grant	VR
Crurithyris sp. b	VR
Derbyia crenulata Girty	VR
Derbyia nasuta Girty	R
Derbyia sp.	R

LOCALITY N722-l - Continued

	Rarity code
Dielasma sp.	VR
Diplanus lamellatus (R.E. King)	C
Dyoros (Dyoros) consanguineus (Girty)	VR
Echinauris sp.	C
Enteletes subcircularis Cooper and Grant	C
Eolyttonia sp.	R
Geyerella hessi Cooper and Grant	VR
Glyptosteges angustus (R.E. King)	C
Glyptosteges intricatus Cooper and Grant	R
Goniarina sp. 3	R
Heteralosia sp. 7	VR
Hustedia cepacea Cooper and Grant	A
Isogramma sp.	VR
Kochiproductus sp. 5?	R
Kochiproductus sp.	VR
Lepidospirifer sp.	VR
Limbella limbata Cooper and Grant	C
Linoproductus angustus R.E. King	VR
Meekella hessensis R.E. King	A
Meekella sp.	VR
Metriolepis scrupea Cooper and Grant	VR
Metriolepis sp.	VR
Micraphelia sp.	VR
Neophricadothyris sp.	C
Oncosarina sp.	C
Paraspiriferina sp.	VR
Peniculauris sp. 1	R
Phrenophoria repugnans Cooper and Grant	VR
Plectelasma kingi Cooper and Grant	VR
Pontisia nanas (Stehli)	R
Pseudodielasma sp.	R
Reticulariina impressa Cooper and Grant	C
Reticulariina sp.	C
Rhamnaria grandis Cooper and Grant	VR
Rhipidomella hessensis R.E. King	R
Rugaria crassa Cooper and Grant	VR
Sceletonia crassa Cooper and Grant	R
Spyridiophora reticulata (R.E. King)	C
Stenoscisma sp.	VR

LOCALITY N722m : Skinner Ranch Formation

Acritosia peculiaris Cooper and Grant	VR
Antronaria dissona Cooper and Grant	VR
Antronaria voluminosa Cooper and Grant	VR
Cartorhium zoyei Cooper and Grant	VR
Compressoproductus parvus Cooper and Grant	VR
Cyclacantharia gigantea Cooper and Grant	VR
Geyerella hessi Cooper and Grant	VR
Glyptosteges angustus (R.E. King)	VR
Glyptosteges intricatus Cooper and Grant	VR
Limbella limbata Cooper and Grant	VR
Martinia sp.	R
Peniculauris sp. 1	VR
Spyridiophora reticulata (R.E. King)	VR
Stenoscisma hadrum Cooper and Grant	R

LOCALITY N722o : Skinner Ranch Formation

Geyerella hessi Cooper and Grant	VR
Scacchinella titan Cooper and Grant	VR

LOCALITY N722p : Hess Formation

Antronaria speciosa Cooper and Grant	VR
Antronaria transversa (R.E. King)	VR
Dielasma longisulcatum Cooper and Grant	VR
Enteletes subcircularis Cooper and Grant	VR

	Rarity code
Limbella sp.	VR
Linoproductus undatus Cooper and Grant	R
Oncosarina whitei (R.E. King)	C
Peniculauris imitata Cooper and Grant	R
Thamnosia silicica Cooper and Grant	VR

LOCALITY N722t : Word Formation, Appel Ranch Member

Acanthocrania intermedia Cooper and Grant	VR
Allorhynchus permianum wordense Cooper and Grant	R
Bothrionia transversa Cooper and Grant	R
Cartorhium retusum Cooper and Grant	VR
Composita enormis Cooper and Grant	C
Composita parasulcata Cooper and Grant	C
Cooperina inexpectata Termier, Termier and Pajaud	R
Crurithyris major Cooper and Grant	VR
Ctenalosia fixata Cooper and Stehli	A
Ctenalosia sp.	R
Cyclacantharia kingorum Cooper and Grant	C
Derbyia filosa Cooper and Grant	C
Derbyia pannucia Cooper and Grant	R
Dielasma adamanteum Cooper and Grant	R
Dielasma sp.	R
Dielasma zebratum Cooper and Grant	R
Dyoros (Dyoros) extensus Cooper and Grant	VA
Dyoros (Tetragonetes) quadrangulatus Cooper and Grant	A
Eolyttonia progressa Cooper and Grant	C
Glossothyropsis rectangulata Cooper and Grant	C
Grandaurispina crassa Cooper and Grant	R
Grandaurispina rara Cooper and Grant	C
Heteralosia sp.	VR
Hustedia pugilla hebetata Cooper and Grant	A
Leiorhynchoidea scelesta Cooper and Grant	R
Lepidocrania sublamellosa Cooper and Grant	R
Leurosina marginata Cooper and Grant	VA
Liosotella irregularis Cooper and Grant	A
Meekella skenoides Girty	A
Megousia definita Cooper and Grant	R
Neophricadothyris conara Cooper and Grant	VR
Paraspiriferina rotundata Cooper and Grant	C
Paucispinifera auriculata Muir-Wood and Cooper	VR
Petrocrania sp.	VR
Plectelasma dubium Cooper and Grant	VR
Pseudodielasma ovatum Cooper and Grant	VR
Pseudodielasma sp.	A
Reticulariina cerina Cooper and Grant	C
Rhamnaria kingorum Muir-Wood and Cooper	C
Rhynchopora tenera Cooper and Grant	VR
Spiriferella clypeata Cooper and Grant	C
Spiriferellina hilli (Girty)	VR
Texarina elongata Cooper and Grant	R
Thedusia procera Cooper and Grant	R
Tropidelasma anthicum Cooper and Grant	VR
Waagenoconcha magnifica Cooper and Grant	R
Wellerella girtyi girtyi Cooper and Grant	C
Xenosteges quadratus Cooper and Grant	R
Yakovlevia indentata Cooper and Grant	R

LOCALITY N722v : Road Canyon Formation

Acosarina mesoplatys (R.E. King)	VR
Collemataria batilliformis Cooper and Grant	C
Composita sp.	VR
Compressoproductus acuminatus Cooper and Grant	A
Cooperina subcuneata Cooper and Grant	R
Derbyia laqueata Cooper and Grant	R
Echinauris lappacea Cooper and Grant	R

	Rarity code
LOCALITY N722v - Continued	
Edriosteges multispinosus Muir-Wood and Cooper	VR
Hustedia consuta Cooper and Grant	VR
Meekella calathica Cooper and Grant	R
LOCALITY N722w : Neal Ranch Formation	
Geyerella kingorum Cooper and Grant	R
Pontisia magnicostata Cooper and Grant	VR
LOCALITY N722x : Neal Ranch Formation	
Enteletes wolfcampensis R.E. King	VR
Eolyttonia phialiforma Cooper and Grant	R
Neospirifer apothescelus Cooper and Grant	VR
LOCALITY N723a : Road Canyon Formation	
Acosarina mesoplatys (R.E. King)	R
Composita crassa Cooper and Grant	A
Crurithyris minutalis Cooper and Grant	C
Dyoros (*Dyoros*) *transversus* Cooper and Grant	R
Elassonia micraria Cooper and Grant	C
Hustedia connorsi Cooper and Grant	VR
Hustedia consuta Cooper and Grant	C
Meekella calathica Cooper and Grant	R
Neospirifer formulosus Cooper and Grant	R
Petasmatherus nitidus Cooper and Grant	C
Texarina wordensis (R.E. King)	VR
Thedusia mesocostata Cooper and Grant	R
Xenosteges magnus Cooper and Grant	VR
LOCALITY N723b : Hess Formation	
Antronaria titania Cooper and Grant	VR
LOCALITY N723d : Lenox Hills Formation	
Neophricadothyris transversa Cooper and Grant	VR
LOCALITY N723e : Skinner Ranch Formation, Sullivan Peak Member	
Eolyttonia gigantea Cooper and Grant	VR
LOCALITY N723h : Skinner Ranch Formation	
Glyptosteges intricatus Cooper and Grant	R
Meekella hessensis R.E. King	VR
Oncosarina spinicostata Cooper and Grant	VR
Spyridiophora reticulata (R.E. King)	VR
Stenoscisma hadrum Cooper and Grant	VR
Torynechus alectorius Cooper and Grant	VR
LOCALITY N723k : Cathedral Mountain Formation	
Chonosteges costellatus Cooper and Grant	VR
Compressoproductus sp.	VR
Cyclacantharia sp.	VR
Derbyia sp.	VR
Dyoros (*Lissosia*) *vagabundus* Cooper and Grant	VR
Echinauris irregularis Cooper and Grant	R
Enteletes sp.	VR
Eolyttonia sp.	VR
Glyptosteges intricatus Cooper and Grant	R
Hercosia uddeni (Böse)	VR
Hustedia lusca Cooper and Grant	R
Kochiproductus sp.	VR
Meekella calathica Cooper and Grant	R
Megousia umbonata Cooper and Grant	VR
Metriolepis tegulata Cooper and Grant	VR
Peniculauris subcostata (R.E. King)	VR
Thedusia bucrenata Cooper and Grant	VR
Xenosteges adherens Muir-Wood and Cooper	VR

	Rarity code
LOCALITY N723-1 : Skinner Ranch Formation	
Acritosia peculiaris Cooper and Grant	C
Altiplecus sp. 1	VR
Antronaria dissona Cooper and Grant	R
Antronaria voluminosa Cooper and Grant	R
Chonosteges variabilis Cooper and Grant	R
Composita apheles Cooper and Grant	VR
Compressoproductus parvus Cooper and Grant	R
Dielasma hessense Cooper and Grant	VR
Enteletes rotundobesus Cooper and Grant	R
Enteletes sp.	C
Glyptosteges intricatus Cooper and Grant	R
Hustedia hessensis R.E. King	R
Limbella limbata Cooper and Grant	C
Meekella hessensis R.E. King	C
Meekella sp.	VR
Neophricadothyris sp.	VR
Nudauris enigmatica Cooper and Grant	VR
Oncosarina spinicostata Cooper and Grant	R
Rhipidomella hessensis R.E. King	R
Rhipidomella sp.	VR
Spyridiophora reticulata (R.E. King)	R
Stenoscisma hadrum Cooper and Grant	R
Teguliferina compacta Cooper and Grant	VR
Tropidelasma sp. 3	R
LOCALITY N723n : Cathedral Mountain Formation	
Agelesia triagonalis (R.E. King)	VR
Institella leonardensis (R.E. King)	VR
LOCALITY N723o : Skinner Ranch Formation	
Acosarina dorsisulcata Cooper and Grant	R
Antronaria dissona Cooper and Grant	VR
Antronaria voluminosa Cooper and Grant	VR
Composita sp.	C
Crurithyris sp.	R
Derbyia laqueata Cooper and Grant	VR
Enteletes sp.	VR
Glyptosteges intricatus Cooper and Grant	VR
Hustedia catella Cooper and Grant	R
Meekella hessensis R.E. King	R
Neophricadothyris sp.	R
Plectelasma kingi Cooper and Grant	VR
Reticulariina sp.	VR
Rhipidomella hessensis R.E. King	R
Spyridiophora reticulata (R.E. King)	VR
Stenoscisma sp.	VR
LOCALITY N723p : Cathedral Mountain Formation	
Anemonaria sublaevis (R.E. King)	VR
Derbyia informis Cooper and Grant	VR
Dyoros (*Tetragonetes*) *lateralis* Cooper and Grant	VR
Dyoros (*Tetragonetes*) *planus* Cooper and Grant	R
Echinauris irregularis Cooper and Grant	VR
Peniculauris subcostata (R.E. King)	R
LOCALITY N723q : Skinner Ranch Formation	
Glyptosteges angustus (R.E. King)	VR
LOCALITY N723r : Lenox Hills Formation	
Teguliferina boesei R.E. King	VR
LOCALITY N723s : Skinner Ranch Formation	
Acritosia peculiaris Cooper and Grant	VR
Antronaria dissona Cooper and Grant	VR
Antronaria titania Cooper and Grant	VR
Chonosteges limbatus Cooper and Grant	VR

	Rarity code
LOCALITY N723s - Continued	
Composita apheles Cooper and Grant	VR
Derbyia nasuta Girty	VR
Enteletes leonardensis R.E. King	VR
Limbella limbata Cooper and Grant	VR
Stenoscisma hadrum Cooper and Grant	VR
LOCALITY N723t : Word Formation, Willis Ranch Member	
Acanthocrania intermedia Cooper and Grant	VR
Cartorhium chelomatum Cooper and Grant	R
Collemataria elongata Cooper and Grant	A
Composita parasulcata Cooper and Grant	C
Cooperina inexpectata Termier, Termier and Pajaud	R
Cyclacantharia kingorum Cooper and Grant	A
Derbyia filosa Cooper and Grant	C
Derbyia pannucia Cooper and Grant	A
Dielasma compactum Cooper and Grant	C
Dielasma sp.	VR
Dielasma zebratum Cooper and Grant	VR
Dyoros (Dyoros) extensus Cooper and Grant	A
Dyoros (Lissosia) concavus Cooper and Grant	C
Dyoros (Tetragonetes) wordensis Cooper and Grant	VR
Echinauris lateralis Muir-Wood and Cooper	A
Echinosteges tuberculatus (R.E. King)	C
Grandaurispina kingorum Muir-Wood and Cooper	C
Heteralosia hystricula (Girty)	R
Heterelasma concavum Cooper and Grant	R
Hustedia pugilla pugilla Cooper and Grant	A
Hustedia sculptilis Cooper and Grant	R
Hustedia sp.	R
Leurosina lata Cooper and Grant	R
Liosotella wordensis (R.E. King)	A
Meekella skenoides Girty	A
Metriolepis pulvinata Cooper and Grant	VR
Paraspiriferina laqueata Cooper and Grant	C
Paraspiriferina rotundata Cooper and Grant	VR
Paucispinifera magnispina Cooper and Grant	C
Paucispinifera transversa Cooper and Grant	C
Pseudodielasma gibberum Cooper and Grant	C
Pseudodielasma sp.	C
Reticulariina senticosa Cooper and Grant	R
Rhamnaria kingorum Muir-Wood and Cooper	C
Rhynchopora palumbula Cooper and Grant	R
Spiriferella gravis Cooper and Grant	R
Spiriferellina hilli (Girty)	A
Texarina elongata Cooper and Grant	R
Tropidelasma anthicum Cooper and Grant	VR
Waagenoconcha magnifica Cooper and Grant	VR
Wellerella girtyi girtyi Cooper and Grant	C
Xenosteges quadratus Cooper and Grant	VR
Yakovlevia hessorum Cooper and Grant	VR
LOCALITY N723u : Cathedral Mountain Formation	
Agelesia triagonalis (R.E. King)	VA
Cartorhium coristum Cooper and Grant	VR
Chonosteges pulcher Cooper and Grant	C
Chonosteges variabilis Cooper and Grant	VR
Collemataria irregularis Cooper and Grant	R
Cooperina parva Cooper and Grant	R
Derbyia complicata Cooper and Grant	C
Derbyia laqueata Cooper and Grant	VR
Diplanus lamellatus (R.E. King)	VR
Echinauris crassa Cooper and Grant	VR
Echinauris irregularis Cooper and Grant	C
Edriosteges multispinosus Muir-Wood and Cooper	VR

	Rarity code
Enteletes leonardensis R.E. King	C
Hercosia uddeni (Böse)	C
Hustedia lusca Cooper and Grant	R
Hustedia spicata Cooper and Grant	R
Institella leonardensis (R.E. King)	VR
Meekella calathica Cooper and Grant	R
Neospirifer mansuetus Cooper and Grant	VR
Rhipidomella hispidula Cooper and Grant	R
Stenoscisma sp.	VR
LOCALITY N723v : Cathedral Mountain Formation, Wedin Member	
Agelesia triagonalis (R.E. King)	VA
Cartorhium coristum Cooper and Grant	R
Choanodus irregularis Cooper and Grant	VR
Chonosteges pulcher Cooper and Grant	C
Collemataria irregularis Cooper and Grant	R
Composita bucculenta Cooper and Grant	VR
Compressoproductus thomasi Cooper and Grant	R
Cooperina parva Cooper and Grant	R
Derbyia complicata Cooper and Grant	VR
Diplanus lamellatus (R.E. King)	R
Echinauris crassa Cooper and Grant	VR
Echinauris irregularis Cooper and Grant	VR
Enteletes plummeri R.E. King	C
Hercosia uddeni (Böse)	C
Heterelasma angulatum Cooper and Grant	VR
Hustedia ampullacea Cooper and Grant	VR
Institella leonardensis (R.E. King)	C
Meekella calathica Cooper and Grant	C
Neophricadothyris bullata Cooper and Grant	VR
Pseudoleptodus sp.	VR
Reticulariina craticula Cooper and Grant	VR
Rhipidomella hispidula Cooper and Grant	C
Xenosteges adherens Muir-Wood and Cooper	VR
LOCALITY N723w : Word Formation, Willis Ranch Member	
Allorhynchus sp.	VR
Cactosteges anomalus Cooper and Grant	VR
Collemataria sp.	R
Composita parasulcata Cooper and Grant	VR
Composita sp.	VR
Cooperina inexpectata Termier, Termier and Pajaud	VR
Costispinifera costata (R.E. King)	C
Crurithyris tholiaphor Cooper and Grant	VR
Cyclacantharia kingorum Cooper and Grant	C
Derbyia filosa Cooper and Grant	VR
Dielasma sp.	VR
Dyoros (Lissosia) concavus Cooper and Grant	C
Echinauris sp.	VR
Echinosteges tuberculatus (R.E. King)	VR
Enteletes wordensis R.E. King	VR
Grandaurispina kingorum Muir-Wood and Cooper	R
Heteralosia hystricula (Girty)	R
Hustedia pugilla nasiterna Cooper and Grant	VR
Liosotella parva Cooper and Grant	C
Liosotella wordensis (R.E. King)	C
Meekella calathica Cooper and Grant	R
Megousia definita Cooper and Grant	R
Metriolepis pulvinata Cooper and Grant	VR
Paraspiriferina sp.	VR
Paucispinifera rectangulata Cooper and Grant	VR
Paucispinifera sp.	R
Pontisia stehlii stehlii Cooper and Grant	VR
Reticulariina sp.	R

	Rarity code
LOCALITY N723w - Continued	
Rhamnaria sp.	R
Rhamnaria vinnula Cooper and Grant	VR
Rhynchopora palumbula Cooper and Grant	VR
Spiriferinaella limata Cooper and Grant	VR
Stenoscisma sp.	VR
LOCALITY N723x : Road Canyon Formation	
Crurithyris sp.	VR
Cyclacantharia transitoria Cooper and Grant	VR
Derbyia laqueata Cooper and Grant	R
Dielasma sp.	VR
Dyoros (Dyoros) angulatus Cooper and Grant	VR
Dyoros (Dyoros) transversus Cooper and Grant	R
Echinauris lappacea Cooper and Grant	R
Edriosteges compactus Cooper and Grant	VR
Hercosestria cribrosa Cooper and Grant	VR
Hustedia sp.	C
Liosotella costata Cooper and Grant	R
Meekella sp.	R
Megousia auriculata Muir-Wood and Cooper	R
Metriolepis ziczac Cooper and Grant	VR
Neospirifer bakeri bakeri R.E. King	R
Paucispinifera sp.	VR
Paucispinifera sulcata Cooper and Grant	VR
Reticulariina sp.	R
Rhamnaria tenuispinosa Cooper and Grant	VR
Rhytisia rugosa Cooper and Grant	R
Rugatia paraindica (McKee)	VR
Spinarella lobata Cooper and Grant	VR
Stenoscisma sp.	VR
Taphrosestria peculiaris Cooper and Grant	R
Yakovlevia sulcata Cooper and Grant	VR
LOCALITY N723y : Cathedral Mountain Formation	
Chonosteges variabilis Cooper and Grant	VR
Dyoros (Tetragonetes) giganteus Cooper and Grant	VR
Hercosia uddeni (Böse)	VR
Institella leonardensis (R.E. King)	VR
Lepidospirifer angulatus Cooper and Grant	VR
Meekella calathica Cooper and Grant	VR
Nudauris linospina Cooper and Grant	VR
Stenoscisma triquetrum Cooper and Grant	VR
LOCALITY N724a : Road Canyon Formation	
Acosarina mesoplatys (R.E. King)	C
Acritosia? vestibula Cooper and Grant	VR
Chondronia ovalis Cooper and Grant	VR
Composita crassa Cooper and Grant	C
Coscinophora magnifica Cooper and Grant	R
Cyclacantharia transitoria Cooper and Grant	VR
Derbyia cincinnata Cooper and Grant	C
Derbyia complicata Cooper and Grant	R
Derbyia sp.	VR
Dielasma ellipsoideum Cooper and Grant	VR
Dielasma sp.	VR
Dyoros (Dyoros) angulatus Cooper and Grant	A
Dyoros (Dyoros) transversus Cooper and Grant	R
Dyoros (Lissosia) concavus Cooper and Grant	C
Echinauris bella Cooper and Grant	C
Echinauris irregularis Cooper and Grant	R
Edriosteges compactus Cooper and Grant	C
Eolyttonia sp.	VR
Heterelasma glansfagea Cooper and Grant	R
Holotricharina sparsa Cooper and Grant	VR
Hustedia consuta Cooper and Grant	C

	Rarity code
Liosotella costata Cooper and Grant	A
Meekella calathica Cooper and Grant	A
Megousia auriculata Muir-Wood and Cooper	A
Neophricadothyris crassibecca Cooper and Grant	R
Neospirifer bakeri bakeri R.E. King	C
Neospirifer bakeri columbarius Cooper and Grant	R
Paraspiriferina pulchra Cooper and Grant	VR
Paucispinifera sulcata Cooper and Grant	VR
Petasmatherus nitidus Cooper and Grant	VR
Phrenophoria sp.	VR
Reticulariina subulata Cooper and Grant	VR
Rhamnaria vinnula Cooper and Grant	VR
Rhynchopora hebetata Cooper and Grant	VR
Rhynchopora sphenoides Cooper and Grant	VR
Stenoscisma bonum Cooper and Grant	VR
Stenoscisma camurum Cooper and Grant	VR
Taphrosestria peculiaris Cooper and Grant	C
Texarina wordensis (R.E. King)	VR
Waagenoconcha platys Cooper and Grant	VR
Yakovlevia sulcata Cooper and Grant	VR
LOCALITY N724b : Road Canyon Formation	
Acosarina mesoplatys (R.E. King)	A
Anteridocus seminudus Cooper and Grant	C
Bothrostegium derbyoideum Cooper and Grant	R
Cenorhynchia parvula Cooper and Grant	VR
Chondronia ovalis Cooper and Grant	R
Composita sp.	C
Costispinifera rugatula (Girty)	VR
Cyclacantharia transitoria Cooper and Grant	A
Derbyia cincinnata Cooper and Grant	C
Derbyia informis Cooper and Grant	VR
Derbyia laqueata Cooper and Grant	C
Derbyia sp.	VR
Echinauris bella Cooper and Grant	VR
Echinauris irregularis Cooper and Grant	A
Echinauris lappacea Cooper and Grant	R
Echinauris sp.	VR
Edriosteges multispinosus Muir-Wood and Cooper	C
Edriosteges sp.	VR
Eolyttonia sp.	VR
Goniarina striata Cooper and Grant	VR
Holotricharina sparsa Cooper and Grant	R
Hustedia connorsi Cooper and Grant	C
Kutorginella sullivanensis (R.E. King)	VR
Meekella calathica Cooper and Grant	A
Megousia auriculata Muir-Wood and Cooper	VR
Metriolepis ziczac Cooper and Grant	C
Neophricadothyris crassibecca Cooper and Grant	C
Neospirifer bakeri bakeri R.E. King	VR
Paucispinifera sulcata Cooper and Grant	R
Peniculauris costata Cooper and Grant	VR
Rhamnaria tenuispinosa Cooper and Grant	VR
Rhynchopora sphenoides Cooper and Grant	VR
Rugatia incurvata (R.E. King)	R
Stenoscisma bonum Cooper and Grant	C
Taphrosestria expansa Cooper and Grant	C
Taphrosestria peculiaris Cooper and Grant	VR
Texarina wordensis (R.E. King)	VR
Waagenoconcha convexa Cooper and Grant	VR
LOCALITY N724c : Road Canyon Formation	
Acanthocrania densispina Cooper and Grant	VR
Acosarina mesoplatys (R.E. King)	C
Chondronia ovalis Cooper and Grant	VR
Chonetinetes angustisulcatus Cooper and Grant	C

Rarity code

LOCALITY N724c - Continued

	Rarity code
Collemataria batilliformis Cooper and Grant	C
Collemataria sp.	VR
Composita sp.	C
Cooperina subcuneata Cooper and Grant	R
Coscinophora magnifica Cooper and Grant	R
Crurithyris sp.	VR
Cyclacantharia transitoria Cooper and Grant	C
Derbyia cincinnata Cooper and Grant	R
Derbyia laqueata Cooper and Grant	R
Dielasma sp.	VR
Dyoros (*Dyoros*) *transversus* Cooper and Grant	C
Echinauris lappacea Cooper and Grant	C
Edriosteges multispinosus Muir-Wood and Cooper	R
Enteletes densus Cooper and Grant	VR
Goniarina sp.	VR
Heteralosia hystricula (Girty)	VR
Heteralosia sp.	VR
Hustedia consuta Cooper and Grant	A
Lepidocrania tardispinosa Cooper and Grant	VR
Liosotella costata Cooper and Grant	VR
Meekella calathica Cooper and Grant	C
Megousia auriculata Muir-Wood and Cooper	R
Metriolepis ziczac Cooper and Grant	R
Neophricadothyris crassibecca Cooper and Grant	VR
Neospirifer formulosus Cooper and Grant	R
Paraspiriferina cellulana Cooper and Grant	VR
Paucispinifera sulcata Cooper and Grant	C
Peniculauris costata Cooper and Grant	VR
Petasmatherus pumilus Cooper and Grant	C
Pontisia stehlii tumidosa Cooper and Grant	VR
Pseudodielasma sp.	VR
Pseudoleptodus? sp. 7	VR
Rhamnaria vinnula Cooper and Grant	C
Rhytisia rugosa Cooper and Grant	A
Stenoscisma sp.	VR
Tropidelasma corniculum Cooper and Grant	R
Xenosteges trivialis Cooper and Grant	A

LOCALITY N724d : Road Canyon Formation

	Rarity code
Acosarina mesoplatys (R.E. King)	R
Acritosia? vestibula Cooper and Grant	VR
Composita pilula Cooper and Grant	VR
Coscinophora magnifica Cooper and Grant	C
Derbyia cincinnata Cooper and Grant	VR
Derbyia laqueata Cooper and Grant	R
Dielasma bellulum Cooper and Grant	C
Dielasma sp.	R
Echinauris crassa Cooper and Grant	R
Edriosteges compactus Cooper and Grant	VR
Enteletes densus Cooper and Grant	C
Heterelasma magnum Cooper and Grant	VR
Hustedia sp.	VR
Meekella calathica Cooper and Grant	VR
Neospirifer formulosus Cooper and Grant	VR
Notothyris planiplicata Cooper and Grant	R
Rhamnaria vinnula Cooper and Grant	R
Stenoscisma sp.	VR
Tropidelasma corniculum Cooper and Grant	A

LOCALITY N724i : Cathedral Mountain Formation

	Rarity code
Institella leonardensis (R.E. King)	VR
Neospirifer mansuetus Cooper and Grant	VR
Nudauris linospina Cooper and Grant	VR
Peniculauris subcostata (R.E. King)	R

LOCALITY N724j : Road Canyon Formation

	Rarity code
Acanthocrania densispina Cooper and Grant	VR
Acosarina mesoplatys (R.E. King)	VA
Acritosia magnifica Cooper and Grant	VR
Cenorhynchia atmeta Cooper and Grant	C
Collemataria sp.	VR
Composita pilula Cooper and Grant	A
Composita sp.	VR
Crurithyris minutalis Cooper and Grant	C
Cyclacantharia transitoria Cooper and Grant	R
Derbyia informis Cooper and Grant	VR
Derbyia laqueata Cooper and Grant	R
Derbyia sp.	VR
Dielasma ellipsoideum Cooper and Grant	VR
Echinauris bella Cooper and Grant	C
Echinauris irregularis Cooper and Grant	R
Echinauris sp.	VR
Edriosteges multispinosus Muir-Wood and Cooper	C
Elassonia micraria Cooper and Grant	C
Holotricharina sparsa Cooper and Grant	VR
Hustedia narinosa Cooper and Grant	VA
Kutorginella sullivanensis (R.E. King)	VR
Meekella calathica Cooper and Grant	C
Megousia auriculata Muir-Wood and Cooper	VR
Neophricadothyris bullata Cooper and Grant	C
Neophricadothyris crassibecca Cooper and Grant	VR
Neospirifer thescelus Cooper and Grant	R
Paraspiriferina cellulana Cooper and Grant	VR
Paucispinifera sulcata Cooper and Grant	R
Peniculauris costata Cooper and Grant	VR
Rhamnaria tenuispinosa Cooper and Grant	VR
Rhynchopora sphenoides Cooper and Grant	VR
Spiriferella sp.	VR
Stenoscisma bonum Cooper and Grant	A
Texarina wordensis (R.E. King)	R
Waagenoconcha convexa Cooper and Grant	VR

LOCALITY N724k : Cathedral Mountain Formation

	Rarity code
Xestosia schucherti (R.E. King)	VR

LOCALITY N724-l : Skinner Ranch Formation

	Rarity code
Enteletes sp.	VR
Glyptosteges angustus (R.E. King)	VR
Glyptosteges intricatus Cooper and Grant	VR
Neophricadothyris sp.	VR
Torynechus alectorius Cooper and Grant	R

LOCALITY N724m : Cathedral Mountain Formation

	Rarity code
Institella leonardensis (R.E. King)	VR
Neospirifer mansuetus Cooper and Grant	VR

LOCALITY N724n : Cathedral Mountain Formation

	Rarity code
Hercosia uddeni (Böse)	VR
Institella leonardensis (R.E. King)	VR
Kochiproductus sp.	VR
Megousia auriculata Muir-Wood and Cooper	VR
Torynechus caelatus Cooper and Grant	VR
Xestosia schucherti (R.E. King)	R

LOCALITY N724p : Skinner Ranch Formation

	Rarity code
Acosarina dorsisulcata Cooper and Grant	C
Antronaria dissona Cooper and Grant	C
Composita sp.	VR
Crurithyris sp.	R
Derbyia nasuta Girty	VR
Dielasma sp.	VR

	Rarity code
LOCALITY N724p - Continued	
Elliottella varicostata Cooper and Grant	A
Enteletes stehlii Cooper and Grant	C
Hystriculina pumila Cooper and Grant	VR
Kozlowskia subsphaeroidalis Cooper and Grant	A
Meekella caperata Cooper and Grant	VR
Meekella hessensis R.E. King	R
Rhipidomella hessensis R.E. King	A
Scacchinella titan Cooper and Grant	A
Spinifrons delicatula Cooper and Grant	VR
Stenoscisma hadrum Cooper and Grant	VR
Teguliferina conida (Stehli)	R
LOCALITY N724q : Skinner Ranch Formation	
Acosarina dorsisulcata Cooper and Grant	R
Anomalesia perplexa Cooper and Grant	VR
Antronaria dissona Cooper and Grant	R
Chonetinella biplicata (R.E. King)	VR
Composita apheles Cooper and Grant	VR
Crenispirifer angulatus (R.E. King)	VR
Crurithyris sp.	R
Enteletes sp.	R
Fimbrinia ovata Cooper and Grant	VR
Hustedia catella Cooper and Grant	R
Hustedia hessensis R.E. King	VR
Hystriculina pumila Cooper and Grant	C
Kozlowskia subsphaeroidalis Cooper and Grant	C
Meekella sp.	VR
Pontisia costata Cooper and Grant	R
Rhipidomella hessensis R.E. King	R
Scacchinella titan Cooper and Grant	R
Tautosia fastigiata Cooper and Grant	VR
LOCALITY N724r : Cathedral Mountain Formation	
Enteletes plummeri R.E. King	VR
Institella leonardensis (R.E. King)	VR
Rugatia paraindica (McKee)	VR
Torynechus caelatus Cooper and Grant	VR
Xenosteges adherens Muir-Wood and Cooper	VR
LOCALITY N724s : Cathedral Mountain Formation	
Enteletes leonardensis R.E. King	VR
Enteletes plummeri R.E. King	VR
Institella leonardensis (R.E. King)	R
Megousia auriculata Muir-Wood and Cooper	VR
Neospirifer mansuetus Cooper and Grant	VR
Peniculauris subcostata (R.E. King)	VR
Stenoscisma triquetrum Cooper and Grant	VR
Thamnosia anterospinosa Cooper and Grant	VR
Torynechus caelatus Cooper and Grant	VR
LOCALITY N724t : Cathedral Mountain Formation	
Enteletes leonardensis R.E. King	VR
Institella leonardensis (R.E. King)	VR
Neophricadothyris bullata Cooper and Grant	VR
LOCALITY N724u : Word Formation, Willis Ranch Member	
Acanthocrania intermedia Cooper and Grant	VR
Allorhynchus permianum wordense Cooper and Grant	R
Allorhynchus triangulatum Cooper and Grant	VR
Cactosteges anomalus Cooper and Grant	A
Cartorhium chelomatum Cooper and Grant	R
Cartorhium sp.	VR
Collemataria elongata Cooper and Grant	C
Composita enormis Cooper and Grant	R
Composita parasulcata Cooper and Grant	A

	Rarity code
Cooperina inexpectata Termier, Termier and Pajaud	C
Costispinifera costata (R.E. King)	C
Crurithyris tholiaphor Cooper and Grant	R
Cyclacantharia kingorum Cooper and Grant	A
Derbyia filosa Cooper and Grant	VR
Derbyia pannucia Cooper and Grant	R
Derbyia texta Cooper and Grant	VR
Dielasma compactum Cooper and Grant	R
Dielasma gracile Cooper and Grant	R
Dielasma sp.	R
Dielasma zebratum Cooper and Grant	R
Dyoros (Dyoros) extensus Cooper and Grant	C
Dyoros (Dyoros) tenuis Cooper and Grant	R
Dyoros (Lissosia) concavus Cooper and Grant	C
Echinauris lateralis Muir-Wood and Cooper	C
Echinosteges tuberculatus (R.E. King)	C
Enteletes sp.	VR
Glossothyropsis rectangulata Cooper and Grant	VR
Grandaurispina bella Cooper and Grant	R
Grandaurispina kingorum Muir-Wood and Cooper	C
Heteralosia hystricula (Girty)	C
Heterelasma concavum Cooper and Grant	R
Hustedia pugilla pugilla Cooper and Grant	A
Hustedia sculptilis Cooper and Grant	R
Leurosina lata Cooper and Grant	R
Liosotella wordensis (R.E. King)	A
Meekella skenoides Girty	A
Metriolepis pulvinata Cooper and Grant	R
Metriolepis sp.	VR
Neospirifer amphigyus Cooper and Grant	R
Paraspiriferina setulosa Cooper and Grant	C
Paucispinifera auriculata Muir-Wood and Cooper	C
Paucispinifera magnispina Cooper and Grant	R
Paucispinifera transversa Cooper and Grant	VR
Petasmatherus opulus Cooper and Grant	R
Polymorpharia polymorpha Cooper and Grant	VR
Pseudodielasma gibberum Cooper and Grant	R
Pseudodielasma lobatum Cooper and Grant	VR
Pseudodielasma minor (R.E. King)	C
Pseudodielasma pingue Cooper and Grant	R
Pseudodielasma sp.	VA
Reticulariina sp.	VR
Rhamnaria kingorum Muir-Wood and Cooper	C
Rhynchopora palumbula Cooper and Grant	R
Spiriferella calcarata Cooper and Grant	R
Spiriferellina hilli (Girty)	R
Texarina elongata Cooper and Grant	VR
Thedusia procera Cooper and Grant	R
Undulella undulata Cooper and Grant	C
Wellerella girtyi girtyi Cooper and Grant	A
Xenosteges quadratus Cooper and Grant	R
Yakovlevia hessorum Cooper and Grant	VR
LOCALITY N724x : Lenox Hills Formation	
Acosarina sp.	R
LOCALITY N725a : Hueco Formation	
Acosarina sp.	A
Composita mexicana (Hall)	VA
Crurithyris sulcata Stehli	C
Derbyia sp.	VR
Enteletes costellatus Cooper and Grant	R
Enteletes sp.	C
Meekella circularis Cooper and Grant	R
Meekella sp.	R
Orthotichia kozlowskii R.E. King	VR

	Rarity code
LOCALITY N725a - Continued	
Reticulatia sp.	VR
Rhipidomella hessensis R.E. King	VR
Rhipidomella sp.	VR
Scacchinella exasperata Cooper and Grant	VR
LOCALITY N725b : Hueco Formation	
Acritosia silicica Cooper and Grant	A
Composita cracens Cooper and Grant	VR
Composita mexicana (Hall)	C
Enteletes sp.	C
Lowenstamia sp.	C
Meekella circularis Cooper and Grant	C
Meekella sp.	R
Neophricadothyris catatona Cooper and Grant	VR
Texarina sp.	R
LOCALITY N725c : Bone Spring Formation	
Acosarina dorsisulcata Cooper and Grant	A
Acritosia peculiaris Cooper and Grant	C
Antronaria indentata Cooper and Grant	C
Antronaria mesicostalis (Girty)	VR
Chonetinella magna Cooper and Grant	C
Collemataria americana (Girty)	VR
Collemataria marshalli (Stehli)	R
Crenispirifer angulatus (R.E. King)	VR
Crurithyris inflata Stehli	R
Crurithyris sulcata Stehli	R
Derbyia nasuta Girty	R
Derbyia sp.	R
Dielasma sp.	VR
Diplanus lamellatus (R.E. King)	VR
Dyoros (*Dyoros*) *consanguineus* (Girty)	R
Dyoros (*Dyoros*) *magnus* Stehli	VR
Enteletes stehlii Cooper and Grant	A
Fimbrinia ovata Cooper and Grant	VR
Goniarina permiana (Stehli)	A
Hustedia hessensis R.E. King	R
Hustedia sp.	R
Kozlowskia kingi Stehli	R
Limbella victorioensis Stehli	R
Meekella angustiplicata Cooper and Grant	A
Meekella attenuata Girty	R
Meekella hessensis R.E. King	R
Meekella intermedia Cooper and Grant	R
Neophricadothyris catatona Cooper and Grant	C
Neophricadothyris sp.	VR
Pontisia nanas (Stehli)	VR
Rhipidomella hessensis R.E. King	C
Scacchinella americana Stehli	C
Sceletonia crassa Cooper and Grant	VR
Spinifrons quadrata Stehli	VR
Teguliferina conida (Stehli)	R
Thamnosia parvispinosa (Stehli)	VR
LOCALITY N725e : Bell Canyon Formation, Lamar Member	
Allorhynchus venustulum Cooper and Grant	R
Aneuthelasma amygdalinum Cooper and Grant	R
Anomaloria anomala Cooper and Grant	A
Anteridocus bicostatus Cooper and Grant	VR
Anteridocus swallovianus (Shumard)	R
Aphaurosia rotundata Cooper and Grant	C
Aphaurosia scutata Cooper and Grant	VR
Arionthia lamaria Cooper and Grant	C
Astegosia subquadrata (Girty)	VA

	Rarity code
Cleiothyridina pilularis Cooper and Grant	R
Collemataria spatulata Cooper and Grant	C
Composita affinis Girty	A
Crenispirifer myllus Cooper and Grant	C
Crurithyris guadalupensis (Girty)	C
Deltarina magnicostata Cooper and Grant	C
Derbyia sp. 1	R
Derbyia sp.	C
Derbyia texta Cooper and Grant	R
Dielasma cordatum Girty	VR
Dielasma sp.	R
Dielasma sulcatum Girty	R
Dyoros (*Dyoros*) *hillanus* (Girty)	R
Eliva shumardi Cooper and Grant	C
Elivina detecta Cooper and Grant	C
Eolyttonia sp.	VR
Fascicosta longaeva (Girty)	VR
Geyerella americana Girty	VR
Heteralosia magnispina Cooper and Grant	R
Heterelasma venustulum Girty	VR
Hustedia rupinata Cooper and Grant	A
Lirellaria costellata Cooper and Grant	VR
Martinia rhomboidalis Girty	VA
Metriolepis sp.	VR
Micraphelia sp.	VR
Ombonia guadalupensis (Girty)	C
Paraspiriferina sapinea Cooper and Grant	C
Paraspiriferina sp.	VR
Paucispinifera latidorsata (Girty)	VR
Plectelasma guadalupense (Girty)	VR
Ptilotorhynchus delicatum Cooper and Grant	R
Reticulariina sp.	R
Rigbyella girtyi (Wanner and Sieverts)	VR
Sarganostega pressa Cooper and Grant	C
Scapharina levis Cooper and Grant	VR
Sestropoma cribriferum Cooper and Grant	VR
Spiriferellina nuda Cooper and Grant	VR
Stenoscisma trabeatum Cooper and Grant	R
Strigirhynchia indentata (Shumard)	VR
Tautosia elegans (Girty)	C
Tautosia shumardiana (Girty)	R
Thamnosia capitanensis (Girty)	VR
Timorina ovata (Girty)	R
Timorina schuchertensis (Girty)	VR
Tropidelasma gregarium (Girty)	A
LOCALITY N725f : Bell Canyon Formation, Rader Member	
Acanthocrania regularis Cooper and Grant	R
Altiplecus? deltosus Cooper and Grant	C
Altiplecus trapezoidalis Cooper and Grant	C
Anteridocus swallovianus (Shumard)	C
Bryorhynchus bisulcatum (Shumard)	VA
Cartorhium sp.	VR
Chonetinetes varians Cooper and Grant	C
Composita affinis Girty	C
Craspedona newelli Cooper and Grant	C
Crenispirifer myllus Cooper and Grant	C
Deltarina magnicostata Cooper and Grant	R
Derbyia sp.	C
Derbyia texta Cooper and Grant	C
Dielasma sp.	VR
Dielasma subcirculare Cooper and Grant	R

	Rarity code
LOCALITY N725f - Continued	
Dielasma sulcatum Girty	R
Dyoros (*Dyoros*) *intrepidus* Cooper and Grant	A
Echinosteges guadalupensis (Shumard)	R
Eliva shumardi Cooper and Grant	VR
Elivina? *annectans* Cooper and Grant	C
Eolyttonia sp.	VR
Fascicosta bella Cooper and Grant	VR
Fascicosta elongata Cooper and Grant	R
Glossothyropsis cryptacanthoides Cooper and Grant	R
Glossothyropsis juvenis Cooper and Grant	VR
Heteralosia magnispina Cooper and Grant	C
Heterelasma venustulum Girty	VR
Hustedia demissa Cooper and Grant	C
Hustedia rupinata Cooper and Grant	VA
Lepidocrania sp.	VR
Madarosia anterolamellata Cooper and Grant	R
Metriolepis nabis Cooper and Grant	VR
Metriolepis pedicosa Cooper and Grant	R
Metriolepis sp.	R
Micraphelia scitula Cooper and Grant	A
Micraphelia subalata Cooper and Grant	VA
Neophricadothyris sp.	VR
Paraspiriferina sapinea Cooper and Grant	C
Paucispinifera sp.	R
Petrocrania sp.	VR
Phrenophoria perplexa Cooper and Grant	R
Plectelasma guadalupense (Girty)	C
Pseudoleptodus guadalupensis (Stehli)	C
Rallacosta imporcata Cooper and Grant	C
Reticulariina echinata Cooper and Grant	R
Reticulariina sp.	C
Reticulariina welleri (Girty)	VR
Rhamnaria shumardi Cooper and Grant	VR
Sarganostega transversalis Cooper and Grant	R
Scapharina levis Cooper and Grant	VR
Scapharina rugosa Cooper and Grant	C
Sestropoma cribriferum Cooper and Grant	A
Spiriferella sulcifer (Shumard)	C
Stenoscisma aberrans Cooper and Grant	R
Stenoscisma trabeatum Cooper and Grant	VR
Thamnosia capitanensis (Girty)	R
Timorina ovata (Girty)	VR
Timorina schuchertensis (Girty)	VR
Tropidelasma gregarium (Girty)	VR
Xenosteges umbonatus Cooper and Grant	VR
LOCALITY N725g : Bell Canyon Formation, Rader Member	
Acanthocrania sp.	VR
Allorhynchus venustulum Cooper and Grant	VR
Altiplecus? *deltosus* Cooper and Grant	R
Anteridocus swallovianus (Shumard)	C
Arionthia lamaria Cooper and Grant	VR
Bryorhynchus bisulcatum (Shumard)	A
Cartorhium sp.	VR
Chonetinetes sp.	R
Composita emarginata Girty	C
Composita pyriformis Cooper and Grant	R
Composita sp.	VR
Craspedona newelli Cooper and Grant	VR
Crenispirifer myllus Cooper and Grant	C
Crurithyris guadalupensis (Girty)	VR

	Rarity code
Derbyia sp.	R
Derbyia texta Cooper and Grant	R
Dielasma sp.	VR
Dielasma sulcatum Girty	VR
Dyoros (*Dyoros*) *intrepidus* Cooper and Grant	C
Echinosteges guadalupensis (Shumard)	VR
Elivina? *annectans* Cooper and Grant	R
Fascicosta bella Cooper and Grant	VR
Fascicosta elongata Cooper and Grant	VR
Fascicosta longaeva (Girty)	VR
Glossothyropsis cryptacanthoides Cooper and Grant	C
Glossothyropsis juvenis Cooper and Grant	VR
Heteralosia magnispina Cooper and Grant	R
Heterelasma shumardianum Girty	VR
Hustedia demissa Cooper and Grant	R
Hustedia rupinata Cooper and Grant	C
Hustedia sp.	A
Metriolepis nabis Cooper and Grant	VR
Metriolepis pedicosa Cooper and Grant	R
Metriolepis sp.	VR
Micraphelia scitula Cooper and Grant	C
Micraphelia subalata Cooper and Grant	A
Notothyris sp.	VR
Ombonia guadalupensis (Girty)	VR
Paraspiriferina billingsi (Shumard)	R
Paraspiriferina sapinea Cooper and Grant	C
Paucispinifera latidorsata (Girty)	VR
Phrenophoria perplexa Cooper and Grant	R
Plectelasma guadalupense (Girty)	R
Pseudoleptodus guadalupensis (Stehli)	VR
Ptilotorhynchus delicatum Cooper and Grant	VR
Rallacosta imporcata Cooper and Grant	R
Reticulariina sp.	VR
Reticulariina welleri (Girty)	VR
Sarganostega transversalis Cooper and Grant	R
Scapharina levis Cooper and Grant	VR
Scapharina rugosa Cooper and Grant	R
Sestropoma cribriferum Cooper and Grant	R
Spiriferella sulcifer (Shumard)	C
Spiriferellina nuda Cooper and Grant	R
Tautosia elegans (Girty)	VR
Tautosia shumardiana (Girty)	VR
Tautosia sp.	VR
Thamnosia capitanensis (Girty)	VR
Thedusia trigonalis (Girty)	R
Thedusia ventricosa Cooper and Grant	C
Tropidelasma gregarium (Girty)	VR
LOCALITY N725h : Bell Canyon Formation, Pinery Member	
Acanthocrania minutispinosa Cooper and Grant	VR
Allorhynchus venustulum Cooper and Grant	VR
Altiplecus extensus Cooper and Grant	VR
Anteridocus swallovianus (Shumard)	VR
Aphaurosia scutata Cooper and Grant	VR
Bryorhynchus bisulcatum (Shumard)	VA
Composita pyriformis Cooper and Grant	R
Composita sp.	R
Craspedona newelli Cooper and Grant	VR
Crenispirifer jubatus Cooper and Grant	R
Deltarina magnicostata Cooper and Grant	VR
Derbyia sp.	R
Dielasma cordatum Girty	VR
Dielasma sp.	VR

LOCALITY N725h - Continued

	Rarity code
Elivina? annectans Cooper and Grant	R
Fascicosta elongata Cooper and Grant	VR
Glossothyropsis polita Cooper and Grant	C
Glossothyropsis robusta (Girty)	VR
Heteralosia magnispina Cooper and Grant	VR
Heterelasma sp.	VR
Heterelasma venustulum Girty	VR
Hustedia rupinata Cooper and Grant	C
Hustedia samiata Cooper and Grant	R
Hustedia sp.	C
Metriolepis pedicosa Cooper and Grant	VR
Micraphelia scitula Cooper and Grant	VA
Micraphelia subalata Cooper and Grant	C
Neophricadothyris sp.	VR
Paraspiriferina billingsi (Shumard)	VR
Paraspiriferina sapinea Cooper and Grant	R
Paucispinifera rara Cooper and Grant	VR
Petrocrania exasperata Cooper and Grant	VR
Petrocrania septifera Cooper and Grant	VR
Plectelasma guadalupense (Girty)	R
Pseudodielasma brilli Cooper and Grant	VR
Pseudoleptodus guadalupensis (Stehli)	VR
Reticulariina sp.	VR
Rigbyella girtyi (Wanner and Sieverts)	VR
Sarganostega pressa Cooper and Grant	VR
Scapharina rugosa Cooper and Grant	R
Sestropoma cribriferum Cooper and Grant	VR
Spiriferellina nuda Cooper and Grant	R
Thamnosia capitanensis (Girty)	VR
Thedusia trigonalis (Girty)	VR
Timorina attenuata Cooper and Grant	VR

LOCALITY N725i : Capitan Formation

Eliva shumardi Cooper and Grant	VR
Liosotella popei (Shumard)	R
Paraspiriferina billingsi (Shumard)	VR
Scapharina rugosa Cooper and Grant	VR
Strigirhynchia indentata (Shumard)	VR

LOCALITY N725j : Capitan Formation

Anteridocus swallovianus (Shumard)	VR
Liosotella popei (Shumard)	VR
Ptilotorhynchus delicatum Cooper and Grant	VR

LOCALITY N725k : Capitan Formation

Anteridocus swallovianus (Shumard)	C
Composita affinis Girty	VR
Dielasma prolongatum Girty	VR
Eliva shumardi Cooper and Grant	R
Heterelasma shumardianum Girty	VR
Hustedia rupinata Cooper and Grant	VR
Liosotella popei (Shumard)	C
Paraspiriferina billingsi (Shumard)	VR
Scapharina levis Cooper and Grant	VR
Strigirhynchia transversa Cooper and Grant	VR

LOCALITY N725-1 : Capitan Formation

Anteridocus swallovianus (Shumard)	C
Composita affinis Girty	VR
Composita emarginata Girty	R
Dielasma prolongatum Girty	VR
Eliva inflata Cooper and Grant	VR
Eliva shumardi Cooper and Grant	R
Eolyttonia sp. 4	VR
Hustedia opsia Cooper and Grant	VR

	Rarity code
Liosotella popei (Shumard)	A
Paraspiriferina billingsi (Shumard)	VR
Stenoscisma oblisum Cooper and Grant	VR
Strigirhynchia indentata (Shumard)	VR
Strigirhynchia transversa Cooper and Grant	VR
Tautosia shumardiana (Girty)	VR
Thamnosia capitanensis (Girty)	R

LOCALITY N725m : Capitan Formation

Cartorhium mexicanum (Shumard)	VR

LOCALITY N725n : Bell Canyon Formation, Pinery Member

Acanthocrania minutispinosa Cooper and Grant	VR
Acanthocrania sp.	VR
Altiplecus? deltosus Cooper and Grant	C
Anteridocus subcarinatus Cooper and Grant	VR
Anteridocus swallovianus (Shumard)	R
Arionthia lamaria Cooper and Grant	VR
Arionthia polypleura (Girty)	R
Bryorhynchus bisulcatum (Shumard)	C
Composita emarginata Girty	C
Composita pyriformis Cooper and Grant	VR
Crenispirifer jubatus Cooper and Grant	R
Deltarina magnicostata Cooper and Grant	VR
Derbyia sp.	C
Dielasma sulcatum Girty	R
Echinosteges guadalupensis (Shumard)	VR
Elivina? annectans Cooper and Grant	C
Fascicosta longaeva (Girty)	VR
Glossothyropsis polita Cooper and Grant	VR
Heteralosia magnispina Cooper and Grant	VR
Hustedia demissa Cooper and Grant	VR
Hustedia rupinata Cooper and Grant	A
Hustedia samiata Cooper and Grant	R
Metriolepis nabis Cooper and Grant	VR
Metriolepis pedicosa Cooper and Grant	VR
Metriolepis sp.	VR
Micraphelia scitula Cooper and Grant	R
Paraspiriferina sapinea Cooper and Grant	R
Paucispinifera sp.	VR
Phrenophoria perplexa Cooper and Grant	VR
Phrenophoria pinguis (Girty)	VR
Plectelasma guadalupense (Girty)	R
Plectelasma planidorsatum Cooper and Grant	VR
Pseudoleptodus guadalupensis (Stehli)	VR
Rallacosta importata Cooper and Grant	VR
Reticulariina sp.	VR
Sarganostega transversalis Cooper and Grant	R
Scapharina rugosa Cooper and Grant	R
Sestropoma cribriferum Cooper and Grant	VR
Spiriferella sulcifer (Shumard)	VR
Spiriferellina nuda Cooper and Grant	R
Tautosia shumardiana (Girty)	VR
Thamnosia capitanensis (Girty)	VR
Thedusia emarginata Cooper and Grant	VR
Thedusia trigonalis (Girty)	R
Thedusia ventricosa Cooper and Grant	C

LOCALITY N725o : Bell Canyon Formation, Rader Member

Bryorhynchus bisulcatum (Shumard)	C
Composita emarginata Girty	R
Crenispirifer myllus Cooper and Grant	VR
Derbyia sp.	VR
Dielasma sp.	VR

Rarity code

LOCALITY N725o - Continued

Dielasma sulcatum Girty	VR
Dyoros (Dyoros) intrepidus Cooper and Grant	VR
Elivina? annectans Cooper and Grant	C
Hustedia rupinata Cooper and Grant	C
Metriolepis sp.	VR
Micraphelia scitula Cooper and Grant	R
Paraspiriferina sapinea Cooper and Grant	R
Plectelasma guadalupense (Girty)	VR
Reticulariina sp.	C
Reticulariina welleri (Girty)	VR
Sarganostega transversalis Cooper and Grant	VR
Scapharina rugosa Cooper and Grant	VR
Sestropoma cribriferum Cooper and Grant	VR
Spiriferella sulcifer (Shumard)	VR
Thedusia trigonalis (Girty)	R

LOCALITY N725p : Capitan Formation

Astegosia subquadrata (Girty)	R
Collemataria sp.	VR
Composita affinis Girty	VR
Eliva inflata Cooper and Grant	VR
Heterelasma shumardianum Girty	VR
Hustedia opsia Cooper and Grant	VR
Martinia rhomboidalis Girty	VR
Ombonia guadalupensis (Girty)	VR
Paraspiriferina billingsi (Shumard)	VR
Paucispinifera sp.	VR
Stenoscisma trabeatum Cooper and Grant	VR
Thamnosia capitanensis (Girty)	VR

LOCALITY N725s : Bone Spring Formation

Acosarina dorsisulcata Cooper and Grant	VR
Anemonaria sublaevis (R.E. King)	VR
Derbyia sp.	VR
Echinauris sp.	VR
Enteletes stehlii Cooper and Grant	VR
Meekella angustiplicata Cooper and Grant	VR
Meekella hessensis R.E. King	VR
Neophricadothyris sp.	VR

LOCALITY N725v : Cibolo Formation, Spicule Zone

Acosarina mesoplatys (R.E. King)	R
Cartorhium sp.	VR
Choanodus irregularis Cooper and Grant	R
Chonosteges pulcher Cooper and Grant	VR
Composita sp.	VR
Compressoproductus sp.	VR
Derbyia sp.	R
Dielasma sp.	VR
Diplanus rarus Cooper and Grant	R
Echinauris sp.	R
Enteletes sp.	VR
Eolyttonia sp.	R
Hustedia sp.	R
Institella leonardensis (R.E. King)	R
Meekella sp.	C
Megousia auriculata Muir-Wood and Cooper	VR
Metriolepis carotica Cooper and Grant	VR
Neophricadothyris sp.	VR
Rhamnaria sp.	VR
Rhipidomella hispidula Cooper and Grant	R
Teguliferina sp.	R
Xenosteges adherens Muir-Wood and Cooper	VR

LOCALITY N725y : Bone Spring Formation

Composita costata Cooper and Grant	C

Rarity code

Echinauris sp.	VR
Glossothyropsis sp. 1 (Girty)	VR
Isogramma diabloense Cooper and Grant	R
Kochiproductus sp.	VR
Leurosina sinesulca (Stehli)	R
Meekella hessensis R.E. King	VR

LOCALITY N725z : Hueco Formation

Composita cracens Cooper and Grant	R
Composita sp.	R
Dasysaria wolfcampensis (R.E. King)	C
Derbyia sp.	VR
Dielasma sp. 3	VR
Echinauris cf. *boulei* (Kozlowski)	R
Echinauris sp.	R
Enteletes costellatus Cooper and Grant	R
Gypospirifer anancites Cooper and Grant	C
Hustedia huecoensis R.E. King	VR
Hustedia sp.	R
Kochiproductus quadratus Cooper and Grant	C
Kutorginella sp.	VR
Nudauris transversa Cooper and Grant	C
Pontisia franklinensis Cooper and Grant	R
Reticulariina powwowensis Cooper and Grant	VR
Waagenoconcha sulcata Cooper and Grant	VR

LOCALITY N726c : Road Canyon Formation

Anteridocus seminudus Cooper and Grant	VR

LOCALITY N726d : Road Canyon Formation

Acosarina mesoplatys (R.E. King)	VA
Anteridocus seminudus Cooper and Grant	VR
Bothrostegium derbyoideum Cooper and Grant	R
Bothrostegium sp.	R
Chonetinetes angustisulcatus Cooper and Grant	C
Cleiothyridina nana Cooper and Grant	VR
Collemataria batilliformis Cooper and Grant	VA
Composita sp.	C
Compressoproductus acuminatus Cooper and Grant	VR
Compressoproductus sp. 1	R
Cooperina subcuneata Cooper and Grant	C
Coscinophora magnifica Cooper and Grant	R
Crurithyris sp.	R
Cyclacantharia transitoria Cooper and Grant	C
Derbyia cincinnata Cooper and Grant	R
Derbyia complicata Cooper and Grant	VR
Derbyia informis Cooper and Grant	VR
Derbyia laqueata Cooper and Grant	C
Derbyia sp.	C
Dielasma bellulum Cooper and Grant	VR
Dielasma ellipsoideum Cooper and Grant	VR
Dielasma sp.	VR
Dyoros (Dyoros) angulatus Cooper and Grant	R
Dyoros (Dyoros) transversus Cooper and Grant	C
Dyoros (Lissosia) parvus Cooper and Grant	C
Echinauris bella Cooper and Grant	C
Echinauris lappacea Cooper and Grant	A
Echinauris sp.	VR
Edriosteges compactus Cooper and Grant	R
Edriosteges multispinosus Muir-Wood and Cooper	C
Eolyttonia chaotica Cooper and Grant	C
Eolyttonia parviconica Cooper and Grant	R
Heteralosia sp.	VR
Holotricharina sparsa Cooper and Grant	R
Hustedia consuta Cooper and Grant	A
Hustedia sp.	R

	Rarity code
LOCALITY N726d - Continued	
Kochiproductus sp.	R
Lepidocrania tardispinosa Cooper and Grant	VR
Leurosina sp.	VR
Liosotella costata Cooper and Grant	R
Meekella calathica Cooper and Grant	VA
Meekella sp.	C
Megousia auriculata Muir-Wood and Cooper	C
Metriolepis ziczac Cooper and Grant	R
Neophricadothyris crassibecca Cooper and Grant	VR
Neophricadothyris sp.	VR
Neospirifer bakeri bakeri R.E. King	VR
Neospirifer formulosus Cooper and Grant	C
Paranorella sp. 5	VR
Paraspiriferina cellulana Cooper and Grant	VR
Paucispinifera sulcata Cooper and Grant	C
Peniculauris costata Cooper and Grant	VR
Petasmatherus nitidus Cooper and Grant	R
Reticulariina pristina Cooper and Grant	R
Rhamnaria tenuispinosa Cooper and Grant	VR
Rhamnaria vinnula Cooper and Grant	A
Rhynchopora hebetata Cooper and Grant	R
Rhytisia rugosa Cooper and Grant	C
Simplicarina incompta Cooper and Grant	VR
Spinarella perfecta Cooper and Grant	VR
Spiriferinaella sp.	VR
Texarina parallela Cooper and Grant	VR
Texarina wordensis (R.E. King)	VR
Thedusia mesocostata Cooper and Grant	R
Waagenoconcha convexa Cooper and Grant	VR
Xenosteges magnus Cooper and Grant	C
Yakovlevia sulcata Cooper and Grant	VR
LOCALITY N726e : Road Canyon Formation	
Acosarina mesoplatys (R.E. King)	C
Composita sp.	C
Cooperina subcuneata Cooper and Grant	R
Coscinophora magnifica Cooper and Grant	VR
Crurithyris sp.	VR
Cyclacantharia transitoria Cooper and Grant	R
Derbyia cincinnata Cooper and Grant	R
Derbyia laqueata Cooper and Grant	VR
Dyoros (*Dyoros*) *angulatus* Cooper and Grant	R
Dyoros (*Dyoros*) *transversus* Cooper and Grant	R
Dyoros (*Tetragonetes*) *solidus* Cooper and Grant	R
Echinauris lappacea Cooper and Grant	C
Echinauris sp.	R
Edriosteges compactus Cooper and Grant	VR
Enteletes sp.	VR
Geyerella inexpectata Cooper and Grant	VR
Goniarina striata Cooper and Grant	C
Heterelasma sp.	VR
Hustedia sp.	VR
Meekella sp.	VR
Metriolepis sp.	VR
Neospirifer formulosus Cooper and Grant	R
Paraspiriferina pulchra Cooper and Grant	VR
Petasmatherus nitidus Cooper and Grant	R
Pseudodielasma sp.	VR
Rhamnaria tenuispinosa Cooper and Grant	R
Rhytisia rugosa Cooper and Grant	R
Tropidelasma corniculum Cooper and Grant	VR
Xenosteges trivialis Cooper and Grant	R
LOCALITY N726f : Road Canyon Formation	
Acosarina mesoplatys (R.E. King)	C

	Rarity code
Cenorhynchia atmeta Cooper and Grant	VR
Chondronia ovalis Cooper and Grant	R
Composita bucculenta Cooper and Grant	C
Composita stalagmium Cooper and Grant	A
Cyclacantharia paucispinosa Cooper and Grant	R
Derbyia cincinnata Cooper and Grant	VR
Derbyia laqueata Cooper and Grant	R
Dielasma ellipsoideum Cooper and Grant	VR
Edriosteges compactus Cooper and Grant	R
Hercosestria cribrosa Cooper and Grant	R
Heterelasma glansfagea Cooper and Grant	VR
Hustedia narinosa Cooper and Grant	C
Meekella calathica Cooper and Grant	C
Neophricadothyris bullata Cooper and Grant	A
Pontisia stehlii stehlii Cooper and Grant	VR
Reticulariina sp.	VR
Reticulariina venustula Cooper and Grant	C
LOCALITY N726h : Skinner Ranch Formation	
Acritosia peculiaris Cooper and Grant	VR
Antronaria dissona Cooper and Grant	VR
Antronaria emarginata Cooper and Grant	VR
Cenorhynchia sp. 1	VR
Composita apheles Cooper and Grant	R
Echinauris sp.	VR
Elliottella varicostata Cooper and Grant	VR
Enteletes sp.	VR
Kozlowskia sp.	R
Neophricadothyris catatona Cooper and Grant	VR
Nudauris enigmatica Cooper and Grant	VR
Peniculauris sp. 1	VR
Scacchinella titan Cooper and Grant	VR
Stenoscisma hadrum Cooper and Grant	VR
Tricoria hirpex Cooper and Grant	VR
LOCALITY N726j : Skinner Ranch Formation	
Antronaria titania Cooper and Grant	VR
Cartorhium zoyei Cooper and Grant	VR
Dielasma hessense Cooper and Grant	VR
Scacchinella titan Cooper and Grant	R
Stenoscisma pyraustoides Cooper and Grant	VR
LOCALITY N726-1 : Skinner Ranch Formation	
Acosarina dorsisulcata Cooper and Grant	VR
Geyerella hessi Cooper and Grant	VR
Spyridiophora reticulata (R.E. King)	VR
LOCALITY N726n : Hess Formation	
Acosarina dorsisulcata Cooper and Grant	C
Acosarina sp.	C
Acritosia peculiaris Cooper and Grant	C
Composita apheles Cooper and Grant	VR
Composita bucculenta Cooper and Grant	VA
Composita sp.	C
Derbyia sp.	R
Echinauris sp.	VR
Heterelasma sp. 3	VR
Hustedia sp.	R
Kochiproductus sp.	VR
Meekella hessensis R.E. King	A
Micraphelia sp.	VR
Neophricadothyris sp.	VR
Peniculauris imitata Cooper and Grant	VR
Plectelasma kingi Cooper and Grant	R
Pontisia ventricola Cooper and Grant	A
Reticulariina pusilla Cooper and Grant	C
Rhipidomella hessensis R.E. King	VR

LOCALITY N726n - Continued

	Rarity code
Stenoscisma hadrum Cooper and Grant	VR

LOCALITY N726o : Cathedral Mountain Formation

	Rarity code
Acanthocrania magna Cooper and Grant	VR
Acanthocrania sp.	VR
Acosarina mesoplatys (R.E. King)	VA
Anemonaria sublaevis (R.E. King)	R
Choanodus irregularis Cooper and Grant	R
Chondronia bella Cooper and Grant	C
Chonosteges costellatus Cooper and Grant	A
Chonosteges pulcher Cooper and Grant	VR
Chonosteges variabilis Cooper and Grant	VR
Composita imbricata Cooper and Grant	VR
Composita sp.	R
Derbyia cincinnata Cooper and Grant	C
Derbyia complicata Cooper and Grant	VR
Derbyia informis Cooper and Grant	VR
Derbyia laqueata Cooper and Grant	C
Derbyia sp.	R
Dielasma anterolatum Cooper and Grant	VR
Dielasma ellipsoideum Cooper and Grant	VR
Dielasma sp.	VR
Echinauris irregularis Cooper and Grant	C
Echinauris sp.	C
Echinauris venustula Cooper and Grant	A
Edriosteges multispinosus Muir-Wood and Cooper	C
Eolyttonia chaotica Cooper and Grant	R
Hercosia delicata Cooper and Grant	VA
Hercosia uddeni (Böse)	A
Heterelasma glansfagea Cooper and Grant	R
Holotricharina hirsuta Cooper and Grant	VR
Hustedia consuta Cooper and Grant	VA
Hustedia sp.	A
Kochiproductus sp. 6	VR
Lepidospirifer demissus Cooper and Grant	VR
Lepidospirifer inferus Cooper and Grant	VR
Meekella calathica Cooper and Grant	VA
Megousia auriculata Muir-Wood and Cooper	R
Metriolepis sp.	VR
Neophricadothyris bullata Cooper and Grant	C
Neospirifer mansuetus Cooper and Grant	R
Nudauris linospina Cooper and Grant	VR
Peniculauris subcostata (R.E. King)	VR
Pontisia stehlii stehlii Cooper and Grant	C
Pontisia stehlii tumidosa Cooper and Grant	R
Reticulariina craticula Cooper and Grant	A
Reticulariina sp.	VR
Rhamnaria tenuispinosa Cooper and Grant	C
Rhynchopora hebetata Cooper and Grant	VR
Rugatia paraindica (McKee)	VR
Stenoscisma sp.	VR
Texarina wordensis (R.E. King)	C
Xenosteges adherens Muir-Wood and Cooper	R

LOCALITY N726r : Word Formation, China Tank Member

	Rarity code
Allorhynchus permianum wordense Cooper and Grant	R
Bothrionia nasuta Cooper and Grant	VR
Cactosteges anomalus Cooper and Grant	VR
Collemataria elongata Cooper and Grant	C
Composita parasulcata Cooper and Grant	C
Cooperina inexpectata Termier, Termier and Pajaud	VR
Costispinifera rugatula (Girty)	R
Crurithyris tholiaphor Cooper and Grant	R
Cyclacantharia kingorum Cooper and Grant	C

	Rarity code
Derbyia pannucia Cooper and Grant	R
Derbyia texta Cooper and Grant	VR
Dielasma compactum Cooper and Grant	R
Dyoros (*Lissosia*) *concavus* Cooper and Grant	C
Echinauris lateralis Muir-Wood and Cooper	VR
Echinosteges tuberculatus (R.E. King)	R
Enteletes wordensis R.E. King	A
Glossothyropsis rectangulata Cooper and Grant	VR
Grandaurispina kingorum Muir-Wood and Cooper	VR
Heteralosia hystricula (Girty)	R
Hustedia pugilla nasiterna Cooper and Grant	C
Leurosina lata Cooper and Grant	VR
Liosotella parva Cooper and Grant	R
Liosotella wordensis (R.E. King)	R
Meekella skenoides Girty	C
Megousia mucronata Cooper and Grant	C
Metriolepis pulvinata Cooper and Grant	VR
Neophricadothyris conara Cooper and Grant	R
Neospirifer amphigyus Cooper and Grant	C
Paraspiriferina laqueata Cooper and Grant	R
Paucispinifera quadrata Cooper and Grant	R
Petasmatherus opulus Cooper and Grant	VR
Reticulariina senticosa Cooper and Grant	VR
Rhamnaria kingorum delicata Muir-Wood and Cooper	C
Rhynchopora palumbula Cooper and Grant	VR
Spiriferellina hilli (Girty)	R
Spiriferinaella limata Cooper and Grant	VR
Stenoscisma renode Cooper and Grant	VR
Thedusia procera Cooper and Grant	R
Tropidelasma anthicum Cooper and Grant	R
Waagenoconcha magnifica Cooper and Grant	VR

LOCALITY N726s : Word Formation, China Tank Member

	Rarity code
Composita enormis Cooper and Grant	R
Crurithyris tholiaphor Cooper and Grant	VR
Dielasma sp.	VR
Dyoros (*Lissosia*) *concavus* Cooper and Grant	VR
Enteletes wordensis R.E. King	VR
Hustedia pugilla nasiterna Cooper and Grant	VR
Meekella skenoides Girty	VR
Megousia mucronata Cooper and Grant	R
Metriolepis pulvinata Cooper and Grant	VR
Neospirifer amphigyus Cooper and Grant	R
Paucispinifera auriculata Muir-Wood and Cooper	VR
Rhynchopora palumbula Cooper and Grant	VR
Spiriferella embrithes Cooper and Grant	VR
Spiriferellina hilli (Girty)	VR
Stenoscisma renode Cooper and Grant	VR

LOCALITY N726t : Word Formation, Appel Ranch Member

	Rarity code
Cartorhium orbiculatum Cooper and Grant	VR
Cartorhium retusum Cooper and Grant	VR
Composita enormis Cooper and Grant	R
Cyclacantharia kingorum Cooper and Grant	C
Derbyia filosa Cooper and Grant	C
Dielasma zebratum Cooper and Grant	C
Echinauris lateralis Muir-Wood and Cooper	VR
Echinosteges tuberculatus (R.E. King)	R
Eolyttonia sp.	R
Grandaurispina crassa Cooper and Grant	R
Heteralosia hystricula (Girty)	C
Hustedia pugilla hebetata Cooper and Grant	C
Liosotella wordensis (R.E. King)	C
Meekella skenoides Girty	R

	Rarity code
LOCALITY N726t - Continued	
Neophricadothyris conara Cooper and Grant	R
Paucispinifera auriculata Muir-Wood and Cooper	A
Petasmatherus opulus Cooper and Grant	VR
Reticulariina cerina Cooper and Grant	C
Rhamnaria kingorum Muir-Wood and Cooper	VR
Spiriferella propria Cooper and Grant	VR
Xenosteges quadratus Cooper and Grant	R
LOCALITY N726u : Cathedral Mountain Formation	
Acanthocrania sp.	VR
Acosarina mesoplatys (R.E. King)	A
Choanodus irregularis Cooper and Grant	C
Choanodus perfectus Cooper and Grant	VR
Chonosteges costellatus Cooper and Grant	VR
Chonosteges pulcher Cooper and Grant	C
Chonosteges variabilis Cooper and Grant	C
Collemataria gregaria Cooper and Grant	VA
Composita imbricata Cooper and Grant	C
Composita sp.	R
Compressoproductus flabellatus Cooper and Grant	R
Derbyia cincinnata Cooper and Grant	VR
Derbyia complicata Cooper and Grant	VR
Derbyia informis Cooper and Grant	C
Derbyia laqueata Cooper and Grant	C
Dielasma sp.	VR
Dyoros (Lissosia) vagabundus Cooper and Grant	A
Dyoros (Tetragonetes) giganteus Cooper and Grant	VR
Echinauris circularis Cooper and Grant	VR
Echinauris irregularis Cooper and Grant	A
Edriosteges multispinosus Muir-Wood and Cooper	C
Eolyttonia circularis Cooper and Grant	C
Hercosia uddeni (Böse)	A
Heterelasma sp.	VR
Hustedia lusca Cooper and Grant	A
Hustedia spicata Cooper and Grant	VR
Lepidospirifer demissus Cooper and Grant	C
Meekella calathica Cooper and Grant	VA
Meekella sp.	C
Megousia auriculata Muir-Wood and Cooper	R
Megousia umbonata Cooper and Grant	VR
Metriolepis tegulata Cooper and Grant	R
Neophricadothyris bullata Cooper and Grant	VR
Neophricadothyris sp.	R
Neospirifer mansuetus Cooper and Grant	C
Nudauris linospina Cooper and Grant	VR
Peniculauris subcostata (R.E. King)	VR
Petasmaia expansa Cooper and Grant	R
Pontisia stehlii stehlii Cooper and Grant	R
Pontisia stehlii tumidosa Cooper and Grant	R
Rhamnaria tenuispinosa Cooper and Grant	C
Rugatia paraindica (McKee)	VR
Stenoscisma sp.	R
Stenoscisma triquetrum Cooper and Grant	VR
Xenosteges adherens Muir-Wood and Cooper	A
LOCALITY N726v : Cathedral Mountain Formation	
Anemonaria sublaevis (R.E. King)	R
Megousia umbonata Cooper and Grant	R
LOCALITY N726w : Cathedral Mountain Formation	
Megousia umbonata Cooper and Grant	VR
Nudauris linospina Cooper and Grant	R
LOCALITY N726x : Cathedral Mountain Formation	
Acanthocrania sp.	VR

	Rarity code
Acosarina mesoplatys (R.E. King)	C
Choanodus irregularis Cooper and Grant	VR
Chonosteges variabilis Cooper and Grant	VR
Composita sp.	R
Derbyia cincinnata Cooper and Grant	VR
Derbyia laqueata Cooper and Grant	R
Dyoros (Lissosia) vagabundus Cooper and Grant	R
Echinauris sp.	VR
Goniarina sp. 7	R
Hercosia uddeni (Böse)	R
Hustedia ampullacea Cooper and Grant	R
Hustedia spicata Cooper and Grant	C
Institella leonardensis (R.E. King)	R
Kochiproductus sp.	VR
Lepidocrania tardispinosa Cooper and Grant	R
Loxophragmus ellipticus Cooper and Grant	R
Martinia miranda Cooper and Grant	C
Meekella calathica Cooper and Grant	A
Meekella sp.	R
Metriolepis tegulata Cooper and Grant	R
Neophricadothyris bullata Cooper and Grant	R
Neospirifer mansuetus Cooper and Grant	C
Niviconia globosa (R.E. King)	C
Petasmaia expansa Cooper and Grant	R
Rhamnaria vinnula Cooper and Grant	VR
Rhipidomella hispidula Cooper and Grant	R
Tautosia fastigiata Cooper and Grant	VR
Xenosteges adherens Muir-Wood and Cooper	C
LOCALITY N726y : Cathedral Mountain Formation	
Acosarina mesoplatys (R.E. King)	VR
Anemonaria sublaevis (R.E. King)	R
Chonosteges variabilis Cooper and Grant	R
Collemataria gregaria Cooper and Grant	R
Composita imbricata Cooper and Grant	R
Compressoproductus curtus Cooper and Grant	VR
Dyoros (Lissosia) vagabundus Cooper and Grant	VR
Dyoros (Tetragonetes) planus Cooper and Grant	VR
Echinauris irregularis Cooper and Grant	VR
Edriosteges multispinosus Muir-Wood and Cooper	VR
Eolyttonia circularis Cooper and Grant	VR
Hercosia uddeni (Böse)	VR
Kochiproductus sp. 6	VR
Lepidospirifer angulatus Cooper and Grant	VR
Lepidospirifer demissus Cooper and Grant	VR
Meekella calathica Cooper and Grant	VR
Meekella occidentalis (Newberry)	VR
Megousia auriculata Muir-Wood and Cooper	VR
Megousia umbonata Cooper and Grant	VR
Neospirifer mansuetus Cooper and Grant	R
Nudauris linospina Cooper and Grant	C
Peniculauris subcostata (R.E. King)	R
Pontisia stehlii stehlii Cooper and Grant	VR
Rhamnaria tenuispinosa Cooper and Grant	R
Rugatia occidentalis parvauris (Newberry)	C
Rugatia paraindica (McKee)	VR
Stenoscisma triquetrum Cooper and Grant	VR
Thamnosia anterospinosa Cooper and Grant	VR
LOCALITY N726z : Road Canyon Formation	
Acosarina mesoplatys (R.E. King)	C
Cenorhynchia saginata Cooper and Grant	R
Chondronia ovalis Cooper and Grant	VR
Composita quantilla Cooper and Grant	C
Composita stalagmium Cooper and Grant	VA

	Rarity code
LOCALITY N726z - Continued	
Cyclacantharia paucispinosa Cooper and Grant	R
Derbyia cincinnata Cooper and Grant	R
Derbyia laqueata Cooper and Grant	R
Dielasma ellipsoideum Cooper and Grant	VR
Echinauris irregularis Cooper and Grant	R
Edriostges multispinosus Muir-Wood and Cooper	C
Eolyttonia chaotica Cooper and Grant	VR
Hercosestria cribrosa Cooper and Grant	C
Holotricharina hirsuta Cooper and Grant	VR
Hustedia cuneata Cooper and Grant	VR
Hustedia narinosa Cooper and Grant	VA
Lepidocrania tardispinosa Cooper and Grant	A
Meekella calathica Cooper and Grant	A
Megousia auriculata Muir-Wood and Cooper	R
Metriolepis sp.	VR
Neophricadothyris bullata Cooper and Grant	R
Neospirifer bakeri bakeri R.E. King	R
Paucispinifera sulcata Cooper and Grant	VR
Peniculauris subcostata (R.E. King)	VR
Pontisia sp.	VR
Reticulariina craticula Cooper and Grant	C
Rhamnaria tenuispinosa Cooper and Grant	VR
Rhynchopora hebetata Cooper and Grant	VR
Stenoscisma calvatum Cooper and Grant	VR
Stenoscisma camurum Cooper and Grant	VR
Stenoscisma triquetrum Cooper and Grant	VR
LOCALITY N726za : Road Canyon Formation	
Acosarina mesoplatys (R.E. King)	VR
Cenorhynchia saginata Cooper and Grant	VR
Composita quantilla Cooper and Grant	R
Composita stalagmium Cooper and Grant	C
Cyclacantharia paucispinosa Cooper and Grant	VR
Derbyia cincinnata Cooper and Grant	VR
Dielasma ellipsoideum Cooper and Grant	R
Hercosestria cribrosa Cooper and Grant	VR
Hustedia connorsi Cooper and Grant	C
Hustedia narinosa Cooper and Grant	R
Meekella calathica Cooper and Grant	VR
Neophricadothyris bullata Cooper and Grant	R
Neospirifer bakeri bakeri R.E. King	VR
Paucispinifera sulcata Cooper and Grant	C
Reticulariina craticula Cooper and Grant	C
Rhynchopora hebetata Cooper and Grant	C
Stenoscisma triquetrum Cooper and Grant	R
LOCALITY N727a : Skinner Ranch Formation, Sullivan Peak Member	
Acosarina dorsisulcata Cooper and Grant	R
Acritosia peculiaris Cooper and Grant	R
Chonosteges variabilis Cooper and Grant	R
Composita apheles Cooper and Grant	R
Compressoproductus parvus Cooper and Grant	VR
Derbyia crenulata Girty	VR
Diplanus lamellatus (R.E. King)	R
Echinauris irregularis Cooper and Grant	VR
Eolyttonia sp.	R
Glyptosteges angustus (R.E. King)	R
Glyptosteges intricatus Cooper and Grant	VR
Goniarina sp. 6	VR
Hustedia hessensis R.E. King	R
Kochiproductus sp. 5	VR
Lepidospirifer sp.	VR
Limbella limbata Cooper and Grant	VR

	Rarity code
Meekella hessensis R.E. King	C
Metriolepis sp.	VR
Neophricadothyris sp.	VR
Peniculauris sp. 1	VR
Petrocrania sp.	VR
Reticulariina impressa Cooper and Grant	VR
Rhamnaria grandis Cooper and Grant	VR
Rhipidomella hessensis R.E. King	R
Sceletonia crassa Cooper and Grant	VR
Spyridiophora reticulata (R.E. King)	C
Tropidelasma sp. 3?	VR
LOCALITY N727b : Skinner Ranch Formation	
Spyridiophora reticulata (R.E. King)	VR
LOCALITY N727d : Neal Ranch Formation	
Cenorhynchia hebata Cooper and Grant	VR
Composita strongyle Cooper and Grant	R
Crurithyris tumibilis Cooper and Grant	VR
Derbyia carteri Cooper and Grant	R
Diplanus catatonus Cooper and Grant	VR
Enteletes wolfcampensis R.E. King	R
Geyerella kingorum Cooper and Grant	R
Isogramma vidriense Cooper and Grant	VR
Meekella prionota Cooper and Grant	R
Orthotetella wolfcampensis R.E. King	VR
Parenteletes cooperi R.E. King	VR
Rhipidomella miscella Cooper and Grant	VR
Teguliferina boesei R.E. King	C
Tropidelasma culmenatum Cooper and Grant	R
LOCALITY N727e : Neal Ranch Formation	
Acanthocrania sp.	VR
Atelestegastus marginatus Cooper and Grant	VR
Beecheria elliptica Cooper and Grant	R
Camarelasma neali Cooper and Grant	R
Cancrinella sp.	VR
Cenorhynchia camerata Cooper and Grant	C
Cenorhynchia hebata Cooper and Grant	C
Chelononia neali Cooper and Grant	C
Cleiothyridina rectimarginata Cooper and Grant	R
Composita sp.	C
Composita strongyle Cooper and Grant	C
Crurithyris tumibilis Cooper and Grant	C
Derbyia bella Cooper and Grant	VA
Derbyia carteri Cooper and Grant	R
Derbyia sp.	R
Dielasma pygmaeum Cooper and Grant	C
Dielasma sp.	VR
Diplanus catatonus Cooper and Grant	VR
Enteletes wolfcampensis R.E. King	R
Eolyttonia fredericksi (R.E. King)	VR
Fimbrinia sp. 2	R
Geyerella kingorum Cooper and Grant	VR
Goniarina sp. 6	R
Hustedia trita trita Cooper and Grant	C
Hystriculina sp.	VR
Hystriculina sulcata Cooper and Grant	R
Isogramma concavum Cooper and Grant	VR
Kochiproductus sp.	VR
Lepidocrania sparsispinosa Cooper and Grant	VR
Limbella wolfcampensis (R.E. King)	R
Linoproductus sp.	VR
Martinia exigua Cooper and Grant	R
Martinia nealranchensis Cooper and Grant	R
Martinia sp.	R

	Rarity code
LOCALITY N727e - Continued	
Meekella prionota Cooper and Grant	A
Neochonetes liratus Cooper and Grant	VR
Neochonetes sp.	VR
Neophricadothyris transversa Cooper and Grant	R
Neospirifer apothescelus Cooper and Grant	R
Neospirifer placidus Cooper and Grant	C
Nudauris tribulosa Cooper and Grant	R.
Orthotetella wolfcampensis R.E. King	VR
Orthotichia koziowskii R.E. King	A
Parenteletes cooperi R.E. King	C
Pontisia kingi Cooper and Grant	C
Pontisia parva Cooper and Grant	R
Pontisia wolfcampensis Cooper and Grant	R
Pseudoleptodus conicus Cooper and Grant	C
Reticulariina sp.	R
Reticulariina strigosa Cooper and Grant	R
Rhipidomella miscella Cooper and Grant	C
Spiriferellina nasuta Cooper and Grant	R
Stenoscisma bellatulum Cooper and Grant	R
Striatifera linoproductiformis Cooper and Grant	VR
Teguliferina boesei R.E. King	C
Tropidelasma culmenatum Cooper and Grant	VR
LOCALITY N727f : Skinner Ranch Formation	
Acosarina dorsisulcata Cooper and Grant	R
Acritosia solida Cooper and Grant	R
Choanodus irregularis Cooper and Grant	VR
Composita sp.	R
Derbyia sp.	R
Echinauris sp.	R
Enteletes subcircularis Cooper and Grant	VR
Hustedia sp.	VR
Limbella limbata Cooper and Grant	VR
Meekella hessensis R.E. King	C
Neospirifer sp.	VR
Rhipidomella hessensis R.E. King	C
Spyridiophora reticulata (R.E. King)	VR
LOCALITY N727h : Skinner Ranch Formation	
Cartorhium zoyei Cooper and Grant	VR
LOCALITY N727i : Lenox Hills Formation	
Reticulatia sp.	VR
LOCALITY N727j : Word Formation, Appel Ranch Member	
Bothrionia transversa Cooper and Grant	C
Cartorhium orbiculatum Cooper and Grant	R
Cenorhynchia fracida Cooper and Grant	VR
Composita enormis Cooper and Grant	VR
Composita parasulcata Cooper and Grant	C
Cooperina sp.	VR
Crurithyris tholiaphor Cooper and Grant	VR
Ctenalosia fixata Cooper and Stehli	A
Cyclacantharia kingorum Cooper and Grant	C
Derbyia pannucia Cooper and Grant	VR
Derbyia texta Cooper and Grant	C
Dielasma sp.	VR
Dielasma zebratum Cooper and Grant	R
Divaricosta vagabunda Cooper and Grant	R
Dyoros (Dyoros) extensus Cooper and Grant	A
Dyoros (Tetragonetes) quadrangulatus Cooper and Grant	A
Eolyttonia progressa Cooper and Grant	C
Glossothyropsis rectangulata Cooper and Grant	R
Grandaurispina crassa Cooper and Grant	C
Heteralosia hystricula (Girty)	VR

	Rarity code
Hustedia pugilla hebetata Cooper and Grant	C.
Leiorhynchoidea scelesta Cooper and Grant	VR
Leurosina marginata Cooper and Grant	A
Liosotella irregularis Cooper and Grant	A
Meekella skenoides Girty	C
Megousia definita Cooper and Grant	R
Metriolepis pulvinata Cooper and Grant	VR
Metriolepis sp.	VR
Neophricadothyris sp.	VR
Paraspiriferina rotundata Cooper and Grant	C
Paucispinifera sp.	R
Phrenophoria subcarinata Cooper and Grant	R
Pseudodielasma globulum Cooper and Grant	C
Pseudodielasma ovatum Cooper and Grant	C
Pseudoleptodus grandis Cooper and Grant	VR
Reticulariina cerina Cooper and Grant	C
Rhamnaria kingorum Muir-Wood and Cooper	C
Rhynchopora palumbula Cooper and Grant	R
Spiriferella clypeata Cooper and Grant	C
Spiriferellina hilli (Girty)	VR
Spiriferinaella scalpata Cooper and Grant	VR
Stenoscisma sp.	VR
Tautosia distorta Cooper and Grant	VR
Texarina elongata Cooper and Grant	VR
Texarina sp.	VR
Thamnosia phragmophora Cooper and Grant	VR
Thedusia procera Cooper and Grant	VR
Tropidelasma anthicum Cooper and Grant	VR
Waagenoconcha magnifica Cooper and Grant	R
Wellerella girtyi girtyi Cooper and Grant	C
Xenosteges quadratus Cooper and Grant	R
Yakovlevia indentata Cooper and Grant	C
LOCALITY N727m : Skinner Ranch Formation	
Chonosteges variabilis Cooper and Grant	VR
Glyptosteges intricatus Cooper and Grant	R
Stenoscisma hadrum Cooper and Grant	VR
LOCALITY N727n : Skinner Ranch Formation	
Glyptosteges intricatus Cooper and Grant	VR
LOCALITY N727o : Cathedral Mountain Formation	
Agelesia triagonalis (R.E. King)	R
Composita sp.	VR
Compressoproductus curtus Cooper and Grant	VR
Enteletes leonardensis R.E. King	VR
Hustedia sp.	VR
Neospirifer mansuetus Cooper and Grant	VR
Stenoscisma triquetrum Cooper and Grant	VR
LOCALITY N727p : Cathedral Mountain Formation, Wedin Member	
Agelesia triagonalis (R.E. King)	C
Cartorhium coristum Cooper and Grant	R
Cenorhynchia mitigata Cooper and Grant	VR
Choanodus perfectus Cooper and Grant	R
Chonosteges pulcher Cooper and Grant	R
Compressoproductus thomasi Cooper and Grant	VR
Derbyia complicata Cooper and Grant	R
Dielasma ellipsoideum Cooper and Grant	VR
Diplanus lamellatus (R.E. King)	R
Dyoros (Lissosia) vagabundus Cooper and Grant	VR
Echinauris irregularis Cooper and Grant	R
Enteletes plummeri R.E. King	A
Hercosia uddeni (Böse)	VR
Heterelasma angulatum Cooper and Grant	VR
Hustedia lusca Cooper and Grant	R

	Rarity code
LOCALITY N727p - Continued	
Institella leonardensis (R.E. King)	A
Lepidocrania tardispinosa Cooper and Grant	VR
Meekella calathica Cooper and Grant	C
Metriolepis larina Cooper and Grant	C
Neophricadothyris bullata Cooper and Grant	VR
Rhipidomella hispidula Cooper and Grant	A
Stenoscisma exutum Cooper and Grant	VR
Stenoscisma triquetrum Cooper and Grant	VR
Xenosteges adherens Muir-Wood and Cooper	VR
LOCALITY N727q : Cathedral Mountain Formation	
Cartorhium coristum Cooper and Grant	VR
Cenorhynchia mitigata Cooper and Grant	VR
Chonosteges pulcher Cooper and Grant	VR
Compressoproductus thomasi Cooper and Grant	VR
Enteletes plummeri R.E. King	VR
Enteletes sp.	VR
Hercosia uddeni (Böse)	VR
Institella leonardensis (R.E. King)	R
Nudauris linospina Cooper and Grant	VR
Rhipidomella hispidula Cooper and Grant	VR
LOCALITY N727t : Skinner Ranch Formation, Decie Ranch Member	
Spyridiophora reticulata (R.E. King)	VR
LOCALITY N727u : Skinner Ranch Formation, Decie Ranch Member	
Acritosia peculiaris Cooper and Grant	VR
Antronaria emarginata Cooper and Grant	C
Antronaria titania Cooper and Grant	C
Cartorhium zoyei Cooper and Grant	R
Chonosteges matutinus Cooper and Grant	VR
Composita apheles Cooper and Grant	C
Enteletes rotundobesus Cooper and Grant	VR
Geyerella hessi Cooper and Grant	VR
Hustedia sp.	VR
Meekella hessensis R.E. King	VR
Orthotichia newelli Cooper and Grant	VR
Rhipidomella hessensis R.E. King	R
Spyridiophora reticulata (R.E. King)	C
Stenoscisma problematicum Cooper and Grant	C
LOCALITY N727w : Cathedral Mountain Formation	
Agelesia triagonalis (R.E. King)	R
Composita sp.	VR
Crurithyris sp.	VR
Enteletes sp.	VR
Eolyttonia sp.	VR
Hustedia sp.	R
Meekella calathica Cooper and Grant	R
Rhipidomella hispidula Cooper and Grant	R
LOCALITY N727x : Cathedral Mountain Formation	
Agelesia triagonalis (R.E. King)	VR
Chonosteges variabilis Cooper and Grant	VR
Composita sp.	VR
Institella leonardensis (R.E. King)	R
Meekella calathica Cooper and Grant	VR
Peniculauris subcostata (R.E. King)	VR
Stenoscisma sp.	VR
LOCALITY N728 : Cherry Canyon Formation, Getaway Member	
Allorhynchus permianum permianum Stehli	C
Bothrionia guadalupensis Cooper and Grant	R

	Rarity code
Cartorhium retusum Cooper and Grant	C
Cartorhium sp.	VR
Composita enormis Cooper and Grant	R
Composita parasulcata Cooper and Grant	C
Composita prospera Cooper and Grant	A
Composita sp.	VR
Cooperina inexpectata Termier, Termier and Pajaud	VR
Crurithyris tholiaphor Cooper and Grant	C
Ctenalosia fixata Cooper and Stehli	A
Ctenalosia sp.	R
Cyclacantharia robusta Cooper and Grant	C
Derbyia filosa Cooper and Grant	C
Derbyia pannucia Cooper and Grant	VR
Derbyia sp.	VR
Derbyia texta Cooper and Grant	C
Dielasma compactum Cooper and Grant	VR
Dielasma ligonorum Cooper and Grant	R
Dielasma pictile Cooper and Grant	C
Dielasma subcylindricum Cooper and Grant	VR
Divaricosta squarrosa Cooper and Grant	R
Dyoros (*Dyoros*) *convexus* Cooper and Grant	VA
Dyoros (*Tetragonetes*) *auriculatus* Cooper and Grant	C
Dyoros (*Tetragonetes*) *subquadratus* Cooper and Grant	C
Echinauris productelloides Cooper and Grant	C
Echinosteges tuberculatus (R.E. King)	VR
Eolyttonia progressa Cooper and Grant	C
Grandaurispina belliformis Cooper and Grant	VR
Grandaurispina rudis Cooper and Grant	C
Grandaurispina sp.	VR
Heteralosia hystricula (Girty)	VR
Heteralosia magnispina Cooper and Grant	C
Heteralosia sp.	VR
Heterelasma concavum Cooper and Grant	R
Heterelasma sp.	VR
Holosia ovoidea Cooper and Grant	VR
Hustedia citeria Cooper and Grant	VA
Hustedia hapala Cooper and Grant	C
Hustedia tomea Cooper and Grant	C
Isogramma sp.	VR
Leiorhynchoidea rotundidorsa Cooper and Grant	VR
Leiorhynchoidea scelesta Cooper and Grant	R
Lepidocrania sp.	VR
Lepidocrania sublamellosa Cooper and Grant	R
Leurosina delicata Cooper and Grant	R
Liosotella spinumbona Cooper and Grant	A
Liosotella wordensis (R.E. King)	C
Martinia causaria Cooper and Grant	VR
Meekella skenoides Girty	VA
Metriolepis exserta Cooper and Grant	C
Neophricadothyris conara Cooper and Grant	VR
Notothyris sp.	VR
Paraspiriferina paginata Cooper and Grant	R
Paraspiriferina sp.	VR
Paucispinifera tumida Cooper and Grant	C
Petasmatherus opulus Cooper and Grant	VR
Phrenophoria pinguiformis Cooper and Grant	C
Polymorpharia polymorpha Cooper and Grant	C
Pseudodielasma magnum Cooper and Grant	R
Pseudodielasma sp.	VR
Pseudoleptodus getawayensis Stehli	C
Rallacosta sp. 1	VR
Reticulariina roscida Cooper and Grant	C
Reticulariina sp.	VR
Rhamnaria sulcata Cooper and Grant	C
Rhynchopora palumbula Cooper and Grant	VR

	Rarity code
LOCALITY N728 - Continued	
Spiriferella gloverae Cooper and Grant	C
Spiriferinaella medialis Cooper and Grant	VR
Stenoscisma aberrans Cooper and Grant	VR
Stenoscisma renode Cooper and Grant	R
Stenoscisma sp.	VR
Strophalosia inexpectans Cooper and Grant	VR
Tautosia transenna Cooper and Grant	C
Texarina solita Cooper and Grant	VR
Thedusia dischides Cooper and Grant	A
Tropidelasma furcillatum Cooper and Grant	VR
Tropidelasma sp.	VR
Waagenoconcha magnifica Cooper and Grant	R
Wellerella girtyi seorsa Cooper and Grant	A
Xenosteges anomalus Cooper and Grant	C
Xenosteges quadratus Cooper and Grant	C
Yakovlevia costellata Cooper and Grant	R
LOCALITY N728d : Hueco Formation	
Acosarina sp.	R
Cancrinella sp.	VR
Crurithyris sp.	VR
Ctenalosia sp.	VR
Dasysaria undulata Cooper and Grant	R
Derbyia sp.	R
Kochiproductus sp.	VR
Kutorginella sp.	VR
Leurosina serratoseptata Cooper and Grant	C
Meekella sp.	VR
Nudauris reticulata Cooper and Grant	VR
Spuriosa sp.	VR
LOCALITY N728e : Bone Spring Formation	
Acosarina dorsisulcata Cooper and Grant	A
Acritosia teguliferoides (R.E. King)	VA
Altiplecus cooperi Stehli	R
Antiquatonia planumbona Stehli	R
Antronaria dissona Cooper and Grant	C
Antronaria mesicostalis (Girty)	R
Antronaria spectabilis Cooper and Grant	VR
Beecheria sp.	VR
Cancrinella sparsispinosa Cooper and Grant	VR
Cartorhium zoyei Cooper and Grant	C
Chonetinella biplicata (R.E. King)	C
Chonetinella victoriana (Girty)	R
Collemataria americana (Girty)	R
Collemataria marshalli (Stehli)	C
Composita cracens Cooper and Grant	C
Composita sp.	R
Crenispirifer angulatus (R.E. King)	C
Crurithyris inflata Stehli	VR
Crurithyris sulcata Stehli	R
Cryptacanthia glabra Cooper and Grant	VR
Derbyia crenulata Girty	C
Derbyia nasuta Girty	A
Derbyia sp.	R
Dielasma diabloense Stehli	C
Dielasma sp.	VR
Diplanus lamellatus (R.E. King)	A
Dyoros (*Dyoros*) *consanguineus* (Girty)	C
Elliottella minima (Stehli)	A
Elliottella multicostata Cooper and Grant	R
Elliottella transversalis (Stehli)	R
Enallosia rotundovata Cooper and Grant	R
Enteletes stehlii Cooper and Grant	A
Eolyttonia diabloensis (Stehli)	C

	Rarity code
Fimbrinia ovata Cooper and Grant	VR
Glossothyropsis sp. 1 (Girty)	VR
Goniarina diabloensis Cooper and Grant	VR
Goniarina permiana (Stehli)	VR
Goniarina sp.	VR
Gypospirifer infraplicus (R.E. King)	VR
Heterelasma quadratum Cooper and Grant	VR
Hustedia hessensis R.E. King	A
Hustedia sp.	R
Isogramma sp.	VR
Kozlowskia kingi Stehli	VA
Leiorhynchoidea sp.	VR
Lepidocrania sp.	VR
Leurosina sinesulca (Stehli)	A
Leurosina vulgarica Cooper and Grant	C
Limbella victorioensis Stehli	VR
Linoproductus angustus R.E. King	C
Liraria lirata Cooper and Grant	C
Meekella attenuata Girty	VA
Meekella hessensis R.E. King	VR
Meekella intermedia Cooper and Grant	VR
Micraphelia sp.	C
Nudauris diabloensis Stehli	C
Orthotetella wolfcampensis R.E. King	VR
Orthotichia irregularis Cooper and Grant	VA
Paranorella sp. b	VR
Petrocrania diabloensis Cooper and Grant	VR
Pontisia nanas (Stehli)	R
Quadrochonetes girtyi Stehli	C
Ramavectus diabloensis Stehli	C
Reticulariina newelli (Stehli)	R
Reticulariina sp.	VR
Reticulariina tetrica Cooper and Grant	C
Rhipidomella hessensis R.E. King	A
Scacchinella americana Stehli	C
Spinifrons quadrata Stehli	A
Stenoscisma multicostum Stehli	VR
Stenoscisma sp.	VR
Teguliferina conida (Stehli)	A
Thamnosia parvispinosa (Stehli)	C
Undellaria magnifica Cooper and Grant	R
LOCALITY N728f : Bone Spring Formation	
Acanthocrania platys Cooper and Grant	VR
Acanthocrania sp.	VR
Acosarina dorsisulcata Cooper and Grant	C
Acritosia teguliferoides (R.E. King)	C
Altiplecus cooperi Stehli	VR
Antiquatonia planumbona Stehli	R
Antronaria dissona Cooper and Grant	VR
Antronaria spectabilis Cooper and Grant	A
Attenuatella texana Stehli	R
Beecheria sp.	VR
Cancrinella sparsispinosa Cooper and Grant	C
Chonetinella biplicata (R.E. King)	R
Chonetinella victoriana (Girty)	A
Collemataria americana (Girty)	C
Composita cracens Cooper and Grant	A
Cooperina sp.	VR
Crenispirifer angulatus (R.E. King)	A
Crurithyris inflata Stehli	C
Crurithyris sulcata Stehli	VA
Cryptacanthia glabra Cooper and Grant	VR
Cryptacanthia sinuata (Stehli)	R
Cyclacantharia sp. 2	VR

	Rarity code
LOCALITY N728f - Continued	
Derbyia crenulata Girty	R
Derbyia nasuta Girty	R
Dielasma diabloense Stehli	R
Dielasma microrhynchum Cooper and Grant	R
Dielasma sp.	VR
Diplanus lamellatus (R.E. King)	C
Dyoros (Dyoros) consanguineus (Girty)	VA
Elliottella minima (Stehli)	VR
Elliottella transversalis (Stehli)	VA
Enallosia rotundovata Cooper and Grant	VR
Enteletes stehlii Cooper and Grant	A
Eolyttonia diabloensis (Stehli)	C
Eridmatus sp.	VR
Fimbrinia ovata Cooper and Grant	R
Goniarina diabloensis Cooper and Grant	R
Goniarina permiana (Stehli)	VA
Heteralosia sp. 7	VR
Heterelasma geniculatum Stehli	C
Heterelasma quadratum Cooper and Grant	VR
Hustedia glomerosa Cooper and Grant	VA
Kozlowskia kingi Stehli	A
Leiorhynchoidea sp.	VR
Lepidocrania sp.	VR
Limbella victorioensis Stehli	C
Linoproductus angustus R.E. King	A
Martinia fucina Cooper and Grant	R
Meekella attenuata Girty	VR
Meekella hessensis R.E. King	C
Meekella intermedia Cooper and Grant	C
Metriolepis irenae (Stehli)	R
Neophricadothyris catatona Cooper and Grant	R
Nudauris diabloensis Stehli	C
Orthotetella wolfcampensis R.E. King	VR
Orthotichia irregularis Cooper and Grant	VA
Paranorella sp. 2	R
Poikilosakos informis Cooper and Grant	R
Pontisia longicosta (Stehli)	C
Pontisia nanas (Stehli)	A
Pseudoleptodus granulosus Cooper and Grant	VR
Quadrochonetes girtyi Stehli	VA
Reticulariina newelli (Stehli)	C
Reticulariina tetrica Cooper and Grant	C
Rhamnaria eximia Cooper and Grant	R
Rhipidomella hessensis R.E. King	A
Scacchinella americana Stehli	R
Spinifrons magna Cooper and Grant	A
Spyridiophora reticulata (R.E. King)	VR
Stenoscisma kalum Stehli	C
Stenoscisma multicostum Stehli	C
Stenoscisma sp.	VR
Tautosia lenumbona (Stehli)	C
Tautosia magnisepta (Stehli)	R
Teguliferina conida (Stehli)	C
Thamnosia parvispinosa (Stehli)	C
Undellaria magnifica Cooper and Grant	VR
LOCALITY N728g : Bone Spring Formation	
Acosarina mesoplatys (R.E. King)	VA
Antronaria specialis Cooper and Grant	C
Antronaria spectabilis Cooper and Grant	C
Chonosteges limbatus Cooper and Grant	R
Composita cracens Cooper and Grant	C
Composita sp.	VR
Heterelasma sp.	VR
Heterelasma sulciplicatum Cooper and Grant	C

	Rarity code
Hustedia decollatensis Cooper and Grant	C
Hustedia hessensis R.E. King	VR
Meekella hessensis R.E. King	C
Neophricadothyris sp.	C
Rhipidomella hessensis R.E. King	C
Spyridiophora reticulata (R.E. King)	VR
Stenoscisma levicostum Cooper and Grant	C
Stenoscisma sp.	VR
Wellerella? nitidula Cooper and Grant	VA
LOCALITY N728h : Bone Spring Formation	
Acosarina dorsisulcata Cooper and Grant	R
Acritosia teguliferoides (R.E. King)	R
Antronaria spectabilis Cooper and Grant	R
Cancrinella sparsispinosa Cooper and Grant	C
Chonetinella victoriana (Girty)	C
Collemataria americana (Girty)	VR
Composita cracens Cooper and Grant	C
Crenispirifer angulatus (R.E. King)	C
Crurithyris sulcata Stehli	A
Cryptacanthia glabra Cooper and Grant	VR
Derbyia crenulata Girty	C
Dielasma sp.	R
Diplanus lamellatus (R.E. King)	C
Dyoros (Dyoros) consanguineus (Girty)	C
Elliottella multicostata Cooper and Grant	VA
Elliottella transversalis (Stehli)	C
Enteletes stehlii Cooper and Grant	C
Fimbrinia ovata Cooper and Grant	R
Goniarina permiana (Stehli)	A
Heteralosia sp.	VR
Heterelasma quadratum Cooper and Grant	VR
Hustedia glomerosa Cooper and Grant	A
Kozlowskia kingi Stehli	C
Leiorhynchoidea sp.	VR
Lepidocrania sp.	VR
Limbella victorioensis Stehli	VR
Linoproductus angustus R.E. King	R
Meekella attenuata Girty	C
Meekella intermedia Cooper and Grant	VR
Orthotichia irregularis Cooper and Grant	VA
Pontisia longicosta (Stehli)	R
Pontisia nanas (Stehli)	R
Quadrochonetes girtyi Stehli	A
Reticulariina tetrica Cooper and Grant	R
Rhamnaria eximia Cooper and Grant	VR
Rhipidomella hessensis R.E. King	C
Scacchinella americana Stehli	VR
Spinifrons magna Cooper and Grant	VA
Spinifrons quadrata Stehli	C
Stenoscisma multicostum Stehli	VR
Tautosia lenumbona (Stehli)	VR
Thamnosia parvispinosa (Stehli)	C
LOCALITY N728i : Bell Canyon Formation, Lamar Member	
Acanthocrania sp.	VR
Allorhynchus venustulum Cooper and Grant	VR
Aphaurosia scutata Cooper and Grant	VR
Arionthia lamaria Cooper and Grant	R
Arionthia polypleura (Girty)	VR
Astegosia subquadrata (Girty)	C
Collemataria spatulata Cooper and Grant	R
Composita affinis Girty	C
Crenispirifer myllus Cooper and Grant	R
Crurithyris guadalupensis (Girty)	R

	Rarity code
LOCALITY N728i - Continued	
Derbyia sp.	R
Dielasma sp.	R
Dielasma sulcatum Girty	R
Elivina detecta Cooper and Grant	R
Fascicosta bella Cooper and Grant	VR
Heteralosia magnispina Cooper and Grant	VR
Hustedia opsia Cooper and Grant	C
Martinia rhomboidalis Girty	C
Ombonia guadalupensis (Girty)	C
Paraspiriferina billingsi (Shumard)	R
Plectelasma guadalupense (Girty)	VR
Reticulariina sp.	VR
Sarganostega pressa Cooper and Grant	R
Sestropoma cribriferum Cooper and Grant	VR
Timorina ovata (Girty)	VR
Tropidelasma gregarium (Girty)	A
LOCALITY N728j : Cibolo Formation, Breccia Zone	
Scacchinella titan Cooper and Grant	VR
LOCALITY N728k : Cibolo Formation, Breccia Zone	
Scacchinella titan Cooper and Grant	C
LOCALITY N728-l : Cibolo Formation, Breccia Zone	
Acosarina dorsisulcata Cooper and Grant	VR
Acosarina sp.	VR
Acritosia teguliferoides (R.E. King)	VR
Antronaria dissona Cooper and Grant	R
Chonetinella ciboloensis Cooper and Grant	VR
Cleiothyridina rectimarginata Cooper and Grant	VR
Composita sp.	VR
Crenispirifer angulatus (R.E. King)	VR
Derbyia crenulata Girty	R
Derbyia aff. *nasuta* Girty	R
Derbyia sp.	R
Dielasma sp.	VR
Diplanus rarus Cooper and Grant	C
Diplanus sp.	C
Echinauris? sp.	R
Elliottella cf. *varicostata* Cooper and Grant	R
Enteletes sp.	VR
Eolyttonia gigantea Cooper and Grant	C
Eolyttonia sp.	A
Fimbrinia sp. 3	VR
Hustedia sp.	VR
Hystriculina sp.	R
Juresania? sp.	VR
Kozlowskia alata Cooper and Grant	R
Meekella attenuata Girty	R
Meekella prionota Cooper and Grant	R
Pontisia robusta Cooper and Grant	VR
Scacchinella titan Cooper and Grant	VR
Stenoscisma problematicum Cooper and Grant	C
Teguliferina conida (Stehli)	R
LOCALITY N728m : Cibolo Formation, Breccia Zone	
Stenoscisma multicostum Stehli	VR
LOCALITY N728p : Bell Canyon Formation, Lamar Member	
Allorhynchus venustulum Cooper and Grant	C
Anomaloria anomala Cooper and Grant	A
Anteridocus swallovianus (Shumard)	R
Aphaurosia rotundata Cooper and Grant	C

	Rarity code
Aphaurosia scutata Cooper and Grant	VR
Arionthia lamaria Cooper and Grant	C
Astegosia subquadrata (Girty)	VA
Bryorhynchus bisulcatum (Shumard)	VR
Callispirina rotunda Cooper and Grant	C
Cartorhium sp.	VR
Cleiothyridina pilularis Cooper and Grant	R
Cleiothyridina sp.	VR
Collemataria spatulata Cooper and Grant	R
Composita affinis Girty	A
Composita sp.	VR
Crenispirifer myllus Cooper and Grant	A
Crurithyris guadalupensis (Girty)	VA
Ctenalosia sp.	VR
Deltarina magnicostata Cooper and Grant	A
Derbyia sp. 1	C
Derbyia sp.	C
Dielasma cordatum Girty	R
Dielasma sp.	R
Dielasma sulcatum Girty	C
Dielasma uniplicatum Cooper and Grant	VR
Dyoros (Dyoros) hillanus (Girty)	C
Echinosteges guadalupensis (Shumard)	VR
Eliva inflata Cooper and Grant	C
Eliva shumardi Cooper and Grant	A
Fascicosta longaeva (Girty)	R
Geyerella americana Girty	VR
Heteralosia magnispina Cooper and Grant	C
Heterelasma shumardianum Girty	VR
Heterelasma venustulum Girty	R
Hustedia rupinata Cooper and Grant	VA
Hustedia sp.	A
Lirellaria costellata Cooper and Grant	A
Lirellaria crassa Cooper and Grant	R
Martinia rhomboidalis Girty	VA
Metriolepis nabis Cooper and Grant	VR
Notothyris sp.	R
Ombonia guadalupensis (Girty)	C
Paraspiriferina billingsi (Shumard)	A
Paucispinifera latidorsata (Girty)	VR
Plectelasma guadalupense (Girty)	R
Pseudodielasma pinyonense Cooper and Grant	R
Ptilotorhynchus delicatum Cooper and Grant	R
Rallacosta sp.	VR
Reticulariina sp.	R
Rigbyella girtyi (Wanner and Sieverts)	VR
Sarganostega pressa Cooper and Grant	C
Scapharina levis Cooper and Grant	R
Sestropoma cribriferum Cooper and Grant	R
Spiriferellina nuda Cooper and Grant	C
Stenoscisma abbreviatum Cooper and Grant	R
Stenoscisma sp.	VR
Stenoscisma trabeatum Cooper and Grant	R
Strigirhynchia elongata Cooper and Grant	R
Strigirhynchia indentata (Shumard)	R
Tautosia elegans (Girty)	C
Tautosia shumardiana (Girty)	C
Thamnosia capitanensis (Girty)	VR
Thamnosia sp.	VR
Thedusia biconvexa Cooper and Grant	R
Thedusia trigonalis (Girty)	C
Thedusia ventricosa Cooper and Grant	C
Timorina ovata (Girty)	R
Tropidelasma gregarium (Girty)	C
Xenosaria exotica Cooper and Grant	VR

	Rarity code
LOCALITY N728q : Bell Canyon Formation, Lamar Member	
Anteridocus swallovianus (Shumard)	VR
Composita affinis Girty	VR
Crenispirifer myllus Cooper and Grant	VR
Deltarina magnicostata Cooper and Grant	VR
Derbyia sp.	VR
Dielasma sulcatum Girty	VR
Eliva inflata Cooper and Grant	VR
Geyerella americana Girty	VR
Heterelasma shumardianum Girty	VR
Hustedia rupinata Cooper and Grant	R
Martinia rhomboidalis Girty	C
Metriolepis nabis Cooper and Grant	VR
Ombonia guadalupensis (Girty)	VR
Paraspiriferina billingsi (Shumard)	VR
Plectelasma guadalupense (Girty)	VR
Sestropoma cribriferum Cooper and Grant	R
Spiriferella sulcifer (Shumard)	VR
Thedusia trigonalis (Girty)	VR
Thedusia ventricosa Cooper and Grant	VR
Timorina ovata (Girty)	VR
Tropidelasma gregarium (Girty)	R
Xenosteges umbonatus Cooper and Grant	VR
LOCALITY N728r : Bell Canyon Formation, Lamar Member	
Allorhynchus sp.	VR
Allorhynchus venustulum Cooper and Grant	R
Aneuthelasma amygdalinum Cooper and Grant	VR
Anteridocus swallovianus (Shumard)	C
Composita pyriformis Cooper and Grant	VR
Elivina detecta Cooper and Grant	VR
Fascicosta longaeva (Girty)	VR
Heterelasma shumardianum Girty	VR
Hustedia sp.	VR
Martinia rhomboidalis Girty	R
Paraspiriferina evax (Girty)	VR
Pseudoleptodus guadalupensis (Stehli)	VR
Tautosia shumardiana (Girty)	VR
LOCALITY N728s : Bell Canyon Formation, Lamar Member	
Astegosia subquadrata (Girty)	VR
Pseudoleptodus guadalupensis (Stehli)	VR
Stenoscisma trabeatum Cooper and Grant	VR
LOCALITY N728t : Bone Spring Formation	
Acosarina dorsisulcata Cooper and Grant	R
Chonetinella biplicata (R.E. King)	VR
Crenispirifer angulatus (R.E. King)	VR
Crurithyris sulcata Stehli	VR
Enteletes stehlii Cooper and Grant	VR
Hustedia sp.	VR
Meekella angustiplicata Cooper and Grant	VR
Quadrochonetes girtyi Stehli	VR
Rhipidomella hessensis R.E. King	VR
Thamnosia parvispinosa (Stehli)	VR
LOCALITY N728u : Capitan Formation	
Anteridocus swallovianus (Shumard)	VR
LOCALITY N728v : Bone Spring Formation	
Enteletes sp.	VR
Meekella hessensis R.E. King	VR

	Rarity code
LOCALITY N728w : Cherry Canyon Formation, Getaway Member	
Stenoscisma repigratum Cooper and Grant	VR
LOCALITY N728x : Graham Formation	
Gypospirifer gryphus Cooper and Grant	VR
LOCALITY N728y : Hueco Formation	
Gypospirifer nelsoni Cooper and Grant	VR
LOCALITY N729 : Bone Spring Formation	
Hustedia decollatensis Cooper and Grant	VR
Isogramma sp.	VR
Meekella hessensis R.E. King	R
Megousia auriculata Muir-Wood and Cooper	VR
LOCALITY N729e : Hess Formation	
Reticulatia sp.	VR
LOCALITY N729f : Skinner Ranch Formation, Poplar Tank Member	
Paranorella sp. 2	VR
LOCALITY N729h : Skinner Ranch Formation, Sullivan Peak Member	
Antronaria speciosa Cooper and Grant	VR
LOCALITY N729i : Skinner Ranch Formation, Decie Ranch Member	
Rugaria crassa Cooper and Grant	VR
Stenoscisma problematicum Cooper and Grant	VR
LOCALITY N729j : Skinner Ranch Formation	
Enteletes rotundobesus Cooper and Grant	VR
Stenoscisma pyraustoides Cooper and Grant	VR
LOCALITY N729ʹ-1 : Skinner Ranch Formation	
Geyerella hessi Cooper and Grant	VR
Limbella limbata Cooper and Grant	VR
LOCALITY N729m : Skinner Ranch Formation, Sullivan Peak Member	
Glyptosteges intricatus Cooper and Grant	VR
LOCALITY N729o : Skinner Ranch Formation, Sullivan Peak Member	
Oncosarina spinicostata Cooper and Grant	VR
LOCALITY N729p : Skinner Ranch Formation, Sullivan Peak Member	
Glyptosteges angustus (R.E. King)	VR
Megousia sp.	VR
Stenoscisma hadrum Cooper and Grant	VR
Torynechus alectorius Cooper and Grant	R
LOCALITY N729q : Skinner Ranch Formation, Poplar Tank Member	
Spyridiophora reticulata (R.E. King)	VR
LOCALITY N729r : Cathedral Mountain Formation	
Neophricadothyris bullata Cooper and Grant	VR
Neospirifer mansuetus Cooper and Grant	VR
LOCALITY N729u : Hess Formation	
Glyptosteges angustus (R.E. King)	VR
LOCALITY N729z : Cathedral Mountain Formation	
Stenoscisma triquetrum Cooper and Grant	VR
LOCALITY N730 : Cherry Canyon Formation, Getaway Member	
Acanthocrania conferta Cooper and Grant	VR

	Rarity code
LOCALITY N730 - Continued	
Allorhynchus formulosum Cooper and Grant	VR
Bothrionia pulchra Cooper and Grant	VR
Cartorhium retusum Cooper and Grant	VR
Cenorhynchia fracida Cooper and Grant	VR
Composita parasulcata Cooper and Grant	VR
Composita prospera Cooper and Grant	R
Cyclacantharia kingorum Cooper and Grant	C
Derbyia filosa Cooper and Grant	VR
Derbyia pannucia Cooper and Grant	VR
Dielasma pictile Cooper and Grant	VR
Dyoros (Dyoros) convexus Cooper and Grant	R
Dyoros (Tetragonetes) auriculatus Cooper and Grant	VR
Dyoros (Tetragonetes) complanatus Cooper and Grant	R
Echinauris productelloides Cooper and Grant	R
Echinosteges tuberculatus (R.E. King)	VR
Eolyttonia progressa Cooper and Grant	C
Grandaurispina undulata Cooper and Grant	VR
Heteralosia magnispina Cooper and Grant	VR
Heterelasma sp.	VR
Hustedia citeria Cooper and Grant	C
Hustedia hapala Cooper and Grant	R
Hustedia tomea Cooper and Grant	VR
Leiorhynchoidea scelesta Cooper and Grant	VR
Lepidocrania sublamellosa Cooper and Grant	VR
Liosotella wordensis (R.E. King)	C
Meekella skenoides Girty	C
Neophricadothyris conara Cooper and Grant	VR
Paraspiriferina paginata Cooper and Grant	VR
Paucispinifera tumida Cooper and Grant	VR
Petasmatherus opulus Cooper and Grant	VR
Pseudodielasma magnum Cooper and Grant	VR
Reticulariina girtyi Cooper and Grant	R
Rhamnaria sulcata Cooper and Grant	R
Rhynchopora guadalupensis Cooper and Grant	VR
Spiriferella sp.	VR
Thedusia dischides Cooper and Grant	R
Undulella guadalupensis Cooper and Grant	R
Wellerella girtyi seorsa Cooper and Grant	R
Xenosteges quadratus Cooper and Grant	VR
LOCALITY N730a : Lenox Hills Formation	
Stenoscisma sp. 1	VR
LOCALITY N730c : Neal Ranch Formation	
Crurithyris tumibilis Cooper and Grant	VR
LOCALITY N730k : Skinner Ranch Formation, Sullivan Peak Member	
Neophricadothyris catatona Cooper and Grant	VR
LOCALITY N730m : Gaptank Formation	
Echinaria cf. *moorei* (Dunbar and Condra)	VR
LOCALITY N730n : Gaptank Formation, Uddenites Member	
Nudauris splendens Cooper and Grant	VR
LOCALITY N730o : Skinner Ranch Formation	
Compressoproductus parvus Cooper and Grant	VR
Derbyia sp.	VR
Oncosarina sp.	VR
Spyridiophora reticulata (R.E. King)	VR
LOCALITY N730q : Cathedral Mountain Formation	
Compressoproductus thomasi Cooper and Grant	VR

	Rarity code
Enteletes plummeri R.E. King	VR
Institella leonardensis (R.E. King)	VR
Kochiproductus sp.	VR
Linoproductus sp.	VR
Rhynchopora hebetata Cooper and Grant	VR
Waagenoconcha convexa Cooper and Grant	VR
LOCALITY N730r : Skinner Ranch Formation	
Composita apheles Cooper and Grant	VR
Dielasma sp.	VR
Spyridiophora reticulata (R.E. King)	VR
Stenoscisma problematicum Cooper and Grant	VR
LOCALITY N730s : Skinner Ranch Formation	
Chonosteges variabilis Cooper and Grant	VR
Compressoproductus parvus Cooper and Grant	VR
Rhipidomella hessensis R.E. King	VR
Spyridiophora reticulata (R.E. King)	VR
LOCALITY N730u : Cathedral Mountain Formation	
Institella leonardensis (R.E. King)	VR
Torynechus caelatus Cooper and Grant	VR
Xestosia schucherti (R.E. King)	VR
LOCALITY N730v : Skinner Ranch Formation	
Neophricadothyris sp.	VR
Spyridiophora reticulata (R.E. King)	VR
Stenoscisma pansum Cooper and Grant	VR
LOCALITY N731 : Bell Canyon Formation, Hegler Member	
Acanthocrania sp.	VR
Acanthocrania vasta Cooper and Grant	R
Allorhynchus sp.	R
Allorhynchus venustulum Cooper and Grant	R
Altiplecus? deltosus Cooper and Grant	R
Altiplecus extensus Cooper and Grant	VR
Anteridocus bicostatus Cooper and Grant	VR
Anteridocus subcarinatus Cooper and Grant	VR
Anteridocus swallovianus (Shumard)	C
Aphaurosia scutata Cooper and Grant	VR
Arionthia lamaria Cooper and Grant	VR
Arionthia polypleura (Girty)	R
Bryorhynchus bisulcatum (Shumard)	VA
Bryorhynchus gratiosum (Girty)	R
Cartorhium sp.	R
Chonetinetes sp.	VR
Chonetinetes varians Cooper and Grant	A
Composita emarginata Girty	R
Composita pyriformis Cooper and Grant	A
Composita sp.	C
Cooperina inexpectata Termier, Termier and Pajaud	R
Cooperina sp.	VR
Craspedona newelli Cooper and Grant	C
Crenispirifer jubatus Cooper and Grant	C
Deltarina magnicostata Cooper and Grant	R
Derbyia sp. 1	R
Derbyia sp.	A
Derbyia texta Cooper and Grant	R
Dielasma cordatum Girty	VR
Dielasma sp.	C
Dielasma subcirculare Cooper and Grant	VR
Dielasma sulcatum Girty	R
Dyoros (Dyoros) attenuatus Cooper and Grant	VR
Dyoros (Dyoros) intrepidus Cooper and Grant	C
Dyoros (Dyoros) robustus Cooper and Grant	C
Echinosteges guadalupensis (Shumard)	VR

	Rarity code
LOCALITY N731 - Continued	
Eliva shumardi Cooper and Grant	VR
Elivina? annectans Cooper and Grant	C
Fascicosta bella Cooper and Grant	VR
Fascicosta elongata Cooper and Grant	R
Glossothyropsis cryptacanthoides Cooper and Grant	VR
Glossothyropsis polita Cooper and Grant	R
Glossothyropsis robusta (Girty)	C
Grandaurispina sp. 4	VR
Heteralosia magnispina Cooper and Grant	C
Heteralosia paucispinosa Cooper and Grant	R
Heteralosia tenuispina Cooper and Grant	R
Heterelasma shumardianum Girty	R
Heterelasma sp.	VR
Hustedia demissa Cooper and Grant	VR
Hustedia rupinata Cooper and Grant	VA
Hustedia samiata Cooper and Grant	C
Hustedia sp.	A
Lepidocrania sp.	R
Liosotella opima (Girty)	C
Madarosia anterolamellata Cooper and Grant	VR
Metriolepis nabis Cooper and Grant	R
Metriolepis pedicosa Cooper and Grant	R
Metriolepis sp.	R
Micraphelia scitula Cooper and Grant	VA
Micraphelia sp.	C
Micraphelia subalata Cooper and Grant	C
Paraspiriferina billingsi (Shumard)	C
Paraspiriferina sapinea Cooper and Grant	C
Paucispinifera indentata (Girty)	R
Paucispinifera latidorsata (Girty)	R
Paucispinifera sp.	R
Paucispinifera spinosa Cooper and Grant	C
Petrocrania exasperata Cooper and Grant	VR
Petrocrania septifera Cooper and Grant	VR
Phrenophoria perplexa Cooper and Grant	VR
Plectelasma guadalupense (Girty)	C
Pseudodielasma brilli Cooper and Grant	C
Pseudodielasma pinyonense Cooper and Grant	C
Pseudoleptodus guadalupensis (Stehli)	C
Pseudoleptodus? sp. 3	R
Ptilotorhynchus delicatum Cooper and Grant	VR
Rallacosta imporcata Cooper and Grant	VR
Reticulariina echinata Cooper and Grant	R
Reticulariina laxa (Girty)	R
Reticulariina phoxa Cooper and Grant	VR
Reticulariina sp.	C
Reticulariina welleri (Girty)	C
Rhamnaria shumardi Cooper and Grant	VR
Rhamnaria sp.	VR
Sarganostega pressa Cooper and Grant	C
Sarganostega transversalis Cooper and Grant	C
Scapharina levis Cooper and Grant	R
Scapharina quadrata Cooper and Grant	R
Scapharina rugosa Cooper and Grant	C
Sestropoma cribriferum Cooper and Grant	A
Spiriferella sp.	VR
Spiriferella sulcifer (Shumard)	C
Spiriferellina nuda Cooper and Grant	C
Stenoscisma aberrans Cooper and Grant	VR
Stenoscisma sp.	VR
Tautosia shumardiana (Girty)	VR
Thamnosia capitanensis (Girty)	R
Thedusia trigonalis (Girty)	C
Thedusia ventricosa Cooper and Grant	C

	Rarity code
Timorina attenuata Cooper and Grant	VR
Timorina ovata (Girty)	R
Tropidelasma gregarium (Girty)	VR
Xenosaria exotica Cooper and Grant	R
Xenosteges umbonatus Cooper and Grant	C
LOCALITY N731b : Cathedral Mountain Formation	
Acosarina mesoplatys (R.E. King)	R
Agelesia triagonalis (R.E. King)	VR
Cenorhynchia mitigata Cooper and Grant	R
Chonosteges pulcher Cooper and Grant	VR
Composita sp.	R
Enteletes plummeri R.E. King	C
Enteletes sp.	VR
Heterelasma gibbosum Cooper and Grant	VR
Hustedia lusca Cooper and Grant	C
Hustedia sp.	VR
Institella leonardensis (R.E. King)	VR
Lepidospirifer demissus Cooper and Grant	VR
Linoproductus sp.	VR
Neophricadothyris bullata Cooper and Grant	VR
Neophricadothyris sp.	VR
Rhipidomella hispidula Cooper and Grant	C
Rugatia paraindica (McKee)	VR
Stenoscisma sp.	VR
Stenoscisma triquetrum Cooper and Grant	VR
Tautosia fastigiata Cooper and Grant	VR
LOCALITY N731e : Road Canyon Formation	
Paraspiriferina cellulana Cooper and Grant	VR
LOCALITY N731f : Skinner Ranch Formation, Poplar Tank Member	
Derbyia sp.	VR
LOCALITY N731g : Skinner Ranch Formation, Sullivan Peak Member	
Spyridiophora reticulata (R.E. King)	VR
LOCALITY N731h : Word Formation, Willis Ranch Member	
Cyclacantharia kingorum Cooper and Grant	VR
LOCALITY N731i : Neal Ranch Formation	
Reticulatia sp. 1	VR
LOCALITY N731j : Capitan Formation	
Liosotella popei (Shumard)	VR
LOCALITY N731k : Lenox Hills Formation	
Linoproductus semisulcatus Cooper and Grant	VR
LOCALITY N731-1 : Neal Ranch Formation	
Linoproductus sp.	VR
LOCALITY N731m : Word Formation, Willis Ranch Member	
Allorhynchus sp.	VR
Composita sp.	VR
Costispinifera rugatula (Girty)	C
Cyclacantharia kingorum Cooper and Grant	VR
Dyoros (Dyoros) convexus Cooper and Grant	VR
Enteletes wordensis R.E. King	VR
Liosotella wordensis (R.E. King)	R
Meekella skenoides Girty	VR
Megousia sp.	VR
Neospirifer amphigyus Cooper and Grant	VR
Paucispinifera sp.	VR
Rhamnaria kingorum delicata Muir-Wood and Cooper	VR

Rarity code

LOCALITY N731m - Continued
Spiriferinaella sp. .... VR
Yakovlevia hessorum Cooper and Grant .... VR

LOCALITY N731n : Cathedral Mountain Formation
Agelesia triagonalis (R.E. King) .... VR
Compressoproductus thomasi Cooper and Grant .... VR
Institella leonardensis (R.E. King) .... VR

LOCALITY N731o : Skinner Ranch Formation
Glyptosteges intricatus Cooper and Grant...................... VR
Megousia sp. .... VR
Torynechus alectorius Cooper and Grant .... VR

LOCALITY N731p : Word Formation
Allorhynchus permianum wordense Cooper and Grant ...... VR
Derbyia pannucia Cooper and Grant .... VR
Echinauris sp. .... VR
Enteletes wordensis R.E. King .... VR
Hustedia pugilla nasiterna Cooper and Grant .... VR
Meekella skenoides Girty .... VR
Rhamnaria kingorum delicata Muir-Wood and Cooper ...... VR

LOCALITY N731q : Cathedral Mountain Formation
Glyptosteges intricatus Cooper and Grant....................... VR

LOCALITY N731t : Cathedral Mountain Formation
Chonosteges variabilis Cooper and Grant....................... VR
Enteletes sp. .... VR
Neophricadothyris sp. .... R
Peniculauris sp. 1 .... VR
Rhynchopora hebetata Cooper and Grant....................... VR
Scacchinella sp. .... VR
Stenoscisma exutum Cooper and Grant .... VR

LOCALITY N731u : Word Formation
Allorhynchus sp. .... VR
Allorhynchus triangulatum Cooper and Grant .... VR
Cenorhynchia pentagonalis Cooper and Grant .... R
Composita sp. .... R
Costispinifera costata (R.E. King) C
Cyclacantharia kingorum Cooper and Grant.................... VR
Dielasma sp. .... VR
Dyoros (Dyoros) convexus Cooper and Grant .... VR
Enteletes wordensis R.E. King .... VR
Hustedia pugilla nasiterna Cooper and Grant .... VR
Hustedia sp. .... VR
Liosotella wordensis (R.E. King) C
Meekella skenoides Girty .... VR
Megousia sp. .... VR
Paraspiriferina laqueata Cooper and Grant.................... VR
Paucispinifera sp. .... VR
Rhamnaria kingorum cf. delicata Muir-Wood and Cooper. VR
Rhynchopora palumbula Cooper and Grant..................... R
Spiriferinaella sp. .... VR
Stenoscisma renode Cooper and Grant........................... R

LOCALITY N731z : Word Formation, Appel Ranch Member
Bryorhynchus plicatum Cooper and Grant....................... R
Cancrinella distorta Cooper and Grant .... VR
Leiorhynchoidea scelesta Cooper and Grant .... VR
Linoproductus nasutus R.E. King C
Liosotella irregularis Cooper and Grant .... VR
Neophricadothyris conara Cooper and Grant .... VR
Spiriferella clypeata Cooper and Grant .... R

Rarity code

LOCALITY N732 : Cherry Canyon Formation, Getaway Member
Acanthocrania conferta Cooper and Grant...................... VR
Allorhynchus circulare Cooper and Grant....................... R
Bothrionia pulchra Cooper and Grant............................ VR
Bryorhynchus bisulcatum (Shumard) .... R
Cancrinella sp. .... VR
Cartorhium retusum Cooper and Grant.......................... R
Composita enormis Cooper and Grant............................ VR
Composita parasulcata Cooper and Grant .... R
Cooperina inexpectata Termier, Termier and Pajaud .... VR
Crenispirifer effrenus Cooper and Grant........................ R
Cyclacantharia kingorum Cooper and Grant C
Derbyia filosa Cooper and Grant .... R
Derbyia pannucia Cooper and Grant.............................. VR
Derbyia texta Cooper and Grant C
Dielasma pictile Cooper and Grant................................ VR
Dielasma sp. .... R
Dielasma sulcatum Girty .... VR
Dyoros (Dyoros) extensus Cooper and Grant .... R
Dyoros (Lissosia) concavus Cooper and Grant................. R
Dyoros (Tetragonetes) auriculatus Cooper and Grant .... R
Dyoros (Tetragonetes) complanatus Cooper and Grant C
Echinauris productelloides Cooper and Grant C
Echinosteges tuberculatus (R.E. King) .... VR
Eolyttonia progressa Cooper and Grant C
Eolyttonia sp. .... VR
Glossothyropsis sp. 1 (Girty)....................................... VR
Grandaurispina sp. .... VR
Grandaurispina undulata Cooper and Grant.................... R
Heteralosia magnispina Cooper and Grant...................... R
Heterelasma concavum Cooper and Grant .... VR
Hustedia citeria Cooper and Grant .... A
Hustedia hapala Cooper and Grant................................ C
Hustedia tomea Cooper and Grant................................. R
Lepidocrania sublamellosa Cooper and Grant .... VR
Liosotella wordensis (R.E. King) C
Martinia causaria Cooper and Grant C
Meekella skenoides Girty .... A
Megousia definita Cooper and Grant.............................. VR
Metriolepis exserta Cooper and Grant............................ R
Neophricadothyris conara Cooper and Grant .... R
Ombonia sp. 1 .... R
Paraspiriferina paginata Cooper and Grant.................... R
Paucispinifera sp. .... R
Petasmatherus opulus Cooper and Grant .... R
Phrenophoria pinguiformis Cooper and Grant .... VR
Plectelasma nitidum Cooper and Grant .... VR
Pseudodielasma magnum Cooper and Grant.................... VR
Pseudodielasma sp. .... R
Pseudoleptodus annosus Cooper and Grant .... VR
Pseudoleptodus getawayensis Stehli .... VR
Ptilotorhynchus delicatum Cooper and Grant.................. VR
Reticulariina girtyi Cooper and Grant .... R
Reticulariina sp. .... VR
Rhamnaria sulcata Cooper and Grant C
Rhynchopora guadalupensis Cooper and Grant................ VR
Sarganostega murata Cooper and Grant......................... R
Spiriferella sp. .... R
Tautosia transenna Cooper and Grant .... R
Texarina elongata Cooper and Grant.............................. VR
Tropidelasma furcillatum Cooper and Grant C
Tropidelasma sp. .... VR
Undulella guadalupensis Cooper and Grant C
Waagenoconcha magnifica Cooper and Grant.................. VR

	Rarity code

LOCALITY N732 - Continued

	Rarity code
Wellerella girtyi seorsa Cooper and Grant	R
Xenosteges quadratus Cooper and Grant	C

LOCALITY N732a : Bell Canyon Formation, Hegler Member

Acanthocrania sp.	VR
Allorhynchus sp.	VR
Altiplecus? deltosus Cooper and Grant	R
Altiplecus extensus Cooper and Grant	R
Anteridocus bicostatus Cooper and Grant	R
Anteridocus swallovianus (Shumard)	VR
Arionthia polypleura (Girty)	R
Bryorhynchus bisulcatum (Shumard)	C
Cancrinella sp.	VR
Cartorhium sp.	R
Chonetinetes sp.	C
Chonetinetes varians Cooper and Grant	A
Composita pyriformis Cooper and Grant	C
Composita sp.	R
Cooperina inexpectata Termier, Termier and Pajaud	R
Craspedona newelli Cooper and Grant	VR
Crenispirifer jubatus Cooper and Grant	R
Crurithyris sp.	VR
Ctenalosia fixata Cooper and Stehli	VR
Ctenalosia rotunda Cooper and Grant	VR
Derbyia sp.	A
Dielasma cordatum Girty	R
Dielasma rigbyi Cooper and Grant	R
Dielasma sp.	R
Dielasma sulcatum Girty	VR
Dyoros (Dyoros) intrepidus Cooper and Grant	VR
Dyoros (Dyoros) robustus Cooper and Grant	R
Echinosteges guadalupensis (Shumard)	VR
Fascicosta elongata Cooper and Grant	VR
Glossothyropsis juvenis Cooper and Grant	VR
Glossothyropsis polita Cooper and Grant	VR
Glossothyropsis robusta (Girty)	VR
Grandaurispina sp.	VR
Heteralosia magnispina Cooper and Grant	C
Heteralosia paucispinosa Cooper and Grant	VR
Heterelasma sp.	VR
Hustedia demissa Cooper and Grant	R
Hustedia opsia Cooper and Grant	C
Hustedia rupinata Cooper and Grant	VA
Hustedia sp.	A
Lamellosia lamellosa Cooper and Grant	R
Liosotella opima (Girty)	R
Metriolepis nabis Cooper and Grant	VR
Metriolepis pedicosa Cooper and Grant	R
Metriolepis sp.	VR
Micraphelia scitula Cooper and Grant	VA
Micraphelia subalata Cooper and Grant	C
Notothyris sp.	VR
Paraspiriferina billingsi (Shumard)	C
Paucispinifera indentata (Girty)	R
Paucispinifera latidorsata (Girty)	VR
Petrocrania sp.	R
Phrenophoria perplexa Cooper and Grant	VR
Phrenophoria pinguis (Girty)	VR
Plectelasma guadalupense (Girty)	R
Pseudodielasma brilli Cooper and Grant	R
Pseudoleptodus guadalupensis (Stehli)	C
Rallacosta imporcata Cooper and Grant	VR
Reticulariina echinata Cooper and Grant	VR

	Rarity code
Reticulariina sp.	C
Sarganostega pressa Cooper and Grant	R
Sarganostega transversalis Cooper and Grant	R
Scapharina levis Cooper and Grant	VR
Scapharina quadrata Cooper and Grant	VR
Scapharina rugosa Cooper and Grant	R
Sestropoma cribriferum Cooper and Grant	C
Spiriferella sulcifer (Shumard)	C
Thamnosia capitanensis (Girty)	VR
Thedusia magna Cooper and Grant	VR
Thedusia trigonalis (Girty)	R
Thedusia ventricosa Cooper and Grant	C
Timorina attenuata Cooper and Grant	VR
Timorina ovata (Girty)	VR
Tropidelasma gregarium (Girty)	VR
Xenosaria exotica Cooper and Grant	VR
Xenosteges umbonatus Cooper and Grant	C

LOCALITY N732b : Skinner Ranch Formation, Decie Ranch Member

Eolyttonia gigantea Cooper and Grant	VR

LOCALITY N732c : Word Formation, Lens

Allorhynchus permianum wordense Cooper and Grant	VR
Arionthia germana Cooper and Grant	R
Cartorhium chelomatum Cooper and Grant	VR
Collemataria elongata Cooper and Grant	R
Composita enormis Cooper and Grant	VR
Composita parasulcata Cooper and Grant	R
Cyclacantharia kingorum Cooper and Grant	VR
Derbyia texta Cooper and Grant	R
Dielasma sp.	VR
Dyoros (Dyoros) convexus Cooper and Grant	A
Echinauris lateralis Muir-Wood and Cooper	C
Echinosteges tuberculatus (R.E. King)	VR
Grandaurispina gibbosa Cooper and Grant	R
Heteralosia hystricula (Girty)	VR
Hustedia sp.	R
Liosotella tetragonalis Cooper and Grant	VR
Liosotella wordensis (R.E. King)	R
Meekella skenoides Girty	VR
Paraspiriferina rotundata Cooper and Grant	VR
Paucispinifera quadrata Cooper and Grant	R
Pseudoleptodus grandis Cooper and Grant	VR
Reticulariina cerina Cooper and Grant	R
Rhamnaria kingorum Muir-Wood and Cooper	C
Spiriferella clypeata Cooper and Grant	R
Spiriferellina hilli (Girty)	VR
Spiriferinaella scalpata Cooper and Grant	VR
Stenoscisma renode Cooper and Grant	VR
Tropidelasma sp.	VR
Xenosteges quadratus Cooper and Grant	VR

LOCALITY N732d : Skinner Ranch Formation, Dugout Mtn Member

Glyptosteges intricatus Cooper and Grant	VR
Sceletonia crassa Cooper and Grant	VR

LOCALITY N732e : Skinner Ranch Formation, Dugout Mtn Member

Acritosia solida Cooper and Grant	VR
Choanodus perfectus Cooper and Grant	VR
Choanodus sp.	VR
Chonosteges variabilis Cooper and Grant	R
Composita sp.	VR
Derbyia sp.	VR

	Rarity code
LOCALITY N732e - Continued	
Dielasma sp.	VR
Dyoros (Dyoros) consanguineus (Girty)	R
Echinauris irregularis Cooper and Grant	C
Enteletes sp.	VR
Glyptosteges intricatus Cooper and Grant	C
Hercosia cf. *uddeni* (Böse)	R
Hustedia sp.	VR
Lepidospirifer sp.	VR
Limbella limbata Cooper and Grant	VR
Meekella hessensis R.E. King	R
Neophricadothyris sp.	R
Paranorella sp. 6	VR
Peniculauris sp.	VR
Rallacosta? sp.	VR
Rhamnaria grandis Cooper and Grant	R
Rhipidomella hessensis R.E. King	VR
Sceletonia crassa Cooper and Grant	R
Sceletonia sp.	VR
Stenoscisma sp.	VR
Torynechus alectorius Cooper and Grant	R
LOCALITY N732i : Road Canyon Formation	
Cyclacantharia transitoria Cooper and Grant	VR
Echinauris sp.	R
Enteletes exiguus Cooper and Grant	R
Enteletes sp.	R
Hustedia connorsi Cooper and Grant	C
Kutorginella umbonata (Muir-Wood and Cooper)	VR
Meekella skenoides Girty	VR
Megousia mucronata Cooper and Grant	R
Metriolepis ziczac Cooper and Grant	VR
Neophricadothyris sp.	VR
Neospirifer formulosus Cooper and Grant	VR
Paraspiriferina pulchra Cooper and Grant	VR
Paucispinifera sp.	VR
Rhamnaria tenuispinosa Cooper and Grant	VR
Rhynchopora hebetata Cooper and Grant	VR
Tropidelasma corniculum Cooper and Grant	VR
LOCALITY N732j : Road Canyon Formation	
Acosarina mesoplatys (R.E. King)	VR
Allorhynchus concentricum Cooper and Grant	VR
Anteridocus triangulatus Cooper and Grant	VR
Cenorhynchia transversa Cooper and Grant	R
Chondronia sp.	R
Chonetinella geronica Cooper and Grant	C
Collemataria batilliformis Cooper and Grant	VR
Collumatus solitarius Cooper and Grant	C
Composita cf. *enormis* Cooper and Grant	R
Composita pilula Cooper and Grant	C
Composita sp.	C
Cooperina subcuneata Cooper and Grant	VR
Coscinophora magnifica Cooper and Grant	VR
Costispinifera rugatula (Girty)	VR
Cyclacantharia transitoria Cooper and Grant	C
Derbyia cincinnata Cooper and Grant	VR
Derbyia complicata Cooper and Grant	R
Derbyia laqueata Cooper and Grant	R
Derbyia sp.	R
Dielasma sp.	R
Dyoros (Dyoros) transversus Cooper and Grant	R
Dyoros (Dyoros) vulgaris Cooper and Grant	A
Echinauris lappacea Cooper and Grant	A
Echinosteges sp.	VR

	Rarity code
Echinosteges cf. *tuberculatus* (R.E. King)	VR
Enteletes exiguus Cooper and Grant	A
Enteletes sp.	A
Heteralosia sp.	VR
Heterelasma sp.	R
Holotricharina sparsa Cooper and Grant	VR
Hustedia connorsi Cooper and Grant	C
Hustedia sp.	C
Kutorginella umbonata (Muir-Wood and Cooper)	VR
Lepidocrania sublamellosa Cooper and Grant	R
Leurosina lata Cooper and Grant	R
Liosotella costata Cooper and Grant	VR
Liosotella rotunda Cooper and Grant	C
Meekella calathica Cooper and Grant	A
Meekella skenoides Girty	C
Megousia mucronata Cooper and Grant	A
Metriolepis pinea Cooper and Grant	A
Metriolepis sp.	VR
Metriolepis ziczac Cooper and Grant	VR
Neophricadothyris cordata Cooper and Grant	C
Neospirifer bakeri bakeri R.E. King	C
Notothyris gillilandensis Cooper and Grant	R
Notothyris planiplicata Cooper and Grant	R
Paranorella sp. 5	R
Paraspiriferina pulchra Cooper and Grant	C
Paucispinifera parasulcata Cooper and Grant	C
Paucispinifera sp.	VR
Paucispinifera sulcata Cooper and Grant	C
Peniculauris sp.	VR
Petasmatherus pumilus Cooper and Grant	C
Petrocrania sp.	VR
Phrenophoria sp.	VR
Pontisia truncata Cooper and Grant	R
Ptygmactrum sp.	VR
Rhamnaria tenuispinosa Cooper and Grant	C
Rhamnaria vinnula Cooper and Grant	R
Rhynchopora hebetata Cooper and Grant	R
Rhytisia rugosa Cooper and Grant	VR
Spiriferella sp.	R
Spiriferellina tricosa Cooper and Grant	VR
Spiriferellina vescula Cooper and Grant	C
Stenoscisma sp.	VR
Tautosia angulata Cooper and Grant	VR
Texarina parallela Cooper and Grant	VR
Texarina wordensis (R.E. King)	VR
Thedusia mesocostata Cooper and Grant	C
Tropidelasma corniculum Cooper and Grant	A
Undulella matutina Cooper and Grant	R
Waagenoconcha convexa Cooper and Grant	VR
Xenosteges trivialis Cooper and Grant	C
Yakovlevia anterospinosa Cooper and Grant	VR
Yakovlevia sulcata Cooper and Grant	R
LOCALITY N732m : Road Canyon Formation	
Cyclacantharia paucispinosa Cooper and Grant	VR
Edriosteges multispinosus Muir-Wood and Cooper,	R
Meekella calathica Cooper and Grant	VR
LOCALITY N732q : Capitan Formation	
Anteridocus swallovianus (Shumard)	R
Cartorhium mexicanum (Shumard)	VR
Composita affinis Girty	VR
Dielasma prolongatum Girty	VR
Liosotella popei (Shumard)	VR
Paraspiriferina billingsi (Shumard)	VR

	Rarity code
LOCALITY N732q - Continued	
Pseudoleptodus guadalupensis (Stehli)	VR
Reticulariina sp.	VR
Stenoscisma trabeatum Cooper and Grant	VR
Tautosia shumardiana (Girty)	VR
LOCALITY N732r : Road Canyon Formation	
Reticulariina sp.	VR
LOCALITY N732s : Word Formation	
Allorhynchus triangulatum Cooper and Grant	VR
Cactosteges anomalus Cooper and Grant	VR
Collemataria elongata Cooper and Grant	R
Compressoproductus rarus Cooper and Grant	VR
Cooperina inexpectata Termier, Termier and Pajaud	VR
Costispinifera rugatula (Girty)	C
Cyclacantharia kingorum Cooper and Grant	R
Derbyia filosa Cooper and Grant	VR
Derbyia sp.	VR
Dielasma sp.	VR
Dyoros (*Dyoros*) *tenuis* Cooper and Grant	VR
Dyoros (*Lissosia*) *concavus* Cooper and Grant	R
Echinauris sp.	R
Echinosteges tuberculatus (R.E. King)	VR
Enteletes sp.	VR
Heteralosia hystricula (Girty)	R
Hustedia pugilla nasiterna Cooper and Grant	VR
Hustedia sp.	R
Liosotella wordensis (R.E. King)	VR
Meekella skenoides Girty	R
Megousia mucronata Cooper and Grant	R
Paraspiriferina laqueata Cooper and Grant	VR
Paucispinifera intermedia Cooper and Grant	VR
Paucispinifera sp.	VR
Rhamnaria kingorum delicata Muir-Wood and Cooper	R
Spiriferellina hilli (Girty)	VR
Xenosteges quadratus Cooper and Grant	VR
LOCALITY N732t : Road Canyon Formation	
Coscinophora magnifica Cooper and Grant	VR
Paucispinifera sp.	VR
LOCALITY N732u : Cathedral Mountain Formation	
Acritosia sp.	VR
Anemonaria sublaevis (R.E. King)	VR
Chonosteges sp.	VR
Collemataria gregaria Cooper and Grant	VR
Derbyia sp.	VR
Echinauris sp.	VR
Edriosteges multispinosus Muir-Wood and Cooper	VR
Eolyttonia pocillata Cooper and Grant	VR
Hercosia uddeni (Böse)	VR
Lepidospirifer demissus Cooper and Grant	VR
Meekella calathica Cooper and Grant	R
Neophricadothyris sp.	VR
Neospirifer mansuetus Cooper and Grant	VR
Peniculauris subcostata (R.E. King)	R
Rhamnaria tenuispinosa Cooper and Grant	VR
Rugatia paraindica (McKee)	R
LOCALITY N732w : Road Canyon Formation	
Coscinophora magnifica Cooper and Grant	VR
LOCALITY N733 : Bell Canyon Formation, Pinery Member	
Altiplecus? deltosus Cooper and Grant	R
Altiplecus trapezoidalis Cooper and Grant	R

	Rarity code
Anteridocus swallovianus (Shumard)	R
Bryorhynchus bisulcatum (Shumard)	C
Composita emarginata Girty	R
Craspedona newelli Cooper and Grant	R
Crenispirifer jubatus Cooper and Grant	R
Deltarina magnicostata Cooper and Grant	VR
Derbyia sp.	C
Dielasma sulcatum Girty	R
Dyoros (*Dyoros*) *intrepidus* Cooper and Grant	R
Elivina? annectans Cooper and Grant	C
Glossothyropsis cryptacanthoides Cooper and Grant	R
Heteralosia magnispina Cooper and Grant	VR
Heterelasma shumardianum Girty	VR
Hustedia demissa Cooper and Grant	R
Hustedia rupinata Cooper and Grant	A
Metriolepis nabis Cooper and Grant	R
Metriolepis pedicosa Cooper and Grant	VR
Micraphelia scitula Cooper and Grant	C
Micraphelia subalata Cooper and Grant	C
Paraspiriferina sapinea Cooper and Grant	R
Paucispinifera spinosa Cooper and Grant	R
Paucispinifera suspecta Cooper and Grant	C
Phrenophoria perplexa Cooper and Grant	VR
Plectelasma guadalupense (Girty)	R
Pseudoleptodus guadalupensis (Stehli)	VR
Ptilotorhynchus delicatum Cooper and Grant	VR
Rallacosta imporcata Cooper and Grant	R
Reticulariina echinata Cooper and Grant	VR
Reticulariina sp.	VR
Rhamnaria shumardi Cooper and Grant	VR
Sarganostega transversalis Cooper and Grant	R
Scapharina levis Cooper and Grant	R
Sestropoma cribriferum Cooper and Grant	R
Spiriferella sulcifer (Shumard)	R
Tautosia elegans (Girty)	VR
Thamnosia capitanensis (Girty)	R
Thedusia trigonalis (Girty)	R
Thedusia ventricosa Cooper and Grant	C
Tropidelasma gregarium (Girty)	VR
LOCALITY N733a : Road Canyon Formation	
Coscinophora magnifica Cooper and Grant	VR
LOCALITY N733b : Road Canyon Formation	
Megousia sp.	VR
LOCALITY N733h : Skinner Ranch Formation, Decie Ranch Member	
Antronaria titania Cooper and Grant	VR
Meekella caperata Cooper and Grant	VR
Scacchinella titan Cooper and Grant	R
LOCALITY N733j : Skinner Ranch Formation, Sullivan Peak Member	
Acosarina dorsisulcata Cooper and Grant	A
Acritosia peculiaris Cooper and Grant	C
Anteridocus paucicostatus Cooper and Grant	C
Chondronia sp.	R
Chonosteges limbatus Cooper and Grant	VR
Composita sp.	VR
Compressoproductus sp.	VR
Coscinophora monilifera Cooper and Grant	A
Derbyia nasuta Girty	R
Dielasma sp.	VR
Diplanus rarus Cooper and Grant	VR
Diplanus sp.	VR
Enteletes sp.	R

LOCALITY N733j - Continued	Rarity code
Geyerella hessi Cooper and Grant	A
Glyptosteges angustus (R.E. King)	VR
Hustedia sp.	R
Limbella limbata Cooper and Grant	VR
Meekella hessensis R.E. King	C
Oncosarina sp.	C
Reticulariina sp.	VR
Rhipidomella hessensis R.E. King	VR
Scacchinella titan Cooper and Grant	VR
Spyridiophora reticulata (R.E. King)	VR
Stenoscisma sp.	VR
Tropidelasma robertsi Cooper and Grant	R

LOCALITY N733-1 : Skinner Ranch Formation, Dugout Mtn Member

	Rarity code
Acritosia peculiaris Cooper and Grant	VR
Chondronia ningula Cooper and Grant	VR
Chonosteges variabilis Cooper and Grant	VR
Compressoproductus parvus Cooper and Grant	VR
Echinauris sp.	VR
Glyptosteges intricatus Cooper and Grant	VR
Goniarina sp.	VR
Rhipidomella hessensis R.E. King	VR
Torynechus alectorius Cooper and Grant	VR

LOCALITY N733m : Cathedral Mountain Formation

	Rarity code
Acosarina mesoplatys (R.E. King)	VR
Choanodus irregularis Cooper and Grant	VR
Chonosteges variabilis Cooper and Grant	R
Composita sp.	VR
Derbyia laqueata Cooper and Grant	R
Echinauris irregularis Cooper and Grant	R
Grandaurispina sp.	VR
Hercosia uddeni (Böse)	C
Heterelasma gibbosum Cooper and Grant	VR
Hustedia sp.	R
Lepidospirifer demissus Cooper and Grant	VR
Meekella calathica Cooper and Grant	R
Megousia umbonata Cooper and Grant	VR
Metriolepis tegulata Cooper and Grant	VR
Nudauris linospina Cooper and Grant	VR
Rhamnaria tenuispinosa Cooper and Grant	R
Rugatia paraindica (McKee)	R

LOCALITY N733n : Road Canyon Formation

	Rarity code
Coscinophora magnifica Cooper and Grant	VR

LOCALITY N733q : Word Formation, China Tank Member

	Rarity code
Allorhynchus triangulatum Cooper and Grant	VR
Cactosteges anomalus Cooper and Grant	VR
Cartorhium chelomatum Cooper and Grant	R
Collemataria elongata Cooper and Grant	C
Composita parasulcata Cooper and Grant	R
Compressoproductus rarus Cooper and Grant	VR
Cooperina inexpectata Termier, Termier and Pajaud	VR
Costispinifera rugatula (Girty)	R
Cyclacantharia kingorum Cooper and Grant	C
Derbyia filosa Cooper and Grant	R
Derbyia pannucia Cooper and Grant	C
Dielasma compactum Cooper and Grant	VR
Dielasma zebratum Cooper and Grant	R
Dyoros (Lissosia) concavus Cooper and Grant	C
Echinauris lateralis Muir-Wood and Cooper	A
Echinosteges tuberculatus (R.E. King)	VR
Enteletes wordensis R.E. King	C

	Rarity code
Grandaurispina sp.	VR
Heteralosia hystricula (Girty)	R
Hustedia pugilla nasiterna Cooper and Grant	VR
Hustedia sp.	C
Liosotella wordensis (R.E. King)	C
Meekella skenoides Girty	A
Megousia mucronata Cooper and Grant	C
Neophricadothyris conara Cooper and Grant	R
Notothyris venusta Cooper and Grant	VR
Paraspiriferina laqueata Cooper and Grant	R
Paraspiriferina sp.	VR
Paucispinifera intermedia Cooper and Grant	C
Reticulariina cerina Cooper and Grant	VR
Rhamnaria kingorum delicata Muir-Wood and Cooper	R
Rhynchopora palumbula Cooper and Grant	VR
Spiriferella sp.	VR
Spiriferellina hilli (Girty)	R
Thamnosia phragmophora Cooper and Grant	VR
Thedusia procera Cooper and Grant	VR
Tropidelasma anthicum Cooper and Grant	VR
Waagenoconcha magnifica Cooper and Grant	VR
Wellerella girtyi girtyi Cooper and Grant	VR
Xenosteges quadratus Cooper and Grant	R

LOCALITY N733r : Skinner Ranch Formation

	Rarity code
Derbyia sp.	VR
Enteletes stehlii Cooper and Grant	VR
Hustedia hessensis R.E. King	R
Kochiproductus sp.	R
Kozlowskia alata Cooper and Grant	R
Kozlowskia sp.	VR
Linoproductus angustus R.E. King	VR
Meekella hessensis R.E. King	R
Scacchinella titan Cooper and Grant	VR
Teguliferina conida (Stehli)	R

LOCALITY N733z : Ross Mine Formation

	Rarity code
Yakovlevia sulcata Cooper and Grant	VR

LOCALITY N734 : Bell Canyon Formation, Pinery Member

	Rarity code
Edriosteges sp.	VR

LOCALITY N734j : Road Canyon Formation

	Rarity code
Acosarina sp.	VR
Composita sp.	VR
Edriosteges multispinosus Muir-Wood and Cooper	VR
Hustedia sp.	VR
Meekella calathica Cooper and Grant	VR
Neophricadothyris sp.	VR

LOCALITY N735 : Bell Canyon Formation, Rader Member

	Rarity code
Bryorhynchus gratiosum (Girty)	C

LOCALITY N735a : Road Canyon Formation

	Rarity code
Derbyia sp.	VR
Dyoros (Dyoros) transversus Cooper and Grant	VR
Echinauris sp.	VR
Horridonia texana R.E. King	VR
Hustedia cuneata Cooper and Grant	VR
Megousia auriculata Muir-Wood and Cooper	VR
Neospirifer bakeri bakeri R.E. King	VR
Ptygmactrum mordicum Cooper and Grant	VR
Rugatia mckeei Cooper and Grant	VR
Thedusia mesocostata Cooper and Grant	R
Waagenoconcha platys Cooper and Grant	VR

Rarity code

LOCALITY N735b : Cathedral Mountain Formation *

Acosarina mesoplatys (R.E. King)	R
Anteridocus gongylus Cooper and Grant	R
Cartorhium latum (R.E. King)	VR
Chaeniorhynchus inauris Cooper and Grant	VR
Chondronia bella Cooper and Grant	R
Chonosteges variabilis Cooper and Grant	VR
Cleiothyridina sp.	VR
Collemataria gregaria Cooper and Grant	R
Composita imbricata Cooper and Grant	R
Derbyia laqueata Cooper and Grant	R
Derbyia sp.	VR
Dielasma sp.	VR
Dyoros (*Lissosia*) *vagabundus* Cooper and Grant	C
Echinauris irregularis Cooper and Grant	C
Edriosteges multispinosus Muir-Wood and Cooper	VR
Eolyttonia circularis Cooper and Grant	VR
Eolyttonia pocillata Cooper and Grant	VR
Grandaurispina? vaga Cooper and Grant	VR
Hercosia uddeni (Böse)	C
Heterelasma gibbosum Cooper and Grant	VR
Hustedia spicata Cooper and Grant	A
Institella leonardensis (R.E. King)	C
Lepidospirifer demissus Cooper and Grant	R
Loxophragmus ellipticus Cooper and Grant	R
Martinia miranda Cooper and Grant	C
Meekella calathica Cooper and Grant	R
Megousia auriculata Muir-Wood and Cooper	VR
Metriolepis tegulata Cooper and Grant	R
Neophricadothyris sp.	VR
Neospirifer mansuetus Cooper and Grant	R
Niviconia globosa (R.E. King)	R
Nudauris linospina Cooper and Grant	R
Peniculauris subcostata (R.E. King)	VR
Petasmaia expansa Cooper and Grant	R
Phrenophoria sp.	VR
Pontisia stehlii stehlii Cooper and Grant	VR
Reticulariina craticula Cooper and Grant	VR
Reticulariina sp.	VR
Rhamnaria tenuispinosa Cooper and Grant	R
Rhipidomella hispidula Cooper and Grant	VR
Rhynchopora hebetata Cooper and Grant	VR
Rugatia paraindica (McKee)	VR
Stenoscisma calvatum Cooper and Grant	VR
Stenoscisma doricranum Cooper and Grant	R
Stenoscisma sp.	VR
Stenoscisma triquetrum Cooper and Grant	R
Tautosia fastigiata Cooper and Grant	VR
Texarina wordensis (R.E. King)	VR
Torynechus caelatus Cooper and Grant	R
Trophisina fenaria Cooper and Grant	VR
Xenosteges adherens Muir-Wood and Cooper	R

LOCALITY N735c : Word Formation, Willis Ranch Member

Cactosteges anomalus Cooper and Grant	R
Cancrinella subquadrata Cooper and Grant	VR
Cenorhynchia fracida Cooper and Grant	R
Collemataria elongata Cooper and Grant	C
Composita enormis Cooper and Grant	R
Cooperina inexpectata Termier, Termier and Pajaud	VR
Cyclacantharia kingorum Cooper and Grant	VR
Derbyia sp.	R
Dielasma sp.	VR
Dielasma zebratum Cooper and Grant	R

Rarity code

Dyoros (*Dyoros*) *extensus* Cooper and Grant	A
Dyoros (*Lissosia*) *concavus* Cooper and Grant	VR
Dyoros (*Tetragonetes*) *giganteus* Cooper and Grant	VR
Echinauris lateralis Muir-Wood and Cooper	VR
Echinosteges tuberculatus (R.E. King)	C
Ectoposia grandis Cooper and Grant	VR
Glossothyropsis rectangulata Cooper and Grant	VR
Grandaurispina kingorum Muir-Wood and Cooper	C
Heteralosia hystricula (Girty)	C
Heterelasma concavum Cooper and Grant	VR
Hustedia pugilla pugilla Cooper and Grant	R
Lepidocrania sublamellosa Cooper and Grant	VR
Liosotella wordensis (R.E. King)	VR
Neophricadothyris sp.	VR
Paucispinifera auriculata Muir-Wood and Cooper	C
Petasmatherus opulus Cooper and Grant	VR
Pseudodielasma sp.	A
Rhamnaria kingorum Muir-Wood and Cooper	C
Rhynchopora palumbula Cooper and Grant	VR
Spiriferella gravis Cooper and Grant	VR
Spiriferellina hilli (Girty)	C
Thedusia procera Cooper and Grant	R
Undulella undulata Cooper and Grant	VR
Wellerella girtyi girtyi Cooper and Grant	R
Xenosteges quadratus Cooper and Grant	VR
Yakovlevia hessorum Cooper and Grant	R

LOCALITY N735f : Skinner Ranch Formation, Sullivan Peak Member

Spyridiophora reticulata (R.E. King)	VR

LOCALITY N735g : Cathedral Mountain Formation

Derbyia cincinnata Cooper and Grant	VR
Peniculauris subcostata (R.E. King)	VR
Rugatia paraindica (McKee)	VR

LOCALITY N735i : Cathedral Mountain Formation

Rugatia paraindica (McKee)	VR

LOCALITY N735j : Capitan Formation

Anteridocus swallovianus (Shumard)	R

LOCALITY N735w : Road Canyon Formation

Hercosestria cribrosa Cooper and Grant	VR
Meekella calathica Cooper and Grant	VR

LOCALITY N736 : Bell Canyon Formation, Pinery Member

Altiplecus? deltosus Cooper and Grant	R
Altiplecus trapezoidalis Cooper and Grant	R
Bryorhynchus gratiosum (Girty)	C
Composita emarginata Girty	VR
Composita sp.	R
Crenispirifer jubatus Cooper and Grant	R
Derbyia texta Cooper and Grant	C
Dielasma sp.	VR
Dielasma subcirculare Cooper and Grant	VR
Dielasma sulcatum Girty	VR
Dyoros (*Dyoros*) *intrepidus* Cooper and Grant	R
Echinosteges guadalupensis (Shumard)	VR
Elivina? annectans Cooper and Grant	C
Fascicosta longaeva (Girty)	VR
Heterelasma shumardianum Girty	VR
Hustedia rupinata Cooper and Grant	A
Hustedia sp.	VR
Lepidocrania sp.	VR
Madarosia anterolamellata Cooper and Grant	R
Metriolepis nabis Cooper and Grant	VR

	Rarity code
LOCALITY N736 - Continued	
Metriolepis pedicosa Cooper and Grant	VR
Metriolepis sp.	VR
Micraphelia scitula Cooper and Grant	VR
Paraspiriferina sapinea Cooper and Grant	C
Paucispinifera suspecta Cooper and Grant	R
Petrocrania exasperata Cooper and Grant	VR
Plectelasma guadalupense (Girty)	R
Pseudoleptodus guadalupensis (Stehli)	R
Rallacosta imporcata Cooper and Grant	VR
Reticulariina echinata Cooper and Grant	VR
Reticulariina sp.	R
Reticulariina welleri (Girty)	VR
Sarganostega transversalis Cooper and Grant	VR
Scapharina rugosa Cooper and Grant	C
Sestropoma cribriferum Cooper and Grant	R
Spiriferella sulcifer (Shumard)	VR
Thamnosia capitanensis (Girty)	VR
Thedusia angustata Cooper and Grant	R
Thedusia trigonalis (Girty)	R
Tropidelasma gregarium (Girty)	VR
LOCALITY N736a : Bell Canyon Formation, Pinery Member	
Altiplecus? deltosus Cooper and Grant	VR
Composita emarginata Girty	VR
Craspedona newelli Cooper and Grant	VR
Crenispirifer jubatus Cooper and Grant	VR
Derbyia sp.	VR
Elivina? annectans Cooper and Grant	VR
Hustedia rupinata Cooper and Grant	R
Metriolepis pedicosa Cooper and Grant	VR
Paraspiriferina sapinea Cooper and Grant	VR
Plectelasma guadalupense (Girty)	VR
Reticulariina laxa (Girty)	R
Thedusia trigonalis (Girty)	VR
Thedusia ventricosa Cooper and Grant	VR
LOCALITY N736t : Cathedral Mountain Formation	
Cenorhynchia sp.	VR
Echinauris sp.	VR
Enteletes sp.	VR
Institella leonardensis (R.E. King)	VR
LOCALITY N736x : Road Canyon Formation	
Chondronia ovalis Cooper and Grant	C
Collumatus solitarius Cooper and Grant	C
Composita cf. *enormis* Cooper and Grant	VR
Composita pilula Cooper and Grant	R
Cooperina subcuneata Cooper and Grant	VR
Cyclacantharia transitoria Cooper and Grant	R
Derbyia cincinnata Cooper and Grant	VR
Derbyia complicata Cooper and Grant	R
Derbyia laqueata Cooper and Grant	R
Derbyia sp.	VR
Dielasma sp.	VR
Dyoros (*Dyoros*) *vulgaris* Cooper and Grant	R
Echinauris lappacea Cooper and Grant	C
Enteletes exiguus Cooper and Grant	C
Enteletes sp.	C
Heterelasma sp.	VR
Holotricharina sparsa Cooper and Grant	VR
Hustedia connorsi Cooper and Grant	C
Kutorginella umbonata (Muir-Wood and Cooper)	VR
Lepidocrania tardispinosa Cooper and Grant	VR
Leurosina lata Cooper and Grant	VR

	Rarity code
Liosotella cf. *costata* Cooper and Grant	VR
Liosotella rotunda Cooper and Grant	R
Meekella calathica Cooper and Grant	R
Megousia mucronata Cooper and Grant	R
Metriolepis sp.	R
Metriolepis ziczac Cooper and Grant	VR
Neophricadothyris cordata Cooper and Grant	R
Neospirifer bakeri bakeri R.E. King	VR
Notothyris gillilandensis Cooper and Grant	R
Notothyris planiplicata Cooper and Grant	VR
Paraspiriferina pulchra Cooper and Grant	R
Paucispinifera parasulcata Cooper and Grant	VR
Paucispinifera sp.	VR
Paucispinifera sulcata Cooper and Grant	R
Petasmaia sp. 1	VR
Petasmatherus nitidus Cooper and Grant	R
Petasmatherus pumilus Cooper and Grant	R
Rhamnaria tenuispinosa Cooper and Grant	R
Rhynchopora hebetata Cooper and Grant	R
Rhytisia rugosa Cooper and Grant	VR
Spiriferella sp.	VR
Spiriferellina sp.	VR
Spiriferellina vescula Cooper and Grant	R
Texarina parallela Cooper and Grant	VR
Thedusia mesocostata Cooper and Grant	R
Tropidelasma corniculum Cooper and Grant	C
Undulella matutina Cooper and Grant	VR
Xenosteges trivialis Cooper and Grant	R
Yakovlevia sulcata Cooper and Grant	VR
LOCALITY N737a : Capitan Formation	
Aneuthelasma amygdalinum Cooper and Grant	VR
Anomaloria anomala Cooper and Grant	R
Astegosia subquadrata (Girty)	A
Collemataria spatulata Cooper and Grant	VR
Composita affinis Girty	VR
Composita emarginata Girty	VR
Compressoproductus pinniformis (Girty)	VR
Crurithyris guadalupensis (Girty)	VR
Elivina compacta (Girty)	R
Fascicosta longaeva (Girty)	VR
Heterelasma shumardianum Girty	VR
Hustedia opsia Cooper and Grant	VR
Martinia rhomboidalis Girty	R
Ombonia guadalupensis (Girty)	C
Paraspiriferina billingsi (Shumard)	VR
Paucispinifera latidorsata (Girty)	R
Reticulariina sp.	VR
Sarganostega pressa Cooper and Grant	VR
Stenoscisma trabeatum Cooper and Grant	VR
Strigirhynchia indentata (Shumard)	VR
Tautosia elegans (Girty)	VR
Tautosia shumardiana (Girty)	R
Thamnosia capitanensis (Girty)	VR
Xenosteges umbonatus Cooper and Grant	VR
LOCALITY N737b : Word Formation	
Composita sp.	VR
Crurithyris tholiaphor Cooper and Grant	VR
Derbyia sp.	R
Dyoros (*Dyoros*) *convexus* Cooper and Grant	VR
Echinauris lateralis Muir-Wood and Cooper	VR
Echinosteges sp.	VR
Glossothyropsis carinata (Girty)	VR
Glossothyropsis robusta (Girty)	VR
Heteralosia sp.	VR

	Rarity code
LOCALITY N737b - Continued	
Hustedia sp.	C
Lepidocrania sublamellosa Cooper and Grant	VR
Leurosina lata Cooper and Grant	VR
Liosotella irregularis Cooper and Grant	VR
Liosotella wordensis (R.E. King)	VR
Meekella skenoides Girty	R
Metriolepis sp.	VR
Paraspiriferina sp.	VR
Paucispinifera auriculata Muir-Wood and Cooper	VR
Pseudoleptodus? sp. 8	VR
Reticulariina cerina Cooper and Grant	VR
Rhamnaria kingorum Muir-Wood and Cooper	VR
Spiriferella sp.	VR
Xenosteges quadratus Cooper and Grant	VR
LOCALITY N737f : Cathedral Mountain Formation	
Peniculauris subcostata (R.E. King)	VR
LOCALITY N737j : Cathedral Mountain Formation	
Neospirifer sp.	VR
LOCALITY N737n : Road Canyon Formation	
Ombonia invecta Cooper and Grant	VR
LOCALITY N737q : Road Canyon Formation	
Acosarina mesoplatys (R.E. King)	VR
Echinauris bella Cooper and Grant	R
Hustedia sp.	VR
Liosotella costata Cooper and Grant	R
LOCALITY N737s : Cathedral Mountain Formation	
Peniculauris subcostata (R.E. King)	VR
LOCALITY N737u : Lenox Hills Formation	
Enteletes sp.	R
Eolyttonia cf. *fredericksi* (R.E. King)	VR
Hustedia sp.	VR
Limbella wolfcampensis (R.E. King)	VR
Linoproductus semisulcatus Cooper and Grant	VR
Neophricadothyris transversa Cooper and Grant	VR
Spyridiophora compacta Cooper and Grant	VR
Teguliferina cf. *boesei* R.E. King	VR
LOCALITY N737v : Cathedral Mountain Formation	
Choanodus irregularis Cooper and Grant	VR
Institella leonardensis (R.E. King)	VR
Stenoscisma triquetrum Cooper and Grant	VR
LOCALITY N737w : Word Formation, Lens	
Allorhynchus permianum wordense Cooper and Grant	VR
Arionthia germana Cooper and Grant	R
Cartorhium retusum Cooper and Grant	VR
Composita enormis Cooper and Grant	VR
Composita parasulcata Cooper and Grant	VR
Cooperina inexpectata Termier, Termier and Pajaud	R
Cyclacantharia kingorum Cooper and Grant	VR
Derbyia sp.	VR
Dielasma sp.	VR
Dyoros (*Dyoros*) *convexus* Cooper and Grant	C
Echinauris lateralis Muir-Wood and Cooper	C
Eolyttonia progressa Cooper and Grant	R
Grandaurispina gibbosa Cooper and Grant	R
Hustedia pugilla pugilla Cooper and Grant	VR
Hustedia sp.	VR
Liosotella irregularis Cooper and Grant	VR
Liosotella tetragonalis Cooper and Grant	VR

	Rarity code
Liosotella wordensis (R.E. King)	R
Neophricadothyris sp.	VR
Paraspiriferina sp.	VR
Paucispinifera quadrata Cooper and Grant	R
Pseudoleptodus grandis Cooper and Grant	VR
Reticulariina sp.	VR
Rhamnaria kingorum Muir-Wood and Cooper	R
Spiriferella sp.	R
Stenoscisma sp.	VR
LOCALITY N737y : Road Canyon Formation	
Collumatus solitarius Cooper and Grant	VR
Echinauris sp.	VR
Enteletes sp.	VR
Megousia auriculata Muir-Wood and Cooper	VR
Thedusia sp.	VR
LOCALITY N738 : Bell Canyon Formation, Lamar Member	
Allorhynchus venustulum Cooper and Grant	R
Aneuthelasma amygdalinum Cooper and Grant	R
Anomaloria anomala Cooper and Grant	R
Anteridocus swallovianus (Shumard)	R
Aphaurosia rotundata Cooper and Grant	R
Aphaurosia scutata Cooper and Grant	R
Arionthia lamaria Cooper and Grant	C
Astegosia subquadrata (Girty)	VA
Collemataria spatulata Cooper and Grant	R
Composita affinis Girty	A
Composita pyriformis Cooper and Grant	VR
Crenispirifer myllus Cooper and Grant	C
Crurithyris guadalupensis (Girty)	C
Deltarina magnicostata Cooper and Grant	C
Derbyia filosa Cooper and Grant	R
Derbyia sp. 1	VR
Dielasma cordatum Girty	R
Dielasma sp.	C
Dielasma sulcatum Girty	R
Eliva shumardi Cooper and Grant	VR
Elivina detecta Cooper and Grant	C
Fascicosta longaeva (Girty)	VR
Geyerella americana Girty	VR
Heteralosia magnispina Cooper and Grant	VR
Heterelasma shumardianum Girty	VR
Heterelasma venustulum Girty	VR
Hustedia opsia Cooper and Grant	A
Lirellaria costellata Cooper and Grant	VR
Martinia rhomboidalis Girty	VA
Ombonia guadalupensis (Girty)	C
Paraspiriferina billingsi (Shumard)	C
Paucispinifera latidorsata (Girty)	VR
Ptilotorhynchus delicatum Cooper and Grant	VR
Reticulariina sp.	R
Rigbyella girtyi (Wanner and Sieverts)	VR
Sarganostega pressa Cooper and Grant	C
Spiriferellina nuda Cooper and Grant	VR
Stenoscisma sp.	VR
Stenoscisma trabeatum Cooper and Grant	C
Strigirhynchia indentata (Shumard)	R
Tautosia elegans (Girty)	C
Tautosia shumardiana (Girty)	R
Thedusia emarginata Cooper and Grant	VR
Thedusia trigonalis (Girty)	R
Timorina schuchertensis (Girty)	R
Tropidelasma gregarium (Girty)	C

	Rarity code
LOCALITY N738a : Capitan Formation	
Allorhynchus sp.	VR
Altiplecus periosus Cooper and Grant	R
Anteridocus swallovianus (Shumard)	C
Cartorhium mexicanum (Shumard)	VR
Composita emarginata Girty	R
Dielasma prolongatum Girty	VR
Dielasma sp. 5	VR
Echinosteges guadalupensis (Shumard)	VR
Eliva inflata Cooper and Grant	VR
Hustedia rupinata Cooper and Grant	R
Liosotella popei (Shumard)	A
Paraspiriferina evax (Girty)	VR
Plectelasma guadalupense (Girty)	VR
Pleurelasma costatum Cooper and Grant	R
Rhamnaria shumardi Cooper and Grant	R
Scapharina levis Cooper and Grant	R
Strigirhynchia indentata (Shumard)	R
Strigirhynchia transversa Cooper and Grant	VR
Tautosia shumardiana (Girty)	R
Thamnosia capitanensis (Girty)	R
Timorina schuchertensis (Girty)	VR
LOCALITY N738b : Bell Canyon Formation, Lamar Member	
Acanthocrania vasta Cooper and Grant	VR
Allorhynchus venustulum Cooper and Grant	C
Aneuthelasma amygdalinum Cooper and Grant	C
Anomaloria anomala Cooper and Grant	A
Anteridocus bicostatus Cooper and Grant	VR
Anteridocus swallovianus (Shumard)	VR
Aphaurosia scutata Cooper and Grant	C
Arionthia lamaria Cooper and Grant	C
Astegosia subquadrata (Girty)	VA
Cleiothyridina pilularis Cooper and Grant	C
Collemataria sp.	VR
Collemataria spatulata Cooper and Grant	C
Composita affinis Girty	A
Composita emarginata Girty	R
Crenispirifer myllus Cooper and Grant	C
Crurithyris guadalupensis (Girty)	A
Crurithyris sp.	VR
Deltarina magnicostata Cooper and Grant	C
Derbyia sp. 1	C
Derbyia texta Cooper and Grant	R
Dielasma cordatum Girty	C
Dielasma sp.	C
Dielasma subcirculare Cooper and Grant	R
Dielasma sulcatum Girty	C
Dyoros (*Dyoros*) *hillanus* (Girty)	R
Dyoros (*Dyoros*) *subliratus* (Girty)	VR
Elivina? annectans Cooper and Grant	VR
Elivina detecta Cooper and Grant	C
Eolyttonia sp. 3	VR
Fascicosta longaeva (Girty)	VR
Geyerella americana Girty	VR
Heteralosia magnispina Cooper and Grant	C
Heteralosia sp.	VR
Heterelasma shumardianum Girty	VR
Heterelasma venustulum Girty	VR
Hustedia opsia Cooper and Grant	VA
Martinia rhomboidalis Girty	VA
Metriolepis nabis Cooper and Grant	VR
Metriolepis sp.	VR
Notothyris sp.	VR

	Rarity code
Ombonia guadalupensis (Girty)	C
Paraspiriferina billingsi (Shumard)	C
Paraspiriferina evax (Girty)	VR
Paucispinifera latidorsata (Girty)	R
Ptilotorhynchus delicatum Cooper and Grant	VR
Reticulariina laxa (Girty)	VR
Reticulariina sp.	C
Rigbyella girtyi (Wanner and Sieverts)	R
Sarganostega pressa Cooper and Grant	C
Scapharina levis Cooper and Grant	C
Scapharina rugosa Cooper and Grant	VR
Sestropoma cribriferum Cooper and Grant	VR
Spiriferellina nuda Cooper and Grant	VR
Stenoscisma trabeatum Cooper and Grant	R
Tautosia elegans (Girty)	C
Thamnosia capitanensis (Girty)	VR
Thedusia ventricosa Cooper and Grant	R
Timorina ovata (Girty)	C
Timorina schuchertensis (Girty)	VR
Tropidelasma gregarium (Girty)	C
LOCALITY N738c : Cibolo Formation, Breccia Zone	
Antronaria mesicostalis (Girty)	VR
Composita sp.	VR
Dielasma longisulcatum Cooper and Grant	VR
Echinauris sp.	VR
Enteletes sp.	VR
Gypospirifer infraplicus (R.E. King)	VR
Limbella limbata Cooper and Grant	VR
Orthotichia irregularis Cooper and Grant	VR
Rhipidomella hessensis R.E. King	VR
Scacchinella titan Cooper and Grant	R
Stenoscisma multicostum Stehli	VR
Tropidelasma robertsi Cooper and Grant	VR
LOCALITY N738d : Cibolo Formation, Transition Zone	
Nudauris whitei Cooper and Grant	VR
LOCALITY N738f : Cibolo Formation, Spicule Zone	
Acritosia teguliferoides (R.E. King)	VR
Institella leonardensis (R.E. King)	VR
Rhipidomella hessensis R.E. King	R
Xenosteges adherens Muir-Wood and Cooper	VR
LOCALITY N738g : Cibolo Formation, Thin-Bedded Zone	
Cenorhynchia saginata Cooper and Grant	VR
Composita sp.	R
Dyoros (*Dyoros*) *transversus* Cooper and Grant	VR
Echinauris bella Cooper and Grant	R
Heterelasma sp.	VR
Hustedia sp.	R
Megousia auriculata Muir-Wood and Cooper	VR
Neophricadothyris cordata Cooper and Grant	VR
Paraspiriferina cellulana Cooper and Grant	VR
Petasmatherus pumilus Cooper and Grant	C
Reticulariina sp.	VR
LOCALITY N738h : Cibolo Formation, Transition Zone	
Enteletes sp.	VR
Hustedia hessensis R.E. King	VR
Meekella magnifica Cooper and Grant	VR
Nudauris sp.	VR
Orthotichia newelli Cooper and Grant	VR

	Rarity code
LOCALITY N738h - Continued	
Reticulariina sp.	VR
Rhipidomella hessensis R.E. King	VR
Stenoscisma multicostum Stehli	VR

LOCALITY N738l : Cibolo Formation, Thin-Bedded Zone

Acosarina mesoplatys (R.E. King)	VR
Cenorhynchia saginata Cooper and Grant	R
Composita sp.	R
Dielasma sp.	VR
Dyoros (Dyoros) transversus Cooper and Grant	R
Echinauris bella Cooper and Grant	C
Echinauris sp.	VR
Heterelasma sp.	VR
Hustedia consuta Cooper and Grant	C
Hustedia cf. *cuneata* Cooper and Grant	VR
Liosotella costata Cooper and Grant	A
Meekella sp.	VR
Megousia auriculata Muir-Wood and Cooper	VR
Neophricadothyris cordata Cooper and Grant	R
Paraspiriferina cellulana Cooper and Grant	R
Paucispinifera sp.	VR
Petasmatherus pumilus Cooper and Grant	C
Phrenophoria sp.	VR
Reticulariina bufala Cooper and Grant	R
Reticulariina sp.	VR
Rhamnaria sp.	VR
Stenoscisma sp.	VR

LOCALITY N738n : Cibolo Formation, Transition Zone

Enteletes sp.	VR
Nudauris sp.	VR
Reticulatia robusta Cooper and Grant	VR
Scacchinella titan Cooper and Grant	VR

LOCALITY N738o : Cibolo Formation, Spicule Zone

Institella leonardensis (R.E. King)	VR

LOCALITY N738q : Cibolo Formation, Spicule Zone

Dielasma sp.	VR
Limbella limbata Cooper and Grant	VR

LOCALITY N738r : Cibolo Formation, Breccia Zone

Acosarina dorsisulcata Cooper and Grant	R
Acritosia teguliferoides (R.E. King)	R
Crenispirifer angulatus (R.E. King)	VR
Derbyia aff. *nasuta* Girty	R
Diplanus rarus Cooper and Grant	VR
Elliottella cf. *varicostata* Cooper and Grant	VR
Enteletes sp.	VR
Eolyttonia gigantea Cooper and Grant	VR
Eolyttonia sp.	VR
Geyerella cf. *hessi* Cooper and Grant	R
Gypospirifer infraplicus (R.E. King)	VR
Hustedia sp.	VR
Meekella attenuata Girty	C
Meekella caperata Cooper and Grant	VR
Meekella sp.	VR
Orthotichia cf. *newelli* Cooper and Grant	A
Scacchinella titan Cooper and Grant	VA
Teguliferina conida (Stehli)	VR

LOCALITY N738s : Cibolo Formation, Breccia Zone

Antronaria mesicostalis (Girty)	VR
Crenispirifer angulatus (R.E. King)	VR
Diplanus rarus Cooper and Grant	VR
Scacchinella titan Cooper and Grant	VR

LOCALITY N738t : Cibolo Formation, Transition Zone

Stenoscisma multicostum Stehli	VR

LOCALITY N739 : Capitan Formation

Anteridocus swallovianus (Shumard)	C
Composita affinis Girty	R
Dielasma prolongatum Girty	VR
Dielasma sp. 5	VR
Dyoros (Dyoros) hillanus (Girty)	VR
Eliva shumardi Cooper and Grant	R
Elivina compacta (Girty)	VR
Heterelasma shumardianum Girty	VR
Heterelasma venustulum Girty	VR
Hustedia opsia Cooper and Grant	R
Liosotella popei (Shumard)	VR
Paraspiriferina billingsi (Shumard)	VR
Paraspiriferina evax (Girty)	VR
Ptilotorhynchus delicatum Cooper and Grant	VR
Stenoscisma oblisum Cooper and Grant	R
Strigirhynchia indentata (Shumard)	VR
Tautosia elegans (Girty)	VR
Tautosia shumardiana (Girty)	VR
Timorina schuchertensis (Girty)	VR

LOCALITY N739g : Skinner Ranch Formation, Sullivan Peak Member

Acosarina dorsisulcata Cooper and Grant	VR
Acritosia peculiaris Cooper and Grant	VR
Chonosteges limbatus Cooper and Grant	R
Derbyia sp.	VR
Diplanus sp.	VR
Enteletes sp.	VR
Limbella limbata Cooper and Grant	VR
Scacchinella titan Cooper and Grant	VR
Spyridiophora reticulata (R.E. King)	VR

LOCALITY N739k : Cibolo Formation, Spicule Zone

Xestosia schucherti (R.E. King)	VR

LOCALITY N739l : Skinner Ranch Formation

Antronaria mesicostalis (Girty)	VR
Limbella limbata Cooper and Grant	VR
Neophricadothyris catatona Cooper and Grant	VR
Pontisia sp.	VR
Stenoscisma pyraustoides Cooper and Grant	VR

LOCALITY N739m : Cibolo Formation, Breccia Zone

Acosarina dorsisulcata Cooper and Grant	VR

LOCALITY N740 : Capitan Formation

Allorhynchus sp.	VR
Anteridocus swallovianus (Shumard)	C
Composita emarginata Girty	R
Dielasma sp.	VR
Dyoros (Dyoros) hillanus (Girty)	VR
Eliva shumardi Cooper and Grant	R
Heterelasma shumardianum Girty	VR
Hustedia opsia Cooper and Grant	VR
Liosotella popei (Shumard)	VR
Paraspiriferina billingsi (Shumard)	VR
Paraspiriferina evax (Girty)	VR
Ptilotorhynchus delicatum Cooper and Grant	VR

	Rarity code
LOCALITY N740 - Continued	
Ptilotorhynchus sp.	VR
Scapharina levis Cooper and Grant	R
Stenoscisma oblisum Cooper and Grant	VR
Strigirhynchia transversa Cooper and Grant	VR
Tautosia elegans (Girty)	R
Tautosia shumardiana (Girty)	VR
Thamnosia capitanensis (Girty)	VR
Timorina ovata (Girty)	VR
LOCALITY N740a : Bell Canyon Formation, Rader Member	
Altiplecus? deltosus Cooper and Grant	VR
Altiplecus extensus Cooper and Grant	VR
Altiplecus trapezoidalis Cooper and Grant	VR
Anteridocus swallovianus (Shumard)	R
Arionthia polypleura (Girty)	VR
Bryorhynchus bisulcatum (Shumard)	C
Chonetinetes sp.	VR
Chonetinetes varians Cooper and Grant	VR
Composita affinis Girty	R
Composita sp.	R
Craspedona newelli Cooper and Grant	VR
Crenispirifer jubatus Cooper and Grant	R
Deltarina magnicostata Cooper and Grant	VR
Derbyia sp.	R
Dielasma sp.	VR
Dielasma sulcatum Girty	VR
Dyoros (Dyoros) intrepidus Cooper and Grant	R
Elivina? annectans Cooper and Grant	C
Glossothyropsis cryptacanthoides Cooper and Grant	R
Glossothyropsis juvenis Cooper and Grant	VR
Heteralosia magnispina Cooper and Grant	VR
Heteralosia paucispinosa Cooper and Grant	VR
Heteralosia sp.	VR
Heterelasma shumardianum Girty	VR
Hustedia demissa Cooper and Grant	R
Hustedia opsia Cooper and Grant	C
Hustedia rupinata Cooper and Grant	R
Hustedia samiata Cooper and Grant	C
Hustedia sp.	C
Madarosia anterolamellata Cooper and Grant	VR
Metriolepis nabis Cooper and Grant	VR
Metriolepis pedicosa Cooper and Grant	R
Micraphelia scitula Cooper and Grant	C
Micraphelia subalata Cooper and Grant	C
Paraspiriferina billingsi (Shumard)	R
Phrenophoria perplexa Cooper and Grant	VR
Plectelasma guadalupense (Girty)	VR
Pseudoleptodus guadalupensis (Stehli)	VR
Ptilotorhynchus delicatum Cooper and Grant	VR
Rallacosta imporcata Cooper and Grant	R
Reticulariina echinata Cooper and Grant	VR
Reticulariina sp.	VR
Sarganostega transversalis Cooper and Grant	R
Scapharina levis Cooper and Grant	VR
Scapharina rugosa Cooper and Grant	VR
Sestropoma cribriferum Cooper and Grant	R
Spiriferella sulcifer (Shumard)	C
Stenoscisma sp.	VR
Tautosia shumardiana (Girty)	VR
Thamnosia capitanensis (Girty)	VR
Thedusia trigonalis (Girty)	R
Thedusia ventricosa Cooper and Grant	R
Tropidelasma gregarium (Girty)	VR

	Rarity code
LOCALITY N740c : Bell Canyon Formation, Hegler Member	
Acanthocrania sp.	VR
Altiplecus? deltosus Cooper and Grant	R
Altiplecus extensus Cooper and Grant	VR
Anteridocus swallovianus (Shumard)	VR
Arionthia alata Cooper and Grant	VR
Arionthia lamaria Cooper and Grant	R
Arionthia polypleura (Girty)	R
Bryorhynchus bisulcatum (Shumard)	C
Composita sp.	C
Craspedona newelli Cooper and Grant	VR
Crenispirifer jubatus Cooper and Grant	R
Derbyia sp.	C
Dielasma cordatum Girty	VR
Dielasma sulcatum Girty	VR
Dyoros (Dyoros) intrepidus Cooper and Grant	R
Echinosteges guadalupensis (Shumard)	VR
Elivina? annectans Cooper and Grant	VR
Fascicosta elongata Cooper and Grant	VR
Glossothyropsis juvenis Cooper and Grant	R
Heteralosia paucispinosa Cooper and Grant	VR
Heterelasma shumardianum Girty	VR
Hustedia rupinata Cooper and Grant	VR
Hustedia samiata Cooper and Grant	R
Hustedia sp.	A
Metriolepis nabis Cooper and Grant	VR
Metriolepis pedicosa Cooper and Grant	VR
Micraphelia scitula Cooper and Grant	C
Micraphelia sp.	R
Paraspiriferina billingsi (Shumard)	R
Paucispinifera sp.	R
Petrocrania sp.	VR
Phrenophoria perplexa Cooper and Grant	VR
Plectelasma guadalupense (Girty)	R
Pseudoleptodus guadalupensis (Stehli)	R
Ptilotorhynchus delicatum Cooper and Grant	R
Rallacosta imporcata Cooper and Grant	VR
Reticulariina sp.	R
Sarganostega pressa Cooper and Grant	R
Sarganostega transversalis Cooper and Grant	R
Scapharina levis Cooper and Grant	VR
Scapharina rugosa Cooper and Grant	R
Sestropoma cribriferum Cooper and Grant	R
Spiriferella sulcifer (Shumard)	VR
Thamnosia capitanensis (Girty)	VR
Thedusia emarginata Cooper and Grant	VR
Thedusia trigonalis (Girty)	R
Thedusia ventricosa Cooper and Grant	R
Timorina attenuata Cooper and Grant	R
Xenosaria exotica Cooper and Grant	R
LOCALITY N740d : Bell Canyon Formation, Hegler Member	
Acanthocrania sp.	VR
Altiplecus? deltosus Cooper and Grant	C
Altiplecus extensus Cooper and Grant	VR
Arionthia alata Cooper and Grant	VR
Arionthia lamaria Cooper and Grant	VR
Bryorhynchus bisulcatum (Shumard)	VR
Chonetinetes sp.	VR
Chonetinetes varians Cooper and Grant	VR
Composita sp.	R
Craspedona newelli Cooper and Grant	VR
Crenispirifer jubatus Cooper and Grant	C

	Rarity code
LOCALITY N740d - Continued	
Derbyia sp.	C
Dielasma sp.	R
Dielasma sulcatum Girty	R
Elivina? annectans Cooper and Grant	C
Glossothyropsis cryptacanthoides Cooper and Grant	R
Glossothyropsis juvenis Cooper and Grant	VR
Glossothyropsis sp. (Girty)	VR
Heteralosia paucispinosa Cooper and Grant	R
Heteralosia sp.	VR
Heterelasma shumardianum Girty	VR
Hustedia demissa Cooper and Grant	R
Hustedia opsia Cooper and Grant	C
Hustedia rupinata Cooper and Grant	C
Hustedia samiata Cooper and Grant	C
Hustedia sp.	C
Metriolepis nabis Cooper and Grant	R
Metriolepis pedicosa Cooper and Grant	R
Metriolepis sp.	VR
Micraphelia scitula Cooper and Grant	A
Micraphelia sp.	C
Micraphelia subalata Cooper and Grant	R
Paraspiriferina billingsi (Shumard)	A
Petrocrania sp.	VR
Plectelasma guadalupense (Girty)	C
Pseudodielasma sp.	VR
Pseudoleptodus guadalupensis (Stehli)	VR
Rallacosta importata Cooper and Grant	VR
Reticulariina echinata Cooper and Grant	R
Reticulariina phoxa Cooper and Grant	VR
Reticulariina sp.	VR
Sarganostega transversalis Cooper and Grant	VR
Scapharina rugosa Cooper and Grant	R
Sestropoma cribriferum Cooper and Grant	R
Spiriferella sulcifer (Shumard)	C
Thamnosia capitanensis (Girty)	VR
Thedusia trigonalis (Girty)	C
Thedusia ventricosa Cooper and Grant	VR
Timorina attenuata Cooper and Grant	VR
LOCALITY N740g : Bell Canyon Formation, Rader Member	
Arionthia lamaria Cooper and Grant	VR
Craspedona newelli Cooper and Grant	R
Eliva inflata Cooper and Grant	VR
Ptilotorhynchus delicatum Cooper and Grant	VR
Strigirhynchia indentata (Shumard)	VR
Tropidelasma sp.	VR
LOCALITY N740h : Bell Canyon Formation, Rader Member	
Anteridocus swallovianus (Shumard)	VR
Arionthia alata Cooper and Grant	VR
Composita emarginata Girty	R
Derbyia sp.	R
Eliva inflata Cooper and Grant	VR
Thamnosia capitanensis (Girty)	VR
LOCALITY N740i : Bell Canyon Formation, Rader Member	
Acanthocrania sp.	VR
Altiplecus? deltosus Cooper and Grant	C
Anteridocus swallovianus (Shumard)	R

	Rarity code
Arionthia lamaria Cooper and Grant	R
Bryorhynchus bisulcatum (Shumard)	C
Chonetinetes sp.	R
Composita affinis Girty	C
Craspedona newelli Cooper and Grant	VR
Crenispirifer jubatus Cooper and Grant	C
Derbyia sp.	C
Dielasma sp.	VR
Dielasma sulcatum Girty	R
Dyoros (Dyoros) intrepidus Cooper and Grant	C
Echinosteges guadalupensis (Shumard)	VR
Eliva shumardi Cooper and Grant	C
Fascicosta bella Cooper and Grant	VR
Glossothyropsis juvenis Cooper and Grant	VR
Glossothyropsis polita Cooper and Grant	R
Heteralosia magnispina Cooper and Grant	C
Heterelasma shumardianum Girty	VR
Hustedia rupinata Cooper and Grant	VA
Hustedia samiata Cooper and Grant	C
Metriolepis nabis Cooper and Grant	R
Metriolepis pedicosa Cooper and Grant	VR
Micraphelia subalata Cooper and Grant	C
Paraspiriferina billingsi (Shumard)	A
Paucispinifera latidorsata (Girty)	VR
Phrenophoria perplexa Cooper and Grant	VR
Plectelasma guadalupense (Girty)	C
Pseudoleptodus guadalupensis (Stehli)	VR
Ptilotorhynchus delicatum Cooper and Grant	VR
Rallacosta importata Cooper and Grant	VR
Sarganostega transversalis Cooper and Grant	R
Scapharina levis Cooper and Grant	R
Scapharina rugosa Cooper and Grant	R
Sestropoma cribriferum Cooper and Grant	C
Spiriferella sulcifer (Shumard)	C
Tautosia shumardiana (Girty)	VR
Thamnosia capitanensis (Girty)	R
Thedusia trigonalis (Girty)	C
Timorina attenuata Cooper and Grant	VR
Timorina ovata (Girty)	VR
LOCALITY N740j : Bell Canyon Formation, Rader Member	
Acanthocrania sp.	VR
Altiplecus? deltosus Cooper and Grant	R
Anteridocus swallovianus (Shumard)	R
Bryorhynchus bisulcatum (Shumard)	A
Chonetinetes sp.	R
Chonetinetes varians Cooper and Grant	R
Composita affinis Girty	C
Composita sp.	R
Craspedona newelli Cooper and Grant	R
Crenispirifer jubatus Cooper and Grant	C
Derbyia sp.	C
Dielasma sp.	VR
Dielasma sulcatum Girty	R
Dyoros (Dyoros) intrepidus Cooper and Grant	C
Echinosteges guadalupensis (Shumard)	VR
Elivina? annectans Cooper and Grant	C
Fascicosta bella Cooper and Grant	VR
Glossothyropsis cryptacanthoides Cooper and Grant	VR
Glossothyropsis juvenis Cooper and Grant	R
Heteralosia paucispinosa Cooper and Grant	R
Heteralosia sp.	VR
Heterelasma shumardianum Girty	VR
Hustedia demissa Cooper and Grant	R

	Rarity code
LOCALITY N740j - Continued	
Hustedia rupinata Cooper and Grant	C
Hustedia samiata Cooper and Grant	C
Hustedia sp.	A
Madarosia anterolamellata Cooper and Grant	R
Metriolepis pedicosa Cooper and Grant	R
Micraphelia scitula Cooper and Grant	C
Micraphelia subalata Cooper and Grant	A
Paraspiriferina billingsi (Shumard)	C
Petrocrania sp.	VR
Phrenophoria perplexa Cooper and Grant	R
Plectelasma guadalupense (Girty)	C
Pseudoleptodus guadalupensis (Stehli)	VR
Ptilotorhynchus delicatum Cooper and Grant	VR
Rallacosta imporcata Cooper and Grant	VR
Reticulariina sp.	R
Rhamnaria sp.	VR
Sarganostega transversalis Cooper and Grant	R
Scapharina levis Cooper and Grant	VR
Scapharina rugosa Cooper and Grant	R
Sestropoma cribriferum Cooper and Grant	C
Spiriferella sulcifer (Shumard)	C
Stenoscisma sp.	VR
Tautosia elegans (Girty)	VR
Thamnosia capitanensis (Girty)	VR
Thedusia angustata Cooper and Grant	VR
Thedusia trigonalis (Girty)	C
Thedusia ventricosa Cooper and Grant	R
Timorina attenuata Cooper and Grant	VR
LOCALITY N740k : Capitan Formation	
Arionthia lamaria Cooper and Grant	VR
Astegosia subquadrata (Girty)	C
Composita emarginata Girty	R
Dielasma sp.	VR
Dielasma sulcatum Girty	VR
Eliva inflata Cooper and Grant	VR
Heterelasma shumardianum Girty	VR
Hustedia sp.	VR
Martinia rhomboidalis Girty	R
Ombonia guadalupensis (Girty)	VR
Paraspiriferina billingsi (Shumard)	VR
Strigirhynchia indentata (Shumard)	VR
Tautosia elegans (Girty)	VR
Tautosia shumardiana (Girty)	VR
Thamnosia capitanensis (Girty)	VR
LOCALITY N740-1 : Capitan Formation	
Anteridocus swallovianus (Shumard)	VR
Composita emarginata Girty	R
Eliva inflata Cooper and Grant	R
Heterelasma shumardianum Girty	VR
Liosotella popei (Shumard)	R
Paraspiriferina billingsi (Shumard)	R
Pseudoleptodus guadalupensis (Stehli)	R
Reticulariina sp.	VR
Scapharina levis Cooper and Grant	VR
Stenoscisma sp.	VR
Stenoscisma trabeatum Cooper and Grant	VR
Thamnosia capitanensis (Girty)	R
LOCALITY N740m : Capitan Formation	
Anteridocus swallovianus (Shumard)	VR
Astegosia subquadrata (Girty)	R
Composita emarginata Girty	VR

	Rarity code
Martinia rhomboidalis Girty	R
Ombonia guadalupensis (Girty)	VR
Stenoscisma trabeatum Cooper and Grant	VR
Tautosia shumardiana (Girty)	VR
Thamnosia capitanensis (Girty)	VR
LOCALITY N740n : Capitan Formation	
Anteridocus swallovianus (Shumard)	R
Arionthia lamaria Cooper and Grant	R
Astegosia subquadrata (Girty)	VR
Composita emarginata Girty	C
Dielasma sp.	VR
Dielasma sulcatum Girty	VR
Eliva inflata Cooper and Grant	R
Eliva shumardi Cooper and Grant	C
Heterelasma shumardianum Girty	VR
Hustedia sp.	VR
Paraspiriferina billingsi (Shumard)	C
Stenoscisma trabeatum Cooper and Grant	C
Strigirhynchia indentata (Shumard)	R
Tautosia elegans (Girty)	C
Tautosia shumardiana (Girty)	R
Timorina attenuata Cooper and Grant	VR
Timorina schuchertensis (Girty)	VR
Tropidelasma gregarium (Girty)	VR
LOCALITY N740o : Capitan Formation	
Anteridocus swallovianus (Shumard)	VR
Astegosia subquadrata (Girty)	VR
Eliva inflata Cooper and Grant	VR
Elivina compacta (Girty)	VR
Fascicosta longaeva (Girty)	VR
Strigirhynchia indentata (Shumard)	VR
LOCALITY N741 : Bone Spring Formation	
Enteletes stehlii Cooper and Grant	VR
Hustedia hessensis R.E. King	VR
Reticulariina newelli (Stehli)	VR
Reticulariina tetrica Cooper and Grant	VR
LOCALITY N741a : Road Canyon Formation	
Acosarina mesoplatys (R.E. King)	VR
Cenorhynchia atmeta Cooper and Grant	R
Cenorhynchia parvula Cooper and Grant	VR
Chondronia ovalis Cooper and Grant	R
Composita crassa Cooper and Grant	R
Cyclacantharia paucispinosa Cooper and Grant	VR
Derbyia informis Cooper and Grant	VR
Edriosteges multispinosus Muir-Wood and Cooper	VR
Hercosestria cribrosa Cooper and Grant	VR
Meekella calathica Cooper and Grant	VR
Neophricadothyris bullata Cooper and Grant	VR
Neospirifer bakeri columbarius Cooper and Grant	VR
Paucispinifera sulcata Cooper and Grant	VR
Peniculauris peniculifera Cooper and Grant	VR
Spiriferellina tricosa Cooper and Grant	VR
Stenoscisma calvatum Cooper and Grant	R
LOCALITY N741h : Hueco Formation	
Reticulariina hueconiana Cooper and Grant	VR
Stenoscisma hueconianum (Girty)	A
LOCALITY N741i : Road Canyon Formation	
Stenoscisma sp.	VR
LOCALITY N741k : Skinner Ranch Formation, Poplar Tank Member	
Cancrinella parva Cooper and Grant	R

	Rarity code

LOCALITY N741k - Continued

Chonosteges aff. limbatus Cooper and Grant	R
Compressoproductus sp. 2	VR
Compressoproductus sp.	VR
Derbyia sp.	VR
Diplanus lamellatus (R.E. King)	R
Glyptosteges sulcatus Cooper and Grant	VR
Hustedia sp.	R
Kochiproductus sp.	VR
Limbella limbata Cooper and Grant	R
Meekella sp.	VR
Oncosarina spinicostata Cooper and Grant	C
Parenteletes cooperi R.E. King	R
Pseudoleptodus sp.	VR
Rhipidomella aff. hessensis R.E. King	VR
Spyridiophora reticulata (R.E. King)	R
Teguliferina boesei R.E. King	R

LOCALITY N741p : Word Formation, Lens

Arionthia germana Cooper and Grant	R
Composita parasulcata Cooper and Grant	R
Composita sp.	R
Cooperina inexpectata Termier, Termier and Pajaud	VR
Cyclacantharia kingorum Cooper and Grant	VR
Derbyia pannucia Cooper and Grant	VR
Derbyia texta Cooper and Grant	C
Dielasma sp.	VR
Dyoros (Dyoros) convexus Cooper and Grant	A
Echinauris lateralis Muir-Wood and Cooper	R
Echinosteges tuberculatus (R.E. King)	VR
Eolyttonia progressa Cooper and Grant	R
Grandaurispina crassa Cooper and Grant	R
Grandaurispina gibbosa Cooper and Grant	R
Hustedia pugilla hebetata Cooper and Grant	R
Hustedia sp.	C
Liosotella irregularis Cooper and Grant	R
Liosotella tetragonalis Cooper and Grant	R
Liosotella wordensis (R.E. King)	C
Meekella skenoides Girty	VR
Megousia definita Cooper and Grant	VR
Neospirifer amphigyus Cooper and Grant	VR
Paraspiriferina rotundata Cooper and Grant	R
Paucispinifera quadrata Cooper and Grant	R
Pseudoleptodus grandis Cooper and Grant	VR
Reticulariina cerina Cooper and Grant	R
Rhamnaria kingorum Muir-Wood and Cooper	C
Rhynchopora tenera Cooper and Grant	VR
Spiriferella sp.	R
Stenoscisma sp.	VR
Xenosteges quadratus Cooper and Grant	VR

LOCALITY N741q : Word Formation, Lens

Arionthia germana Cooper and Grant	C
Composita parasulcata Cooper and Grant	R
Cyclacantharia kingorum Cooper and Grant	VR
Dyoros (Dyoros) convexus Cooper and Grant	VA
Echinauris lateralis Muir-Wood and Cooper	C
Eolyttonia progressa Cooper and Grant	R
Grandaurispina crassa Cooper and Grant	R
Grandaurispina elongata Cooper and Grant	VR
Hustedia sp.	C
Liosotella wordensis (R.E. King)	C
Meekella skenoides Girty	R
Neospirifer amphigyus	VR
Paraspiriferina rotundata Cooper and Grant	R
Paucispinifera sp.	R

Pseudoleptodus grandis Cooper and Grant	R
Reticulariina cerina Cooper and Grant	VR
Spiriferella sp.	C
Xenosteges quadratus Cooper and Grant	VR

LOCALITY N741s : Cathedral Mountain Formation

Agelesia triagonalis (R.E. King)	VR
Enteletes sp.	VR
Institella leonardensis (R.E. King)	VR
Meekella sp.	VR
Rhipidomella hispidula Cooper and Grant	VR

LOCALITY N742 : Bone Spring Formation

Crenispirifer angulatus (R.E. King)	VR
Elliottella transversalis (Stehli)	R
Kozlowskia kingi Stehli	VR
Limbella victorioensis Stehli	VR

LOCALITY N742a : Hess Formation

Scacchinella titan Cooper and Grant	VR

LOCALITY N742b : Word Formation, Lens

Allorhynchus triangulatum Cooper and Grant	VR
Cartorhium orbiculatum Cooper and Grant	VR
Composita sp.	VR
Cooperina inexpectata Termier, Termier and Pajaud	VR
Cyclacantharia kingorum Cooper and Grant	VR
Derbyia sp.	R
Derbyia texta Cooper and Grant	R
Dyoros (Dyoros) convexus Cooper and Grant	A
Dyoros (Dyoros) extensus Cooper and Grant	R
Echinauris lateralis Muir-Wood and Cooper	C
Echinosteges tuberculatus (R.E. King)	VR
Grandaurispina crassa Cooper and Grant	R
Hustedia sp.	C
Liosotella irregularis Cooper and Grant	R
Liosotella wordensis (R.E. King)	C
Meekella skenoides Girty	VR
Paucispinifera quadrata Cooper and Grant	R
Pseudoleptodus grandis Cooper and Grant	R
Reticulariina cerina Cooper and Grant	C
Reticulariina sp.	R
Rhamnaria kingorum Muir-Wood and Cooper	R
Spiriferella clypeata Cooper and Grant	R
Spiriferellina hilli (Girty)	R
Spiriferinaella scalpata Cooper and Grant	VR
Stenoscisma renode Cooper and Grant	VR
Thamnosia phragmophora Cooper and Grant	VR
Xenosteges quadratus Cooper and Grant	VR

LOCALITY N742c : Neal Ranch Formation

Camarelasma neali Cooper and Grant	VR
Cenorhynchia hebata Cooper and Grant	R
Chondronia rectimarginata Cooper and Grant	R
Cleiothyridina rectimarginata Cooper and Grant	R
Composita sp.	VR
Crurithyris tumibilis Cooper and Grant	VR
Derbyia carteri Cooper and Grant	VR
Derbyia sp.	VR
Diplanus catatonus Cooper and Grant	VR
Geyerella kingorum Cooper and Grant	VR
Hustedia sp.	VR
Limbella wolfcampensis (R.E. King)	R
Meekella prionota Cooper and Grant	R
Orthotichia kozlowskii R.E. King	R
Teguliferina boesei R.E. King	C
Tropidelasma sp.	VR

Rarity code

LOCALITY N742d : Lenox Hills Formation

Reticulatia robusta Cooper and Grant .... VR

LOCALITY N744 : Bone Spring Formation

Enteletes stehlii Cooper and Grant .... VR

LOCALITY N745 : Bone Spring Formation

Antronaria spectabilis Cooper and Grant .... VR
Chonetinella victoriana (Girty)....................................... VR
Elliottella minima (Stehli)... VR
Goniarina permiana (Stehli)... R
Hustedia hessensis R.E. King... VR
Kozlowskia kingi Stehli... VR
Meekella hessensis R.E. King... VR
Meekella intermedia Cooper and Grant .... VR
Pontisia nanas (Stehli) .... VR
Rhipidomella hessensis R.E. King.................................... VR

LOCALITY N746 : Bone Spring Formation

Acosarina dorsisulcata Cooper and Grant .... VR
Antronaria spectabilis Cooper and Grant .... VR
Cancrinella sp. .... R
Chonetinella victoriana (Girty)....................................... R
Cyclacantharia sp. 3 .... R
Derbyia sp. .... VR
Dyoros (*Dyoros*) *consanguineus* (Girty)...................... VR
Elliottella multicostata Cooper and Grant......................... C
Enteletes stehlii Cooper and Grant .... R
Heteralosia sp. .... VR
Hustedia glomerosa Cooper and Grant .... VR
Kozlowskia kingi Stehli... C
Limbella victorioensis Stehli .... VR
Meekella intermedia Cooper and Grant .... R
Quadrochonetes girtyi Stehli.. R
Rhipidomella hessensis R.E. King.................................... VR
Scacchinella americana Stehli .... R
Spinifrons quadrata Stehli... VR
Teguliferina conida (Stehli) .... VR

LOCALITY N747 : Bone Spring Formation, Cutoff Member

Composita nucella Cooper and Grant C
Hustedia decollatensis Cooper and Grant.......................... VR
Megousia auriculata Muir-Wood and Cooper...................... VR
Phrenophoria corpulenta Cooper and Grant....................... VR
Tautosia expansa Cooper and Grant .... R

LOCALITY N748 : Bell Canyon Formation, Pinery Member

Altiplecus trapezoidalis Cooper and Grant .... R
Arionthia lamaria Cooper and Grant .... VR
Composita sp. .... R
Craspedona newelli Cooper and Grant.............................. VR
Crenispirifer jubatus Cooper and Grant .... VR
Derbyia sp. .... VR
Dielasma prolongatum Girty... VR
Dielasma sulcatum Girty .... R
Elivina? annectans Cooper and Grant .... R
Glossothyropsis cryptacanthoides Cooper and Grant........... VR
Heterelasma shumardianum Girty .... VR
Hustedia rupinata Cooper and Grant C
Metriolepis nabis Cooper and Grant .... VR
Micraphelia subalata Cooper and Grant .... VR
Paraspiriferina sapinea Cooper and Grant C
Plectelasma guadalupense (Girty).................................... R
Plectelasma sp. .... VR
Sarganostega transversalis Cooper and Grant.................... VR

Rarity code

Scapharina rugosa Cooper and Grant .... VR
Spiriferella sulcifer (Shumard) .... VR
Spiriferellina nuda Cooper and Grant .... R
Thedusia trigonalis (Girty) .... R
Thedusia ventricosa Cooper and Grant .... R

LOCALITY N748a : Capitan Formation

Anteridocus swallovianus (Shumard)................................. VR
Bryorhynchus bisulcatum (Shumard) .... R
Dyoros (*Dyoros*) *subliratus* (Girty) .... VR
Liosotella popei (Shumard) .... VR
Micraphelia subalata Cooper and Grant .... R
Phrenophoria pinguis (Girty).. VR
Reticulariina sp. .... VR
Sestropoma cribriferum Cooper and Grant .... R
Stenoscisma sp. .... VR
Thamnosia capitanensis (Girty)....................................... VR

LOCALITY N750 : Capitan Formation

Allorhynchus sp. .... VR
Aneuthelasma amygdalinum Cooper and Grant.................... R
Anomaloria anomala Cooper and Grant .... R
Astegosia subquadrata (Girty) .... A
Cleiothyridina pilularis Cooper and Grant .... VR
Compressoproductus pinniformis (Girty) .... A
Dielasma sp. .... VR
Dielasma subcirculare Cooper and Grant.......................... VR
Martinia rhomboidalis Girty C
Ombonia guadalupensis (Girty)....................................... C
Paucispinifera latidorsata (Girty) .... R
Plectelasma guadalupense (Girty).................................... VR
Plectelasma planidorsatum Cooper and Grant .... VR
Tropidelasma gregarium (Girty) .... VR

LOCALITY N750a : Capitan Formation

Anteridocus swallovianus (Shumard).................................. C
Collemataria sp. .... VR
Composita emarginata Girty .... R
Dielasma prolongatum Girty... VR
Dyoros (*Dyoros*) *subliratus* (Girty) .... VR
Eliva inflata Cooper and Grant....................................... C
Fascicosta longaeva (Girty) .... VR
Grandaurispina sp. 5 .... VR
Hustedia opsia Cooper and Grant .... VR
Liosotella popei (Shumard) .... R
Paraspiriferina billingsi (Shumard)................................... VR
Paucispinifera sp. .... R
Reticulariina sp. .... VR
Scapharina levis Cooper and Grant.................................. VR
Stenoscisma trabeatum Cooper and Grant .... R
Strigirhynchia transversa Cooper and Grant...................... VR
Tautosia shumardiana (Girty) .... VR
Thamnosia capitanensis (Girty)....................................... C

LOCALITY N750b : Capitan Formation

Astegosia subquadrata (Girty) .... R
Composita affinis Girty.. VR
Compressoproductus pinniformis (Girty) .... VR
Elivina compacta (Girty).. VR
Fascicosta longaeva (Girty) .... VR
Martinia rhomboidalis Girty .... VR
Megousia sp. .... R
Paraspiriferina billingsi (Shumard)................................... R
Paucispinifera latidorsata (Girty) .... R
Stenoscisma trabeatum Cooper and Grant........................ VR
Strigirhynchia transversa Cooper and Grant...................... VR
Tautosia shumardiana (Girty) .... VR

	Rarity code
LOCALITY N750e : Capitan Formation	
Martinia rhomboidalis Girty	VR
Plectelasma planidorsatum Cooper and Grant	VR
LOCALITY N750f : Capitan Formation	
Astegosia subquadrata (Girty)	VR

	Rarity code
Paraspiriferina billingsi (Shumard).................................	VR
LOCALITY N750g : Capitan Formation	
Plectelasma guadalupense (Girty)...................................	VR

TABLE 2.—Stratigraphic distribution of brachiopod species in Glass and Guadalupe mountains

GENUS AND SPECIES	Gaptank	Uddenites	Neal Ranch	Lenox Hills	Decie Ranch	Poplar Tank	Dugout Mtn.	Sullivan Peak	Skinner Ranch undivided	Hess	Taylor Ranch	Cathedral Mtn.	Wedin	Road Canyon	China Tank	Willis Ranch	Lens	Appel Ranch	Word undivided	Hueco	Bone Spring	Getaway	Hegler	Pinery	Rader	Lamar	Capitan
Acanthocrania																											
alta	-	-	-	-	-	-	-	-	X	-	-	-	-	-	-	-	-	-	-	-	-	-	-	-	-	-	-
conferta	-	-	-	-	-	-	-	-	-	-	-	-	-	-	X	-	-	-	-	-	-	X	-	-	-	-	-
densispina	-	-	-	-	-	-	-	-	-	-	X	-	X	-	-	-	-	-	-	-	-	-	-	-	-	-	-
intermedia	-	-	-	-	-	-	-	-	-	-	-	-	-	-	X	X	-	X	-	-	-	-	-	-	-	-	-
magna	-	-	-	-	-	-	-	-	-	-	X	-	-	-	-	-	-	-	-	-	-	-	-	-	-	-	-
minutispinosa	-	-	-	-	-	-	-	-	-	-	-	-	-	-	-	-	-	-	-	-	-	-	-	X	X	-	-
platys	-	-	-	-	-	-	-	-	-	-	-	-	-	-	-	-	-	-	-	-	X	-	-	-	-	-	-
regularis	-	-	-	-	-	-	-	-	-	-	-	-	-	-	-	-	-	-	-	-	-	-	-	-	-	X	-
vasta	-	-	-	-	-	-	-	-	-	-	-	-	-	-	-	-	-	-	-	-	-	-	X	-	-	X	-
Acolosia																											
?anomala	-	-	-	-	-	-	-	-	-	-	-	-	-	-	X	-	-	-	-	-	-	-	-	-	-	-	-
elliptica	-	-	-	-	-	-	-	-	-	-	X	-	-	-	-	-	-	-	-	-	-	-	-	-	-	-	-
?exasperata	-	-	-	-	-	-	-	X	-	-	-	-	-	-	-	-	-	-	-	-	-	-	-	-	-	-	-
glabra	-	-	-	-	-	-	-	-	-	-	-	-	-	-	X	-	-	-	-	-	-	-	-	-	-	-	-
magna	-	-	-	X	-	-	-	-	-	-	-	-	-	-	-	-	-	-	-	-	-	-	-	-	-	-	-
recepta	-	-	-	-	-	-	-	X	-	-	-	-	-	-	-	-	-	-	-	-	-	-	-	-	-	-	-
Acosarina																											
baylorensis (REK)	-	-	-	-	-	-	-	-	-	-	-	-	-	-	-	-	-	-	-	-	X	-	-	-	-	-	-
dorsisulcata C&G	-	-	-	X	X	-	X	X	X	X	-	-	-	-	-	-	-	-	-	-	X	-	-	-	-	-	-
mesoplatys (REK)	-	-	-	-	-	-	-	-	-	-	X	X	X	-	-	-	-	-	-	-	X	-	-	-	-	-	-
rectimarginata	-	X	-	-	-	-	-	-	-	-	-	-	-	-	-	-	-	-	-	-	-	-	-	-	-	-	-
Acritosia																											
magna C&G	-	-	X	-	-	-	-	-	-	-	-	-	-	-	-	-	-	-	-	-	-	-	-	-	-	-	-
magnifica	-	-	-	-	-	-	-	-	-	-	-	-	-	-	X	-	-	-	-	-	-	-	-	-	-	-	-
peculiaris	-	-	-	X	X	X	X	X	X	X	X	-	-	-	-	-	-	-	-	-	X	-	-	-	-	-	-
silicica	-	-	-	-	-	-	-	-	-	-	-	-	-	-	-	-	-	-	-	X	-	-	-	-	-	-	-
solida	-	-	-	-	-	X	-	X	-	X	-	-	-	-	-	-	-	-	-	-	-	-	-	-	-	-	-
teguliferoides (REK)	-	-	-	X	-	-	-	X	-	-	-	-	-	-	-	-	-	-	-	-	X	-	-	-	-	-	-
?vestibula	-	-	-	-	-	-	-	-	-	-	-	X	-	-	-	-	-	-	-	-	-	-	-	-	-	-	-
Agelesia																											
triagonalis (REK)	-	-	-	-	-	-	-	X	-	-	X	X	-	-	-	-	-	-	-	-	X	-	-	-	-	-	-
Allorhynchus																											
circulare	-	-	-	-	-	-	-	-	-	-	-	-	-	-	-	-	-	-	-	-	-	X	-	-	-	-	-
concentricum	-	-	-	-	-	-	-	-	-	-	-	X	-	-	-	-	-	-	-	-	-	-	-	-	-	-	-
formulosum	-	-	-	-	-	-	-	-	-	-	-	-	-	-	-	-	-	-	-	-	-	X	-	-	-	-	-
permianum permianum Stehli	-	-	-	-	-	-	-	-	-	-	-	-	-	-	-	-	-	-	-	-	-	X	-	-	-	-	-
permianum wordense	-	-	-	-	-	-	-	-	-	-	-	-	-	-	X	X	X	X	X	-	-	-	-	-	-	-	-
triangulatum	-	-	-	-	-	-	-	-	-	-	-	-	-	-	X	X	X	X	X	-	-	-	-	-	-	-	-
variable	-	-	-	-	-	-	-	-	-	-	-	-	-	-	X	X	-	-	-	-	-	-	-	-	-	-	-
venustulum	-	-	-	-	-	-	-	-	-	-	-	-	-	-	-	-	-	-	-	-	-	-	X	X	X	X	-
Altiplecus																											
argutus	-	-	X	-	-	-	-	-	-	-	-	-	-	-	-	-	-	-	-	-	-	-	-	-	-	-	-
cooperi Stehli	-	-	-	-	-	-	-	-	-	-	-	-	-	-	-	-	-	X	-	-	-	-	-	-	-	-	-
?deltosus	-	-	-	-	-	-	-	-	-	-	-	-	-	-	-	-	-	-	-	-	-	-	X	X	X	-	-
extensus	-	-	-	-	-	-	-	-	-	-	-	-	-	-	-	-	-	-	-	-	-	-	X	X	X	-	-
glebosus	-	-	-	X	-	-	-	X	-	-	-	-	-	-	-	-	-	-	-	-	-	-	-	-	-	-	-
periosus	-	-	-	-	-	-	-	-	-	-	-	-	-	-	-	-	-	-	-	-	-	-	-	-	-	-	X
trapezoidalis	-	-	-	-	-	-	-	-	-	-	-	-	-	-	-	-	-	-	-	-	-	-	-	X	X	-	-
sp.	-	-	-	-	-	-	-	X	-	-	X	-	X	-	-	-	-	-	-	-	-	-	-	-	-	-	-
Ametoria																											
residua	-	-	-	-	-	-	-	-	-	-	-	-	-	X	-	-	-	-	-	-	-	-	-	-	-	-	-
Amphipella																											
arcaria C&G	-	-	-	-	-	-	-	-	-	-	X	-	-	-	-	-	-	-	-	-	-	-	-	-	-	-	-
attenuata	-	-	-	-	-	-	-	-	-	-	X	-	-	-	-	-	-	-	-	-	-	-	-	-	-	-	-
Anemonaria																											
sublaevis (REK)	-	-	-	-	-	-	-	-	-	-	X	-	X	-	-	-	-	-	-	-	X	-	-	-	-	-	-
Aneuthelasma																											
amygdalinum	-	-	-	-	-	-	-	-	-	-	-	-	-	-	-	-	-	-	-	-	-	-	-	-	-	X	X
Anomalesia																											
perplexa	-	-	-	-	-	-	-	X	-	-	-	-	-	-	-	-	-	-	-	-	X	-	-	-	-	-	-

GENUS AND SPECIES	Gaptank	Uddenites	Neal Ranch	Lenox Hills	Decie Ranch	Poplar Tank	Dugout Mtn.	Sullivan Peak	Skinner Ranch undivided	Hess	Taylor Ranch	Cathedral Mtn.	Wedin	Road Canyon	China Tank	Willis Ranch	Lens	Appel Ranch	Word undivided	Hueco	Bone Spring	Getaway	Hegler	Pinery	Rader	Lamar	Capitan
Anomaloria																											
anomala C&G	-	-	-	-	-	-	-	-	-	-	-	-	-	-	-	-	-	-	-	-	-	-	-	-	-	X	X
Anteridocus																											
bicostatus	-	-	-	-	-	-	-	-	-	-	-	-	-	-	-	-	-	-	-	-	X	-	X	X	-	X	-
erugatus	-	-	-	-	-	-	-	-	-	-	-	X	-	X	-	-	-	-	-	-	-	-	-	-	-	-	-
eximius	-	-	-	-	-	-	-	-	-	-	-	-	-	-	-	-	-	-	-	-	X	-	-	-	-	-	-
gongylus	-	-	-	-	-	-	-	-	-	-	-	X	-	-	-	-	-	-	-	-	-	-	-	-	-	-	-
paucicostatus	-	-	-	-	-	-	-	X	X	-	-	-	-	-	-	-	-	-	-	-	-	-	-	-	-	-	-
seminudus	-	-	-	-	-	-	-	-	-	-	-	-	-	X	-	-	-	-	-	-	-	-	-	-	-	-	-
subcarinatus	-	-	-	-	-	-	-	-	-	-	-	-	-	-	-	-	-	-	-	-	-	-	X	X	-	-	-
swallovianus (Shumard)	-	-	-	-	-	-	-	-	-	-	-	-	-	-	-	-	-	-	-	-	-	-	X	X	X	X	X
triangulatus	-	-	-	-	-	-	-	-	-	-	-	-	-	X	-	-	-	-	-	-	-	-	-	-	-	-	-
Antiquatonia																											
costella	-	-	-	X	-	-	-	-	-	-	-	-	-	-	-	-	-	-	-	-	-	-	-	-	-	-	-
hessensis (REK)	-	-	-	-	X	-	-	X	X	-	-	-	-	-	-	-	-	-	-	-	-	-	-	-	-	-	-
inflativentra	X	X	X	-	-	-	-	-	-	-	-	-	-	-	-	-	-	-	-	-	-	-	-	-	-	-	-
planumbona Stehli	-	-	-	-	-	-	-	-	-	-	-	-	-	-	-	-	-	-	-	-	X	-	-	-	-	-	-
regularis	-	-	-	X	-	-	-	-	-	-	-	-	-	-	-	-	-	-	-	-	-	-	-	-	-	-	-
Antronaria																											
dissona	-	-	-	-	X	-	-	X	X	-	-	-	-	-	-	-	-	-	-	-	X	-	-	-	-	-	-
emarginata	-	-	-	-	X	-	-	X	X	-	-	-	-	-	-	-	-	-	-	-	-	-	-	-	-	-	-
indentata	-	-	-	-	-	-	-	-	-	-	-	-	-	-	-	-	-	-	-	-	X	-	-	-	-	-	-
mesicostalis (Girty)	-	-	-	-	-	-	-	X	-	-	-	-	-	-	-	-	-	-	-	-	X	-	-	-	-	-	-
pluricosta	-	-	-	-	-	-	-	-	-	-	-	-	-	-	-	-	-	-	-	-	X	-	-	-	-	-	-
specialis	-	-	-	-	-	-	-	-	-	-	-	-	-	-	-	-	-	-	-	-	X	-	-	-	-	-	-
speciosa	-	-	-	-	-	-	-	X	-	X	X	X	-	X	-	-	-	-	-	-	-	-	-	-	-	-	-
spectabilis	-	-	-	-	-	-	-	-	-	-	-	-	-	-	-	-	-	-	-	-	X	-	-	-	-	-	-
titania	-	-	-	-	X	-	-	X	X	X	-	-	-	-	-	-	-	-	-	-	-	-	-	-	-	-	-
transversa (REK)	-	-	-	-	X	-	-	X	X	X	X	-	-	-	-	-	-	-	-	-	-	-	-	-	-	-	-
voluminosa	-	-	-	-	X	X	-	X	X	-	-	-	-	-	-	-	-	-	-	-	X	-	-	-	-	-	-
Aphaurosia																											
rotundata	-	-	-	-	-	-	-	-	-	-	-	-	-	-	-	-	-	-	-	-	-	-	-	-	X	X	-
scutata	-	-	-	-	-	-	-	-	-	-	-	-	-	-	-	-	-	-	-	-	-	-	X	X	-	X	-
Arionthia																											
alata	-	-	-	-	-	-	-	-	-	-	-	-	-	-	-	-	-	-	-	-	-	-	X	-	-	X	-
blothrhachis	-	-	-	-	-	-	-	-	-	-	-	-	-	X	X	-	-	-	-	-	-	-	-	-	-	-	-
germana	-	-	-	-	-	-	-	-	-	-	-	-	-	-	X	X	-	-	-	-	-	-	-	-	-	-	-
lamaria	-	-	-	-	-	-	-	-	-	-	-	-	-	-	-	-	-	-	-	-	-	-	X	X	X	X	X
polypleura (Girty)	-	-	-	-	-	-	-	-	-	-	-	-	-	-	-	-	-	-	-	-	-	-	X	X	X	X	-
Astegosia																											
subquadrata (Girty)	-	-	-	-	-	-	-	-	-	-	-	-	-	-	-	-	-	-	-	-	-	-	-	-	X	X	X
Atelestegastus																											
marginatus	-	-	X	-	-	-	-	-	-	-	-	-	-	-	-	-	-	-	-	-	-	-	-	-	-	-	-
Attenuatella																											
texana Stehli	-	-	-	-	-	-	-	-	-	-	-	-	-	-	-	-	-	-	-	-	X	-	-	-	-	-	-
Beecheria																											
elliptica	-	-	X	-	-	-	-	-	-	-	-	-	-	-	-	-	-	-	-	-	-	-	-	-	-	-	-
expansa	-	-	X	X	-	-	-	-	-	-	-	-	-	-	-	-	-	-	-	-	-	-	-	-	-	-	-
Bothrionia																											
guadalupensis	-	-	-	-	-	-	-	-	-	-	-	-	-	-	-	-	-	-	-	-	-	X	-	-	-	-	-
nasuta	-	-	-	-	-	-	-	-	-	-	-	-	-	-	X	X	X	-	-	-	-	-	-	-	-	-	-
pulchra	-	-	-	-	-	-	-	-	-	-	-	-	-	-	X	-	-	-	-	-	-	X	-	-	-	-	-
transversa	-	-	-	-	-	-	-	-	-	-	-	-	-	-	X	X	X	-	-	-	-	-	-	-	-	-	-
Bothrostegium																											
compactum	-	-	-	-	-	-	-	-	-	-	-	-	-	X	-	-	-	-	-	-	-	-	-	-	-	-	-
derbyoideum	-	-	-	-	-	-	-	-	-	-	-	-	-	X	-	-	-	-	-	-	-	-	-	-	-	-	-
pusillum	-	-	-	-	-	-	-	-	-	-	-	-	-	X	-	-	-	-	-	-	-	-	-	-	-	-	-
Bryorhynchus																											
bisulcatum (Shumard)	-	-	-	-	-	-	-	-	-	-	-	-	-	-	-	-	-	-	-	-	-	X	X	X	X	X	X
gratiosum (Girty)	-	-	-	-	-	-	-	-	-	-	-	-	-	-	-	-	-	-	-	-	-	X	X	X	X	-	-
?nitidum (Girty)	-	-	-	-	-	-	-	-	-	-	-	-	-	-	-	-	-	-	-	-	X	-	-	-	-	-	-

GENUS AND SPECIES	Gaptank	Uddenites	Neal Ranch	Lenox Hills	Decie Ranch	Poplar Tank	Dugout Mtn.	Sullivan Peak	Skinner Ranch undivided	Hess	Taylor Ranch	Cathedral Mtn.	Wedin	Road Canyon	China Tank	Willis Ranch	Lens	Appel Ranch	Word undivided	Hueco	Bone Spring	Getaway	Hegler	Pinery	Rader	Lamar	Capitan
Bryorhynchus (cont'd.)																											
plicatum	-	-	-	-	-	-	-	-	-	-	-	-	-	-	-	-	-	X	-	-	-	-	-	-	-	-	-
Cactosteges																											
anomalus	-	-	-	-	-	-	-	-	-	-	-	-	-	X	X	X	-	-	X	-	-	-	-	-	-	-	-
Calliprotonia																											
sp.	-	-	X	-	-	-	-	-	-	-	-	-	-	-	-	-	-	-	-	-	-	-	-	-	-	-	-
Callispirina																											
rotunda	-	-	-	-	-	-	-	-	-	-	-	-	-	-	-	-	-	-	-	-	-	-	-	-	-	X	-
Camarelasma																											
neali	-	-	X	-	-	-	-	-	-	-	-	-	-	-	-	-	-	-	-	-	-	-	-	-	-	-	-
Cancrinella																											
distorta	-	-	-	-	-	-	-	-	-	-	-	-	-	-	-	-	-	X	-	-	-	-	-	-	-	-	-
expansa	-	-	-	-	-	-	-	-	-	-	-	-	-	-	X	-	-	-	-	-	-	-	-	-	-	-	-
fragosa	-	-	-	-	-	-	-	X	X	-	-	-	-	-	-	-	-	-	-	-	-	-	-	-	-	-	-
parva	-	-	X	-	X	-	-	-	-	-	-	-	-	-	-	-	-	-	-	-	-	-	-	-	-	-	-
planumbona	-	-	-	-	-	-	-	-	-	-	-	-	-	-	X	-	-	-	-	-	-	-	-	-	-	-	-
sparsispinosa	-	-	-	-	-	-	-	-	X	-	-	-	-	-	-	-	-	-	-	-	X	-	-	-	-	-	-
subquadrata	-	-	-	-	-	-	-	-	-	-	-	-	-	-	-	X	-	X	-	-	-	-	-	-	-	-	-
sp. 1	-	-	-	-	-	-	-	-	-	-	-	X	-	-	-	-	-	-	-	-	-	-	-	-	-	-	-
Cartorhium																											
chelomatum	-	-	-	-	-	-	-	-	-	-	-	-	-	-	X	X	X	X	-	-	-	-	-	-	-	-	-
coristum	-	-	-	-	-	-	-	-	-	-	X	X	-	-	-	-	-	-	-	-	-	-	-	-	-	-	-
latum (REK)	-	-	-	-	-	-	-	-	-	-	X	X	-	-	-	-	-	-	-	-	X	-	-	-	-	-	-
mexicanum (Shumard)	-	-	-	-	-	-	-	-	-	-	-	-	-	-	-	-	-	-	-	-	-	-	-	-	-	-	X
orbiculatum	-	-	-	-	-	-	-	-	-	-	-	-	-	-	X	X	-	-	-	-	-	-	-	-	-	-	-
retusum	-	-	-	-	-	-	-	-	-	-	-	-	-	-	X	X	-	-	-	-	-	-	-	-	X	-	-
vidriense	-	-	-	-	-	-	-	-	-	-	-	-	-	-	X	X	-	-	-	-	-	-	-	-	-	-	-
zoyei	-	-	-	-	X	X	-	X	X	-	-	-	-	-	-	-	-	-	-	-	X	-	-	-	-	-	-
Cenorhynchia																											
atmeta	-	-	-	-	-	-	-	-	-	-	-	-	-	X	-	-	-	-	-	-	-	-	-	-	-	-	-
camerata	-	-	X	-	-	-	-	-	-	-	-	-	-	-	-	-	-	-	-	-	-	-	-	-	-	-	-
fracida	-	-	-	-	-	-	-	-	-	-	-	-	*	-	X	X	X	X	-	-	X	-	-	-	-	-	-
hebata	-	-	X	-	-	-	-	-	-	-	-	-	-	-	-	-	-	-	-	-	-	-	-	-	-	-	-
mitigata	-	-	-	-	-	-	-	-	-	-	-	X	-	X	X	-	-	-	-	-	-	-	-	-	-	-	-
nasuta	-	-	-	-	-	-	-	-	-	-	-	-	-	X	-	-	-	-	-	-	-	-	-	X	-	-	-
parvula	-	-	-	-	-	-	-	-	-	-	-	X	-	-	X	-	-	-	-	-	-	-	-	-	-	-	-
pentagonalis	-	-	-	-	-	-	-	-	-	-	-	-	-	-	X	-	-	-	X	-	-	-	-	-	-	-	-
saginata	-	-	-	-	-	-	-	-	-	-	-	X	-	-	X	-	-	-	-	-	-	-	-	-	-	-	-
transversa	-	-	-	-	-	-	-	-	-	-	-	-	-	-	X	-	-	-	-	-	-	-	-	-	-	-	-
triangulata	-	-	-	-	-	-	-	-	-	-	-	-	-	-	-	X	-	-	-	-	-	-	-	-	-	-	-
unicostata	-	-	-	-	-	-	-	-	-	-	-	X	-	-	-	-	-	-	-	-	-	-	-	-	-	-	-
ventricosa	-	-	X	-	-	-	-	-	-	-	-	-	-	-	-	-	-	-	-	-	-	-	-	-	-	-	-
Chaeniorhynchus																											
inauris	-	-	-	-	-	-	-	-	-	-	-	X	-	-	-	-	-	-	-	-	-	-	-	-	-	-	-
salutare	-	-	-	-	-	-	-	-	-	-	-	-	-	X	-	-	-	-	-	-	-	-	-	-	-	-	-
transversum	-	-	-	-	-	-	-	-	-	-	-	X	-	-	-	-	-	-	-	-	-	-	-	-	-	-	-
Chelononia																											
neali	-	-	X	-	-	-	-	-	-	-	-	-	-	-	-	-	-	-	-	-	-	-	-	-	-	-	-
straminea	-	-	X	-	-	-	-	-	-	-	-	-	-	-	-	-	-	-	-	-	-	-	-	-	-	-	-
Choanodus																											
anomalus	-	-	-	-	-	-	-	-	-	-	-	X	-	-	-	-	-	-	-	-	-	-	-	-	-	-	-
irregularis	-	-	-	-	-	-	-	X	-	-	-	X	X	-	-	-	-	-	-	-	X	-	-	-	-	-	-
perfectus	-	-	-	-	-	-	X	-	-	-	-	X	X	-	-	-	-	-	-	-	X	-	-	-	-	-	-
Chondronia																											
bella	-	-	-	-	-	-	-	-	-	-	-	X	X	-	-	-	-	-	-	-	X	-	-	-	-	-	-
ningula	-	-	-	-	-	X	-	X	-	X	-	-	-	-	-	-	-	-	-	-	-	-	-	-	-	-	-
obesa	-	-	-	-	-	-	-	-	-	-	-	-	-	-	-	-	-	-	-	X	-	-	-	-	-	-	-
ovalis	-	-	-	-	-	-	-	-	-	-	-	X	-	-	-	-	-	-	-	-	-	-	-	-	-	-	-
parva	-	-	-	-	X	-	-	-	-	-	-	-	-	-	-	-	-	-	-	-	-	-	-	-	-	-	-
rectimarginata	-	-	X	-	-	-	-	-	-	-	-	-	-	-	-	-	-	-	-	-	-	-	-	-	-	-	-

GENUS AND SPECIES	Gaptank	Uddenites	Neal Ranch	Lenox Hills	Decie Ranch	Poplar Tank	Dugout Mtn.	Sullivan Peak	Skinner Ranch undivided	Hess	Taylor Ranch	Cathedral Mtn.	Wedin	Road Canyon	China Tank	Willis Ranch	Lens	Appel Ranch	Word undivided	Hueco	Bone Spring	Getaway	Hegler	Pinery	Rader	Lamar	Capitan
Chonetinella																											
biplicata (REK)	-	-	-	-	-	-	-	-	X	-	X	-	-	-	-	-	-	-	-	-	X	-	-	-	-	-	-
costellata	X	X	X	-	-	-	-	-	-	-	-	-	-	-	-	-	-	-	-	-	-	-	-	-	-	-	-
crassiparva	-	-	X	-	-	-	-	-	-	-	-	-	-	-	-	-	-	-	-	-	-	-	-	-	-	-	-
gerontica	-	-	-	-	-	-	-	-	-	-	-	-	-	X	-	-	-	-	-	-	-	-	-	-	-	-	-
magna	-	-	-	-	-	-	-	-	-	-	-	-	-	-	-	-	-	-	-	-	X	-	-	-	-	-	-
parva	X	X	-	-	-	-	-	-	-	-	-	-	-	-	-	-	-	-	-	-	-	-	-	-	-	-	-
spinolirata (REK)	-	-	X	-	-	-	-	-	-	-	-	-	-	-	-	-	-	-	-	-	-	-	-	-	-	-	-
victoriana (Girty)	-	-	-	-	-	-	-	-	-	-	-	-	-	-	-	-	-	-	-	-	X	-	-	-	-	-	-
Chonetinetes																											
angustisulcatus	-	-	-	-	-	-	-	-	-	-	-	-	-	X	-	-	-	-	-	-	-	-	-	-	-	-	-
reversus C&G	-	-	-	-	-	-	-	-	-	-	-	-	-	X	-	-	-	-	-	-	-	-	-	-	-	-	-
varians	-	-	-	-	-	-	-	-	-	-	-	-	-	-	-	-	-	-	-	-	-	-	X	X	X	-	-
Chonosteges																											
costellatus	-	-	-	-	-	-	-	-	-	-	-	X	-	X	-	-	-	-	-	-	-	-	-	-	-	-	-
limbatus	-	-	-	-	-	X	-	X	X	-	X	-	-	-	-	-	-	-	-	-	-	-	-	-	-	-	-
matutinus	-	-	-	-	X	-	-	-	-	-	-	-	-	-	-	-	-	-	-	-	-	-	-	-	-	-	-
multicostatus	-	-	-	-	-	-	-	-	-	-	-	X	-	-	-	-	-	-	-	-	-	-	-	-	-	-	-
pulcher	-	-	-	-	-	-	-	-	-	-	-	X	X	-	-	-	-	-	-	-	X	-	-	-	-	-	-
variabilis	-	-	-	-	X	X	X	X	X	-	-	X	X	-	-	-	-	-	-	-	X	-	-	-	-	-	-
Cleiothyridina																											
mulsa	-	-	-	-	-	-	-	-	X	-	-	-	-	-	-	-	-	-	-	-	-	-	-	-	-	-	-
nana	-	-	-	-	-	-	-	-	-	-	-	-	-	X	-	-	-	-	-	-	-	-	-	-	-	-	-
pilularis	-	-	-	-	-	-	-	-	-	-	-	-	-	-	-	-	-	-	-	-	-	-	-	-	-	X	X
rara	-	-	-	-	-	-	-	-	-	-	-	-	-	-	-	X	-	-	-	-	-	-	-	-	-	-	-
rectimarginata	-	-	X	-	-	-	-	-	-	-	-	-	-	-	-	-	-	-	-	-	-	-	-	-	-	-	-
Collemataria																											
americana (Girty)	-	-	-	-	-	-	-	-	-	-	-	-	-	-	-	-	-	-	-	-	X	-	-	-	-	-	-
batilliformis	-	-	-	-	-	-	-	-	-	-	-	-	-	X	-	-	-	-	-	-	-	-	-	-	-	-	-
elongata	-	-	-	-	-	-	-	-	-	-	-	-	-	-	X	X	X	-	X	-	-	-	-	-	-	-	-
gregaria	-	-	-	-	-	-	-	-	-	-	-	X	-	X	-	-	-	-	-	-	-	-	-	-	-	-	-
irregularis	-	-	-	-	-	-	-	-	-	-	-	X	X	-	-	-	-	-	-	-	-	-	-	-	-	-	-
marshalli (Stehli)	-	-	-	-	-	-	-	-	X	-	-	-	-	-	-	-	-	-	-	-	X	-	-	-	-	-	-
platys	-	-	-	-	X	-	-	X	X	-	-	-	-	-	-	-	-	-	-	-	-	-	-	-	-	-	-
spatulata	-	-	-	-	-	-	-	-	-	-	-	-	-	-	-	-	-	-	-	-	-	-	-	X	-	X	X
Collumatus																											
solitarius C&G	-	-	-	-	-	-	-	-	-	-	-	-	-	X	-	-	-	-	-	-	-	-	-	-	-	-	-
Composita																											
affinis Girty	-	-	-	-	-	-	-	-	-	-	-	-	-	-	-	-	-	-	-	-	-	-	-	X	X	X	X
apheles	-	-	-	-	X	X	-	X	X	X	-	-	-	-	-	-	-	-	-	-	-	-	-	-	-	-	-
apsidata	-	-	-	-	-	-	-	-	-	-	X	-	-	-	-	-	-	-	-	-	-	-	-	-	-	-	-
bucculenta	-	-	-	-	-	-	-	X	-	X	X	X	X	X	-	-	-	-	-	-	-	-	-	-	-	-	-
costata	-	-	-	-	-	-	-	-	-	-	-	-	-	-	-	-	-	-	-	-	X	-	-	-	-	-	-
cracens	-	-	-	-	-	-	-	-	-	-	-	-	-	-	-	-	-	-	-	X	X	-	-	-	-	-	-
crassa	-	-	-	-	-	-	-	-	-	-	-	X	-	X	-	-	-	-	-	-	-	-	-	-	-	-	-
discina	X	X	-	X	X	-	-	-	X	-	-	-	-	-	-	-	-	-	-	-	-	-	-	-	-	-	-
emarginata Girty	-	-	-	-	-	-	-	-	-	-	-	-	-	-	-	-	-	-	-	-	-	-	X	X	X	X	X
enormis	-	-	-	-	-	-	-	-	-	-	-	-	-	X	X	X	X	X	-	-	-	X	-	-	-	-	-
imbricata	-	-	-	-	-	-	-	-	-	-	-	X	-	-	-	-	-	-	-	-	-	-	-	-	-	-	-
mexicana (Hall)	-	-	-	-	-	-	-	-	-	-	-	-	-	-	-	-	-	-	-	X	-	-	-	-	-	-	-
nucella	-	-	-	-	-	-	-	-	-	-	-	-	-	-	-	-	-	-	-	-	X	-	-	-	-	-	-
parasulcata	-	-	-	-	-	-	-	-	-	-	-	-	-	-	X	X	X	X	-	-	-	X	-	-	-	-	-
pilula	-	-	-	-	-	-	-	-	-	-	-	-	-	X	-	-	-	-	-	-	-	-	-	-	-	-	-
prospera	-	-	-	-	-	-	-	-	-	-	-	-	-	-	-	-	-	-	-	-	-	X	-	-	-	-	-
pyriformis	-	-	-	-	-	-	-	-	-	-	-	-	-	-	-	-	-	-	-	-	-	-	X	X	X	X	-
quantilla	-	-	-	-	-	-	-	-	-	-	-	-	-	X	-	-	-	-	-	-	-	-	-	-	-	-	-
stalagmium	-	-	-	-	-	-	-	-	-	-	-	X	-	X	-	-	-	-	-	-	-	-	-	-	-	-	-
strongyle	-	X	X	X	-	-	-	-	-	-	-	-	-	-	-	-	-	-	-	X	-	-	-	-	-	-	-
Compressoproductus																											
acuminatus	-	-	-	-	-	-	-	-	-	-	-	-	-	X	-	-	-	-	-	-	-	-	-	-	-	-	-
concentricus	-	-	-	-	X	-	-	-	X	-	X	-	-	-	-	-	-	-	-	-	-	-	-	-	-	-	-
curtus	-	-	-	-	-	-	-	-	-	-	-	X	-	-	-	-	-	-	-	-	-	-	-	-	-	-	-
flabellatus	-	-	-	-	-	-	-	-	-	-	-	X	-	-	-	-	-	-	-	-	-	-	-	-	-	-	-
parvus	-	-	-	-	X	X	X	X	X	-	-	-	-	-	-	-	-	-	-	-	-	-	-	-	-	-	-
pinniformis (Girty)	-	-	-	-	-	-	-	-	-	-	-	-	-	-	-	-	-	-	-	-	-	-	-	-	-	-	X

Genus and species	Gaptank	Uddenites	Neal Ranch	Lenox Hills	Decie Ranch	Poplar Tank	Dugout Mtn.	Sullivan Peak	Skinner Ranch undivided	Hess	Taylor Ranch	Cathedral Mtn.	Wedin	Road Canyon	China Tank	Willis Ranch	Lens	Appel Ranch	Word undivided	Hueco	Bone Spring	Getaway	Hegler	Pinery	Rader	Lamar	Capitan
Compressoproductus (Cont'd.)																											
rarus	-	-	-	-	-	-	-	-	-	-	-	-	-	-	X	-	X	-	X	-	-	-	-	-	-	-	-
thomasi	-	-	-	-	-	-	-	-	-	-	-	X	X	-	-	-	-	-	-	-	-	-	-	-	-	-	-
Cooperina																											
inexpectata T,T,&P	-	-	-	-	-	-	-	-	-	-	-	-	-	-	X	X	X	X	X	-	-	X	X	-	-	-	-
parva	-	-	-	-	-	-	-	-	-	-	X	X	X	X	-	-	-	-	-	-	-	-	-	-	-	-	-
subcuneata	-	-	-	-	-	-	-	-	-	-	-	-	-	X	-	-	-	-	-	-	-	-	-	-	-	-	-
triangulata	-	-	X	-	-	-	-	-	-	-	-	-	-	-	-	-	-	-	-	-	-	-	-	-	-	-	-
Coscinophora																											
hortoni (REK)	-	-	-	-	-	-	-	-	-	-	-	-	X	-	-	-	-	-	-	-	-	-	-	-	-	-	-
magnifica	-	-	-	-	-	-	-	-	-	-	-	-	-	X	-	-	-	-	-	-	-	-	-	-	-	-	-
monilifera	-	-	-	-	X	X	-	X	X	-	-	-	-	-	-	-	-	-	-	-	-	-	-	-	-	-	-
nodosa (C&S)	-	-	-	-	-	-	-	-	-	-	-	-	-	X	-	-	-	-	-	-	-	-	-	-	-	-	-
Costispinifera																											
costata (REK)	-	-	-	-	-	-	-	-	-	-	-	-	-	-	X	X	X	X	-	-	-	-	-	-	-	-	-
rugatula (Girty)	-	-	-	-	-	-	-	-	-	-	-	-	-	X	X	X	X	-	X	-	-	-	-	-	-	-	-
walcottiana (Girty)	-	-	-	-	-	-	-	-	-	-	-	-	-	-	-	-	-	-	-	-	-	X?	-	-	-	-	-
Craspedona																											
newelli	-	-	-	-	-	-	-	-	-	-	-	-	-	-	-	-	-	-	-	-	-	X	X	X	X	-	-
Crenispirifer																											
angulatus (REK)	-	-	-	-	X	-	-	X	-	-	-	-	-	-	-	-	-	-	-	-	X	-	-	-	-	-	-
effrenus	-	-	-	-	-	-	-	-	-	-	-	-	-	-	-	-	-	-	-	-	X	-	X	-	-	-	-
jubatus	-	-	-	-	-	-	-	-	-	-	-	-	-	-	-	-	-	-	-	-	-	-	X	X	X	-	-
myllus	-	-	-	-	-	-	-	-	-	-	-	-	-	-	-	-	-	-	-	-	-	-	-	-	X	X	-
sagus	-	-	-	-	-	-	-	-	-	-	-	-	-	-	-	-	-	-	-	-	X	-	-	-	-	-	-
Crurithyris																											
guadalupensis (Girty)	-	-	-	-	-	-	-	-	-	-	-	-	-	-	-	-	-	-	-	-	-	-	-	X	X	X	X
inflata Stehli	-	-	-	-	-	-	-	-	-	-	-	-	-	-	-	-	-	-	-	-	X	-	-	-	-	-	-
longirostris	-	-	-	-	-	-	-	-	-	-	-	-	-	-	-	-	-	-	-	-	X	-	-	-	-	-	-
major	-	-	-	-	-	-	-	-	-	-	-	-	-	-	-	-	X	-	-	-	-	-	-	-	-	-	-
minutalis	-	-	-	-	-	-	-	-	-	-	-	-	-	X	-	-	-	-	-	-	-	-	-	-	-	-	-
sulcata Stehli	-	-	-	-	-	-	-	-	-	-	-	-	-	-	-	-	-	-	X	X	-	-	-	-	-	-	-
tholiaphor	-	-	-	-	-	-	-	-	-	-	-	-	-	-	X	X	X	X	X	-	X	-	-	-	-	-	-
tumibilis	-	X	X	X	-	-	-	-	-	-	-	-	-	-	-	-	-	-	-	-	-	-	-	-	-	-	-
Cryptacanthia																											
glabra	-	-	-	-	-	-	-	-	-	-	-	-	-	-	-	-	-	-	-	-	X	-	-	-	-	-	-
sinuata (Stehli)	-	-	-	-	-	-	-	-	-	-	-	-	-	-	-	-	-	-	-	-	X	-	-	-	-	-	-
sp. 1	-	-	-	-	X	-	-	-	-	-	-	-	-	-	-	-	-	-	-	-	-	-	-	-	-	-	-
Ctenalosia																											
fixata C&S	-	-	-	-	-	-	-	-	-	-	-	-	-	-	X	-	X	X	-	-	-	X	X	-	-	-	-
primitiva	-	-	X	-	-	-	-	-	-	-	-	-	-	-	-	-	-	-	-	-	-	-	-	-	-	-	-
rotunda	-	-	-	-	-	-	-	-	-	-	-	-	-	-	-	-	-	-	-	-	-	-	X	-	-	-	-
Cyclacantharia																											
gigantea	-	-	-	-	X	-	-	X	-	-	-	-	-	-	-	-	-	-	-	-	-	-	-	-	-	-	-
kingorum C&G	-	-	-	-	-	-	-	-	-	-	-	-	-	-	X	X	X	X	X	-	-	X	-	-	-	-	-
kingorum agaricoidea	-	-	-	-	-	-	-	-	-	-	-	-	-	-	-	-	X	-	-	-	-	-	-	-	-	-	-
paucispinosa	-	-	-	-	-	-	-	-	-	-	-	-	X	X	-	-	-	-	-	-	-	-	-	-	-	-	-
robusta	-	-	-	-	-	-	-	-	-	-	-	-	-	-	-	-	-	-	-	-	-	-	-	-	X	-	-
transitoria	-	-	-	-	-	-	-	-	-	-	-	-	-	X	X	-	-	-	-	-	-	-	-	-	-	-	-
Dasysaria																											
undulata C&G	-	-	-	-	-	-	-	-	-	-	-	-	-	-	-	-	-	-	-	-	X	X?	-	-	-	-	-
wolfcampensis (REK)	-	-	-	X	-	-	-	-	-	-	-	-	-	-	-	-	-	-	-	-	X	-	-	-	-	-	-
Deltarina																											
magnicostata	-	-	-	-	-	-	-	-	-	-	-	-	-	-	-	-	-	-	-	-	-	-	X	X	X	X	-
Derbyia																											
bella	-	-	X	-	-	-	-	-	-	-	-	-	-	-	-	-	-	-	-	-	-	-	-	-	-	-	-
carteri	-	X	X	-	-	-	-	-	-	-	-	-	-	-	-	-	-	-	-	-	-	-	-	-	-	-	-
cincinnata	-	-	-	-	-	-	-	-	-	-	X	-	X	-	-	-	-	-	-	-	-	-	-	-	-	-	-
complicata	-	-	-	-	-	-	-	-	-	-	X	X	X	-	-	-	-	-	-	-	-	-	-	-	-	-	-
crenulata Girty	-	-	-	-	X	X	-	X	X	-	X	-	X	-	-	-	-	-	-	-	-	X	-	-	-	-	-
elevata REK	-	-	-	-	-	-	-	-	-	-	-	-	-	-	-	-	-	-	X	-	-	-	-	-	-	-	-

GENUS AND SPECIES	Gaptank	Uddenites	Neal Ranch	Lenox Hills	Decie Ranch	Poplar Tank	Dugout Mtn.	Sullivan Peak	Skinner Ranch undivided	Hess	Taylor Ranch	Cathedral Mtn.	Wedin	Road Canyon	China Tank	Willis Ranch	Lens	Appel Ranch	Word undivided	Hueco	Bone Spring	Getaway	Hegler	Pinery	Rader	Lamar	Capitan
Derbyia (Cont'd.)																											
filosa	-	-	-	-	-	-	-	-	-	-	-	-	-	X	X	X	-	X	X	-	-	X	-	-	-	X	-
informis	-	-	-	-	-	-	-	-	-	-	X	X	X	-	-	-	-	-	-	-	-	-	-	-	-	-	-
laqueata	-	-	-	-	-	-	-	X	-	-	X	X	X	-	-	-	-	-	-	-	-	-	-	-	-	-	-
nasuta Girty	-	-	-	X	X	-	-	X	X	-	-	-	-	-	-	-	-	-	-	-	-	X	-	-	-	-	-
pannucia	-	-	-	-	-	-	-	-	-	-	-	-	-	X	X	X	X	X	-	-	-	X	-	-	-	-	-
profunda	-	X	X	X	-	-	-	-	-	-	-	-	-	-	-	-	-	-	-	-	-	-	-	-	-	-	-
scitula	-	-	X	-	-	-	-	-	-	-	-	-	-	-	-	-	-	-	-	-	-	-	-	-	-	-	-
strophomenoidea	-	-	X	-	-	-	-	-	-	-	-	-	-	-	-	-	-	-	-	-	-	-	-	-	-	-	-
texta	-	-	-	-	-	-	-	-	-	-	-	-	-	X	X	X	X	X	-	-	-	X	X	X	X	X	-
Derbyoides																											
dunbari	-	-	X	-	-	-	-	-	-	-	-	-	-	-	-	-	-	-	-	-	-	-	-	-	-	-	-
marathonensis	-	-	X	-	-	-	-	-	-	-	-	-	-	-	-	-	-	-	-	-	-	-	-	-	-	-	-
sp.	X	X	-	-	-	-	-	-	-	-	-	-	-	-	-	-	-	-	-	-	-	-	-	-	-	-	-
Dielasma																											
adamanteum	-	-	-	-	-	-	-	-	-	-	-	-	-	X	X	X	X	-	-	-	-	-	-	-	-	-	-
a. angulatum	-	-	-	-	-	-	-	-	-	-	-	-	-	X	X	-	-	-	-	-	-	-	-	-	-	-	-
anterolatum	-	-	-	-	-	-	-	-	-	-	-	X	-	-	-	-	-	-	-	-	-	-	-	-	-	-	-
bellulum	-	-	-	-	-	-	-	-	-	-	-	-	-	X	-	-	-	-	-	-	-	-	-	-	-	-	-
compactum	-	-	-	-	-	-	-	-	-	-	-	-	-	X	X	X	X	-	-	-	-	X	-	-	-	-	-
cordatum Girty	-	-	-	-	-	-	-	-	-	-	-	-	-	-	-	-	-	-	-	-	-	-	X	X	-	X	-
diabloense Stehli	-	-	-	-	-	-	-	-	-	-	-	-	-	-	-	-	-	-	-	-	X	-	-	-	-	-	-
ellipsoideum	-	-	-	-	-	-	-	-	-	-	X	X	X	-	-	-	-	-	-	-	-	-	-	-	-	-	-
emarginatum	-	-	-	-	-	-	-	-	-	-	-	-	-	X	-	-	-	-	-	-	-	-	-	-	-	-	-
expansum	-	-	-	-	-	-	-	-	-	-	-	-	-	X	-	-	-	-	-	-	-	-	-	-	-	-	-
gracile	-	-	-	-	-	-	-	-	-	-	-	-	-	-	X	X	-	-	-	-	-	-	-	-	-	-	-
hessense	-	-	-	-	X	-	-	X	X	-	-	-	-	-	-	-	-	-	-	-	-	-	-	-	-	-	-
labiatum	-	-	-	-	-	-	-	-	-	-	-	-	-	X	-	-	-	-	-	-	-	-	-	-	-	-	-
ligonorum	-	-	-	-	-	-	-	-	-	-	-	-	-	-	-	-	-	-	-	-	-	-	-	X	-	-	-
longisulcatum	-	-	-	-	-	-	-	-	-	X	X	-	-	-	-	-	-	-	-	-	-	-	-	-	-	-	-
microrhynchum	-	-	-	-	-	-	-	-	-	-	-	-	-	-	-	-	-	-	-	-	X	-	-	-	-	-	-
obesum	-	-	-	-	-	-	-	-	-	-	X	X	-	-	-	-	-	-	-	-	-	-	-	-	-	-	-
perplexum	-	-	-	-	-	-	-	-	-	-	X	X	-	-	-	-	-	-	-	-	-	-	-	-	-	-	-
pictile	-	-	-	-	-	-	-	-	-	-	-	-	-	-	-	-	-	-	-	-	-	X	-	-	-	-	-
planidorsatum	-	-	-	-	-	-	-	-	-	-	-	-	-	-	X	X	-	-	-	-	-	-	-	-	-	-	-
prolongatum Girty	-	-	-	-	-	-	-	-	-	-	-	-	-	-	-	-	-	-	-	-	-	-	-	X	-	-	X
pygmaeum	-	-	X	-	-	-	-	-	-	-	-	-	-	-	-	-	-	-	-	-	-	-	-	-	-	-	-
rigbyi	-	-	-	-	-	-	-	-	-	-	-	-	-	-	-	-	-	-	-	-	-	-	X	-	-	-	-
spatulatum Girty	-	-	-	-	-	-	-	-	-	-	-	-	-	-	-	-	-	-	-	-	-	-	-	-	-	-	X
subcirculare	-	-	-	-	-	-	-	-	-	-	-	-	-	-	-	-	-	-	-	-	-	-	X	X	X	X	X
subcylindricum	-	-	-	-	-	-	-	-	-	-	-	-	-	-	-	-	-	-	-	-	-	X	-	-	-	-	-
sulcatum Girty	-	-	-	-	-	-	-	-	-	-	-	-	-	-	-	-	-	-	-	-	-	X	X	X	X	X	X
uniplicatum	-	-	-	-	-	-	-	-	-	-	-	-	-	-	-	-	-	-	-	-	-	-	-	-	-	X	-
zebratum	-	-	-	-	-	-	-	-	-	-	-	-	-	X	X	X	X	X	-	-	-	-	-	-	-	-	-
Diplanus																											
apochordus	-	-	-	-	X	-	-	-	-	-	-	-	-	-	-	-	-	-	-	-	-	-	-	-	-	-	-
catatonus	-	-	X	-	-	-	-	-	-	-	-	-	-	-	-	-	-	-	-	-	-	-	-	-	-	-	-
lamellatus (REK)	-	-	-	-	X	X	-	X	X	-	X	X	X	-	-	-	-	-	-	-	X	-	-	-	-	-	-
rarus	-	-	-	-	X	X	-	X	X	-	-	-	-	-	-	-	-	-	-	-	-	-	-	-	-	-	-
redactus	X	X	X	-	-	-	-	-	-	-	-	-	-	-	-	-	-	-	-	-	-	-	-	-	-	-	-
Divaricosta																											
squarrosa C&G	-	-	-	-	-	-	-	-	-	-	-	-	-	-	-	-	-	-	-	-	-	X	-	-	-	-	-
vagabunda	-	-	-	-	-	-	-	-	-	-	-	-	-	-	-	-	-	-	X	-	-	-	-	-	-	-	-
Dyoros (Dyoros)																											
angulatus	-	-	-	-	-	-	-	-	-	-	-	-	-	X	-	-	-	-	-	-	-	-	-	-	-	-	-
attenuatus	-	-	-	-	-	-	-	-	-	-	-	-	-	-	-	-	-	-	-	-	-	-	X	-	-	-	-
consanguineus (Girty)	-	-	-	-	X	X	X	-	-	-	-	-	-	-	-	-	-	-	-	-	-	X	-	-	-	-	-
convexus	-	-	-	-	-	-	-	-	-	-	-	-	-	-	X	X	X	X	-	-	-	X	-	-	-	-	-
endospinus	-	-	-	-	-	-	-	-	-	-	-	-	-	X	-	-	-	-	-	-	-	-	-	-	-	-	-
extensiformis	-	-	-	-	-	-	-	-	-	-	-	X	-	X	-	-	-	-	-	-	-	-	-	-	-	-	-
extensus	-	-	-	-	-	-	-	-	-	-	-	-	-	X	X	X	X	X	-	-	-	X	-	-	-	-	-
hillanus (Girty)	-	-	-	-	-	-	-	-	-	-	-	-	-	-	-	-	-	-	-	-	-	-	-	-	-	X	X
intrepidus	-	-	-	-	-	-	-	-	-	-	-	-	-	-	-	-	-	-	-	-	-	-	X	X	X	-	-
magnus (Stehli)	-	-	-	-	-	-	-	-	-	-	-	-	-	-	-	-	-	-	-	-	X	-	-	-	-	-	-
planiextensus	-	-	-	-	-	-	-	-	-	-	-	-	-	-	-	-	-	X	-	-	-	-	-	-	-	-	-
robustus	-	-	-	-	-	-	-	-	-	-	-	-	-	-	-	-	-	-	-	-	-	-	-	X	-	-	-
subliratus (Girty)	-	-	-	-	-	-	-	-	-	-	-	-	-	-	-	-	-	-	-	-	-	-	-	-	-	X	X
tenuis	-	-	-	-	-	-	-	-	-	-	-	-	-	-	X	-	X	-	-	-	-	-	-	-	-	-	-

GENUS AND SPECIES	Gaptank	Uddenites	Neal Ranch	Lenox Hills	Decie Ranch	Poplar Tank	Dugout Mtn.	Sullivan Peak	Skinner Ranch undivided	Hess	Taylor Ranch	Cathedral Mtn.	Wedin	Road Canyon	China Tank	Willis Ranch	Lens	Appel Ranch	Word undivided	Hueco	Bone Spring	Getaway	Hegler	Pinery	Rader	Lamar	Capitan
Dyoros (Dyoros) (Cont'd.)																											
transversus	-	-	-	-	-	-	-	-	-	-	-	-	-	X	-	-	-	-	-	-	-	-	-	-	-	-	-
vulgaris	-	-	-	-	-	-	-	-	-	-	-	-	-	X	-	-	-	-	-	-	-	-	-	-	-	-	-
Dyoros (Lissosia)																											
concavus	-	-	-	-	-	-	-	-	-	-	-	-	-	X	X	X	X	-	X	-	-	X	-	-	-	-	-
parvus	-	-	-	-	-	-	-	-	-	-	-	-	-	X	-	-	-	X	-	-	-	-	-	-	-	-	-
vagabundus	-	-	-	-	-	-	-	-	-	-	-	X	X	X	-	-	-	-	-	-	X	-	-	-	-	-	-
Dyoros (Tetragonetes)																											
auriculatus	-	-	-	-	-	-	-	-	-	-	-	-	-	-	-	-	-	-	-	-	-	-	X	-	-	-	-
complanatus	-	-	-	-	-	-	-	-	-	-	-	-	-	-	-	-	-	-	-	-	-	-	X	-	-	-	-
giganteus	-	-	-	-	-	-	-	-	-	-	-	X	-	-	X	-	-	-	-	-	-	-	-	-	-	-	-
lateralis	-	-	-	-	-	-	-	-	-	-	-	X	-	X	-	-	-	-	-	-	-	-	-	-	-	-	-
planus	-	-	-	-	-	-	-	-	-	-	-	X	-	X	-	-	-	-	-	-	-	-	-	-	-	-	-
quadrangulatus	-	-	-	-	-	-	-	-	-	-	-	-	-	-	-	-	-	X	-	-	-	-	-	-	-	-	-
rectangulatus	-	-	-	-	-	-	-	-	-	-	-	X	-	X	-	-	-	-	-	-	X	-	-	-	-	-	-
solidus	-	-	-	-	-	-	-	-	-	-	-	-	-	X	-	-	-	-	-	-	-	-	-	-	-	-	-
strigosus	-	-	-	-	-	-	-	-	-	-	-	-	-	X	-	-	-	-	-	-	-	-	-	-	-	-	-
subquadratus	-	-	-	-	-	-	-	-	-	-	-	-	-	-	-	-	-	-	-	-	-	-	-	X	-	-	-
wordensis	-	-	-	-	-	-	-	-	-	-	-	-	-	-	-	X	X	-	-	-	-	-	-	-	-	-	-
Echinaria																											
cf. E. moorei (D&C)	X	X	X	-	-	-	-	-	-	-	-	-	-	-	-	-	-	-	-	-	-	-	-	-	-	-	-
Echinauris																											
bella	-	-	-	-	-	-	-	-	-	-	-	-	-	X	-	-	-	-	-	-	-	-	-	-	-	-	-
cf. E. boulei (Koz)	-	-	-	-	-	-	-	-	-	-	-	-	-	-	-	-	-	-	-	X	-	-	-	-	-	-	-
circularis	-	-	-	-	-	-	-	-	-	-	-	X	-	-	-	-	-	-	-	-	-	-	-	-	-	-	-
crassa	-	-	-	-	-	-	-	-	-	-	-	X	X	X	-	-	-	-	-	-	-	-	-	-	-	-	-
interrupta	-	-	X	X	-	-	-	-	-	-	-	-	-	-	-	-	-	-	-	-	-	-	-	-	-	-	-
irregularis	-	-	-	-	-	X	X	-	-	-	-	X	X	X	-	-	-	-	-	-	X	-	-	-	-	-	-
lappacea	-	-	-	-	-	-	-	-	-	-	-	-	-	X	-	-	-	-	-	-	-	-	-	-	-	-	-
lateralis M-W&C	-	-	-	-	-	-	-	-	-	-	-	-	-	X	X	X	X	X	X	-	-	-	-	-	-	-	-
liumbona	-	-	-	-	-	-	-	-	-	-	-	-	-	X	-	-	-	-	-	-	-	-	-	-	-	-	-
parva	-	-	-	-	-	-	-	-	-	-	-	-	-	X	-	-	-	-	-	-	-	-	-	-	-	-	-
productelloides	-	-	-	-	-	-	-	-	-	-	-	-	-	-	-	-	-	-	-	-	-	-	-	X	-	-	-
subquadrata	X	X	X	X	-	-	-	-	-	-	-	-	-	-	-	-	-	-	-	-	-	-	-	-	-	-	-
venustula	-	-	-	-	-	-	-	-	-	-	-	X	-	-	-	-	-	-	-	-	-	-	-	-	-	-	-
Echinosteges																											
guadalupensis (Shumard)	-	-	-	-	-	-	-	-	-	-	-	-	-	-	-	-	-	-	-	-	-	-	X	X	X	X	X
tuberculatus (REK)	-	-	-	-	-	-	-	-	-	-	-	-	-	X	X	X	X	X	X	-	X	-	-	-	-	-	-
sp.	-	-	X	-	-	-	-	-	-	-	-	-	-	-	-	-	-	-	-	-	-	-	-	-	-	-	-
Ectoposia																											
grandis	-	-	-	-	-	-	-	-	-	-	-	-	-	X	X	-	-	-	-	-	-	-	-	-	-	-	-
wildei	-	-	-	-	-	-	-	-	-	-	-	-	-	-	X	X	-	-	-	-	-	-	-	-	-	-	-
Edriosteges																											
beedei (REK)	-	-	-	-	-	-	-	-	-	-	-	X	-	-	-	-	-	-	-	-	-	-	-	-	-	-	-
compactus	-	-	-	-	-	-	-	-	-	-	-	-	-	-	X	-	-	-	-	-	-	-	-	-	-	-	-
multispinosus M-W&C	-	-	-	-	-	-	-	-	-	-	-	X	X	X	-	-	-	-	-	-	-	-	-	-	-	-	-
tenuispinosus	-	-	-	-	-	-	-	-	-	-	-	X	-	-	-	-	-	-	-	-	-	-	-	-	-	-	-
Elassonia																											
micraria	-	-	-	-	-	-	-	-	-	-	-	-	-	X	-	-	-	-	-	-	-	-	-	-	-	-	-
petila	-	-	-	-	-	-	-	-	-	-	-	X	-	-	-	-	-	-	-	-	-	-	-	-	-	-	-
scitula	-	-	-	-	-	-	-	-	-	-	-	X	-	-	-	-	-	-	-	-	-	-	-	-	-	-	-
sobrina	-	-	-	-	-	-	-	-	X	-	-	-	-	-	-	-	-	-	-	-	-	-	-	-	-	-	-
Eliva																											
inflata	-	-	-	-	-	-	-	-	-	-	-	-	-	-	-	-	-	-	-	-	-	-	-	-	X	X	X
shumardi	-	-	-	-	-	-	-	-	-	-	-	-	-	-	-	-	-	-	-	-	-	-	X	-	X	X	X
Elivina																											
?annectans	-	-	-	-	-	-	-	-	-	-	-	-	-	-	-	-	-	-	-	-	-	-	X	X	X	X	-
compacta (Girty)	-	-	-	-	-	-	-	-	-	-	-	-	-	-	-	-	-	-	-	-	-	-	-	-	-	-	X
detecta	-	-	-	-	-	-	-	-	-	-	-	-	-	-	-	-	-	-	-	-	-	-	X	-	X	-	-
Elliottella																											
minima (Stehli)	-	-	-	-	-	-	-	-	X	-	-	-	-	-	-	-	-	-	-	-	X	-	-	-	-	-	-
multicostata	-	-	-	-	-	-	-	-	-	-	-	-	-	-	-	-	-	-	-	-	X	-	-	-	-	-	-

GENUS AND SPECIES	Gaptank	Uddenites	Neal Ranch	Lenox Hills	Decie Ranch	Poplar Tank	Dugout Mtn.	Sullivan Peak	Skinner Ranch undivided	Hess	Taylor Ranch	Cathedral Mtn.	Wedin	Road Canyon	China Tank	Willis Ranch	Lens	Appel Ranch	Word undivided	Hueco	Bone Spring	Getaway	Hegler	Pinery	Rader	Lamar	Capitan
Elliottella (Cont'd.)																											
transversalis (Stehli)	-	-	-	-	-	-	-	-	-	-	-	-	-	-	-	-	-	-	-	-	X	-	-	-	-	-	-
varicostata	-	-	-	-	X	-	-	-	X	-	-	-	-	-	-	-	-	-	-	-	-	-	-	-	-	-	-
Enallosia																											
rotundovata	-	-	-	-	-	-	-	-	-	-	-	-	-	-	-	-	-	-	-	-	X	-	-	-	-	-	-
Enteletes																											
costellatus	-	-	-	-	-	-	-	-	-	-	-	-	-	-	-	-	-	-	-	X	-	-	-	-	-	-	-
densus	-	-	-	-	-	-	-	-	-	-	-	-	-	X	-	-	-	-	-	-	-	-	-	-	-	-	-
dumblei Girty	-	-	-	-	-	-	-	-	-	-	-	-	-	-	-	-	-	-	-	X?	-	-	-	-	-	-	-
exiguus	-	-	-	-	-	-	-	-	-	-	-	-	-	X	-	-	-	-	-	-	-	-	-	-	-	-	-
leonardensis REK	-	-	-	-	-	-	-	-	X	-	-	X	X	-	-	-	-	-	-	-	X	-	-	-	-	-	-
plummeri REK	-	-	-	-	-	-	-	-	-	-	-	X	X	-	-	-	-	-	-	-	X	-	-	-	-	-	-
rotundobesus	-	-	-	-	X	-	-	X	-	-	-	-	-	-	-	-	-	-	-	-	X	-	-	-	-	-	-
stehlii	-	-	-	-	X	-	-	X	-	-	-	-	-	-	-	-	-	-	-	-	X	-	-	-	-	-	-
subcircularis	-	-	-	-	-	-	-	X	X	X	X	-	-	-	-	-	-	-	-	-	X	-	-	-	-	-	-
subnudus	-	-	-	-	-	-	-	-	-	-	-	-	-	X	-	-	-	-	-	-	-	-	-	-	-	-	-
wolfcampensis REK	X	X	X	X	-	-	-	-	-	-	-	-	-	-	-	-	-	-	-	-	-	-	-	-	-	-	-
wordensis REK	-	-	-	-	-	-	-	-	-	-	-	-	-	-	X	X	-	X	-	-	-	-	-	-	-	-	-
Eolyttonia																											
catilla	-	-	X	-	-	-	-	-	-	-	-	-	-	-	-	-	-	-	-	-	-	-	-	-	-	-	-
chaotica	-	-	-	-	-	-	-	-	-	-	-	X	-	X	-	-	-	-	-	-	-	-	-	-	-	-	-
circularis	-	-	-	-	-	-	-	-	-	-	-	X	-	-	-	-	-	-	-	-	X	-	-	-	-	-	-
cornucopia	-	-	-	-	-	-	-	X	-	-	-	-	-	-	-	-	-	-	-	-	X	-	-	-	-	-	-
diabloensis (Stehli)	-	-	-	-	-	-	-	-	-	-	-	-	-	-	-	-	-	-	-	-	X	-	-	-	-	-	-
fredericksi (REK)	-	-	X	X	-	-	-	-	-	-	-	-	-	-	-	-	-	-	-	-	-	-	-	-	-	-	-
gigantea	-	-	-	X	-	-	-	X	X	-	-	-	-	-	-	-	-	-	-	-	-	-	-	-	-	-	-
parviconica	-	-	-	-	-	-	-	-	-	-	-	-	-	X	-	-	-	-	-	-	-	-	-	-	-	-	-
phialiforma	-	-	X	-	-	-	-	-	-	-	-	-	-	-	-	-	-	-	-	-	-	-	-	-	-	-	-
pocillata	-	-	-	-	-	-	-	-	-	-	-	X	-	-	-	-	-	-	-	-	X	-	-	-	-	-	-
progressa	-	-	-	-	-	-	-	-	-	-	-	-	-	-	-	-	X	X	-	-	-	X	-	-	-	-	-
Eridmatus																											
marathonensis	X	X	X	-	-	-	-	-	-	-	-	-	-	-	-	-	-	-	-	-	-	-	-	-	-	-	-
Fascicosta																											
bella	-	-	-	-	-	-	-	-	-	-	-	-	-	-	-	-	-	-	-	-	-	-	X	-	X	X	-
elongata	-	-	-	-	-	-	-	-	-	-	-	-	-	-	-	-	-	-	-	-	-	-	X	X	X	X	-
longaeva (Girty)	-	-	-	-	-	-	-	-	-	-	-	-	-	-	-	-	-	-	-	-	-	-	-	X	X	X	X
Fimbrinia																											
ovata	-	-	-	-	-	-	-	X	-	-	-	-	-	-	-	-	-	-	-	-	X	-	-	-	-	-	-
plummeri (RHK)	-	-	X	-	-	-	-	-	-	-	-	-	-	-	-	-	-	-	-	-	-	-	-	-	-	-	-
Geyerella																											
americana Girty	-	-	-	-	-	-	-	-	-	-	-	-	-	-	-	-	-	-	-	-	-	-	-	-	-	X	X
hessi	-	-	-	-	X	-	-	X	X	-	-	-	-	-	-	-	-	-	-	-	-	-	-	-	-	-	-
inexpectata	-	-	-	-	-	-	-	-	-	-	-	-	-	X	-	-	-	-	-	-	-	-	-	-	-	-	-
kingorum	-	-	X	X	-	-	-	-	-	-	-	-	-	-	-	-	-	-	-	-	-	-	-	-	-	-	-
sp. 1	-	-	-	X	-	-	-	-	-	-	-	-	-	-	-	-	-	-	-	-	-	-	-	-	-	-	-
Glossothyropsis																											
carinata	-	-	-	-	-	-	-	-	-	-	-	-	-	-	-	-	-	-	-	X	-	-	-	-	-	-	-
cryptacanthoides	-	-	-	-	-	-	-	-	-	-	-	-	-	-	-	-	-	-	-	-	-	-	X	X	X	-	-
immatura	-	-	-	-	-	-	-	-	-	-	-	X	-	-	-	-	-	-	-	-	-	-	X	-	X	-	-
juvenis	-	-	-	-	-	-	-	-	-	-	-	-	*	-	-	-	-	-	-	-	-	-	X	-	X	-	-
polita	-	-	-	-	-	-	-	-	-	-	-	-	-	-	-	-	-	-	-	-	-	-	X	X	X	-	-
rectangulata	-	-	-	-	-	-	-	-	-	-	-	-	-	-	X	X	X	X	-	-	-	-	-	-	-	-	-
robusta (Girty)	-	-	-	-	-	-	-	-	-	-	-	-	-	-	-	-	-	X	-	-	-	-	X	-	X	-	-
superba	-	-	-	-	-	-	-	-	-	-	-	-	-	X	-	-	-	-	-	-	-	-	-	-	-	-	-
Glyptosteges																											
angustus (REK)	-	-	-	-	X	X	-	X	X	X	-	-	-	-	-	-	-	-	-	-	-	-	-	-	-	-	-
insculptus	-	-	-	-	-	-	-	-	-	-	-	-	-	-	-	-	-	-	-	-	X	-	-	-	-	-	-
intricatus	-	-	-	-	X	-	X	X	X	-	-	X	-	-	-	-	-	-	-	-	-	-	-	-	-	-	-
sulcatus	-	-	-	-	-	X	-	-	-	-	-	X	-	-	-	-	-	-	-	-	-	-	-	-	-	-	-
Goniarina																											
appeli	-	-	-	-	-	-	-	-	-	-	X	-	-	-	-	-	-	-	-	-	-	-	-	-	-	-	-
diabloensis	-	-	-	-	-	-	-	-	-	-	-	-	-	-	-	-	-	-	-	-	X	-	-	-	-	-	-
futilis	-	-	-	-	X	-	-	-	-	-	X	X	X	-	-	-	-	-	-	-	-	-	-	-	-	-	-

GENUS AND SPECIES	Gaptank	Uddenites	Neal Ranch	Lenox Hills	Decie Ranch	Poplar Tank	Dugout Mtn.	Sullivan Peak	Skinner Ranch undivided	Hess	Taylor Ranch	Cathedral Mtn.	Wedin	Road Canyon	China Tank	Willis Ranch	Lens	Appel Ranch	Word undivided	Hueco	Bone Spring	Getaway	Hegler	Pinery	Rader	Lamar	Capitan
Goniarina (Cont'd.)																											
magniextensa	-	-	-	-	-	-	-	-	X	-	-	-	-	-	-	-	-	-	-	-	-	-	-	-	-	-	-
permiana (Stehli)	-	-	-	-	-	-	-	-	-	-	-	-	-	-	-	-	-	-	-	-	X	-	-	-	-	-	-
pyelodes C&G	-	-	X	-	-	-	-	-	-	-	-	-	-	-	-	-	-	-	-	-	-	-	-	-	-	-	-
striata	-	-	-	-	-	-	-	-	-	-	-	-	-	X	-	-	-	-	-	-	-	-	-	-	-	-	-
Grandaurispina																											
bella	-	-	-	-	-	-	-	-	-	-	-	-	-	-	-	X	-	X	-	-	-	-	-	-	-	-	-
belliformis	-	-	-	-	-	-	-	-	-	-	-	-	-	-	-	-	-	-	-	-	-	X	-	-	-	-	-
crassa	-	-	-	-	-	-	-	-	-	-	-	-	-	-	X	X	-	-	-	-	-	-	-	-	-	-	-
elongata	-	-	-	-	-	-	-	-	-	-	-	-	-	-	X	X	-	-	-	-	-	-	-	-	-	-	-
gibbosa	-	-	-	-	-	-	-	-	-	-	-	-	-	-	-	X	-	-	-	-	-	-	-	-	-	-	-
kingorum M-W&C	-	-	-	-	-	-	-	-	-	-	-	-	-	-	-	X	X	-	-	-	-	-	-	-	-	-	-
rara	-	-	-	-	-	-	-	-	-	-	-	-	-	-	-	-	-	X	-	-	-	-	-	-	-	-	-
rudis	-	-	-	-	-	-	-	-	-	-	-	-	-	-	-	-	-	-	-	-	X	-	-	-	-	-	-
undulata	-	-	-	-	-	-	-	-	-	-	-	-	-	-	-	-	-	-	-	-	X	-	-	-	-	-	-
?vaga	-	-	-	-	-	-	-	-	-	X	-	-	-	-	-	-	-	-	-	-	-	-	-	-	-	-	-
Gypospirifer																											
anancites	-	X	-	X	-	-	-	-	-	-	-	-	-	-	-	-	-	-	-	X	-	-	-	-	-	-	-
infraplicus (REK)	-	-	-	-	-	-	-	-	X	-	-	-	-	-	-	-	-	-	-	-	X	-	-	-	-	-	-
nelsoni	-	-	-	-	-	-	-	-	-	-	-	-	-	-	-	-	-	-	-	-	X	-	-	-	-	-	-
Hemileurus																											
runcinatus	-	-	X	-	-	-	-	-	-	-	-	-	-	-	-	-	-	-	-	-	-	-	-	-	-	-	-
Hercosestria																											
cribrosa C&G	-	-	-	-	-	-	-	-	-	X	-	X	-	-	-	-	-	-	-	-	-	-	-	-	-	-	-
laevis	-	-	-	-	-	-	-	-	-	X	-	-	-	-	-	-	-	-	-	-	-	-	-	-	-	-	-
Hercosia																											
delicata	-	-	-	-	-	-	-	-	-	X	-	-	-	-	-	-	-	-	-	-	-	-	-	-	-	-	-
uddeni (Böse)	-	-	-	-	-	-	X	X	X	-	-	X	X	X	-	-	-	-	-	-	X	-	-	-	-	-	-
Heteralosia																											
hystricula (Girty)	-	-	-	-	-	-	-	-	-	-	-	-	-	X	X	X	X	X	X	-	X	-	-	-	-	-	-
magnispina	-	-	-	-	-	-	-	-	-	-	-	-	-	-	-	-	-	-	-	-	-	X	X	X	X	-	-
paucispinosa	-	-	-	-	-	-	-	-	-	-	-	-	-	-	-	-	-	-	-	-	-	X	X	X	X	-	-
tenuispina	-	-	-	-	-	-	-	-	-	-	-	-	-	-	-	-	-	-	-	-	-	X	-	-	-	-	-
vidriensis	-	-	-	-	-	-	-	-	-	X	-	X	-	-	-	-	-	-	-	-	-	-	-	-	-	-	-
Heteraria																											
blakemorei	-	-	-	-	-	-	-	-	-	X	-	-	-	-	-	-	-	-	-	-	-	-	-	-	-	-	-
Heterelasma																											
angulatum	-	-	-	-	-	-	-	-	-	-	-	-	X	-	-	-	-	-	-	-	-	-	-	-	-	-	-
concavum	-	-	-	-	-	-	-	-	-	-	-	-	-	-	X	X	X	X	-	-	-	X	-	-	-	-	-
contortum	-	-	-	-	-	-	-	-	-	X	-	-	-	-	-	-	-	-	-	-	-	-	-	-	-	-	-
geniculatum Stehli	-	-	-	-	-	-	-	-	-	-	-	-	-	-	-	-	-	-	-	-	-	X	-	-	-	-	-
gibbosum	-	-	-	-	-	-	-	X	-	-	-	X	X	-	-	-	-	-	-	-	-	-	-	-	-	-	-
glansfagea	-	-	-	-	-	-	-	-	-	X	-	X	-	-	-	-	-	-	-	-	-	-	-	-	-	-	-
magnum	-	-	-	-	-	-	-	-	-	-	-	-	X	-	-	-	-	-	-	-	-	-	-	-	-	-	-
pentagonum	-	-	-	-	-	-	-	-	-	-	-	-	-	-	X	X	X	-	-	-	-	-	-	-	-	-	-
quadratum	-	-	-	-	-	-	-	-	-	-	-	-	-	-	-	-	-	-	-	-	-	X	-	-	-	-	-
shumardianum Girty	-	-	-	-	-	-	-	-	-	-	-	-	-	-	-	-	-	-	-	-	-	-	X	X	X	X	X
solidum	-	-	-	-	-	-	-	-	-	-	-	-	-	-	X	X	X	X	-	-	-	-	-	-	-	-	-
sulciplicatum	-	-	-	-	-	-	-	-	-	-	-	-	-	-	-	-	-	-	-	-	-	X	-	-	-	-	-
venustulum Girty	-	-	-	-	-	-	-	-	-	-	-	-	-	-	-	-	-	-	-	-	-	-	X	X	X	X	X
Holosia																											
ovalis	-	-	-	-	-	-	-	-	-	-	-	-	X	-	-	-	-	-	-	-	-	-	-	-	-	-	-
ovoidea	-	-	-	-	-	-	-	-	-	-	-	-	-	-	-	-	-	-	-	-	-	-	X	-	-	-	-
regularis	-	-	-	-	-	-	-	-	-	-	-	-	-	-	-	-	-	-	-	-	-	-	-	X	-	-	-
Holotricharina																											
hirsuta	-	-	-	-	-	-	-	-	-	X	-	-	X	-	-	-	-	-	-	-	-	-	-	-	-	-	-
sparsa	-	-	-	-	-	-	-	-	-	-	-	-	X	-	-	-	-	-	-	-	-	-	-	-	-	-	-
Horridonia																											
texana REK	-	-	-	-	-	-	-	-	-	-	-	-	X	-	-	-	-	-	-	-	-	-	-	-	-	-	-
Hustedia																											
ampullacea	-	-	-	-	-	-	-	-	-	-	-	X	X	X	-	-	-	-	-	-	X	-	-	-	-	-	-

GENUS AND SPECIES	Gaptank	Uddenites	Neal Ranch	Lenox Hills	Decie Ranch	Poplar Tank	Dugout Mtn.	Sullivan Peak	Skinner Ranch undivided	Hess	Taylor Ranch	Cathedral Mtn.	Wedin	Road Canyon	China Tank	Willis Ranch	Lens	Appel Ranch	Word undivided	Hueco	Bone Spring	Getaway	Hegler	Pinery	Rader	Lamar	Capitan
Hustedia (Cont'd.)																											
bipartita Girty	-	-	-	-	-	-	-	-	-	-	-	-	-	-	X	-	-	-	-	-	-	-	-	-	-	-	-
catella	-	-	-	-	X	X	-	X	X	-	-	-	-	-	-	-	-	-	-	-	-	-	-	-	-	-	-
cepacea	-	-	-	-	X	X	-	X	-	-	X	-	-	-	-	-	-	-	-	-	-	-	-	X	-	-	-
citeria	-	-	-	-	-	-	-	-	-	-	-	-	-	-	-	-	-	-	-	-	-	-	-	X	-	-	-
compressa	-	-	-	-	-	-	-	-	-	-	-	X	-	-	-	-	-	-	-	-	-	-	-	-	-	-	-
connorsi	-	-	-	-	-	-	-	-	-	-	-	X	-	X	-	-	-	-	-	-	-	-	-	-	-	-	-
consuta	-	-	-	-	-	-	-	-	-	-	-	X	-	X	-	-	-	-	-	-	-	-	-	-	-	-	-
crepax	-	-	X	-	-	-	-	-	-	-	-	-	-	-	-	-	-	-	-	-	-	-	-	-	-	-	-
culcitula	-	-	X	-	-	-	-	-	-	-	-	-	-	-	-	-	-	-	-	-	-	-	-	-	-	-	-
cuneata	-	-	-	-	-	-	-	-	-	-	-	-	-	-	X	-	-	-	-	-	-	-	-	-	-	-	-
decollatensis	-	-	-	-	-	-	-	-	-	-	-	-	-	-	-	-	-	-	-	-	X	-	-	-	-	-	-
demissa	-	-	-	-	-	-	-	-	-	-	-	-	-	-	-	-	-	-	-	-	X	-	X	X	X	-	-
glomerosa	-	-	-	-	-	-	-	-	-	-	-	-	-	-	-	-	-	-	-	-	X	-	-	-	-	-	-
hapala	-	-	-	-	-	-	-	-	-	-	-	-	-	-	-	-	-	-	-	-	-	X	-	-	-	-	-
hessensis REK	-	-	-	-	X	-	-	X	X	-	-	-	-	-	-	-	-	-	-	-	X	-	-	-	-	-	-
huecoensis REK	-	-	-	-	-	-	-	-	-	-	-	-	-	-	-	-	-	-	-	X	-	-	-	-	-	-	-
inconspicua	-	-	-	-	-	-	X	-	-	-	-	-	-	-	-	-	-	-	-	-	-	-	-	-	-	-	-
lusca	-	-	-	-	-	-	-	-	-	-	-	X	X	X	-	-	-	-	-	-	-	-	-	-	-	-	-
narinosa	-	-	-	-	-	-	-	-	-	-	-	-	-	X	-	-	-	-	-	-	-	-	-	-	-	-	-
opsia	-	-	-	-	-	-	-	-	-	-	-	-	-	-	-	-	-	-	-	-	-	-	X	X	X	X	X
pugilla hebetata	-	-	-	-	-	-	-	-	-	-	-	-	-	-	-	-	X	X	-	-	-	-	-	-	-	-	-
p. nasiterna	-	-	-	-	-	-	-	-	-	-	-	-	-	X	X	X	-	X	X	-	-	-	-	-	-	-	-
p. pluscula	-	-	-	-	-	-	-	-	-	-	-	-	-	-	-	X	X	-	-	-	-	-	-	-	-	-	-
p. pugilla	-	-	-	-	-	-	-	-	-	-	-	-	-	-	-	-	X	X	-	-	-	-	-	-	-	-	-
rupinata	-	-	-	-	-	-	-	-	-	-	-	-	-	-	-	-	-	-	-	-	-	-	X	X	X	X	X
samiata	-	-	-	-	-	-	-	-	-	-	-	-	-	-	X	X	X	X	-	-	-	-	-	-	-	-	-
sculptilis	-	-	-	-	-	-	-	-	-	-	-	X	X	X	-	-	-	-	-	-	-	-	-	-	-	-	-
spicata	-	-	-	-	-	-	-	-	-	-	-	X	X	X	-	-	-	-	-	-	-	-	-	-	-	-	-
stataria	-	-	-	-	-	-	-	-	-	-	-	X	-	-	-	-	-	-	-	-	-	-	-	-	-	-	-
tomea	-	-	-	-	-	-	-	-	-	-	-	-	-	-	-	-	-	-	-	-	-	X	-	-	-	-	-
trisecta	-	-	-	-	-	-	-	-	-	-	-	X	-	-	-	-	-	-	-	-	-	-	-	-	-	-	-
trita leptyca	-	-	X	X	-	-	-	-	-	-	-	-	-	-	-	-	-	-	-	-	-	-	-	-	-	-	-
t. trita	-	-	X	X	-	-	-	-	-	-	-	-	-	-	-	-	-	-	-	-	-	-	-	-	-	-	-
Hypopsia																											
versuta	-	-	X	-	-	-	-	-	-	-	-	-	-	-	-	-	-	-	-	-	-	-	-	-	-	-	-
Hystriculina																											
convexa	-	-	X	X	-	-	-	-	-	-	-	-	-	-	-	-	-	-	-	-	-	-	-	-	-	-	-
dugoutensis (REK)	-	-	-	X	-	-	-	-	-	-	-	-	-	-	-	-	-	-	-	-	-	-	-	-	-	-	-
minima	-	-	X	-	-	-	-	-	-	-	-	-	-	-	-	-	-	-	-	-	-	-	-	-	-	-	-
pumila	-	-	-	-	X	-	-	X	-	-	-	-	-	-	-	-	-	-	-	-	-	-	-	-	-	-	-
sulcata	X	X	X	X	-	-	-	-	-	X?	-	-	-	-	-	-	-	-	-	-	-	-	-	-	-	-	-
ventroplana	X	X	X	X	-	-	-	-	-	-	-	-	-	-	-	-	-	-	-	-	-	-	-	-	-	-	-
Institella																											
leonardensis (REK)	-	-	-	-	-	-	-	-	-	-	X	X	X	-	-	-	-	-	-	-	X	-	-	-	-	-	-
Iotina																											
minuta	-	-	-	-	-	-	-	-	-	-	-	-	-	-	-	-	-	-	-	-	X	-	-	-	-	-	-
Isogramma																											
concavum	-	-	X	-	-	-	-	-	-	-	-	-	-	-	-	-	-	-	-	-	X	-	-	-	-	-	-
diabloense	-	-	-	-	-	-	-	-	-	X	-	-	-	-	-	-	-	-	-	-	X	-	-	-	-	-	-
lobatum	-	-	-	-	-	-	-	-	-	-	-	X	-	-	-	-	-	-	-	-	-	-	-	-	-	-	-
vidriense	-	-	X	-	-	-	-	-	-	-	-	-	-	-	-	-	-	-	-	-	-	-	-	-	-	-	-
Juresania																											
sp. 1	X	X	X	-	-	-	-	-	-	-	-	-	-	-	-	-	-	-	-	-	-	-	-	-	-	-	-
sp. 2	-	-	X	-	-	-	-	-	-	-	-	-	-	-	-	-	-	-	-	-	-	-	-	-	-	-	-
sp. 3	-	-	X	-	-	-	-	-	-	-	-	-	-	-	-	-	-	-	-	-	-	-	-	-	-	-	-
Kochiproductus																											
elongatus	-	-	-	-	-	-	-	X	-	-	-	-	-	-	-	-	-	-	-	-	X	-	-	-	-	-	-
occidentalis (REK)	-	-	X	-	-	-	-	-	-	-	-	-	-	-	-	-	-	-	-	-	-	-	-	-	-	-	-
primitivus	X	X	-	X	-	-	-	-	-	-	-	-	-	-	-	-	-	-	-	-	-	-	-	-	-	-	-
quadratus	-	-	-	-	-	-	-	-	-	-	-	-	-	-	-	-	-	-	-	X	-	-	-	-	-	-	-
victorioensis (REK)	-	-	-	-	-	-	-	X	-	-	-	-	-	-	-	-	-	-	-	-	X	-	-	-	-	-	-
sp. 1	-	-	-	-	X	-	-	-	-	-	-	-	-	-	-	-	-	-	-	-	-	-	-	-	-	-	-
sp. 2	-	-	-	X	-	-	-	-	-	-	-	-	-	-	-	-	-	-	-	-	-	-	-	-	-	-	-
sp. 6	-	-	-	-	-	-	-	-	-	-	-	-	-	X	X	-	-	-	-	-	-	-	-	-	-	-	-

GENUS AND SPECIES	Gaptank	Uddenites	Neal Ranch	Lenox Hills	Decie Ranch	Poplar Tank	Dugout Mtn.	Sullivan Peak	Skinner Ranch undivided	Hess	Taylor Ranch	Cathedral Mtn.	Wedin	Road Canyon	China Tank	Willis Ranch	Lens	Appel Ranch	Word undivided	Hueco	Bone Spring	Getaway	Hegler	Pinery	Rader	Lamar	Capitan
Kozlowskia																											
alata	-	-	-	-	-	-	-	-	X	-	-	-	-	-	-	-	-	-	-	-	-	-	-	-	-	-	-
anterosulcata	-	-	X	X	-	-	-	-	-	-	-	-	-	-	-	-	-	-	-	-	-	-	-	-	-	-	-
kingi Stehli	-	-	-	-	X	-	-	-	-	-	-	-	-	-	-	-	-	-	-	-	X	-	-	-	-	-	-
nasuta	-	-	X	-	-	-	-	-	-	-	-	-	-	-	-	-	-	-	-	-	-	-	-	-	-	-	-
subsphaeroidalis	-	-	-	-	X	-	-	-	X	-	-	-	-	-	-	-	-	-	-	-	-	-	-	-	-	-	-
Kutorginella																											
dartoni (REK)	-	-	-	-	-	-	-	-	-	-	-	-	-	-	-	-	-	-	-	X	-	-	-	-	-	-	-
robusta	-	-	-	-	-	-	-	-	-	-	-	-	-	-	X	-	-	-	-	-	-	-	-	-	-	-	-
sullivanensis (REK)	-	-	-	-	-	-	-	-	-	-	-	-	-	-	X	-	-	-	-	-	-	-	-	-	-	-	-
uddeni	X	X	X	X	-	-	-	-	-	-	-	-	-	-	-	-	-	-	-	-	-	-	-	-	-	-	-
umbonata (M-W&C)	-	-	-	-	-	-	-	-	-	-	-	X	-	X	-	-	-	-	-	-	-	-	-	-	-	-	-
Lamellosia																											
lamellosa	-	-	-	-	-	-	-	-	-	-	-	-	-	-	-	-	-	-	-	-	-	-	X	-	-	-	-
Leiorhynchoidea																											
amygdaloidea	-	-	-	-	-	-	-	-	-	-	-	-	-	X	X	X	-	-	-	-	-	-	-	-	-	-	-
rotundidorsa	-	-	-	-	-	-	-	-	-	-	-	-	-	-	-	-	-	-	-	-	-	-	X	-	-	-	-
scelesta	-	-	-	-	-	-	-	-	-	-	-	-	-	-	X	-	-	-	-	-	X	-	-	-	-	-	-
Lepidocrania																											
sparsispinosa	-	-	X	-	-	-	-	-	-	-	-	-	-	-	-	-	-	-	-	-	-	-	-	-	-	-	-
sublamellosa	-	-	-	-	-	-	-	-	-	-	-	-	-	X	X	X	X	X	X	-	-	-	X	-	-	-	-
tardispinosa	-	-	-	-	-	-	-	-	-	-	-	X	X	X	-	-	-	-	-	-	-	-	-	-	-	-	-
Lepidospirifer																											
angulatus C&G	-	-	-	-	-	-	-	-	-	-	-	X	-	-	-	-	-	-	-	-	-	-	-	-	-	-	-
costellus (REK)	-	-	-	-	-	-	-	-	-	-	-	X	-	-	-	-	-	-	-	-	-	-	-	-	-	-	-
demissus	-	-	-	-	-	-	-	-	-	-	-	X	X	-	-	-	-	-	-	-	-	-	-	-	-	-	-
inferus	-	-	-	-	-	-	-	-	-	-	-	X	-	-	-	-	-	-	-	-	-	-	-	-	-	-	-
sp.	-	-	-	-	X	X	X	-	-	-	-	-	-	-	-	-	-	-	-	-	-	-	-	-	-	-	-
Leurosina																											
delicata	-	-	-	-	-	-	-	-	-	-	-	-	-	-	-	-	-	-	-	-	-	X	-	-	-	-	-
lata	-	-	-	-	-	-	-	-	-	-	-	-	-	X	X	X	X	X	X	-	-	-	-	-	-	-	-
marginata	-	-	-	-	-	-	-	-	-	-	-	-	-	-	-	-	-	-	X	-	-	-	-	-	-	-	-
serratoseptata	-	-	-	-	-	-	-	-	-	-	-	-	-	-	-	-	-	-	-	X	-	-	-	-	-	-	-
sinesulca (Stehli)	-	-	-	-	-	-	-	-	-	-	-	-	-	-	-	-	-	-	-	-	X	-	-	-	-	-	-
vulgarica	-	-	-	-	X	-	-	-	X	-	-	-	-	-	-	-	-	-	-	-	X	-	-	-	-	-	-
Limbella																											
costellata	X	X	-	-	-	-	-	-	-	-	-	-	-	-	-	-	-	-	-	-	-	-	-	-	-	-	-
limbata	-	-	-	-	X	X	X	X	X	-	-	-	-	-	-	-	-	-	-	-	-	-	-	-	-	-	-
victorioensis Stehli	-	-	-	-	-	-	-	-	-	-	-	-	-	-	-	-	-	-	-	-	X	-	-	-	-	-	-
wolfcampensis (REK)	-	X	X	X	-	-	-	-	X	-	-	-	-	-	-	-	-	-	-	-	-	-	-	-	-	-	-
sp. 1	-	-	-	-	-	-	-	-	X	X	X	-	-	-	-	-	-	-	-	-	-	-	-	-	-	-	-
Linoproductus																											
angustus REK	-	-	-	-	X	X	-	X	X	-	-	-	-	-	-	-	-	-	-	-	-	X	-	-	-	-	-
delicatus	-	-	-	-	-	-	-	-	-	-	-	X	-	-	-	-	-	-	-	-	-	-	-	-	-	-	-
meniscus D&C	X	X	X	-	-	-	-	-	-	-	-	-	-	-	-	-	-	-	-	-	-	-	-	-	-	-	-
nasutus REK	-	-	-	-	-	-	-	-	-	-	-	-	-	-	-	-	-	X	-	-	-	-	-	-	-	-	-
semisulcatus	-	-	X	X	-	-	-	-	-	-	-	-	-	-	-	-	-	-	-	-	-	-	-	-	-	-	-
undatus	-	-	-	-	-	-	-	-	X	X	-	-	-	-	-	-	-	-	-	-	-	-	-	-	-	-	-
sp. 1	-	X	-	-	-	-	-	-	-	-	-	-	-	-	-	-	-	-	-	-	-	-	-	-	-	-	-
Liosotella																											
costata	-	-	-	-	-	-	-	-	-	-	-	-	-	X	-	-	-	-	-	-	-	-	-	-	-	-	-
irregularis	-	-	-	-	-	-	-	-	-	-	-	-	-	-	X	X	X	-	-	-	-	-	-	-	-	-	-
opima (Girty)	-	-	-	-	-	-	-	-	-	-	-	-	-	-	-	-	-	-	-	-	-	-	-	X	-	-	-
parva	-	-	-	-	-	-	-	-	-	-	-	-	-	-	X	X	X	-	-	-	-	-	-	-	-	-	-
popei (Shumard)	-	-	-	-	-	-	-	-	-	-	-	-	-	-	-	-	-	-	-	-	-	-	-	-	-	-	X
rotunda	-	-	-	-	-	-	-	-	-	-	-	-	-	X	-	-	-	-	-	-	-	-	-	-	-	-	-
spinumbona	-	-	-	-	-	-	-	-	-	-	-	-	-	-	-	-	-	-	-	-	-	-	X	-	-	-	-
tetragonalis	-	-	-	-	-	-	-	-	-	-	-	-	-	-	-	X	X	-	-	-	-	-	-	-	-	-	-
wordensis (REK)	-	-	-	-	-	-	-	-	-	-	-	-	-	X	X	X	X	X	X	-	X	-	-	-	-	-	-
Liraria																											
lirata	-	-	-	-	-	-	-	-	-	-	-	-	-	-	-	-	-	-	-	-	X	-	-	-	-	-	-
Lirellaria																											
costellata	-	-	-	-	-	-	-	-	-	-	-	-	-	-	-	-	-	-	-	-	-	-	-	-	-	X	-

GENUS AND SPECIES	Gaptank	Uddenites	Neal Ranch	Lenox Hills	Decie Ranch	Poplar Tank	Dugout Mtn.	Sullivan Peak	Skinner Ranch undivided	Hess	Taylor Ranch	Cathedral Mtn.	Wedin	Road Canyon	China Tank	Willis Ranch	Lens	Appel Ranch	Word undivided	Hueco	Bone Spring	Getaway	Hegler	Pinery	Rader	Lamar	Capitan
Lirellaria (Cont'd.)																											
crassa	-	-	-	-	-	-	-	-	-	-	-	-	-	-	-	-	-	-	-	-	-	-	-	-	-	X	-
diabloensis	-	-	-	-	-	-	-	-	-	-	-	-	-	-	-	-	-	-	-	-	X	-	-	-	-	-	-
Lissochonetes																											
parvisulcatus	-	X	-	-	-	-	-	-	-	-	-	-	-	-	-	-	-	-	-	-	-	-	-	-	-	-	-
Lowenstamia																											
ampla	-	-	X	-	-	-	-	-	-	-	-	-	-	-	-	-	-	-	-	-	-	-	-	-	-	-	-
sp. 1	-	-	X	-	-	-	-	-	-	-	-	-	-	-	-	-	-	-	-	-	-	-	-	-	-	-	-
Loxophragmus																											
ellipticus	-	-	-	-	-	-	-	-	-	-	-	X	-	-	-	-	-	-	-	-	-	-	-	-	-	-	-
Madarosia																											
anterolamellata	-	-	-	-	-	-	-	-	-	-	-	-	-	-	-	-	-	-	-	-	-	-	X	X	X	-	-
pentagona	-	-	-	-	-	-	-	-	-	-	-	-	-	-	-	-	-	-	-	-	X	-	-	-	-	-	-
Martinia																											
causaria	-	-	-	-	-	-	-	-	-	-	-	-	-	-	-	-	-	-	-	-	X	-	-	-	-	-	-
cruenta	-	-	-	-	-	-	-	-	-	X	-	-	-	-	-	-	-	-	-	-	-	-	-	-	-	-	-
exigua	-	-	X	-	-	-	-	-	-	-	-	-	-	-	-	-	-	-	-	-	-	-	-	-	-	-	-
fucina	-	-	-	-	-	-	-	-	-	-	-	-	-	-	-	-	-	-	-	-	X	-	-	-	-	-	-
miranda	-	-	-	-	-	-	-	-	-	-	-	X	-	-	-	-	-	-	-	-	-	-	-	-	-	-	-
nealranchensis	-	-	X	-	-	-	-	-	-	-	-	-	-	-	-	-	-	-	-	-	-	-	-	-	-	-	-
rhomboidalis Girty	-	-	-	-	-	-	-	-	-	-	-	-	-	-	-	-	-	-	-	-	-	-	-	-	X	X	X
wolfcampensis REK	-	-	X	-	-	-	-	-	-	-	-	-	-	-	-	-	-	-	-	-	-	-	-	-	-	-	-
Meekella																											
angustiplicata	-	-	-	-	-	-	-	-	-	-	-	-	-	-	-	-	-	-	-	-	X	-	-	-	-	-	-
attenuata Girty	-	-	-	-	-	-	-	-	-	-	-	-	-	-	-	-	-	-	-	-	X	-	-	-	-	-	-
calathica	-	-	-	-	-	-	-	-	-	X	X	X	-	X	-	-	-	-	-	-	-	-	-	-	-	-	-
caperata	-	-	-	-	X	-	-	X	X	-	-	-	-	-	-	-	-	-	-	-	-	-	-	-	-	-	-
circularis	-	-	-	-	-	-	-	-	-	-	-	-	-	-	-	-	-	-	-	X	-	-	-	-	-	-	-
enormis	-	-	-	-	X	-	-	X	-	-	-	-	-	-	-	-	-	-	-	-	-	-	-	-	-	-	-
hessensis REK	-	-	-	-	X	X	X	X	X	X	X	-	X	-	-	-	-	-	-	-	X	-	-	-	-	-	-
intermedia	-	-	-	-	-	-	-	-	-	-	-	-	-	-	-	-	-	-	-	-	X	-	-	-	-	-	-
magnifica	-	X	X	X	-	-	-	-	-	-	-	-	-	-	-	-	-	-	-	-	-	-	-	-	-	-	-
occidentalis (Newberry)	-	-	-	-	-	-	-	-	-	-	-	X	-	-	-	-	-	-	-	-	-	-	-	-	-	-	-
prionota	X	X	X	X	-	-	-	-	-	-	-	-	-	-	-	-	-	-	-	-	-	-	-	-	-	-	-
skenoides Girty	-	-	-	-	-	-	-	-	-	-	-	-	-	X	X	X	X	X	X	-	-	X	X	X	-	-	-
texana REK	X	X	-	X	-	-	-	-	-	-	-	-	-	-	-	-	-	-	-	-	-	-	-	-	-	-	-
Megousia																											
auriculata M-W&C	-	-	-	-	-	-	-	-	-	X	-	X	-	-	-	-	-	-	-	-	X	-	X	-	-	-	-
definita	-	-	-	-	-	-	-	-	-	-	-	-	-	X	X	X	X	-	-	-	-	X	-	-	-	-	-
flexuosa	-	-	-	-	-	-	-	-	-	-	-	-	-	X	X	X	-	-	-	-	-	-	-	-	-	-	-
mucronata	-	-	-	-	-	-	-	-	-	-	-	-	-	X	X	X	-	X	-	-	-	-	-	-	-	-	-
umbonata	-	-	-	-	-	-	-	-	-	-	-	X	-	-	-	-	-	-	-	-	-	-	-	-	-	-	-
?waageniana (Girty)	-	-	-	-	-	-	-	-	-	-	-	-	-	-	-	-	-	-	-	-	-	-	-	-	-	-	X
Mesolobus																											
?permianus	-	-	-	-	-	-	-	-	-	-	-	X	-	-	-	-	-	-	-	-	-	-	-	-	-	-	-
Metriolepis																											
carotica	-	-	-	-	-	-	-	-	-	-	-	X	-	-	-	-	-	-	-	-	-	-	-	-	-	-	-
diabloensis	-	-	-	-	-	-	-	-	-	-	-	-	-	-	-	-	-	-	-	-	-	X	-	-	-	-	-
exserta	-	-	-	-	-	-	-	-	-	-	-	-	-	-	-	-	-	-	-	-	-	X	-	-	-	-	-
irenae (Stehli)	-	-	-	-	-	-	-	-	-	-	-	-	-	-	-	-	-	-	-	-	-	X	-	-	-	-	-
larina	-	-	-	-	-	-	-	-	-	X	X	X	-	-	-	-	-	-	-	-	-	-	-	-	-	-	-
nabis	-	-	-	-	-	-	-	-	-	-	-	-	-	-	-	-	-	-	-	-	-	-	X	X	X	-	-
pedicosa	-	-	-	-	-	-	-	-	-	-	-	-	-	-	X	-	-	-	-	-	-	-	-	-	-	-	-
pinea	-	-	-	-	-	-	-	-	-	-	-	X	-	-	-	-	-	-	-	-	-	-	-	-	-	-	-
pulvinata	-	-	-	-	-	-	-	-	-	-	-	-	-	-	X	X	X	X	-	-	-	-	-	-	-	-	-
scrupea	-	-	-	-	X	-	-	X	X	-	-	-	-	-	-	-	-	-	-	-	-	-	-	-	-	-	-
tegulata	-	-	-	-	-	-	-	-	-	-	-	X	-	X	-	-	-	-	-	-	-	-	-	-	-	-	-
ziczac	-	-	-	-	-	-	-	-	-	-	-	X	-	-	-	-	-	-	-	-	-	-	-	-	-	-	-
Micraphelia																											
pumilis	-	-	-	-	-	-	-	-	-	-	-	-	-	-	-	-	-	-	-	-	X	-	-	-	-	-	-
scitula C&G	-	-	-	-	-	-	-	-	-	-	-	-	-	-	-	-	-	-	-	-	-	X	X	X	X	-	-
subalata	-	-	-	-	-	-	-	-	-	-	-	-	-	-	-	-	-	-	-	-	-	X	X	X	-	-	X

GENUS AND SPECIES	Gaptank	Uddenites	Neal Ranch	Lenox Hills	Decie Ranch	Poplar Tank	Dugout Mtn.	Sullivan Peak	Skinner Ranch undivided	Hess	Taylor Ranch	Cathedral Mtn.	Wedin	Road Canyon	China Tank	Willis Ranch	Lens	Appel Ranch	Word undivided	Hueco	Bone Spring	Getaway	Hegler	Pinery	Rader	Lamar	Capitan
Neochonetes																											
liratus	-	X	X	-	-	-	-	-	-	-	-	-	-	-	-	-	-	-	-	-	-	-	-	-	-	-	-
parvus	-	-	X	-	-	-	-	-	-	-	-	-	-	-	-	-	-	-	-	-	-	-	-	-	-	-	-
Neophricadothyris																											
bullata	-	-	-	-	-	-	-	X	-	X	X	X	X	-	-	-	-	-	-	-	X	-	-	-	-	-	-
catatona	-	-	-	X	X	-	-	X	X	-	-	-	-	-	-	-	-	-	-	X	X	-	-	-	-	-	-
conara	-	-	-	-	-	-	-	-	-	-	-	-	-	-	X	X	X	X	-	-	-	X	-	-	-	-	-
cordata	-	-	-	-	-	-	-	-	-	-	-	-	-	X	-	-	-	-	-	-	-	-	-	-	-	-	-
crassibecca	-	-	-	-	-	-	-	-	-	-	-	-	-	X	-	-	-	-	-	-	-	-	-	-	-	-	-
transversa	-	X	X	X	-	-	-	-	-	-	-	-	-	-	-	-	-	-	-	-	-	-	-	-	-	-	-
Neospirifer																											
amphigyus	-	-	-	-	-	-	-	-	-	-	-	-	-	-	X	X	X	X	-	-	-	-	-	-	-	-	-
apothescelus	-	X	X	X	-	-	-	-	-	-	-	-	-	-	-	-	-	-	-	-	-	-	-	-	-	-	-
bakeri bakeri REK	-	-	-	-	-	-	-	-	-	-	-	-	-	X	-	-	-	-	-	-	-	-	-	-	-	-	-
b. columbarius	-	-	-	-	-	-	-	-	-	-	-	-	-	X	-	-	-	-	-	-	-	-	-	-	-	-	-
formulosus	-	-	-	-	-	-	-	-	-	-	-	-	-	X	-	-	-	-	-	-	-	-	-	-	-	-	-
mansuetus	-	-	-	-	-	-	-	-	-	-	X	X	X	-	-	-	-	-	-	-	X	-	-	-	-	-	-
neali	-	-	-	-	-	-	-	-	-	X	-	-	-	-	-	-	-	-	-	-	X	-	-	-	-	-	-
notialis	-	-	-	-	-	-	-	-	-	X	-	-	-	-	-	-	-	-	-	-	-	-	-	-	-	-	-
placidus	-	-	X	-	-	-	-	-	-	-	-	-	-	-	-	-	-	-	-	-	-	-	-	-	-	-	-
thescelus	-	-	-	-	-	-	-	-	-	-	-	-	-	X	-	-	-	-	-	-	-	-	-	-	-	-	-
Niviconia																											
abrupta	-	-	-	-	-	-	-	-	-	-	X	-	-	-	-	-	-	-	-	-	-	-	-	-	-	-	-
globosa (REK)	-	-	-	-	-	-	-	-	-	-	X	-	X	-	-	-	-	-	-	-	-	-	-	-	-	-	-
Nothopindax																											
egregius	-	-	X	-	-	-	-	-	-	-	-	-	-	-	-	-	-	-	-	-	-	-	-	-	-	-	-
Notothyris																											
gillilandensis	-	-	-	-	-	-	-	-	-	-	-	-	-	X	-	-	-	-	-	-	-	-	-	-	-	-	-
planiplicata	-	-	-	-	-	-	-	-	-	-	-	-	-	X	-	-	-	-	-	-	-	-	-	-	-	-	-
venusta	-	-	-	-	-	-	-	-	-	-	-	-	-	-	X	X	X	-	-	-	-	-	-	-	-	-	-
Nucleospira																											
cunctata	-	-	-	-	-	-	-	-	-	-	-	-	-	X	-	-	-	-	-	-	-	-	-	-	-	-	-
Nudauris																											
convexa	-	-	X	-	-	-	-	-	-	-	-	-	-	-	-	-	-	-	-	-	-	-	-	-	-	-	-
diabloensis Stehli	-	-	-	-	-	-	-	-	-	-	-	-	-	-	-	-	-	-	-	-	X	-	-	-	-	-	-
enigmatica	-	-	-	X	X	-	-	X	X	-	-	-	-	-	-	-	-	-	-	-	-	-	-	-	-	-	-
linospina	-	-	-	-	-	-	-	-	-	-	X	X	-	-	-	-	-	-	-	-	-	-	-	-	-	-	-
reticulata	-	-	-	-	-	-	-	-	-	-	-	-	-	-	-	-	-	-	-	-	X	-	-	-	-	-	-
splendens	X	X	X	X	-	-	-	-	-	-	-	-	-	-	-	-	-	-	-	-	-	-	-	-	-	-	-
transversa	-	-	-	-	-	-	-	-	-	-	-	-	-	-	-	-	-	-	-	-	X	-	-	-	-	-	-
tribulosa	-	X	X	-	-	-	-	-	-	-	-	-	-	-	-	-	-	-	-	-	-	-	-	-	-	-	-
Ombonia																											
guadalupensis (Girty)	-	-	-	-	-	-	-	-	-	-	-	-	-	-	-	-	-	-	-	-	-	-	-	X	X	X	X
invecta	-	-	-	-	-	-	-	-	-	-	-	X	-	-	-	-	-	-	-	-	-	-	-	-	-	-	-
sp. 1	-	-	-	-	-	-	-	-	-	-	-	-	-	-	-	-	-	-	-	-	-	X	-	-	-	-	-
Oncosarina																											
rotunda	-	-	-	-	X	-	-	X	-	-	-	-	-	-	-	-	-	-	-	-	-	-	-	-	-	-	-
spinicostata C&G	-	-	-	-	X	X	-	X	X	X	-	-	-	-	-	-	-	-	-	-	-	-	-	-	-	-	-
whitei (REK)	-	-	-	-	-	-	-	-	-	-	X	X	-	-	-	-	-	-	-	-	-	-	-	-	-	-	-
Orthotetella																											
wolfcampensis REK	-	X	X	-	-	-	-	-	-	-	-	-	-	-	-	-	-	-	-	-	X	-	-	-	-	-	-
Orthotichia																											
irregularis	-	-	-	-	-	-	-	-	-	-	-	-	-	-	-	-	-	-	-	-	X	-	-	-	-	-	-
kozlowskii REK	-	X	X	X	-	-	-	-	-	-	-	-	-	-	-	-	-	-	-	X	-	-	-	-	-	-	-
newelli	-	-	-	-	X	-	-	X	-	-	-	-	-	-	-	-	-	-	-	-	-	-	-	-	-	-	-
Paranorella																											
aquilonia	-	-	-	-	-	-	-	-	-	-	-	-	-	-	-	-	-	-	-	-	-	X	-	-	X	-	-
comptula	-	-	-	-	-	-	-	-	-	-	-	-	-	-	X	-	-	-	-	-	X	-	-	-	-	-	-
sp. 1	-	-	-	-	-	-	-	-	-	-	-	-	-	-	X	X	-	-	-	-	X	-	-	-	-	-	-
sp. 2	-	-	-	-	-	X	-	-	-	-	-	-	-	-	-	-	-	-	-	-	X	-	-	-	-	-	-
sp. 4	-	-	-	-	-	-	-	-	-	X	-	-	-	-	-	-	-	-	-	-	X	-	-	-	-	-	-

GENUS AND SPECIES	Gaptank	Uddenites	Neal Ranch	Lenox Hills	Decie Ranch	Poplar Tank	Dugout Mtn.	Sullivan Peak	Skinner Ranch undivided	Hess	Taylor Ranch	Cathedral Mtn.	Wedin	Road Canyon	China Tank	Willis Ranch	Lens	Appel Ranch	Word undivided	Hueco	Bone Spring	Getaway	Hegler	Pinery	Rader	Lamar	Capitan
Paranorella (Cont'd.)																											
sp. 5	-	-	-	-	-	-	-	-	-	-	-	-	-	X	-	-	-	-	-	-	-	-	-	-	-	-	-
sp. 6	-	-	-	-	-	X	-	-	-	-	-	-	-	-	-	-	-	-	-	-	-	-	-	-	-	-	-
Paraspiriferina																											
amoena	-	-	X	-	-	-	-	-	-	-	-	-	-	-	-	-	-	-	-	-	-	-	X	X	X	X	X
billingsi (Shumard)	-	-	-	-	-	-	-	-	-	-	-	-	-	-	-	-	-	-	-	-	-	-	-	-	-	-	X
b. retusa (Girty)	-	-	-	-	-	-	-	-	-	-	-	-	-	X	-	-	-	-	-	-	-	-	-	-	-	-	-
cellulana	-	-	-	-	-	-	-	-	-	-	-	-	-	-	-	-	-	-	-	-	-	-	-	-	-	X	X
evax (Girty)	-	-	-	-	-	-	-	-	-	-	-	-	-	-	X	X	X	-	X	-	-	-	-	-	-	-	-
laqueata	-	-	-	-	-	-	-	-	-	-	-	-	-	-	-	-	-	-	-	-	-	X	-	-	-	-	-
paginata	-	-	-	-	-	-	-	-	-	-	-	-	-	X	-	-	-	-	-	-	-	-	-	-	-	-	-
pulchra	-	-	-	-	-	-	-	-	-	-	-	-	-	-	X	X	X	-	-	-	-	-	-	-	-	-	-
rotundata	-	-	-	-	-	-	-	-	-	-	-	-	-	-	-	-	-	-	-	-	-	-	X	X	X	X	-
sapinea	-	-	-	-	-	-	-	-	-	-	-	-	-	-	X	-	-	-	-	-	-	-	-	-	-	-	-
setulosa	-	-	-	-	-	-	-	-	-	-	-	-	-	-	-	-	-	-	-	-	-	-	-	-	-	-	-
Parenteletes																											
cooperi REK	X	X	X	-	-	X	-	-	-	-	-	-	-	-	-	-	-	-	-	-	-	-	-	-	-	-	-
superbus	-	X	X	X	-	-	-	-	-	-	-	-	-	-	-	-	-	-	-	-	-	-	-	-	-	-	-
Paucispinifera																											
auriculata M-W&C	-	-	-	-	-	-	-	-	-	-	-	-	-	-	X	X	X	X	X	-	-	-	-	-	-	-	-
costellata	-	-	-	-	-	-	-	-	-	-	-	-	-	X	-	-	-	-	-	-	-	-	-	-	-	-	-
indentata (Girty)	-	-	-	-	-	-	-	-	-	-	-	-	-	-	-	-	-	-	-	-	-	-	X	-	-	-	-
intermedia	-	-	-	-	-	-	-	-	-	-	-	-	-	-	X	X	-	X	-	-	-	-	-	X	X	X	X
latidorsata (Girty)	-	-	-	-	-	-	-	-	-	-	-	-	-	-	X	X	-	-	-	-	-	-	-	-	-	-	-
magnispina	-	-	-	-	-	-	-	-	-	-	-	-	-	X	-	-	-	-	-	-	-	-	-	-	-	-	-
parasulcata	-	-	-	-	-	-	-	-	-	-	-	-	-	-	X	X	X	X	-	-	-	-	-	-	-	-	-
quadrata	-	-	-	-	-	-	-	-	-	-	-	-	-	-	-	-	-	-	-	-	-	-	-	X	-	-	-
rara	-	-	-	-	-	-	-	-	-	-	-	-	-	-	X	-	-	-	-	-	-	-	-	-	-	-	-
rectangulata	-	-	-	-	-	-	-	-	-	-	-	-	-	-	-	-	-	-	-	-	-	-	X	X	-	-	-
spinosa	-	-	-	-	-	-	-	-	-	-	-	-	-	X	-	-	-	-	-	-	-	-	-	-	-	-	-
sulcata	-	-	-	-	-	-	-	-	-	-	-	-	-	-	-	-	-	-	-	-	-	-	-	-	X	-	-
suspecta	-	-	-	-	-	-	-	-	-	-	-	-	-	-	X	X	X	X	-	-	-	-	-	-	-	-	-
transversa	-	-	-	-	-	-	-	-	-	-	-	-	-	-	-	-	-	-	-	-	-	X	-	-	-	-	-
tumida	-	-	-	-	-	-	-	-	-	-	-	-	-	-	-	-	-	-	-	-	-	-	-	-	-	-	-
Peniculauris																											
costata	-	-	-	-	-	-	-	-	-	X	X	-	-	-	-	-	-	-	-	-	-	X	-	-	-	-	-
imitata	-	-	-	-	-	-	-	-	-	-	-	-	-	X	-	-	-	-	-	-	-	-	-	-	-	-	-
peniculifera	-	-	-	-	-	-	-	-	-	-	-	X	-	X	-	-	-	-	-	-	-	-	-	-	-	-	-
subcostata (REK)	-	-	-	-	-	-	-	-	-	-	-	-	-	X	-	-	-	-	-	-	-	-	-	-	-	-	-
transversa	-	-	-	-	-	-	-	-	-	-	-	-	-	-	-	-	-	-	-	-	-	-	-	-	-	-	-
sp. 1	-	-	-	X	X	X	X	X	-	-	-	-	-	X	-	-	-	-	-	-	-	-	-	-	-	-	-
Petasmaia																											
expansa C&G	-	-	-	-	-	-	-	-	-	-	-	-	-	X	-	-	-	-	-	-	-	-	-	-	-	-	-
sp. 1	-	-	-	-	-	-	-	-	-	-	-	-	-	X	-	-	-	-	-	-	-	-	-	-	-	-	-
Petasmatherus																											
depressus	-	-	-	-	-	-	-	-	-	-	-	-	-	X	-	-	-	-	-	-	-	-	-	-	-	-	-
mundus	-	-	-	-	-	-	-	-	-	X	-	X	-	X	-	-	-	-	-	-	-	-	-	-	-	-	-
nitidus	-	-	-	-	-	-	-	-	-	-	-	-	-	X	X	X	X	X	-	-	-	-	X	-	-	-	-
opulus C&G	-	-	-	-	-	-	-	-	-	-	-	-	-	X	-	-	-	-	-	-	-	-	-	-	-	-	-
pumilus	-	-	-	-	-	-	-	-	-	-	-	-	-	-	-	-	-	-	-	-	X	-	-	-	-	-	-
pusillus (Girty)	-	-	-	-	-	-	-	-	-	-	-	-	-	-	-	-	-	-	-	-	-	X	-	-	-	-	-
recticardinatus	-	-	-	-	-	-	-	-	-	-	-	-	-	-	-	-	-	-	-	-	-	-	-	-	-	-	-
Petrocrania																											
diabloensis	-	-	-	-	-	-	-	-	-	-	-	-	-	-	-	-	-	-	-	-	X	-	-	X	X	-	-
exasperata	-	-	-	-	-	-	-	-	-	-	-	-	-	-	-	-	-	-	-	-	-	-	-	X	X	-	-
septifera	-	-	-	-	-	-	-	-	-	-	-	-	-	-	X	X	-	-	-	-	-	X	-	-	-	-	-
teretis	-	-	-	-	-	-	-	-	-	-	-	-	-	-	-	-	-	-	-	-	-	-	-	-	-	-	-
Phrenophoria																											
anterocostata	-	-	-	-	-	-	-	-	-	-	-	-	X	-	-	-	-	-	-	-	-	-	-	-	-	-	-
bicostata	-	-	-	-	-	-	-	-	-	-	-	-	-	-	-	-	-	X	-	-	-	-	-	-	-	-	-
?compressa	-	-	-	-	-	-	-	-	-	-	-	-	-	-	X	-	-	-	-	-	-	-	-	-	-	-	-
corpulenta	-	-	-	-	-	-	-	-	-	-	-	-	-	-	-	-	-	-	-	-	X	-	-	-	-	-	-
depressa	-	-	-	-	-	X	-	-	-	-	-	-	-	-	-	-	-	-	-	-	X	-	-	-	-	-	-
incomitata	-	-	-	-	-	-	-	-	-	-	-	-	-	-	-	-	-	-	-	-	-	X	-	-	-	-	-
irregularis	-	-	-	-	-	-	-	-	-	-	-	-	-	-	-	-	-	-	-	-	-	-	-	-	-	-	-

GENUS AND SPECIES	Gaptank	Uddenites	Neal Ranch	Lenox Hills	Decie Ranch	Poplar Tank	Dugout Mtn.	Sullivan Peak	Skinner Ranch undivided	Hess	Taylor Ranch	Cathedral Mtn.	Wedin	Road Canyon	China Tank	Willis Ranch	Lens	Appel Ranch	Word undivided	Hueco	Bone Spring	Getaway	Hegler	Pinery	Rader	Lamar	Capitan
Phrenophoria (Cont'd.)																											
nesiotes	-	-	-	-	-	-	-	-	-	-	X	-	-	-	-	-	-	-	-	-	-	-	-	-	-	-	-
?nudumbona	-	-	-	-	-	-	-	-	-	-	-	-	-	-	X	-	-	-	-	-	-	-	-	-	-	-	-
pentagonalis	-	-	-	-	-	-	-	-	-	-	-	-	-	-	X	-	-	-	-	-	-	-	-	-	-	-	-
perplexa	-	-	-	-	-	-	-	-	-	-	-	-	-	-	-	-	-	-	-	-	-	-	-	-	-	-	-
pinguiformis	-	-	-	-	-	-	-	-	-	-	-	-	-	-	-	-	-	-	-	-	-	-	X	X	X	-	-
pinguis (Girty)	-	-	-	-	-	-	-	-	-	-	-	-	-	-	-	-	-	-	-	-	-	-	X	X	-	-	X
planifrons	-	-	-	-	-	-	-	-	-	-	X	-	-	-	-	-	-	-	-	-	-	-	-	-	-	-	X
planiventra	-	-	-	-	-	-	-	-	-	-	-	-	-	-	X	-	-	-	-	-	-	-	-	-	-	-	-
repugnans	-	-	-	-	-	-	-	X	-	-	-	-	-	-	-	-	-	-	-	X	-	-	-	-	-	-	-
subcarinata C&G	-	-	-	-	-	-	-	-	-	-	-	-	-	-	X	X	X	X	-	-	-	-	-	-	-	-	-
ventricosa	-	-	-	-	-	-	-	-	-	-	-	-	-	-	X	-	-	-	-	-	-	-	-	-	-	-	-
vetula	-	-	-	-	-	-	-	-	-	-	X	-	-	-	-	-	-	-	-	-	-	-	-	-	-	-	-
Plectelasma																											
dubium	-	-	-	-	-	-	-	-	-	-	-	-	-	-	X	-	-	-	-	-	-	-	-	-	-	-	-
guadalupense (Girty)	-	-	-	-	-	-	-	-	-	-	-	-	-	-	-	-	-	-	-	-	-	-	X	X	X	X	X
kingi C&G	-	-	-	-	-	X	-	X	X	X	-	-	-	-	-	-	-	-	-	-	-	-	-	-	-	-	-
nitidum	-	-	-	-	-	-	-	-	-	-	-	-	-	-	-	-	-	-	-	-	-	X	-	-	-	-	-
planidorsatum	-	-	-	-	-	-	-	-	-	-	-	-	-	-	-	-	-	-	-	-	-	-	-	X	-	-	X
Pleurelasma																											
costatum	-	-	-	-	-	-	-	-	-	-	-	-	-	-	-	-	-	-	-	-	-	-	-	-	-	-	X
Poikilosakos																											
informis	-	-	-	-	-	-	-	-	X	-	-	-	-	-	-	-	-	-	-	-	X	-	-	-	-	-	-
Polymorpharia																											
polymorpha	-	-	-	-	-	-	-	-	-	-	-	-	-	-	-	X	-	-	-	-	X	-	-	-	-	-	-
Pontisia																											
costata	-	-	-	-	-	-	-	X	-	-	-	-	-	-	-	-	-	-	-	-	-	-	-	-	-	-	-
franklinensis	-	-	-	-	-	-	-	-	-	-	-	-	-	-	-	-	-	-	X	-	-	-	-	-	-	-	-
kingi	-	X	X	X	-	-	-	-	-	-	-	-	-	-	-	-	-	-	-	-	-	-	-	-	-	-	-
longicosta (Stehli)	-	-	-	-	-	-	-	-	-	-	-	-	-	-	-	-	-	-	-	-	-	X	-	-	-	-	-
magnicostata	-	-	X	-	-	-	-	-	-	-	-	-	-	-	-	-	-	-	-	-	-	-	-	-	-	-	-
nanas (Stehli)	-	-	-	-	-	-	-	X	X	-	X	-	-	-	-	-	-	-	-	-	-	X	-	-	-	-	-
parva	-	-	X	-	-	-	-	-	-	-	-	-	-	-	-	-	-	-	-	-	-	-	-	-	-	-	-
stehlii stehlii C&G	-	-	-	-	-	-	-	X	-	-	X	-	-	X	-	X	-	-	-	-	-	-	-	-	-	-	-
s. tumidosa	-	-	-	-	-	-	-	-	-	-	X	-	-	X	-	-	-	-	-	-	-	-	-	-	-	-	-
truncata	-	-	-	-	-	-	-	-	-	-	-	-	-	X	-	-	-	-	-	-	-	-	-	-	-	-	-
ventricola	-	-	-	-	-	-	-	-	-	X	-	-	-	-	-	-	-	-	-	-	-	-	-	-	-	-	-
wolfcampensis	-	X	-	-	-	-	-	-	-	-	-	-	-	-	-	-	-	-	-	-	-	-	-	-	-	-	-
Pseudodielasma																											
brilli	-	-	-	-	-	-	-	-	-	-	-	-	-	-	-	-	-	-	-	-	-	-	X	X	-	-	-
gibberum	-	-	-	-	-	-	-	-	-	-	-	-	-	-	X	-	-	-	-	-	-	-	-	-	-	-	-
globulum	-	-	-	-	-	-	-	-	-	-	-	-	-	-	-	-	-	-	X	-	-	-	-	-	-	-	-
lobatum	-	-	-	-	-	-	-	-	-	-	-	-	-	X	X	-	-	-	-	-	-	-	-	-	-	-	-
magnum	-	-	-	-	-	-	-	-	-	-	-	-	-	X	X	-	-	-	-	-	-	X	-	-	-	-	-
minor (REK)	-	-	-	-	-	-	-	-	-	-	-	-	-	X	X	-	-	-	-	-	-	-	-	-	-	-	-
ovatum	-	-	-	-	-	-	-	-	-	-	-	-	-	-	X	X	X	-	-	-	-	-	-	-	-	-	-
pingue	-	-	-	-	-	-	-	-	-	-	-	-	-	X	X	-	-	-	-	-	-	-	-	-	-	-	-
pinyonense	-	-	-	-	-	-	-	-	-	-	-	-	-	-	-	-	-	-	-	-	-	-	X	X	-	X	-
plicatum	-	-	-	-	-	-	-	-	-	-	-	-	-	X	X	-	-	-	-	-	-	-	-	-	-	-	-
scutulatum (Girty)	-	-	-	-	-	-	-	-	-	-	-	-	-	-	-	-	-	-	-	-	-	-	-	-	-	-	X
subcirculare	-	-	-	-	-	-	-	-	-	-	-	-	-	X	X	-	-	-	-	-	-	-	-	-	-	-	-
sulcatum	-	-	-	-	-	-	-	-	-	-	-	-	-	-	X	-	-	-	-	-	-	-	-	-	-	-	-
Pseudoleptodus																											
annosus	-	-	-	-	-	-	-	-	-	-	-	-	-	-	X	-	-	-	-	-	-	X	-	-	-	-	-
conicus	-	-	X	-	-	-	-	-	-	-	-	-	-	-	-	-	-	-	-	-	-	-	-	-	-	-	-
cucullatus	-	-	-	-	-	-	-	-	-	-	X	-	-	-	-	-	-	-	-	-	-	-	-	-	-	-	-
getawayensis Stehli	-	-	-	-	-	-	-	-	-	-	-	-	-	-	-	-	-	-	-	-	-	X	-	-	-	-	-
?giganteus	-	-	-	-	-	-	-	-	-	-	-	-	-	X	-	-	-	-	-	-	-	-	-	-	-	-	-
grandis	-	-	-	-	-	-	-	-	-	-	-	-	-	-	-	X	X	-	-	-	-	-	-	-	-	-	-
granulosus	-	-	-	-	-	-	-	-	-	-	-	-	-	-	-	-	-	-	X	-	-	-	-	-	-	-	-
guadalupensis (Stehli)	-	-	-	-	-	-	-	-	-	-	-	-	-	-	-	-	-	-	-	-	-	-	X	X	X	X	X
lepidus	-	-	-	-	-	-	-	-	-	-	-	-	-	-	-	-	X	-	-	-	-	-	-	-	-	-	-
nodosus	-	-	-	-	-	-	-	-	-	-	-	-	-	X	-	-	-	-	-	-	-	-	-	-	-	-	-
primitivus	-	-	X	-	-	-	-	-	-	-	-	-	-	-	-	-	-	-	-	-	-	-	-	-	-	-	-
Psilocamara																											
hesperia	-	-	X	-	-	-	-	-	-	-	-	-	-	-	-	-	-	-	-	-	-	-	-	-	-	-	-

GENUS AND SPECIES	Gaptank	Uddenites	Neal Ranch	Lenox Hills	Decie Ranch	Poplar Tank	Dugout Mtn.	Sullivan Peak	Skinner Ranch undivided	Hess	Taylor Ranch	Cathedral Mtn.	Wedin	Road Canyon	China Tank	Willis Ranch	Lens	Appel Ranch	Word undivided	Hueco	Bone Spring	Getaway	Hegler	Pinery	Rader	Lamar	Capitan
Ptilotorhynchus																											
delicatum	-	-	-	-	-	-	-	-	-	-	-	-	-	-	-	-	-	-	-	-	-	X	X	X	X	X	X
Ptygmactrum																											
acutum	-	-	-	-	-	-	-	-	-	-	-	-	-	X	-	-	-	-	-	-	-	-	-	-	-	-	-
angulatum	-	-	-	-	-	-	-	-	-	-	-	X	-	X	-	-	-	-	-	-	-	-	-	-	-	-	-
depressum	-	-	-	-	-	-	-	-	-	-	-	-	-	X	-	-	-	-	-	-	-	-	-	-	-	-	-
extensum	-	-	-	-	-	-	-	-	-	-	-	-	-	X	-	-	-	-	-	-	-	-	-	-	-	-	-
mordicum	-	-	-	-	-	-	-	-	-	-	-	X	-	X	-	-	-	-	-	-	-	-	-	-	-	-	-
spiculatum	-	-	-	-	-	-	-	-	-	-	-	-	-	-	-	X	-	-	-	-	-	X	-	-	-	-	-
Quadrochonetes																											
girtyi Stehli	-	-	-	-	-	-	-	-	-	-	-	-	-	-	-	-	-	-	-	-	X	-	-	-	-	-	-
praecursor	-	-	-	-	-	-	-	-	-	-	-	-	-	-	-	-	-	-	-	-	X	-	-	-	-	-	-
Rallacosta																											
actina	-	-	-	-	-	-	-	-	-	-	-	X	-	-	-	-	-	-	-	-	-	-	-	-	-	-	-
imporcata	-	-	-	-	-	-	-	-	-	-	-	-	-	-	-	-	-	-	-	-	-	-	X	X	X	-	-
laminata	-	-	-	-	-	-	-	-	-	-	-	X	-	-	-	-	-	-	-	-	-	-	-	-	-	-	-
xystica	-	-	-	-	-	-	-	-	-	-	-	X	-	-	-	-	-	-	-	-	-	-	-	-	-	-	-
sp. 1	-	-	-	-	-	-	-	-	-	-	-	-	-	-	-	-	-	-	-	-	-	-	X	-	-	-	-
sp. 2	-	-	-	-	-	-	-	-	-	-	-	-	-	-	-	-	-	-	-	-	X	-	-	-	-	-	-
Ramavectus																											
diabloensis Stehli	-	-	-	-	-	-	-	-	-	-	-	-	-	-	-	-	-	-	-	-	X	-	-	-	-	-	-
Reticulariina																											
cerina	-	-	-	-	-	-	-	-	-	-	-	-	-	-	X	X	X	X	X	-	-	-	-	-	-	-	-
craticula	-	-	-	-	-	-	-	-	-	-	-	-	-	-	-	-	-	-	-	-	-	-	X	X	X	-	-
echinata	-	-	-	-	-	-	-	-	-	-	-	-	-	-	-	-	-	-	-	-	-	-	X	-	-	-	-
girtyi	-	-	-	-	-	-	-	-	-	-	-	-	-	-	-	-	-	-	-	-	-	X	-	-	-	-	-
hueconiana	-	-	-	-	-	-	-	-	-	-	-	-	-	-	-	-	-	-	-	X	-	-	-	-	-	-	-
impressa	-	-	-	-	-	-	X	-	-	-	-	-	-	-	-	-	-	-	-	-	-	-	-	-	-	-	-
laxa (Girty)	-	-	-	-	-	-	-	-	-	-	-	-	-	-	-	-	-	-	-	-	-	-	X	X	X	X	-
newelli (Stehli)	-	-	-	-	-	-	-	-	-	-	-	-	-	-	-	-	-	-	-	X	-	-	X	-	X	-	-
phoxa	-	-	-	-	-	-	-	-	-	-	-	-	-	-	-	-	-	-	-	X	-	-	-	-	-	-	-
powwowensis	-	-	-	-	-	-	-	-	-	-	-	-	-	-	X	-	-	-	-	-	-	-	-	-	-	-	-
pristina	-	-	-	-	-	-	-	-	X	X	-	-	-	-	-	-	-	-	-	-	-	-	-	-	-	-	-
pusilla	-	-	-	-	-	-	-	-	-	-	-	-	-	-	-	-	-	-	-	-	-	-	X	-	-	-	-
roscida	-	-	-	-	-	-	-	-	-	-	-	-	-	-	X	X	X	-	-	-	-	-	-	-	-	-	-
senticosa	-	-	-	-	-	-	-	-	-	-	-	-	-	-	X	X	X	-	-	-	-	-	-	-	-	-	-
strigosa	-	-	X	-	-	-	-	-	-	-	-	-	-	-	-	-	-	-	-	-	-	-	-	-	-	-	-
subulata	-	-	-	-	-	-	-	-	-	-	-	-	-	X	X	-	-	-	-	-	-	-	-	-	-	-	-
tetrica	-	-	-	X	-	-	X	X	-	-	-	-	-	-	-	-	-	-	-	-	X	-	-	-	-	-	-
venustula	-	-	-	-	-	-	-	-	-	-	-	X	-	X	-	-	-	-	-	-	-	-	X	X	X	X	-
welleri (Girty)	-	-	-	-	-	-	-	-	-	-	-	-	-	-	-	-	-	-	-	-	-	-	X	X	X	X	-
Reticulatia																											
americana (D&C)	-	-	X	-	-	-	-	-	-	-	-	-	-	-	-	-	-	-	-	-	-	-	-	-	-	-	-
huecoensis (REK)	X?	-	X	X	-	-	-	-	-	-	-	-	-	-	-	-	-	-	-	X	-	-	-	-	-	-	-
robusta	-	-	X	X	-	-	-	-	-	-	-	-	-	-	-	-	-	-	-	-	-	-	-	-	-	-	-
sp. 1	-	-	X	-	-	-	-	-	-	-	-	-	-	-	-	-	-	-	-	-	-	-	-	-	-	-	-
sp. 2	-	X	-	-	-	-	-	-	-	-	-	-	-	-	-	-	-	-	-	-	-	-	-	-	-	-	-
Rhamnaria																											
eximia	-	-	-	-	-	-	-	-	-	-	-	-	-	-	-	-	-	-	-	-	X	-	-	-	-	-	-
grandis	-	-	-	-	X	X	X	X	X	-	-	-	-	-	-	-	-	-	-	-	-	-	-	-	-	-	-
kingorum M-W&C	-	-	-	-	-	-	-	-	-	-	-	-	-	-	X	X	X	X	X	-	-	-	-	-	-	-	-
k. delicata	-	-	-	-	-	-	-	-	-	-	-	-	-	-	X	X	X	-	X	-	-	-	-	-	-	-	-
leonardensis (REK)	-	-	-	-	-	-	-	-	-	-	-	-	X	-	X	-	-	-	-	-	-	-	-	-	-	-	-
rectangulata	-	-	-	-	-	-	-	-	-	-	-	-	-	-	-	-	-	-	-	-	-	-	-	X	X	X	X
shumardi	-	-	-	-	-	-	-	-	-	-	-	-	-	-	-	-	-	-	-	-	-	-	X	-	-	-	-
sulcata	-	-	-	-	-	-	-	-	-	-	-	-	X	X	X	-	X	-	-	-	-	-	-	-	-	-	-
tenuispinosa	-	-	-	-	-	-	-	-	-	-	-	-	X	-	X	-	X	-	-	-	-	-	-	-	-	-	-
vinnula	-	-	-	-	-	-	-	-	-	-	-	-	X	-	X	-	-	-	-	-	-	-	-	-	-	-	-
Rhipidomella																											
hessensis REK	-	-	-	-	X	X	X	X	X	X	X	-	-	-	-	-	-	-	-	-	X	X	-	-	-	-	-
hispidula	-	-	-	-	-	-	-	-	-	-	-	-	X	X	X	-	-	-	-	-	-	X	-	-	-	-	-
miscella	-	-	X	X	-	-	-	-	-	-	-	-	-	-	-	-	-	-	-	-	-	-	-	-	-	-	-
Rhynchopora																											
dossena	X	-	-	-	-	-	-	-	-	-	-	-	-	-	-	-	-	-	-	-	-	-	-	-	-	-	-

GENUS AND SPECIES	Gaptank	Uddenites	Neal Ranch	Lenox Hills	Decie Ranch	Poplar Tank	Dugout Mtn.	Sullivan Peak	Skinner Ranch undivided	Hess	Taylor Ranch	Cathedral Mtn.	Wedin	Road Canyon	China Tank	Willis Ranch	Lens	Appel Ranch	Word undivided	Hueco	Bone Spring	Getaway	Hegler	Pinery	Rader	Lamar	Capitan
Rhynchopora (Cont'd.)																											
guadalupensis	-	-	-	-	-	-	-	-	-	-	-	-	-	-	-	-	-	-	-	-	-	X	-	-	-	-	-
hebetata	-	-	-	-	-	-	-	-	-	-	X	X	X	-	-	-	-	-	-	-	-	-	-	-	-	-	-
molina	-	X	X	X	-	-	-	-	-	-	-	-	-	-	-	-	-	-	-	-	-	-	-	-	-	-	-
palumbula	-	-	-	-	-	-	-	-	-	-	-	-	-	-	X	X	X	X	X	-	-	-	-	-	-	-	-
patula	-	-	-	-	X	-	-	-	-	-	-	-	-	-	-	-	-	-	-	-	-	X	-	-	-	-	-
sphenoides	-	-	-	-	-	-	-	-	-	-	-	-	-	X	-	-	-	-	-	-	-	-	-	-	-	-	-
tenera	-	-	-	-	-	-	-	-	-	-	-	-	-	-	-	X	X	-	-	-	-	-	-	-	-	-	-
sp. B	-	-	-	-	-	-	-	-	-	-	-	-	-	-	-	-	-	-	-	-	-	-	-	-	-	X	-
Rhytisia																											
rugosa	-	-	-	-	-	-	-	-	-	-	X	-	X	-	-	-	-	-	-	-	-	-	-	-	-	-	-
Rigbyella																											
girtyi (W&S)	-	-	-	-	-	-	-	-	-	-	-	-	-	-	-	-	-	-	-	-	-	-	X	-	X	-	-
Roemerella																											
gigantissima	-	-	-	-	-	-	-	-	-	-	-	X	-	-	-	-	-	-	-	-	-	-	-	-	-	-	-
Rugaria																											
crassa	-	-	-	-	X	-	X	X	-	-	-	-	-	-	-	-	-	-	-	-	-	-	-	-	-	-	-
hessensis (REK)	-	-	-	-	-	-	-	-	-	-	X	X	-	-	-	-	-	-	-	-	-	-	-	-	-	-	-
Rugatia																											
convexa	-	-	-	-	-	-	-	-	-	-	-	-	-	X	-	-	-	-	-	-	-	-	-	-	-	-	-
incurvata (REK)	-	-	-	-	-	-	-	-	-	-	-	-	-	X	-	-	-	-	-	-	-	-	-	-	-	-	-
mckeei	-	-	-	-	-	-	-	-	-	-	-	-	-	X	-	-	-	-	-	-	-	-	-	-	-	-	-
occidentalis parvauris	-	-	-	-	-	-	-	-	-	-	X	-	X	-	-	-	-	-	-	-	-	-	-	-	-	-	-
paraindica (McKee)	-	-	-	-	-	-	-	-	-	-	X	X	X	-	-	-	-	-	-	-	X	-	-	-	-	-	-
Sarganostega																											
murata	-	-	-	-	-	-	-	-	-	-	-	-	-	-	-	-	-	-	-	-	-	X	-	-	-	-	-
pressa	-	-	-	-	-	-	-	-	-	-	-	-	-	-	-	-	-	-	-	-	-	-	X	X	X	X	X
prisca	-	-	-	-	-	-	-	-	-	-	-	-	-	-	-	-	-	-	X	-	-	-	-	-	-	-	-
pyramidalis (Girty)	-	-	-	-	-	-	-	-	-	-	-	-	-	-	-	-	-	-	-	-	-	-	-	-	-	-	X
transversalis C&G	-	-	-	-	-	-	-	-	-	-	-	-	-	-	-	-	-	-	-	-	-	X	X	X	X	X	-
Scacchinella																											
americana Stehli	-	-	-	-	-	-	-	-	-	-	-	-	-	-	-	-	-	-	-	-	-	X	-	-	-	-	-
exasperata	-	-	-	X	-	-	-	-	-	-	-	-	-	-	-	-	-	-	X	-	-	-	-	-	-	-	-
primitiva	X	-	-	-	-	-	-	-	-	-	-	-	-	-	-	-	-	-	-	-	-	-	-	-	-	-	-
titan	-	-	-	-	X	X	-	X	X	X	X	-	-	-	-	-	-	-	-	-	-	-	-	-	-	-	-
triangulata	-	X	-	-	-	-	-	-	-	-	-	-	-	-	-	-	-	-	-	-	-	-	-	-	-	-	-
Scapharina																											
levis	-	-	-	-	-	-	-	-	-	-	-	-	-	-	-	-	-	-	-	-	-	-	X	X	X	X	X
quadrata	-	-	-	-	-	-	-	-	-	-	-	-	-	-	-	-	-	-	-	-	-	X	-	-	-	-	-
rugosa	-	-	-	-	-	-	-	-	-	-	-	-	-	-	-	-	-	-	-	-	-	-	X	X	X	X	X
Sceletonia																											
crassa	-	-	-	-	-	-	X	X	-	-	-	-	-	-	-	-	-	-	-	-	X	-	-	-	-	-	-
Scenesia																											
extensa	-	-	-	-	-	-	-	-	-	-	-	X	-	-	-	-	-	-	-	-	-	-	-	-	-	-	-
Schuchertella																											
?subvexa	-	-	X	-	-	-	-	-	-	-	-	-	-	-	-	-	-	-	-	-	-	-	-	-	-	-	-
Sestropoma																											
cribriferum C&G	-	-	-	-	-	-	-	-	-	-	-	-	-	-	-	-	-	-	-	-	-	X	X	X	X	X	X
Simplicarina																											
incompta	-	-	-	-	-	-	-	-	-	-	-	-	-	X	-	-	-	-	-	-	-	-	-	-	-	-	-
Siphonosia																											
alleni	-	-	-	-	-	-	-	-	-	-	-	X	-	-	-	-	-	-	-	-	-	-	-	-	-	-	-
Spinarella																											
costellata	-	-	-	-	-	-	-	-	-	-	-	-	-	X	-	-	-	-	-	-	-	-	-	-	-	-	-
lobata	-	-	-	-	-	-	-	-	-	-	-	-	-	X	-	-	-	-	-	-	-	-	-	-	-	-	-
paulula	-	-	-	-	-	-	-	-	-	-	-	-	-	X	-	-	-	-	-	-	-	-	-	-	-	-	-
perfecta	-	-	-	-	-	-	-	-	-	-	-	-	-	X	-	-	-	-	-	-	-	-	-	-	-	-	-

GENUS AND SPECIES	Gaptank	Uddenites	Neal Ranch	Lenox Hills	Decie Ranch	Poplar Tank	Dugout Mtn.	Sullivan Peak	Skinner Ranch undivided	Hess	Taylor Ranch	Cathedral Mtn.	Wedin	Road Canyon	China Tank	Willis Ranch	Lens	Appel Ranch	Word undivided	Hueco	Bone Spring	Getaway	Hegler	Pinery	Rader	Lamar	Capitan
Spinifrons																											
delicatula	-	-	-	-	-	-	-	-	X	-	-	-	-	-	-	-	-	-	-	-	X	-	-	-	-	-	-
magna	-	-	-	-	-	-	-	-	-	-	-	-	-	-	-	-	-	-	-	-	X	-	-	-	-	-	-
quadrata Stehli	-	-	-	-	-	-	-	-	-	-	-	-	-	-	-	-	-	-	-	-	X	-	-	-	-	-	-
Spiriferella																											
calcarata	-	-	-	-	-	-	-	-	-	-	-	-	-	-	X	X	-	-	-	-	-	X	-	-	-	-	-
clypeata	-	-	-	-	-	-	-	-	-	-	-	-	-	-	-	-	X	X	-	-	-	-	-	-	-	-	-
embrithes	-	-	-	-	-	-	-	-	-	-	-	-	-	-	X	-	-	-	-	-	-	-	-	-	-	-	-
gloverae	-	-	-	-	-	-	-	-	-	-	-	-	-	-	-	-	-	-	-	-	-	X	-	-	-	-	-
gravis	-	-	-	-	-	-	-	-	-	-	-	-	-	-	X	X	X	-	-	-	-	-	-	-	-	-	-
levis	-	-	-	-	-	-	-	-	-	-	-	-	-	-	-	-	X	-	-	-	-	-	-	-	-	-	-
propria	-	-	-	-	-	-	-	-	-	-	-	-	-	-	-	-	-	X	-	-	-	-	-	-	-	-	-
sulcifer (Shumard)	-	-	-	-	-	-	-	-	-	-	-	-	-	-	-	-	-	-	-	-	-	-	X	X	X	X	-
Spiriferellina																											
hilli (Girty)	-	-	-	-	-	-	-	-	-	-	-	-	-	-	X	X	X	X	X	-	-	-	-	-	-	-	-
nasuta	-	-	X	-	-	-	-	-	-	-	-	-	-	-	-	-	-	-	-	-	-	-	-	-	-	-	-
nuda	-	-	-	-	-	-	-	-	-	-	-	-	-	-	-	-	-	-	-	-	-	-	X	X	X	X	-
paucicostata	-	-	-	-	-	-	-	-	-	-	-	-	-	-	-	-	X	X	-	-	-	-	-	-	-	-	-
tricosa	-	-	-	-	-	-	-	-	-	-	-	X	X	X	-	-	-	-	-	-	-	-	-	-	-	-	-
vescula	-	-	-	-	-	-	-	-	-	-	-	-	-	X	-	-	-	-	-	-	-	-	-	-	-	-	-
Spiriferinaella																											
limata	-	-	-	-	-	-	-	-	-	-	-	-	-	-	X	X	-	-	-	-	-	-	-	-	-	-	-
medialis	-	-	-	-	-	-	-	-	-	-	-	-	-	-	-	-	-	-	-	-	-	X	-	-	-	-	-
scalpata	-	-	-	-	-	-	-	-	-	-	-	-	-	-	-	X	X	X	-	-	-	-	-	-	-	-	-
sp.	-	-	-	-	-	-	-	-	-	-	-	-	-	-	X	-	X	-	X	-	-	-	-	-	-	-	-
Spuriosa																											
circularis	-	-	X	-	-	-	-	-	-	-	-	-	-	-	-	-	-	-	-	X	-	-	-	-	-	-	-
Spyridiophora																											
compacta	-	-	-	X	-	-	-	-	-	-	-	-	-	-	-	-	-	-	-	-	-	-	-	-	-	-	-
distincta C&S	-	-	X	-	-	-	-	-	-	-	-	-	-	-	-	-	-	-	-	-	-	-	-	-	-	-	-
reticulata (REK)	-	-	-	-	X	X	X	X	X	X	X	X	-	-	-	-	-	-	-	-	X	-	-	-	-	-	-
sp.	-	-	-	X	-	-	-	-	-	-	-	-	-	-	-	-	-	-	-	-	-	-	-	-	-	-	-
Stenoscisma																											
abbreviatum	-	-	-	-	-	-	-	-	-	-	-	-	-	-	-	-	-	-	-	-	-	-	-	-	-	X	-
aberrans	-	-	-	-	-	-	-	-	-	-	-	-	-	-	-	-	-	-	-	-	-	X	X	-	X	-	-
amoenum	-	-	-	X	-	-	-	-	-	-	-	-	-	-	-	-	-	-	-	-	-	-	-	-	-	-	-
aptatum	-	-	-	-	-	-	-	-	-	-	-	X	-	X	-	-	-	-	-	-	-	-	-	-	-	-	-
bellatulum	-	-	X	X	-	-	-	X	-	-	-	-	-	-	-	-	-	-	-	-	-	-	-	-	-	-	-
bonum	-	-	-	-	-	-	-	-	-	-	-	-	-	X	-	-	-	-	-	-	-	-	-	-	-	-	-
calvatum	-	-	-	-	-	-	-	-	-	-	-	X	-	X	-	-	-	-	-	-	-	-	-	-	-	-	-
camurum	-	-	-	-	-	-	-	-	-	-	-	-	-	X	-	-	-	-	-	-	-	X	-	-	-	-	-
doricranum	-	-	-	-	-	-	-	X	-	X	X	-	-	-	-	-	-	-	-	-	-	-	-	-	-	-	-
exutum	-	-	-	-	-	-	-	-	-	X	X	-	-	-	-	-	-	-	-	-	-	-	-	-	-	-	-
fabarium	-	-	-	-	-	-	-	-	-	X	-	-	-	-	-	-	-	-	-	-	-	-	-	-	-	-	-
hadrum	-	-	-	X	X	-	-	X	X	X	X	-	-	-	-	-	-	-	-	-	-	-	-	-	-	-	-
hueconianum (Girty)	-	-	-	-	-	-	-	-	-	-	-	-	-	-	-	-	-	-	-	X	-	-	-	-	-	-	-
inaequale (Girty)	-	-	-	-	-	-	-	-	-	-	-	-	-	-	-	-	-	-	-	-	-	X	-	-	-	-	-
kalum Stehli	-	-	-	-	-	-	-	-	-	-	-	-	-	-	-	-	-	-	-	-	-	X	-	-	-	-	-
levicostum	-	-	-	-	-	-	-	-	-	-	-	-	-	-	-	-	-	-	-	-	-	X	-	-	-	-	-
maniculum	-	-	-	-	-	-	-	-	-	-	-	-	-	X	-	-	-	-	-	-	-	-	-	-	-	-	-
multicostum Stehli	-	-	-	-	-	-	X	-	-	-	-	-	-	-	-	-	-	-	-	-	-	X	-	-	-	-	-
myioides	-	-	-	-	-	-	X	-	-	-	-	-	-	-	-	-	-	-	-	-	-	-	-	-	-	-	-
oblisum	-	-	-	-	-	-	-	-	-	-	-	-	-	-	-	-	-	-	-	-	-	-	-	-	-	-	X
pansum	-	-	-	-	X	X	-	X	-	-	-	-	-	-	-	-	-	-	-	-	-	-	-	-	-	-	-
peneleve	-	-	-	X	-	-	-	-	-	-	-	-	-	-	-	-	-	-	-	-	-	-	-	-	-	-	-
problematicum	-	-	X	X	-	-	X	X	-	-	-	-	-	-	-	-	-	-	-	-	-	-	-	-	-	-	-
pyraustoides	-	-	-	X	-	-	-	X	-	-	X	-	-	-	-	-	-	-	-	-	-	-	-	-	-	-	-
renode	-	-	-	-	-	-	-	-	-	-	-	-	-	-	X	X	X	X	X	-	-	X	-	-	-	-	-
repigratum	-	-	-	-	-	-	-	-	-	-	-	-	-	-	X	-	-	-	-	-	-	X	-	-	-	-	-
trabeatum	-	-	-	-	-	-	-	-	-	-	-	-	-	-	-	-	-	-	-	-	-	-	-	-	X	X	X
triquetrum	-	-	-	-	-	-	-	-	-	-	-	X	X	X	-	-	-	-	-	-	-	-	-	-	-	-	-
Striatifera																											
linoproductiformis	-	-	X	X	-	-	-	-	-	-	-	-	-	-	-	-	-	-	-	-	-	-	-	-	-	-	-
Strigirhynchia																											
elongata	-	-	-	-	-	-	-	-	-	-	-	-	-	-	-	-	-	-	-	-	-	-	-	-	-	X	-

GENUS AND SPECIES	Gaptank	Uddenites	Neal Ranch	Lenox Hills	Decie Ranch	Poplar Tank	Dugout Mtn.	Sullivan Peak	Skinner Ranch undivided	Hess	Taylor Ranch	Cathedral Mtn.	Wedin	Road Canyon	China Tank	Willis Ranch	Lens	Appel Ranch	Word undivided	Hueco	Bone Spring	Getaway	Hegler	Pinery	Rader	Lamar	Capitan
Strigirhynchia (Cont'd.)																											
indentata (Shumard)	-	-	-	-	-	-	-	-	-	-	-	-	-	-	-	-	-	-	-	-	-	-	-	-	X	X	X
transversa	-	-	-	-	-	-	-	-	-	-	-	-	-	-	-	-	-	-	-	-	-	-	-	-	-	-	X
Strophalosia																											
inexpectans	-	-	-	-	-	-	-	-	-	-	-	-	-	-	-	-	-	-	-	-	-	X	-	-	-	-	-
Sulcataria																											
?compacta	-	-	X	-	-	-	-	-	-	-	-	-	-	-	-	-	-	-	-	-	-	-	-	-	-	-	-
latisulcata	-	-	X	-	-	-	-	-	-	-	-	-	-	-	-	-	-	-	-	-	-	-	-	-	-	-	-
sp.	-	X	-	X	-	-	-	-	-	-	-	-	-	-	-	-	-	-	-	-	-	-	-	-	-	-	-
Taphrosestria																											
expansa	-	-	-	-	-	-	-	-	-	-	-	-	-	X	-	-	-	-	-	-	-	-	-	-	-	-	-
peculiaris	-	-	-	-	-	-	-	-	-	-	-	-	-	X	-	-	-	-	-	-	-	-	-	-	-	-	-
?sp.	-	-	-	-	-	-	-	-	-	-	-	X	-	-	-	-	-	-	-	-	-	-	-	-	-	-	-
Tautosia																											
angulata	-	-	-	-	-	-	-	-	-	-	-	-	-	X	-	-	-	-	-	-	-	-	-	-	-	-	-
distorta	-	-	-	-	-	-	-	-	-	-	-	-	-	-	X	-	-	-	-	-	-	-	-	-	-	-	-
elegans (Girty)	-	-	-	-	-	-	-	-	-	-	-	-	-	-	-	-	-	-	-	-	-	-	-	X	X	X	X
fastigiata C&G	-	-	-	-	-	X	-	-	-	-	-	X	-	-	-	-	-	-	-	-	-	-	-	-	-	-	-
galbina	-	-	-	-	-	-	-	-	-	-	-	X	-	-	-	-	-	-	-	-	-	-	-	-	-	-	-
lenumbona (Stehli)	-	-	-	-	-	-	-	-	-	-	-	-	-	-	-	-	-	-	-	X	-	-	-	-	-	-	-
magnisepta (Stehli)	-	-	-	-	-	-	-	-	-	-	-	-	-	-	-	-	-	-	-	X	-	-	-	-	-	-	-
podistra	-	-	-	X	-	-	-	X	X	-	-	-	-	-	-	-	-	-	-	-	-	-	-	-	-	-	-
pulchra	-	-	-	-	-	-	-	-	-	-	-	X	-	-	-	-	-	-	-	-	-	-	-	-	-	-	-
shumardiana (Girty)	-	-	-	-	-	-	-	-	-	-	-	-	-	-	-	-	-	-	-	-	-	-	-	X	X	X	X
transenna	-	-	-	-	-	-	-	-	-	-	-	-	-	X	X	X	X	-	-	-	X	-	-	-	-	-	-
Teguliferina																											
armata (Girty)	X	-	-	-	-	-	-	-	-	-	-	-	-	-	-	-	-	-	-	-	-	-	-	-	-	-	-
boesei REK	X	X	X	X	-	X	-	-	X	-	-	-	-	-	-	-	-	-	-	-	-	-	-	-	-	-	-
compacta	-	-	-	-	-	-	-	-	X	-	X	-	-	-	-	-	-	-	-	-	-	-	-	-	-	-	-
conida (Stehli)	-	-	-	-	X	-	-	X	X	-	-	-	-	-	-	-	-	-	-	-	-	X	-	-	-	-	-
solidispinosa	-	-	X	-	-	-	-	-	-	-	-	-	-	-	-	-	-	-	-	-	-	-	-	-	-	-	-
Texarina																											
elongata	-	-	-	-	-	-	-	-	-	-	-	-	-	X	X	X	X	X	-	-	-	X	-	-	-	-	-
oblongata C&G	-	-	-	-	-	-	-	-	-	-	-	-	-	-	X	X	-	-	-	-	-	-	-	-	-	-	-
parallela	-	-	-	-	-	-	-	-	-	-	-	-	-	-	X	-	-	-	-	-	-	-	-	-	-	-	-
paucula	-	-	-	-	-	-	-	-	-	-	-	X	-	-	-	-	-	-	-	-	-	-	-	-	-	-	-
solita	-	-	-	-	-	-	-	-	-	-	-	-	-	-	-	-	-	-	-	-	-	X	-	-	-	-	-
wordensis (REK)	-	-	-	-	-	-	-	-	-	-	-	-	-	X	X	X	-	-	-	-	-	-	-	-	-	-	-
Thammosia																											
anterospinosa C&G	-	-	-	-	-	-	-	-	-	-	-	X	-	-	-	-	-	-	-	-	-	-	-	-	-	-	-
capitanensis (Girty)	-	-	-	-	-	-	-	-	-	-	-	-	-	-	-	-	-	-	-	-	-	-	-	X	X	X	X
parvispinosa (Stehli)	-	-	-	X	-	-	-	-	X	-	-	-	-	-	-	-	-	-	-	X	-	-	-	-	-	-	-
phragmophora	-	-	-	-	-	-	-	-	-	-	-	-	-	-	X	-	X	X	-	-	-	-	-	-	-	-	-
silicica	-	-	-	-	-	-	-	-	-	X	X	-	-	-	-	-	-	-	-	-	-	-	-	-	-	-	-
Thedusia																											
angustata	-	-	-	-	-	-	-	-	-	-	-	-	-	-	-	-	-	-	-	-	-	-	-	X	X	-	-
biconvexa	-	-	-	-	-	-	-	-	-	-	-	-	-	-	-	-	-	-	-	-	-	-	-	-	X	-	-
bucrenata	-	-	-	-	-	-	-	-	-	-	-	X	-	-	-	-	-	-	-	-	-	-	-	-	-	-	-
dischides	-	-	-	-	-	-	-	-	-	-	-	-	-	-	-	-	-	-	-	-	-	-	X	-	-	-	-
discissa	-	-	-	-	-	-	-	-	-	-	-	X	-	-	-	-	-	-	-	-	-	-	-	-	-	-	-
emarginata	-	-	-	-	-	-	-	-	-	-	-	-	-	-	-	-	-	-	-	-	-	-	-	X	X	-	X
magna	-	-	-	-	-	-	-	-	-	-	-	-	-	-	-	-	-	-	-	-	-	-	X	-	-	-	-
mesocostata	-	-	-	-	-	-	-	-	-	-	-	-	-	-	X	-	-	-	-	-	-	-	-	-	-	-	-
paucicostata	-	-	-	-	-	-	-	-	-	-	-	X	-	-	-	-	-	-	-	-	-	-	-	-	-	-	-
procera	-	-	-	-	-	-	-	-	-	-	-	-	-	-	X	X	X	X	-	-	-	-	-	-	-	-	-
trigonalis (Girty)	-	-	-	-	-	-	-	-	-	-	-	-	-	-	-	-	-	-	-	-	-	-	-	X	X	X	X
ventricosa	-	-	-	-	-	-	-	-	-	-	-	-	-	-	-	-	-	-	-	-	-	-	-	X	X	X	X
Timorina																											
attenuata	-	-	-	-	-	-	-	-	-	-	-	-	-	-	-	-	-	-	-	-	-	-	-	X	X	-	X
ovata (Girty)	-	-	-	-	-	-	-	-	-	-	-	-	-	-	-	-	-	-	-	-	-	-	-	X	X	X	X
schuchertensis (Girty)	-	-	-	-	-	-	-	-	-	-	-	-	-	-	-	-	-	-	-	-	-	-	-	-	X	X	X
Torynechus																											
alectorius	-	-	-	-	-	-	X	X	X	-	-	-	-	-	-	-	-	-	-	-	-	-	-	-	-	-	-

GENUS AND SPECIES	Gaptank	Uddenites	Neal Ranch	Lenox Hills	Decie Ranch	Poplar Tank	Dugout Mtn.	Sullivan Peak	Skinner Ranch undivided	Hess	Taylor Ranch	Cathedral Mtn.	Wedin	Road Canyon	China Tank	Willis Ranch	Lens	Appel Ranch	Word undivided	Hueco	Bone Spring	Getaway	Hegler	Pinery	Rader	Lamar	Capitan
Torynechus (Cont'd.)																											
caelatus C&G	-	-	-	-	-	-	-	-	-	-	-	X	X	-	-	-	-	-	-	-	-	-	-	-	-	-	-
Tricoria																											
hirpex	-	-	-	-	X	-	-	-	X	-	-	-	-	-	-	-	-	-	-	-	-	-	-	-	-	-	-
Trophisina																											
fenaria	-	-	-	-	-	-	-	-	-	-	-	X	-	-	-	-	-	-	-	-	-	-	-	-	-	-	-
Tropidelasma																											
anthicum	-	-	-	-	-	-	-	-	-	-	-	-	-	-	X	X	X	X	-	-	-	-	-	-	-	-	-
corniculum	-	-	-	-	-	-	-	-	-	-	-	-	-	-	X	-	-	-	-	-	-	-	-	-	-	-	-
costellatum	-	-	-	-	-	-	-	-	X	-	X	-	-	-	-	-	-	-	-	-	-	-	-	-	-	-	-
culmenatum C&G	-	X	X	-	-	-	-	-	-	-	-	-	-	-	-	-	-	-	-	-	-	-	-	-	-	-	-
furcillatum	-	-	-	-	-	-	-	-	-	-	-	-	-	-	-	-	-	-	-	-	-	X	-	-	-	-	-
gregarium (Girty)	-	-	-	-	-	-	-	-	-	-	-	-	-	-	-	-	-	-	-	-	-	-	X	X	X	X	X
rhamphodes	-	-	-	-	X	-	-	X	X	-	-	-	-	-	-	-	-	-	-	-	-	-	-	-	-	-	-
robertsi	-	-	-	-	-	-	-	X	-	-	-	-	-	-	-	-	-	-	-	-	-	-	-	-	-	-	-
strobilum	X	-	-	X	-	-	-	-	-	-	-	-	-	-	-	-	-	-	-	-	-	-	-	-	-	-	-
undulatum (REK)	-	-	-	-	-	-	-	-	-	X?	-	-	-	-	-	-	-	-	-	-	-	-	-	-	-	-	-
sp.	-	X	X	-	-	-	-	X	X	-	X	-	-	-	-	-	X	-	-	-	-	X	-	-	X	-	-
Tschernyschewia																											
americana	-	-	-	-	-	-	-	-	-	-	-	-	-	-	-	-	-	-	-	-	X	-	-	-	-	-	-
inexpectans	-	-	-	-	-	-	-	-	-	X	X	-	-	-	-	-	-	-	-	-	-	-	-	-	-	-	-
sp.	-	-	-	-	-	-	-	-	-	-	-	-	-	-	X	-	-	-	-	-	-	-	-	-	-	-	-
Uncinuloides																											
guadalupensis (Shumard)	-	-	-	-	-	-	-	-	-	-	-	-	-	-	-	-	-	-	-	-	-	-	-	-	-	-	X
Undellaria																											
magnifica	-	-	-	-	-	-	-	-	-	-	-	-	-	-	-	-	-	-	-	-	X	-	-	-	-	-	-
Undulella																											
guadalupensis	-	-	-	-	-	-	-	-	-	-	-	-	-	-	-	-	-	-	-	-	-	X	-	-	-	-	-
matutina	-	-	-	-	-	-	-	-	-	-	-	-	-	X	-	-	-	-	-	-	-	-	-	-	-	-	-
undulata C&G	-	-	-	-	-	-	-	-	-	-	-	-	-	-	X	X	X	-	-	-	-	-	-	-	-	-	-
Waagenoconcha																											
convexa	-	-	-	-	-	-	-	-	-	-	X	-	-	X	-	-	-	-	-	-	-	-	-	-	-	-	-
magnifica	-	-	-	-	-	-	-	-	-	-	-	-	-	-	X	X	X	X	-	-	-	X	-	-	-	-	-
platys	-	-	-	-	-	-	-	-	-	-	-	-	-	X	-	-	-	-	-	-	-	-	-	-	-	-	-
prophetica	-	X	X	-	-	-	-	-	-	-	-	-	-	-	-	-	-	-	-	-	-	-	-	-	-	-	-
sulcata	-	-	-	-	-	-	-	-	-	-	-	-	-	-	-	-	-	-	-	X	-	-	-	-	-	-	-
Wellerella																											
girtyi girtyi	-	-	-	-	-	-	-	-	-	-	-	-	-	-	X	X	X	X	-	-	-	-	-	-	-	-	-
g. seorsa	-	-	-	-	-	-	-	-	-	-	-	-	-	-	-	-	-	-	-	-	-	X	-	-	-	-	-
?nitidula	-	-	-	-	-	-	-	-	-	-	-	-	-	-	-	-	-	-	-	-	X	-	-	-	-	-	-
Xenosaria																											
exotica	-	-	-	-	-	-	-	-	-	-	-	-	-	-	-	-	-	-	-	-	-	-	X	-	X	-	-
Xenosteges																											
adherens M-W&C	-	-	-	-	-	-	-	-	-	-	X	X	-	-	-	-	-	-	-	-	-	X	-	-	-	-	-
anomalus	-	-	-	-	-	-	-	-	-	-	-	-	-	-	-	-	-	-	-	-	-	X	-	-	-	-	-
magnus	-	-	-	-	-	-	-	-	-	-	-	-	-	X	-	-	-	-	-	-	-	-	-	-	-	-	-
quadratus	-	-	-	-	-	-	-	-	-	-	-	-	-	-	X	X	X	X	X	-	-	X	-	-	-	-	-
trivialis	-	-	-	-	-	-	-	-	-	-	-	-	-	X	-	-	-	-	-	-	-	-	-	-	-	-	-
umbonatus	-	-	-	-	-	-	-	-	-	-	-	-	-	-	-	-	-	-	-	-	-	-	X	-	X	X	X
Xestosia																											
obsolescens	-	-	-	-	-	-	-	-	-	-	X	-	-	-	-	-	-	-	-	-	-	-	-	-	-	-	-
schucherti (REK)	-	-	-	-	-	-	-	-	-	-	X	X	-	-	-	-	-	-	-	-	-	-	-	-	-	-	-
Yakovlevia																											
anterospinosa	-	-	-	-	-	-	-	-	-	-	-	-	-	X	-	-	-	-	-	-	-	-	-	-	-	-	-
costellata	-	-	-	-	-	-	-	-	-	-	-	-	-	X	-	-	-	-	-	-	-	X	-	-	-	-	-
hessorum	-	-	-	-	-	-	-	-	-	-	-	-	-	-	X	X	-	-	-	-	-	-	-	-	-	-	-
immatura	-	-	-	-	-	-	-	-	-	-	-	-	-	X	-	-	-	-	-	-	-	-	-	-	-	-	-
indentata	-	-	-	-	-	-	-	-	-	-	-	-	-	-	-	-	-	X	-	-	-	-	-	-	-	-	-
intermedia	-	-	-	-	-	-	-	-	-	-	-	-	-	-	X	-	-	-	-	-	-	-	-	-	-	-	-
sulcata	-	-	-	-	-	-	-	-	-	-	-	-	-	X	-	-	-	-	-	-	-	-	-	-	-	-	-

GENUS AND SPECIES	Transition	Breccia	Spicule	Thin-bedded (lower)	Thin-bedded (upper)	GENUS AND SPECIES	Transition	Breccia	Spicule	Thin-bedded (lower)	Thin-bedded (upper)
Acosarina dorsisulcata C&G	–	X	–	–	–	H. cf. H. cuneata	–	–	–	X	–
A. mesoplatys (REK)	–	X	X	–	X	H. hessensis REK	X	–	–	–	–
A. sp.	–	X	–	–	–	Institella leonardensis (REK)	–	–	X	–	–
Acritosia silicica	–	X	–	–	–	Kozlowskia alata	–	X	–	–	–
A. teguliferoides (REK)	–	X	X	–	–	Limbella limbata	–	X	X	–	–
Anemonaria sublaevis (REK)	–	–	X	–	–	Liosotella costata	–	–	–	X	–
Antronaria dissona	–	X	–	–	–	Meekella attenuata Girty	–	X	–	–	–
A. mesicostalis (Girty)	–	X	–	–	–	M. caperata	–	X	–	–	–
Cenorhynchia saginata	–	–	–	–	X	M. magnifica	X	X	–	–	–
Choanodus irregularis	–	–	X	–	–	M. prionota	–	X	–	–	–
Chonetinella ciboloensis	–	X	–	–	–	Megousia auriculata M-W&C	–	–	X	–	X
Chonosteges pulcher	–	–	X	–	–	Metriolepis carotica	–	–	X	–	–
Cleiothyridina rectimarginata	–	X	–	–	–	Neophricadothyris cordata	–	–	–	–	X
Collemataria americana (Girty)	–	X	–	–	–	Nudauris whitei	X	–	–	–	–
Composita crassa	–	X	–	–	–	Orthotichia irregularis	–	X	–	–	–
C. sp.	–	X	X	–	X	O. cf. O. newelli	X	X	–	–	–
Crenispirifer angulatus (REK)	–	X	–	–	–	Paraspiriferina cellulana	–	–	–	–	X
Derbyia crenulata Girty	–	X	–	–	–	Paucispinifera sp.	–	–	–	–	X
D. aff. D. nasuta Girty	–	X	–	–	–	Petasmatherus pumilus	–	–	–	–	X
D. sp.	–	X	X	–	–	Phrenophoria sp.	–	–	–	–	X
Dielasma longisulcatum	–	X	–	–	–	Pontisia robusta	–	X	–	–	–
Diplanus rarus	–	X	X	–	–	Reticulariina bufala	–	–	–	–	X
Dyoros (Dyoros) magnus (Stehli)	–	X	–	–	–	Reticulatia robusta	X	–	–	–	–
D. (D.) transversus	–	–	–	–	X	Rhamnaria sp.	–	–	X	X	X
Echinauris bella	–	–	–	–	X	Rhipidomella hessensis REK	X	X	X	–	–
E. sp.	–	X	X	X	–	R. hispidula	–	–	X	–	–
Elliottella cf. E. varicostata	–	X	–	–	–	Scacchinella titan	X	X	–	–	–
Enteletes wolfcampensis REK	–	X	–	–	–	Stenoscisma multicostum Stehli	X	X	–	–	–
E. sp. indet.	X	X	X	–	–	S. problematicum	–	X	–	–	–
Eolyttonia gigantea	–	X	–	–	–	S. sp. (small)	–	–	–	–	X
Geyerella cf. G. hessi	–	X	–	–	–	Teguliferina conida (Stehli)	–	X	–	–	–
Gypospirifer infraplicus (REK)	–	X	–	–	–	Tropidelasma robertsi	–	X	–	–	–
Heterelasma sp.	–	–	–	X	–	Xenosteges adherens M-W&C	–	–	X	–	–
Hustedia consuta	–	–	–	X	–	Xestosia schucherti (REK)	–	–	X	–	–

Ammonites

Identifications by William M. Furnish and Brian F. Glenister

At the outset of the Glass Mountains work, ammonites were sent to Dr. A. K. Miller at the University of Iowa. He determined the presence of *Perrinites* in the First Limestone Member of the Word [now Road Canyon Formation] near the site of the Old World Ranch (Miller, 1945a) and insisted on the Leonardian age of this original Word member. After Miller's untimely death, Dr. William M. Furnish and later also his colleague Dr. Brian F. Glenister kindly helped us with ammonite identifications and age assignments based on them. They were especially helpful in separating Pennsylvanian (Gaptank Formation) beds from Permian rocks in places where separation was difficult. They collected with us in the field on a number of occasions. As with the fusulinids, brachiopod and ammonite age assignments are not always in accord, a result of the variation in evolving rates

of different phyla. We thank Furnish and Glenister for their generous help. Comments and annotations by them accompany the ammonite lists. The localities are those designated by the National Museum of Natural History (formerly the United States National Museum) and are described in Part I, pages 136–165, or herein in "Corrigenda" under "Additions to Localities."

700e. *Boesites texanus* (Böse)
  Dunbarites rectilaterale (Miller)
  Kargalites parkeri (Heilprin)
  Neopronorites boesei (Smith)
  Neoshumardites gaptankensis (Miller)
  Prothalassoceras kingorum (Miller)
  Prouddenites primus Miller
  Schistoceras hyatti Smith?
  Uddenites schucherti Böse

[This fauna represents one of the more important ammonoid assemblages of West Texas. It was first described in 1930 by A. K. Miller, and can be correlated with similar forms of the Missourian Series in the Midcontinent Region.]

William M. Furnish and Brian F. Glenister, Department of Geology, University of Iowa, Iowa City 52240.

700m. *Bamyaniceras knighti* (Miller and Furnish)
    Eumedlicottia whitneyi (Böse)
    Perrinites sp.
    Pseudovidrioceras dunbari (Miller and Furnish)

[Collections from this locality are representative of the Skinner Ranch Formation in the Dugout Mountain Area. Collectively, the assemblage is fairly distinctive for that part of the section originally designated as lower Leonard. Specimens of *Perrinites* are distinguished by only moderate size (about 50 mm diameter) and differ slightly from those of the Cathedral Mountain Formation in having a more primitive suture.]

700n. *Bamyaniceras knighti* (Miller and Furnish)
    Metalegoceras sp.
    Perrinites sp.

700o. *Bamyaniceras knighti* (Miller and Furnish)

700r. *Bamyaniceras knighti* (Miller and Furnish)
    Perrinites sp.

700s. *Bamyaniceras knighti* (Miller and Furnish)
    Perrinites sp.

700t. *Bamyaniceras knighti* (Miller and Furnish)
    Eothinites hessensis Miller and Furnish
    Perrinites sp.

701. *Almites sellardsi* (Plummer and Scott)
    Artinskia artiensis (Grünewaldt)
    Eoasianites deciensis (Plummer and Scott)
    Neopronorites bakeri Miller and Furnish

[This collection is in the sequence of ammonoid faunas of West Texas. It is regarded as definitely Permian, rather than Pennsylvanian, but cannot be assigned exactly within the Lower Permian on the basis of the known ammonoids. *Properrinites bakeri* (Plummer and Scott) is the usual index for the Neal Ranch Formation.]

701c. *Agathiceras uralicum* (Karpinsky)
    Almites sellardsi (Plummer and Scott)
    Eoasianites cf. *E. modestus* (Böse)
    Prothalassoceras cf. *P. welleri* Böse

701e. *Schistoceras hyatti* Smith

701f. *Marathonites ganti* (Smith)?

701g. *Agathiceras uralicum* (Karpinsky)

701h. *Agathiceras* cf. *A. uralicum* (Karpinsky)

701k. *Agathiceras uralicum* (Karpinsky)
    Almites sellardsi (Plummer and Scott)
    Eoasianites cf. *E. modestus* (Böse)
    Properrinites bakeri (Plummer and Scott)
    Prothalassoceras welleri Böse

701–l. *Agathiceras* sp.
    Boesites sp.
    Eoasianites sp.

    Marathonites sp.
    Schistoceras sp.
    Uddenites? sp.

[Abundant small silicified ammonoids occur at this locality. Although poorly preserved, generic assignments are considered to be reliable. The assemblage of genera is that found in the Gaptank Formation, below the Neal Ranch. This material is therefore assumed to be reworked or from a carbonate erratic in the limestone ledge.]

701m. *Properrinites bakeri* (Plummer and Scott)

701n. *Almites sellardsi* (Plummer and Scott)
    Properrinites cf. *P. bakeri* (Plummer and Scott)

701o. *Agathiceras* sp.
    Almites sellardsi (Plummer and Scott)

701p. *Agathiceras ciscoense* Smith
    Boesites texanus (Böse)
    Dunbarites sp.
    Emilites incertum (Böse)
    Eoasianites modestus (Böse)
    Kargalites parkeri (Heilprin)
    Marathonites ganti (Smith)
    Neodimorphoceras sp.
    Neopronorites boesei (Smith)?
    Schistoceras hyatti Smith
    Uddenites schucherti Böse
    Vidrioceras uddeni Böse

[Ammonoids from this locality were described by Böse in 1917 and this collection constitutes topotypes of several generotypes.]

701q. *Eoasianites modestus* (Böse)
    Marathonites ganti (Smith)
    Neopronorites boesei (Smith)
    Schistoceras hyatti Smith

701r. *Boesites texanus* (Böse)
    Eoasianites modestus (Böse)
    Eothalassoceras? sp.
    Marathonites ganti (Smith)
    Neodimorphoceras lenticulare Ruzhencev?
    Parashumardites senex (Miller and Cline)?
    Schistoceras hyatti Smith
    Stenopronorites sp.
    Uddenoceras oweni (Miller and Furnish)

[This collection contains abundant, well-preserved ammonoids. The locality is approximately equivalent to that providing specimens for the study by Smith in 1929.]

701s. *Marathonites* sp.
    Schistoceras sp.

701t. *Schistoceras* sp.

701v. *Marathonites* sp.
    Neopronorites sp.
    Schistoceras sp.

701w. *Agathiceras ciscoense* Smith

701y. *Schistoceras* sp.

701z. *Almites sellardsi* (Plummer and Scott)
    Properrinites bakeri (Plummer and Scott)

702. *Agathiceras uralicum* (Karpinsky)
    Clinolobus n. sp.
    Neocrimites newelli (Miller and Furnish)
    Perrinites hilli (Smith) sensu lato
    Pseudogastrioceratid [immature]

702a. *Stacheoceras rothi* Miller and Furnish

702b. *Perrinites* sp.

702c. *Glassoceras normani* (Miller and Furnish)
    Paraceltites? sp.
    Perrinites sp.

702d. [Immature multilobed ammonoid, probably *Stacheoceras*]

702e. *Perrinites hilli* (Smith) sensu lato

702t. *Almites?* sp.

703. *Agathiceras* sp.
    Eumedlicottia whitnyei (Böse)
    Glassoceras normani (Miller and Furnish)
    Neocrimites sp.
    Paraceltites sp.
    Perrinites hilli (Smith) sensu stricto
    Propinacoceras sp.
    Pseudogastrioceras cooperi Miller

[The assemblage of ammonoids from this locality was described by Miller and Furnish in 1940, then in more detail by Miller in 1945, and by Miller and Furnish in 1957. The fauna is representative of the Roadian Stage in the type area.]

703a. [Immature pseudogastrioceratid]
    Perrinites sp.

703b. *Perrinites* sp.

703bs. *Pseudovidrioceras* sp.

705c. *Kargalites hargisi* (Böse)

705d. *Kargalites hargisi* (Böse)

705e. *Kargalites?* sp.

705g. *Properrinites bakeri* (Plummer and Scott)

706. *Altudoceras altudense* (Böse)

706b. *Agathiceras girtyi* Böse

706c. *Altudoceras altudense* (Böse)
    Tauroceras bowmani (Böse)

706e. *Atsabites multiliratus* (Plummer and Scott)
    Eumedlicottia burckhardti (Böse)
    Pseudogastrioceras roadense (Böse)

706f. *Neocrimites* sp. [immature]

706x. *Almites sellardsi* (Plummer and Scott)
    Artinskia artiensis (Grünewaldt)
    Kargalites cf. *K. subquadratum* (Plummer and Scott)
    Properrinites bakeri (Plummer and Scott)

706y. *Agathiceras uralicum* (Karpinsky)
    Crimites new species

707a. *Agathiceras* sp.
    Almites sp.
    Perrinites subcumminsi (Haniel)

707d. *Neocrimites newelli* (Miller and Furnish)

707e. *Glassoceras?* sp. [small globular ammonoids]
    Peritrochia erebus Girty?
    Perrinites hilli (Smith) sensu stricto
    Propinacoceras sp.
    Pseudogastrioceras cooperi Miller?

707g. *Metalegoceras schucherti?* Miller and Furnish

707j. *Akmilleria adkinsi* (Plummer and Scott)
    Artinskia artiensis (Grünewaldt)
    Daraelites kingi Plummer and Scott
    Eoasianites deciensis (Plummer and Scott)
    Kargalites subquadratum (Plummer and Scott)
    Properrinites bakeri (Plummer and Scott)
    Prothalassoceras welleri Böse

707k. *Perrinites subcumminsi* (Haniel)?

707m. *Agathiceras uralicum* (Karpinsky)
    Crimites sp.
    Properrinites boesei (Plummer and Scott)
    Prostacheoceras sp.

707n. *Agathiceras uralicum* (Karpinsky)
    Artinskia artiensis (Grünewaldt)
    Eoasianites deciensis (Plummer and Scott)
    Properrinites denhami Miller and Furnish

707o. *Agathiceras uralicum* (Karpinsky)
    Almites sellardsi (Plummer and Scott)

707p. *Akmilleria adkinsi* (Plummer and Scott)
    Eoasianites deciensis (Plummer and Scott)
    Eoasianites cf. *E. modestus* (Böse)
    Properrinites bakeri (Plummer and Scott)
    Prothalassoceras welleri Böse

707q. *Paragastrioceras* new species
    Perrinites hilli (Smith)

707v. *Metalegoceras* sp.

707w. *Kargalites?* sp.

708e. *Almites sellardsi* (Plummer and Scott)
    Perrinites subcumminsi (Haniel)

708q. *Properrinites cumminsi* (White)

709h. *Perrinites subcumminsi* (Haniel)

709o. *Neocrimites newelli* (Miller and Furnish)
    Perrinites hilli (Smith)

709t. *Kargalites subquadratum* (Plummer and Scott)

709u. *Agathiceras uralicum* (Karpinsky)

710g. *Bamyaniceras* cf. *B. knighti* (Miller and Furnish)
  Perrinites hilli (Smith)

710h. [Immature paragastrioceratids]

710r. *Bamyaniceras* cf. *B. knighti* (Miller and Furnish)

711d. *Kargalites* sp.

711q. *Neocrimites* sp.
  Perrinites hilli (Smith)

711r. *Perrinites hilli* (Smith)

713p. *Perrinites hilli* (Smith)

713y. *Almites sellardsi* (Plummer and Scott)

715. *Agathiceras uralicum* (Karpinsky)
  Almites sellardsi (Plummer and Scott)
  Artinskia artiensis (Grünewaldt)
  Crimites glomulus? Ruzhencev
  Daraelites kingi Plummer and Scott
  Metalegoceras colemanense Plummer and Scott
  Neopronorites bakeri Miller and Furnish
  Properrinites bakeri (Plummer and Scott)
  P. denhami Miller and Furnish
  P. new species
  Propopanoceras postsimense Ruzhencev
  Prostacheoceras new species
  Prothalassoceras welleri Böse
  Svetlanoceras sp.

[The ammonoids from this locality represent the best assemblage of upper Wolfcamp species. Except for the representatives of *Properrinites*, there are close counterparts in the upper Sakmarian Series of the southern Ural Mountains.]

715b. *Almites sellardsi* (Plummer and Scott)
  Properrinites bakeri (Plummer and Scott)

715v. *Metalegoceras colemanense* Plummer and Scott

716n. *Perrinites subcumminsi* (Haniel)

718g. *Perrinites* sp.

719x. *Pseudovidrioceras* sp.

720d. *Agathiceras* sp.
  Neocrimites? sp.
  Pseudogastrioceras? sp.

720e. *Agathiceras uralicum* (Karpinsky)

720f. *Bamyaniceras knighti* (Miller and Furnish)
  Perrinites sp.

721j. *Agathiceras* sp.
  Eumedlicottia burckhardti Böse
  Neocrimites new species
  Paraceltites elegans Girty
  Pseudogastrioceras roadense (Böse)

721r. *Waagenoceras dieneri* Böse

721s. [On the basis of the two small but well-preserved ammonoids from this locality, it is preferred to regard the source as Word Formation rather than Road Canyon. The description states that the fossils came from above Road Canyon Limestone, and the block could even have been derived from higher on the slope. There is no uncertainty about the identification of the species, a characteristic element found in the three lower members of the Word in the Glass Mountains. Except for this possible occurrence, we have not been able to verify *Waagenoceras* in the Road Canyon Formation; a similar appearing related globular ammonoid, *Glassoceras*, does occur, though, at that level.]

721u. *Bamyaniceras knighti* (Miller and Furnish)
  Eumedlicottia sp.
  Perrinites hilli (Smith)

721v. *Perrinites hilli* (Smith)

721x. *Perrinites hilli* (Smith)

722e. *Eumedlicottia* sp.

722i. *Almites* sp.
  Neocrimites sp.
  Perrinites sp.

722m. *Stacheoceras rothi* Miller and Furnish [immature]

722u. [Unidentified cyclolobid]

723o. *Eothinites hessensis* Miller and Furnish
  Eumedlicottia whitneyi (Böse)
  Neocrimites sp.
  Perrinites sp.
  Pseudogastrioceras sp.
  Pseudovidrioceras? sp.
  Thalassoceras sp.

723w. *Agathiceras* sp.
  Altudoceras altudense (Böse)
  Eumedlicottia burckhardti (Böse)
  Neocrimites defordi (Miller and Furnish)
  Popanoceras cf. *P. bowmani* (Böse)
  Waagenoceras cf. *W. dieneri* Böse

723y. *Eumedlicottia whitneyi* (Böse)
  Neocrimites newelli (Miller and Furnish)
  Perrinites hilli (Smith)

724f. *Eumedlicottia* sp.
  Neocrimites defordi (Miller and Furnish)
  Pseudogastrioceras sp.

724g. *Neocrimites defordi* (Miller and Furnish)
  Waagenoceras cf. *W. dieneri* Böse

724u. *Eumedlicottia* sp.

725f. *Timorites* sp. [immature]
  Waagenoceras? sp.

725m. [Immature cyclolobid]

726c. *Eumedlicottia whitneyi* Böse
      Perrinites hilli (Smith)

726f. *Pseudogastrioceratid* [indeterminate]

726m. *Kargalites* new species

726n. *Crimites* sp. [immature]
      Stacheoceras sp.

726o. *Perrinites hilli* (Smith)
      Pseudohalorites new species

727d. *Boesites* sp.
      Daixites cf. *D. meglitskyi* Ruzhencev

727m. *Eothinites hessensis* Miller and Furnish

727n. *Bamyaniceras knighti* (Miller and Furnish)
      Perrinites sp.
      Pseudovidrioceras dunbari (Miller and Furnish)

727v. *Bamyaniceras knighti* (Miller and Furnish)
      Perrinites sp.

727w. *Bamyaniceras knighti* (Miller and Furnish)

728e. *Medlicottia* sp.

728h. *Agathiceras* sp.

730e. *Perrinites hilli* (Smith)

730f. *Perrinites hilli* (Smith)

730g. *Perrinites hilli* (Smith)

730i. *Perrinites hilli* (Smith)

730j. *Bamyaniceras knighti* (Miller and Furnish)
      Perrinites hilli (Smith)—sensu lato

730k. *Almites* sp.
      Bamyaniceras knighti (Miller and Furnish)
      Neocrimites sp. [fusiform]
      Perrinites sp.

730w. *Popanoceras* sp.
      Waagenoceras sp.

731. *Mexicoceras guadalupense* (Girty)
     Timorites sp.

731s. *Neocrimites newelli* (Miller and Furnish)
      Perrinites subcumminsi (Haniel)

731u. *Waagenoceras* sp.

732a. *Altudoceras altudense* (Böse)
      Cibolites uddeni Plummer and Scott
      ?Mexicoceras guadalupense (Girty)
      ?Timorites uddeni Miller and Furnish

732c. *Waagenoceras* sp.

732j. *Agathiceras uralicum* (Karpinsky)

732–l. *Perrinites hilli* (Smith)

732s. *Eumedlicottia* sp.

732u. *Eumedlicottia whitneyi* (Böse)
      Perrinites hilli (Smith)
      Prostacheoceras sp.

732y. *Eumedlicottia* sp.
      Paraceltites elegans Girty

732z. *Agathiceras uralicum* (Karpinsky)
      Epithalassoceras new species
      Eumedlicottia whitneyi (Böse)?
      Glassoceras normani (Miller and Furnish)
      Paraceltites elegans Girty
      Peritrochia erebus Girty
      ?Propinacoceras sp.
      Pseudogastrioceras cooperi Miller?
      Texoceras texanum (Girty)
      [This locality, discovered by Cooper and Grant about 1965, has been the source of the largest collection of Permian ammonoids in West Texas. It is also a critical locality in that it combines faunal elements from the basin with those normally found on the shelf and is believed to provide a basis for detailed correlation from the Glass Mountains to the Guadalupes.]

733f. *Agathiceras* sp.
      Paraceltites sp.

733t. *Agathiceras* sp.
      Eumedlicottia sp.
      Paraceltites sp.
      Pseudogastrioceras sp.
      Stacheoceras sp.

734c. *Perrinites* cf. *P. hilli* (Smith)

736d. *Perrinites hilli* (Smith)

736h. *Perrinites hilli* (Smith)

736j. *Pseudogastrioceras* sp.
      Waagenoceras sp.

736r. *Perrinites hilli* (Smith) sensu stricto

736v. *Agathiceras* cf. *A. uralicum* (Karpinsky)

736w. *Waagenoceras* sp.

737b. *Pseudogastrioceras roadense* (Böse)?
      Waagenoceras sp.

737c. *Agathiceras uralicum* (Karpinsky)
      Paraceltites elegans Girty

737g. *Agathiceras uralicum* (Karpinsky)
      Paraceltites elegans Girty

737j. *Bamyaniceras smile* (Haniel)
      Perrinites subcumminsi (Haniel)

737n. *Agathiceras uralicum* (Karpinsky)
      Paraceltites elegans Girty

737r. *Agathiceras* sp.
      Paraceltites elegans Girty

737s. *Perrinites hilli* (Smith)

737t. *Daixites* sp.
    Emilites incertus (Böse)
    Kargalites parkeri (Heilprin)
    Metapronorites pseudotrimorense (Miller)
    Prouddenites primus Miller
    Schistoceras sp.

737u. *?Almites sellardsi* (Plummer and Scott)
    Aristoceras appressum Ruzhencev
    Eoasianites subhanieli Ruzhencev

737z. *Agathiceras girtyi* Böse
    ?Popanoceras bowmani Böse

738c. *Medlicottia chozaensis* Plummer and Scott

738h. *Perrinites* sp.

738o. *Perrinites hilli* (Smith)

739d. *Agathiceras uralicum* (Karpinsky)
    Epithalassoceras new species

740n. *Strigogoniatites fountaini* Miller and Furnish

[The only diagnostic ammonoids found within the more massive carbonate of the Capitan reef front are the same as those known from the Lamar Limestone in the Patterson Hills in the basin facies.]

Fusulinids

Identifications by Garner L. Wilde

In 1957 we asked Garner Wilde to identify a modest number of fusulinid samples for us. He obligingly did so. In the subsequent years, up to 1971, we took advantage of his willingness to help us, which resulted in an enormous amount of information from the 279 samples that he examined. We also had several conferences in the field with him. We believe that his contribution to the paleontology and stratigraphy of the Glass Mountains should be recorded.

In addition to the identifications listed we have included his comments on localities in which there appeared some doubt as to age. An example is locality 723w, the samples from which were labeled "First Limestone Member of the Word" because that was the geological map designation for that locality. Wilde (as did also Furnish and Glenister with reference to ammonites) recognized the locality as an exposure of the "Third Limestone Member of the Word" (= Willis Ranch Member), a discovery that had a far reaching effect on the understanding of the Gilliland Canyon area. The localities are those designated by the National Museum of Natural History (formerly a part of the United States National Museum) and are described in Part I, pages 136–165, or herein in "Corrigenda" under "Additions to Localities."

We must express here our appreciation and thanks for the enormous amount of work performed by Garner Wilde in our behalf. He was especially helpful in locating the base of the Wolfcamp in the

Lenox Hills. The differences of opinion reflected in the contrast of his stratigraphic analysis with our designations for USNM localities result from reliance on different groups of animals whose stages of evolution are not totally parallel.

700a. *Triticites newelli* Burma
    T. aff. *T. primarius* Merchant and Keroher

[Both of the above species occur in the Stanton limestone of the Lansing group in Kansas and are typical Missourian forms. The form identified above as *T.* aff. *T. primarius* is probably an undescribed species, but I related it to that species to give an idea of the type of thing we are dealing with.]

700g. *Triticites* sp. [Virgilian]

700q. *Parafusulina attenuata* Dunbar and Skinner
    P. boesei Dunbar and Skinner
    P. cf. *P. sullivanensis* Ross
    Reichelina? sp.

700v. *Parafusulina deliciasensis* Dunbar and Skinner
    P. rothi Dunbar and Skinner
    P. spp.

[Word Number 2 (= China Tank Member) or slightly higher. I doubt that this could be as old as Road Canyon.]

700w. *Parafusulina rothi* Dunbar and Skinner
    P. sullivanensis Ross

[Again this may be slightly younger than Road Canyon (see locality 700v).]

700z. *Parafusulina deltoides* Ross
    P. spissisepta Ross

[This looks a little younger than most Skinner Ranch (Sullivan Peak) that we have seen, but could be.]

701. *Triticites* cf. *T. creekensis* Thompson
    T. meeki (Moller)
    T. ventricosus (Meek and Hayden)

Garner L. Wilde, Exxon Company USA, Midland, Texas, 79701.

701a. *Schwagerina* sp.
   Triticites creekensis Thompson?

701b. *Schwagerina* sp.
   Triticites creekensis Thompson

702d. *Parafusulina* spp.

   [One form may be *Parafusulina brooksensis* Ross; one is similar to, but smaller than, *Parafusulina leonardensis* Ross.]

703g. *Schwagerina crassitectoria* Dunbar and Skinner
   S. guembeli Dunbar and Skinner
   S. guembeli pseudoregularis Dunbar and Skinner

703h. *Schwagerina crassitectoria* Dunbar and Skinner
   S. guembeli Dunbar and Skinner

703i. *Schwagerina guembeli* Dunbar and Skinner
   Staffella sp.

703j. *Schwagerina crassitectoria* Dunbar and Skinner
   S. guembeli Dunbar and Skinner
   Staffella sp.

703n. *Schwagerina* aff. *S. huecoensis* (Dunbar and Skinner)
   S. cf. *S. neolata* Thompson
   S.? sp. [similar to some lower McCloud forms]

   [This again looks like a typical Wolfcampian fauna, and not too different in age from 705m, perhaps a little older.]

705m. *Ozawainella* sp.
   Pseudoschwagerina sp.
   P. uddeni (Beede and Kniker)
   Schwagerina diversiformis Dunbar and Skinner
   S. neolata Thompson

   [This occurrence of *Schwagerina neolata* in the Glass Mountains section fits very nicely, for Thompson's types came from the middle Hueco limestone in the Hueco Mountains. *Schwagerina diversiformis* was also reported by Thompson from the Hueco limestone, but higher in the section.]

706b. *Parafusulina* sp. [similar in development to *P. boesei attenuata*]
   Rauserella? sp.

706d. *Parafusulina sp.* [elongate, very slender, highly evolved form]

706f. *Parafusulina* sp.
   P. cf. *P. attenuata* Dunbar and Skinner
   Rauserella sp.

707. *Schwagerina dugoutensis* Ross

707a. *Ozawainella?* sp.
   Schubertella melonica Dunbar and Skinner
   S. kingi Dunbar and Skinner
   Schwagerina dugoutensis Ross
   S. hawkinsi Dunbar and Skinner
   S. hessensis Dunbar and Skinner
   S. sp. [with heavy axial fillings]

707c. *Parafusulina boesei* Dunbar and Skinner
   P. attenuata Dunbar and Skinner
   P. splendens Dunbar and Skinner

708e. *Parafusulina spissisepta* Ross

708q. *Paraschwagerina plena* Ross?
   Schwagerina sp.

   [Reworked fusulines?]

709c. *Parafusulina* cf. *P. bakeri* Dunbar and Skinner
   P. cf. *P. attenuata* Dunbar and Skinner
   Rauserella sp.

709d. *"Eoschubertella"* sp.
   Schwagerina tersa Ross

709e. *Schwagerina crassitectoria* Dunbar and Skinner
   S. guembeli pseudoregularis Dunbar and Skinner

709f. *Schwagerina crassitectoria* Dunbar and Skinner
   Staffella lacunosa Dunbar and Skinner

709g. *Schwagerina crassitectoria* Dunbar and Skinner

709h. *Schwagerina guembeli pseudoregularis* Dunbar and Skinner

709i. *Parafusulina allisonensis* Ross
   P. brooksensis Ross
   Staffella lacunosa Dunbar and Skinner

709j. *Parafusulina allisonensis* Ross?

709k. *Parafusulina brooksensis* Ross?
   Staffella sp.

709m. *Parafusulina brooksensis* Ross?
   Staffella sp.

   [Contains same algae as 716h.]

709p. *Schwagerina crassitectoria* Dunbar and Skinner
   Staffella lacunosa Dunbar and Skinner

709q. *Schwagerina crassitectoria* Dunbar and Skinner
   Staffella lacunosa Dunbar and Skinner

709r. *Schwagerina crassitectoria* Dunbar and Skinner
   Staffella lacunosa Dunbar and Skinner

709s. *Paraschwagerina* sp.
   Pseudoschwagerina sp.
   Schubertella sp.

709v. *Monodiexodina linearis* (Dunbar and Skinner)
   Schubertella sp.

709w. *Monodiexodina linearis* (Dunbar and Skinner)
   Schwagerina spp.

709x. *Paraschwagerina* sp.
   Schubertella sp.
   Schwagerina sp.

710i. *Parafusulina* cf. *P. attenuata* Dunbar and Skinner
   P. cf. *P. fountaini* Dunbar and Skinner
   P. sp.

   [These forms are generally larger and more advanced looking than those of 709c and 718k.]

710j. *Parafusulina boesei attenuata* Dunbar and Skinner
  P. cf. *P. fountaini* Dunbar and Skinner
  P. cf. *P. splendens* Dunbar and Skinner

710–l. *Parafusulina boesei* Dunbar and Skinner
  P. attenuata Dunbar and Skinner
  P. splendens Dunbar and Skinner
  P. sp.
  Rauserella sp. [common]
  Schubertella sp.? [massive chomata]

710m. *Parafusulina* cf. *P. boesei attenuata* Dunbar and Skinner
  P. sp.

710n. *Parafusulina* cf. *P. boesei* Dunbar and Skinner
  P. cf. *P. attenuata* Dunbar and Skinner
  Rauserella sp. [rare]

710o. *Parafusulina* cf. *P. boesei* Dunbar and Skinner
  P. cf. *P. splendens* Dunbar and Skinner
  P. sp.

710p. *Parafusulina attenuata* Dunbar and Skinner
  P. boesei Dunbar and Skinner
  Rauserella new species [abundant]

710s. *Schubertella* sp.
  Schwagerina aff. *S. dispansa* Ross
  S. sp.

710t. *Parafusulina* cf. *P. attenuata* Dunbar and Skinner
  P. cf. *P. boesei* Dunbar and Skinner

710w. *Pseudoschwagerina gerontica* Dunbar and Skinner
  Schwagerina sp.

710x. *Schwagerina* cf. *S. dugoutensis* Ross
  S. cf. *S. hessensis* Dunbar and Skinner

711c. *Paraschwagerina* sp.
  Schubertella sp.
  Schwagerina cf. *S. thompsoni* Needham
  S. spp.
  Stewartina cf. *S. laxissima* Dunbar and Skinner

711d. *Parafusulina allisonensis* Ross?

711e. *Pseudoschwagerina* sp.
  Schwagerina cf. *S. diversiformis* Dunbar and Skinner

711f. *Schwagerina?* sp. [may be close to *Chalaroschwagerina nelsoni* Dunbar and Skinner]
  Staffella sp.

711g. *Monodiexodina linearis* (Dunbar and Skinner)
  Paraschwagerina sp.
  Schwagerina spp.

711h. *Chalaroschwagerina nelsoni* Dunbar and Skinner?
  Paraschwagerina sp.
  Schubertella kingi Dunbar and Skinner

711–l. *Schwagerina hawkinsi* Dunbar and Skinner
  S. sp.

711m. *Monodiexodina linearis* (Dunbar and Skinner)
  Pseudoschwagerina sp.
  Schwagerina spp.

711n. *Schubertella* cf. *S. kingi* Dunbar and Skinner
  Schwagerina spp.
  Staffella sp.

711s. *Parafusulina attenuata* Dunbar and Skinner
  P. cf. *P. splendens* Dunbar and Skinner
  Rauserella sp.

711u. *Parafusulina sellardsi* Dunbar and Skinner
  P. spp.

711v. *Parafusulina* cf. *P. attenuata* Dunbar and Skinner
  P. spp.
  Rauserella sp.

711w. *Parafusulina* cf. *P. boesei* Dunbar and Skinner
  P. spp.

711x. *Paraschwagerina* sp.
  Pseudoschwagerina sp.
  Schubertella sp.
  Staffella sp.

711y. *Schubertella melonica* Dunbar and Skinner
  Schwagerina sp.

712p. *Nankinella huecoensis* (Dunbar and Skinner)
  Pseudoschwagerina sp.
  Schwagerina knighti Dunbar and Skinner?
  S. spp.
  Staffella sp.

712q. *Parafusulina attenuata* Dunbar and Skinner
  P. cf. *P. splendens* Dunbar and Skinner
  P. spp. [large]

712u. *Nankinella huecoensis* (Dunbar and Skinner)
  Schwagerina knighti Dunbar and Skinner
  S. sp.

712v. *Nankinella huecoensis* (Dunbar and Skinner)
  Paraschwagerina sp.
  Pseudoschwagerina gerontica Dunbar and Skinner
  Schwagerina knighti Dunbar and Skinner
  S. sp.

712x. *Paraschwagerina* sp.
  Schwagerina spp.

712y. *Pseudofusulina* sp., sensu stricto
  Pseudoschwagerina sp.
  Schwagerina sp.

714a. *Schwagerina diversiformis* Dunbar and Skinner

714b. *Schwagerina crassitectoria* Dunbar and Skinner
  Staffella laucunosa Dunbar and Skinner

714c. *Pseudoschwagerina gerontica* Dunbar and Skinner
  P. texana Dunbar and Skinner
  P. sp.
  Schubertella sp.
  Schwagerina cribrisepta Ross
  S. dispansa Ross

714d. *Schubertella* aff. *S. melonica* Dunbar and Skinner
Schwagerina sp.?

714f. *Pseudoschwagerina* sp.
Schwagerina spp.

714g. *Pseudoschwagerina gerontica* Dunbar and Skinner
Stewartina laxissima Dunbar and Skinner

714h. *Ozawainella?* sp.
Schwagerina crassitectoria Dunbar and Skinner

714i. *Parafusulina vidriensis* Ross

714j. *Parafusulina* aff. *P. spissisepta* Ross

714k. *Parafusulina leonardensis* Ross

714s. *Schwagerina crassitectoria* Dunbar and Skinner
Staffella lacunosa Dunbar and Skinner

714t. *Schwagerina* sp. [vaguely similar to *S. dugoutensis* Ross, but not that form]

714u. *Parafusulina allisonensis* Ross [or *P. leonardensis* Ross]
Schubertella sp.

714v. *Endothyra* sp.
Parafusulina bakeri Dunbar and Skinner?
P. sp.
Rauserella sp.

715. *Nankinella huecoensis* (Dunbar and Skinner)
Pseudoschwagerina gerontica Dunbar and Skinner
P. sp.
Schwagerina complexa Thompson

715b. *Nankinella huecoensis* (Dunbar and Skinner)
Pseudoschwagerina uddeni (Beede and Kniker)
Pseudofusulina spp., sensu stricto
Schwagerina emaciata Dunbar and Skinner
S. pugunculus Ross
S. new species?
Staffella sp.

715c. *Schwagerina crassitectoria* Dunbar and Skinner
Staffella lacunosa Dunbar and Skinner

715i. *Parafusulina* sp. [very close to 706d]

715k. *Schubertella* cf. *S. melonica* Dunbar and Skinner
Schwagerina hawkinsi Dunbar and Skinner
S. hessensis Dunbar and Skinner
S. spp.

715r. *Chalaroschwagerina nelsoni* Dunbar and Skinner
Paraschwagerina? sp.
Pseudoschwagerina sp.
Schubertella sp.
Schwagerina pugunculus Ross

715t. *Schwagerina crassitectoria* Dunbar and Skinner
Staffella lacunosa Dunbar and Skinner

715v. *Monodiexodina linearis* (Dunbar and Skinner)
Pseudoschwagerina sp.
Schwagerina aff. *S. hawkinsi* Dunbar and Skinner

716a. *Ozawainella?* sp.
Schwagerina crassitectoria Dunbar and Skinner
Staffella lacunosa Dunbar and Skinner

716b. *Schwagerina crassitectoria* Dunbar and Skinner
S. guembeli pseudoregularis Dunbar and Skinner

716c. *Schwagerina guembeli pseudoregularis* Dunbar and Skinner

716d. *Schwagerina crassitectoria* Dunbar and Skinner

716e. *Schwagerina crassitectoria* (Dunbar and Skinner)
Staffella lacunosa Dunbar and Skinner

716f. *Parafusulina allisonensis* Ross

716h. *Parafusulina allisonensis* Ross?
P. deltoides Ross?

716i. *Triticites* spp. [Pennsylvanian-Virgilian]

716m. *Schwagerina* sp.
Triticites creekensis Thompson
T. pinguis Dunbar and Skinner

716r. *Monodiexodina linearis* (Dunbar and Skinner)
Paraschwagerina sp.
Schwagerina knighti Dunbar and Skinner
S. cf. *S. hawkinsi* Dunbar and Skinner

716u. *Nankinella huecoensis* (Dunbar and Skinner)
Pseudoschwagerina gerontica Dunbar and Skinner
Paraschwagerina sp.
Schwagerina dispansa Ross
S. sp.

716w. *Parafusulina boesei* Dunbar and Skinner
P. spp.

716y. *Nankinella huecoensis* (Dunbar and Skinner)
Paraschwagerina sp. B?
Pseudoreichelina sp.
Schwagerina hessensis Dunbar and Skinner?

717b. *Parafusulina attenuata* Dunbar and Skinner
Rauserella new species

717c. *Pseudoschwagerina convexa* Thompson?
P. sp.
Schwagerina sp.

718k. *Parafusulina boesei* Dunbar and Skinner
P. cf. *P. bakeri* Dunbar and Skinner
P. sp.

718-l. *Parafusulina rothi* Dunbar and Skinner
P. sp.

718n. *Monodiexodina linearis* (Dunbar and Skinner)
Nankinella huecoensis (Dunbar and Skinner)
Paraschwagerina sp.
Schwagerina sp.

718o. *Monodiexodina linearis* (Dunbar and Skinner)
Paraschwagerina sp.
Pseudoschwagerina sp.
Schwagerina sp.

718p. *Paraschwagerina* sp.
    Schwagerina? sp.

718r. *Pseudoschwagerina* spp.
    Schwagerina spp.
    Triticites sp.

718t. *Schwagerina hawkinsi* Dunbar and Skinner
    S. hessensis Dunbar and Skinner

718u. *Parafusulina allisonensis* Ross?

720e. *Schwagerina* sp. [somewhat similar to *S. dispansa* Ross]
    S. crassitectoria Dunbar and Skinner
    S. sp.
    Schubertella melonica Dunbar and Skinner
    Staffella lacunosa Dunbar and Skinner

    [I believe this is younger than Decie Ranch.]

720h. *Schwagerina* ex. gr. *S. crassitectoria* Dunbar and Skinner

720i. *Schubertella* sp.
    Schwagerina sp.

720j. *Schubertella* sp.
    Schwagerina sp.

720k. *Schubertella* sp.
    Schwagerina sp.

720–1. *Nankinella huecoensis* (Dunbar and Skinner)
    Pseudoschwagerina texana Dunbar and Skinner
    P. uddeni Dunbar and Skinner
    Schwagerina spp.

720m. *Nankinella* sp.
    Staffella sp.

720n. *Oketaella?* sp.
    Schwagerina sp.

720o. *Schwagerina crassitectoria* Dunbar and Skinner
    S. guembeli Dunbar and Skinner

720p. *Schwagerina crassitectoria* Dunbar and Skinner
    S. guembeli Dunbar and Skinner

720q. *Nankinella* sp.
    Schwagerina crassitectoria Dunbar and Skinner
    S. guembeli Dunbar and Skinner
    S. sp.
    Staffella lacunosa Dunbar and Skinner

720r. *Schwagerina crassitectoria* Dunbar and Skinner
    S. sp.
    Staffella sp.

720s. *Schwagerina crassitectoria* Dunbar and Skinner
    S. guembeli Dunbar and Skinner

720t. *Parafusulina* cf. *P. deltoides* Ross

720u. *Ozawainella* sp.
    Parafusulina cf. *P. deltoides* Ross
    Staffella sp.

720v. *Monodiexodina linearis* (Dunbar and Skinner)
    Schwagerina cf. *S. dispansa* Ross var. 2
    Staffella sp.

720w. *Schubertella* sp.
    Schwagerina spp.

720y. *Paraschwagerina* sp.
    Pseudoschwagerina sp. [ex. gr. *P. convexa* Thompson]
    Schubertella sp.
    Schwagerina sp.

720z. *Monodiexodina linearis* (Dunbar and Skinner)
    Paraschwagerina sp.
    Pseudoschwagerina? sp.
    Schubertella kingi Dunbar and Skinner
    Schwagerina extumida Ross

    [This is not Gaptank. Could this be the large slide block on the southeast nose of Leonard Mountain?]

721c. *Monodiexodina linearis* (Dunbar and Skinner)
    Paraschwagerina sp. [large]
    Schwagerina sp.

721d. *Monodiexodina linearis* (Dunbar and Skinner)
    Paraschwagerina spp.
    Schubertella kingi Dunbar and Skinner
    S. sp.

721e. *Monodiexodina linearis* (Dunbar and Skinner)
    Schubertella sp.
    Schwagerina cf. *S. extumida* Ross

721qc. *Parafusulina* aff. *P. splendens* Dunbar and Skinner
    P. n. sp.

722h. *Parafusulina* cf. *P. allisonensis* Ross
    Schubertella [Ross called this *S. muelleriedi* Thompson and Miller]

722m. *Parafusulina leonardensis* Ross
    Schubertella sp.
    Schwagerina dugoutensis Ross

722r. *Monodiexodina?* sp.
    Schwagerina sp.

722y. *Parafusulina?* sp.
    Schwagerina sp. [very poor material]

722z. *Parafusulina? leonardensis* Ross
    Schubertella sp. [same as Ross referred to *S. muelleriedi* Thompson and Miller]
    Schwagerina sp.

723f. *Parafusulina* spp. [all new]

723g. *Schubertella* sp.
    Schwagerina sp.

    [This poses a problem. I would tentatively assign it to Wolfcampian-2 (Lenox Hills), while recognizing that it might be low Leonardian.]

723j. *Parafusulina?* spp.

    [These resemble species of the *Schwagerina hawkinsi-hessensis* group, but seemingly have a better development of incipient cuniculi.]

723–l. *Schubertella melonica* Dunbar and Skinner
   Schwagerina spp. [similar to those of 723j but not the same.]

723s. *Parafusulina allisonensis* Ross
   P. cf. *P. leonardensis* Ross

723t. *Parafusulina kingorum* Dunbar and Skinner
   P. sp.

   [The types come from Word Limestone Number 4 (your Appel Ranch Member). I do not see how this can possibly be as old as Road Canyon (mapped as First Limestone of the Word = Road Canyon).]

723w. *Parafusulina rothi* Dunbar and Skinner
   P. sellardsi Dunbar and Skinner
   P. spp. [beautiful undescribed species, some of which resemble *P. sellardsi*]
   P. wildei Ross
   Rauserella sp.

   [In addition to the above, J. W. Skinner (letter of 26 Nov 1963) identified *Parafusulina boesei* Dunbar and Skinner and *Parafusulina sullivanensis* Ross. I don't believe this material is as old as Road Canyon, and it might be (Word) Limestone 3.] [This bed was originally mapped as First Limestone Member of the Word = Road Canyon Formation) but actually is Willis Ranch Member—GAC]

724b. *Parafusulina attenuata* Dunbar and Skinner
   P. cf. *P. splendens* Dunbar and Skinner

724c. *Parafusulina rothi* Dunbar and Skinner
   P. sp.
   P. splendens Dunbar and Skinner?

724d. *Parafusulina rothi* Dunbar and Skinner
   P. sullivanensis Ross

724e. *Parafusulina sullivanensis* Ross

724h. *Parafusulina boesei* Dunbar and Skinner
   P. cf. *P. sullivanensis* Ross

724o. *Paraschwagerina* sp.
   Schubertella sp.
   Schwagerina spp. [Sierra Diablo type]
   Staffella sp.

   [This ought to be Lenox Hills rather than Skinner Ranch: *Monodiexodina linearis* assemblage-zone.]

724v. *Paraschwagerina plena* Ross
   Schwagerina dispansa Ross

724w. *Chalaroschwagerina nelsoni opima* Dunbar and Skinner
   Schwagerina dispansa Ross?

724x. *Paraschwagerina plena* Ross
   P. sp.
   Schwagerina dispansa Ross
   Triticites sp. [reworked?]

   [This could not be Skinner Ranch.]

724y. *Parafusulina deliciasensis* Dunbar and Skinner
   P. sellardsi Dunbar and Skinner

724z. *Parafusulina* cf. *P. wordensis* Dunbar and Skinner
   P. sp.

725a. *Schwagerina* spp.

   [Wolfcampian (= Lenox Hills) and probably very close to 723g.]

725c. *Schwagerina* sp.
   Stewartina laxissima (Dunbar and Skinner)
   Triticites? sp.

   [This is not Bone Spring as supposed, but Late Wolfcampian Hueco.]

725q. *Parafusulina* cf. *P. boesei* Dunbar and Skinner

   [Very few sections for study, but this appears to be about Road Canyon.]

725u. *Parafusulina boesei* Dunbar and Skinner
   P. cf. *P. splendens* Dunbar and Skinner
   Rauserella sp.

   [About Road Canyon.]

726c. *Parafusulina sullivanensis* Ross

   [J. W. Skinner (letter of 26 Nov 1963) identified *Parafusulina boesei* Dunbar and Skinner and *P. wildei* Ross in addition to *P. sullivanensis*—GAC]

726g. *Parafusulina deltoides* Ross

   [This might be as old as Skinner Ranch.]

726i. *Monodiexodina linearis* (Dunbar and Skinner)
   Paraschwagerina plena Ross
   Schwagerina extumida Ross

726k. *Schwagerina crassitectoria* Dunbar and Skinner
   S. guembeli Dunbar and Skinner
   Staffella lacunosa Dunbar and Skinner

   [Assemblage-zone of *S. crassitectoria*.]

726n. *Parafusulina?* sp. [large, elongate]
   Schubertella melonica Dunbar and Skinner [abundant]

726q. *Parafusulina lineata* Dunbar and Skinner
   P. n. sp. [extremely thin walls]
   Rauserella sp.
   Skinnerina cf. *S. typicalis* Ross

726y. *Parafusulina leonardensis* Ross?
   Schubertella sp.

727c. *Schwagerina* cf. *S. longissimoidea* (Beede)
   Triticites subventricosus Dunbar and Skinner

727d. *Schwagerina emaciata* (Beede)
   S. sp.
   Triticites pinguis Dunbar and Skinner
   T. sp.

727h. *Schwagerina crassitectoria* Dunbar and Skinner
   S. guembeli Dunbar and Skinner
   Parafusulina cf. *P. allisonensis* Ross

727k. *Parafusulina leonardensis* Ross
   Schubertella sp.

   [Should be Leonard Number 1 Limestone (= Sullivan Peak Member).]

727-l. *Parafusulina leonardensis* Ross?
   Schubertella melonica Dunbar and Skinner
   S. sp.

   [All have been rolled about and redeposited: Leonard Number 1 Limestone or slightly higher.]

727q. *Parafusulina* sp.
   Schubertella melonica Dunbar and Skinner
   S. sp.

   [Leonard Number 1 Limestone or slightly higher.]

727s. *Parafusulina* aff. *P. durhami* Thompson [probably a new species]

727t. *Parafusulina* cf. *P. leonardensis* Ross
   Pseudoreichelina sp.
   Schwagerina dugoutensis Ross

727y. *Schwagerina crassitectoria* Dunbar and Skinner
   Staffella lacunosa Dunbar and Skinner

   [This cannot be Lenox Hills, but is Skinner Ranch equivalent.]

727z. *Schwagerina crassitectoria* Dunbar and Skinner
   S. guembeli Dunbar and Skinner

   [Not Lenox Hills.]

728m. *Chalaroschwagerina nelsoni* (Dunbar and Skinner)
   Pseudoschwagerina convexa Thompson
   Schwagerina cf. *S. diversiformis* Dunbar and Skinner
      [some resemble *S. wildei* Stewart]
   S. sp.

   [Assemblage-zone of *Monodiexodina linearis*. Late Wolfcampian, Lenox Hills equivalent.]

728n. *Schubertella* aff. *S. melonica* Dunbar and Skinner
   Schwagerina spp.

   [Some schwagerinas resemble *S. diversiformis* Dunbar and Skinner; others resemble some elongate species just below Leonard Number 1 Limestone (= Sullivan Peak Member) in the Lenox Hills. I would suggest a Skinner Ranch equivalent.]

728o. *Eoparafusulina* spp.
   Schwagerina sp.

   [Assemblage zone of *S. crassitectoria*.]

729a. *Schwagerina crassitectoria* Dunbar and Skinner
   S. guembeli Dunbar and Skinner

729b. *Parafusulina* sp. [axial filling to poles]
   Schwagerina cf. *S. hawkinsi* Dunbar and Skinner

   [Should be higher than Lenox Hills.]

730-l. *Schubertella melonica* Dunbar and Skinner
   Schwagerina aff. *S. hawkinsi* Dunbar and Skinner
   S. aff. *S. hessensis* Dunbar and Skinner

730o. *Parafusulina* sp.
   Schubertella melonica Dunbar and Skinner

730p. *Parafusulina* [large, elongate, with axial filling similar to *P. brooksensis* Ross]

730r. *Schwagerina* cf. *S. hawkinsi* Dunbar and Skinner
   S. cf. *S. hessensis* Dunbar and Skinner
   S. spp.

730t. *Parafusulina* spp.? [in detrital limestone with abundant *Tubiphytes*]

730x. *Parafusulina* cf. *P. allisonensis* Ross
   P. brooksensis Ross

730y. *Parafusulina* sp. [squeezed specimens]

730z. *Parafusulina* cf. *P. deliciasensis* Dunbar and Skinner
   P. cf. *P. sellardsi* Dunbar and Skinner
   P. sp.

   [This should be about Word Number 3 (= Willis Ranch Member).]

731. *Polydiexodina shumardi* Dunbar and Skinner
   Rauserella? sp.

731c. *Pseudoreichelina* sp.
   Schwagerina sp.
   Staffella lacunosa Dunbar and Skinner [abundant]

   [This should be low in the Hess.]

731e. *Parafusulina* cf. *P. attenuata* Dunbar and Skinner
   P. cf. *P. boesei* Dunbar and Skinner
   P. cf. *P. splendens* Dunbar and Skinner

731m. *Parafusulina* cf. *P. rothi* Dunbar and Skinner
   P. cf. *P. wordensis* Dunbar and Skinner
   P. sp. [Probably the same species that Ross called *P. antimonioensis* Dunbar which it is not]

   [This ought to be Word Number 4]

   Parafusulina cf. *P. rothi*

   [These appear to be somewhat younger than Word Number 2, or China Tank, but I am not sure]

731p. *Parafusulina sellardsi* Dunbar and Skinner
   P. spp.

   [This ought to be a Word Number 3 fauna.]

731u. *Parafusulina* sp. [completely silicified]

   [Difficult to say because of poor preservation, but probably Word Number 2 or 3.]

   Parafusulina cf. *P. maleyi* Dunbar and Skinner
   P. sp. [large]

   [Again this material is very poor but it should be as high as Word Number 2.]

731v. *Parafusulina* spp.

731w. *Parafusulina attenuata* Dunbar and Skinner
   P. boesei Dunbar and Skinner [not common]

P. splendens Dunbar and Skinner
Rauserella sp.

[Upper Road Canyon to Word Number 2 is about right.]

731x. *Parafusulina ironensis* Ross
P. cf. *P. sellardsi* Dunbar and Skinner
P. sullivanensis Ross
Rauserella sp.

[This appears to be about Word Number 2.]
Parafusulina spp.

[Two other species, broken up badly, but apparently about Road Canyon]

731y. *Parafusulina boesei* Dunbar and Skinner
P. sp.

[Probably Word Number 1, but possibly Number 2.]

Parafusulina boesei Dunbar and Skinner
P. cf. *P. splendens* Dunbar and Skinner
P. sp.
Rauserella sp.

[This appears to be good Road Canyon; two thin sections appear to be of different lithology and contain *Parafusulina rothi* Dunbar and Skinner.]

732c. *Parafusulina sellardsi* Dunbar and Skinner [not common]
P. cf. *P. wildei* Ross [Abundant; this latter form is a problem (other than just the name); Ross described three species (*P. wildei, P. deliciasensis,* and *P. antimonioensis*) missing on the last two identifications and mixing more than one species on the first.]

[I would say that this is Limestone Number 3 or younger, but not Limestone Number 4.]

732g. *Parafusulina attenuata* Dunbar and Skinner
P. cf. *P. rothi* Dunbar and Skinner
P. splendens Dunbar and Skinner
P. sullivanensis Ross

[Could be high as Word Number 2, but probably Word Number 1.]

732h. *Parafusulina attenuata* Dunbar and Skinner
P. aff. *P. bakeri* Dunbar and Skinner
P. boesei Dunbar and Skinner
P. splendens Dunbar and Skinner
P. sullivanensis Ross
Rauserella sp.

732i. *Parafusulina* cf. *P. bakeri* Dunbar and Skinner?
P. rothi Dunbar and Skinner
P. cf. *P. splendens* Dunbar and Skinner

[I believe that *P. bakeri* really is a Word species and one mistakenly called Leonard by Dunbar and Skinner; its proper location in the section has always been in doubt.]

P. sellardsi Dunbar and Skinner [loose specimens]

[Should be Word Number 3 with *P. sellardsi*.]

Parafusulina rothi Dunbar and Skinner
P. spp.

[This is probably very high Road Canyon if not younger.]

732j. *Parafusulina* cf. *P. sellardsi* Dunbar and Skinner
P. aff. *P. wordensis* Dunbar and Skinner
P. spp.

[It is difficult to believe that these are Road Canyon. I would say that they are closer to Word Number 3. You (Cooper & Grant) noted "definite Road Canyon" for 732j. That is pretty definite; but I identified *Parafusulina* cf. *sellardsi* and *P.* aff. *wordensis* from it along with *P.* spp. If this really is Road Canyon, then you must have gotten your collections mixed up, because there is no way that these fusulines could be that old.]

732n. *Parafusulina attenuata* Dunbar and Skinner
P. spp.

732o. *Parafusulina* spp. [with reefoid cobbles]

732p. *Parafusulina* sp. [very small, rather primitive-looking species]

732q. *Leella bellula* Dunbar and Skinner?
Polydiexodina sp.

732s. *Parafusulina* cf. *deliciasensis* Dunbar and Skinner
P. sp. [One extremely large microspheric specimen]

[This ought to be about Word Number 3.]

732t. *Parafusulina attenuata* Dunbar and Skinner
P. boesei Dunbar and Skinner
P. splendens Dunbar and Skinner
P. sullivanensis Ross
Rauserella [possibly 2 species]

732w. *Parafusulina attenuata* Dunbar and Skinner
P. splendens Dunbar and Skinner

732x. *Parafusulina boesei* Dunbar and Skinner
P. splendens Dunbar and Skinner
P. n. sp. [this looks like the form Ross called *P. deliciasensis,* but we do not think him correct on this point]
P. sp.
Rauserella [abundant]

[Are you sure about this being basal Road Canyon? It looks younger.]

Parafusulina attenuata Dunbar and Skinner [abundant]
P. boesei Dunbar and Skinner [abundant]
P. n. sp. [not common]
P. splendens Dunbar and Skinner [not common]

732y. *Parafusulina* cf. *P. ironensis* Ross
P. n. sp. [as in 732x]

[This could be as high as the lower part of Word Number 2.]

732z. *Parafusulina attenuata* Dunbar and Skinner [abundant]
P. boesei Dunbar & Skinner [abundant]

P. n. sp. [not common]
P. splendens Dunbar and Skinner [not common]

733b. *Parafusulina* cf. *P. boesei* Dunbar and Skinner
P. sp.

[Why isn't this also Road Canyon?]

733c. *Parafusulina* aff. *P. rothi* Dunbar and Skinner
P. spp.

[About Word Number 2.]

733d. *Parafusulina splendens* Dunbar and Skinner
P. sp.

[About Word Number 2.]

733e. *Parafusulina splendens* Dunbar and Skinner
P. sp.

[About Word Number 2.]

733h. *Schwagerina* aff. *S. hessensis* Dunbar and Skinner

733i. *Parafusulina* sp.
Schwagerina? aff. *S. hessensis* Dunbar and Skinner

[This looks younger than Decie Ranch.]

733k. *Parafusulina deltoides* Ross
P. sp.
Staffella sp. [abundant]

733n. *Parafusulina splendens* Dunbar and Skinner
P. sp.

733o. *Parafusulina* spp.

[This looks younger than Road Canyon.]

733p. *Parafusulina attenuata* Dunbar and Skinner
P. boesei Dunbar and Skinner
P. splendens Dunbar and Skinner?

733s. *Schwagerina* spp. [or primitive *Parafusulina*]
Staffella sp.

733u. *Parafusulina boesei* Dunbar and Skinner
P. sullivanensis Ross
P. sp.

733v. *Parafusulina attenuata* Dunbar and Skinner
P. boesei Dunbar and Skinner
P. sp. [slender with axial filling]
Rauserella sp. [very abundant]

733w. *Parafusulina* cf. *P. boesei* Dunbar and Skinner
P. cf. *P. maleyi* Dunbar and Skinner
P. sp.
Rauserella sp.

733x. *Parafusulina boesei* Dunbar and Skinner
P. sp.

733y. *Parafusulina* spp. [silicified]

733z. *Parafusulina* spp. [much silicification]

[This might be Word Number 2 or 3 equivalent.]

734b. *Parafusulina* spp.

734d. *Parafusulina* spp.

734e. *Parafusulina* spp.

735e. *Parafusulina boesei* Dunbar and Skinner
P. sp.

736b. *Schubertella melonica* Dunbar and Skinner
Schwagerina cf. *S. pseudoregularis* Dunbar and Skinner
S. sp.

736c. *Parafusulina* cf. *P. allisonensis* Ross

736e. *Parafusulina durhami* Thompson and Miller
P. sp.

[Late Leonardian.]

736f. *Parafusulina* cf. *P. durhami* Thompson and Miller

[This is obviously not as young as Road Canyon seen anywhere previously.]

736g. *Parafusulina* spp. [one resembles an "underdeveloped" *P. boesei*]

736o. *Parafusulina rothi* Dunbar and Skinner

736p. *Parafusulina boesei* Dunbar and Skinner

736q. *Parafusulina* cf. *P. boesei* Dunbar and Skinner
P. sp.

737c. *Parafusulina splendens* Dunbar and Skinner
P. cf. *P. sullivanensis* Ross

737h. *Parafusulina* cf. *P. rothi* Dunbar and Skinner
P. splendens Dunbar and Skinner

737i. *Parafusulina attenuata* Dunbar and Skinner
P. boesei Dunbar and Skinner [rare]
P. splendens Dunbar and Skinner [rare]

737m. *Parafusulina boesei* Dunbar and Skinner
P. rothi Dunbar and Skinner
P. splendens Dunbar and Skinner

737n. *Parafusulina attenuata* Dunbar and Skinner
P. boesei Dunbar and Skinner

737o. *Parafusulina rothi* Dunbar and Skinner [rare]
P. sp. [fragmental]

737p. *Parafusulina rothi* Dunbar and Skinner
P. sp.
Skinnerina sp. [elongate]

737q. *Parafusulina splendens* Dunbar and Skinner?
P. spp. [One is a beautiful, thin-walled, delicate species; the other is inflated fusiform, but is very rare. Material is fragmentary.]

737r. *Parafusulina* cf. *P. rothi* Dunbar and Skinner
P. splendens Dunbar and Skinner
Skinnerina sp. [rare]

[Probably Road Canyon, but could be China Tank.]

737t. *Triticites* cf. *T. acutuloides* Ross
T. cf. *T. marathonensis* Ross

[This cannot possibly be Lenox Hills; it is clearly Missourian (Gaptank).]

737x. *Parafusulina* spp.

[This material is difficult to assess. I would suspect it to be from somewhere low in the Road Canyon, but I am not sure. The species has/have large proloculi, large shells, but the cuniculi do not appear to be too advanced.]

737y. *Parafusulina attenuata* Dunbar and Skinner
P. boesei Dunbar and Skinner
P. cf. *P. rothi* Dunbar and Skinner
P. sp. [as one in 737q]
P. splendens Dunbar and Skinner

738d. *Skinnerella* spp.

738e. [Forms which I have suggested in the past as representing an undescribed genus, characterized by having primitive cuniculi, very thin spirotheca, tight coiling, rather small proloculi, and intense septal fluting. Similar, if not identical forms occur in the Bone Spring Limestone above Kriz Lens and in Victorio Canyon in the Sierra Diablo, and in the lower parts of your Skinner Ranch in the eastern Glass Mountains. One specimen resembles *Schwagerina diversiformis* Dunbar and Skinner (Late Wolfcampian–Early Leonardian). We have good Lenox Hills fauna from Udden's "Transition Beds," his bed 4, Cibolo ("Brecciated Zone"). Primitive *Parafusulina* similar, if not identical to some of Ross' small species from the Hess. I would interpret these as Early Leonardian. *Nankinella* sp. and dasyclad algae are also present. We have good Wolfcamp from the ("Lower Brecciated Zone"), Udden's bed 5.]

738g. *Schwagerina* cf. *S. hawkinsi* Dunbar and Skinner
S. sp.

738k. *Parafusulina* spp.

[Badly squeezed material but similar to Victorio Peak species seen elsewhere; Leonardian.]

738m. *Parafusulina* aff. *P. fountaini* Dunbar and Skinner
P. leonardensis Ross
P. sp.

[Early Leonardian.]

738q. *Chalaroschwagerina* sp.
Schwagerina cf. *S. hessensis* Dunbar and Skinner

[I would consider this late Wolfcampian or earliest Leonardian.]

738x. *Parafusulina* cf. *P. leonardensis* Ross
P. spp.

[Material very similar to 738m; Leonardian.]

738y. *Parafusulina* cf. *P. brooksensis* Ross
P. cf. *P. vidriensis* Ross
P. sp.

[Leonardian; upper Hess.]

738z. *Parafusulina* spp. [poor specimens, but not too different from below. One form looks rather intermediate between *P. leonardensis* Ross and *P. durhami* Thompson and Miller.]

[Leonardian.]

739a. *Parafusulina* cf. *P. rothi* Dunbar and Skinner
P. splendens Dunbar and Skinner
P. wildei Ross

[This material could be upper Road Canyon, but I would place it higher, possibly China Tank (Word Number 2).

739b. *Parafusulina deliciasensis* Dunbar and Skinner
P. sellardsi Dunbar and Skinner
Rauserella erratica Dunbar

[Appears to be a clear-cut Willis Ranch (Word Number 3) fauna.]

739e. *Parafusulina boesei* Dunbar and Skinner
P. maleyi Dunbar and Skinner
P. rothi Dunbar and Skinner
P. splendens Dunbar and Skinner

739f. *Parafusulina splendens* Dunbar and Skinner?

[Not common and poorly preserved; Road Canyon.]

739i. *Parafusulina spissisepta* Ross
P. vidriensis Ross

[Leonardian; upper Hess.]

739j. *Parafusulina* sp.
Schwagerina? sp.

[Leonardian.]

Identifications by Carl O. Dunbar

When we were studying the Hess Ranch Horst and parts of the Wolf Camp Hills and their extension to the east, we were unable to get good brachiopod faunas in the conglomerates, thin-bedded limestones, and dolomites that occur in these areas.

Fusulinids are abundant in some of the thin limestone beds. We asked Dr. Carl O. Dunbar, then of Yale University, to help us. He identified the specimens from the USNM localities in the list below. We are most grateful to Dr. Dunbar for his help in identifying the fusulinids and for his counsel on stratigraphic problems.

Carl O. Dunbar, formerly of the Department of Geology, Yale University, New Haven, Connecticut.

702v. *Schwagerina guembeli* Dunbar and Skinner
 S. guembeli pseudoregularis Dunbar and Skinner

702w. *Schwagerina guembeli* Dunbar and Skinner

703f. *Schwagerina crassitectoria* Dunbar and Skinner

703g. *Schwagerina guembeli* Dunbar and Skinner
 S. guembeli pseudoregularis Dunbar and Skinner

703h. *Schwagerina crassitectoria* Dunbar and Skinner
 S. guembeli Dunbar and Skinner

703i. *Schwagerina guembeli* Dunbar and Skinner [rare]
 Staffella sp. [very abundant]

703j. *Schwagerina crassitectoria* Dunbar and Skinner
 S. guembeli Dunbar and Skinner
 Staffella sp.

703n. *Schwagerina hawkinsi* Dunbar and Skinner
 S. hessensis Dunbar and Skinner

703q. *Parafusulina* n. sp.

703u. *Parafusulina* sp.

704k. *Monodiexodina linearis* (Dunbar and Skinner)
 Schubertella kingi Dunbar and Skinner
 Schwagerina nelsoni Dunbar and Skinner

704–l. *Parafusulina* n. sp.

704m. *Parafusulina* n. sp.

704o. *Monodiexodina linearis* (Dunbar and Skinner)
 Paraschwagerina acuminata Dunbar and Skinner
 Schwagerina nelsoni Dunbar and Skinner

704p. *Monodiexodina linearis* (Dunbar and Skinner) [very
 abundant]
 Schubertella sp.

704r. *Pseudoschwagerina uddeni* (Beede and Kniker) [rare]
 [rare]
 Schwagerina diversiformis Dunbar and Skinner [abundant]

704u. *Pseudoschwagerina texana* Dunbar and Skinner
 Schwagerina compacta (White)
 S. nelsoni Dunbar and Skinner

705ca. *Monodiexodina linearis* Dunbar and Skinner
 Schwagerina hessensis Dunbar and Skinner
 S. nelsoni Dunbar and Skinner

705r. *Parafusulina* sp.

705u. *Parafusulina* sp.

706j. *Parafusulina* n. sp.

706k. *Parafusulina* n. sp.

706–l. *Schwagerina guembeli* Dunbar and Skinner

706r. *Parafusulina boesei* Dunbar and Skinner
 P. boesei attenuata Dunbar and Skinner

706s. *Triticites primarius* Burma?
 T. sp.

 [These all appear to be redeposited but are a Gaptank Formation fauna.]

706t. *Schwagerina emaciata* (Beede)
 Triticites pinguis Dunbar and Skinner
 T. ventricosus (Meek and Hayden)

706u. *Pseudoschwagerina uddeni* (Beede and Kniker)
 Schwagerina sp.
 Triticites ventricosus (Meek and Hayden)

706w. *Monodiexodina linearis* (Dunbar and Skinner)
 Schwagerina sp.

707r. *Schwagerina* sp. [near *Parafusulina*]

708f. *Schubertella melonica* Dunbar and Skinner [abundant]
 Schwagerina sp.

708i. *Schubertella melonica* Dunbar and Skinner [very abundant

715b. *Pseudoschwagerina uddeni* Dunbar and Skinner [including microspheric shells]
 Schwagerina emaciata (Beede)
 S. pugunculus Ross [including microspheric shells]
 S. n. sp.?

Identifications by Charles A. Ross

Dr. Charles A. Ross, while at Yale, identified many samples from USNM localities sent there for study. He was, at that time, studying the stratigraphy and fusulinids of the Glass Mountains and later he published extensively on these subjects (see Ross, 1959, 1960, 1962b, 1963a, 1963b, 1965). We are most grateful to Dr. Ross for his identifications and the comments included in his list.

Charles A. Ross, Department of Geology, Western Washington State College, Bellingham, Washington 98225.

700a. *Triticites newelli* Burma
 Triticites aff. *T. primarius* Burma

701f. *Triticites cullomensis* Dunbar and Skinner
 T. primarius Burma

701x. *Triticites primarius* Burma

701y. *Triticites comptus* Ross

702i. *Triticites cullomensis* Dunbar and Skinner

702k. *Triticites cullomensis* Dunbar and Skinner?

702–l. *Pseudoschwagerina texana* Dunbar and Skinner
 Schwagerina gracilitatis Dunbar and Skinner

702n. *Triticites cullomensis* Dunbar and Skinner

702o. *Triticites beedei* Dunbar and Skinner
    T. primarius Burma

702p. *Triticites cullomensis* Dunbar and Skinner

702q. *Triticites cullomensis* Dunbar and Skinner

702s. *Triticites beedei* Dunbar and Skinner?
    T. comptus Ross

702t. *Paraschwagerina acuminata* Dunbar and Skinner?
    Schwagerina compacta (White)
    S. gracilitatis Dunbar and Skinner

702u. *Triticites beedei* Dunbar and Skinner
    T. primarius Burma

702x. *Pseudoschwagerina parabeedei* Ross?
    Schwagerina compacta (White)
    S. spp.

702z. *Triticites primarius* Burma

703k. *Triticites cullomensis* Dunbar and Skinner

703–l. *Triticites beedei* Dunbar and Skinner
    T. cullomensis Dunbar and Skinner

703m. *Schwagerina pugunculus* Ross
    Triticites pinguis Dunbar and Skinner
    T. uddeni Dunbar and Skinner
    T. ventricosus (Meek and Hayden)

703p. *Triticites cullomensis* Dunbar and Skinner

703r. *Triticites cullomensis* Dunbar and Skinner

703t. *Pseudoschwagerina texana* Dunbar and Skinner
    P. uddeni (Beede and Kniker)
    Schwagerina gracilitatus Dunbar and Skinner

703v. *Triticites cullomensis* Dunbar and Skinner

703x. *Triticites cullomensis* Dunbar and Skinner

704a. *Triticites primarius* Burma

704b. *Chalaroschwagerina? nelsoni* (Dunbar and Skinner)

704c. *Triticites comptus* Dunbar and Skinner

704e. *Monodiexodina linearis* (Dunbar and Skinner)
    Schwagerina diversiformis Dunbar and Skinner

704h. *Triticites beedei* Dunbar and Skinner

704i. *Chalaroschwagerina? nelsoni* (Dunbar and Skinner)
    Monodiexodina linearis (Dunbar and Skinner)

704j. *Pseudoschwagerina parabeedei* Ross
    Schwagerina diversiformis Dunbar and Skinner

704q. *Chalaroschwagerina? nelsoni* (Dunbar and Skinner)
    Monodiexodina linearis (Dunbar and Skinner)

704r. *Pseudoschwagerina parabeedei* Ross?
    Schwagerina diversiformis Dunbar and Skinner

704t. *Chalaroschwagerina? nelsoni* (Dunbar and Skinner)
    Monodiexodina linearis (Dunbar and Skinner)

704u. *Chalaroschwagerina? nelsoni* (Dunbar and Skinner)
    Pseudoschwagerina cf. *P. texana* Dunbar and Skinner?

704v. *Chalaroschwagerina? nelsoni* (Dunbar and Skinner)
    Pseudoschwagerina parabeedei Ross

704w. *Triticites primarius* Burma

705f. *Triticites joensis* Thompson

705j. *Triticites cullomensis* Dunbar and Skinner

705k. *Monodiexodina linearis* (Dunbar and Skinner)
    Pseudoschwagerina cf. *P. texana* Dunbar and Skinner
    Schwagerina crebrisepta Ross
    S. diversiformis Dunbar and Skinner
    Stewartina laxissima (Dunbar and Skinner)

705m. *Pseudoschwagerina robusta* (Meek)
    P. cf. *P. texana* Dunbar and Skinner
    Schwagerina diversiformis Dunbar and Skinner

705q. *Triticites cullomensis* Dunbar and Skinner

705t. *Pseudoschwagerina* cf. *P. texana* Dunbar and Skinner

705v. *Triticites primarius* Burma

705x. *Triticites primarius* Burma

705y. *Triticites cullomensis* Dunbar and Skinner

706h. *Monodiexodina linearis* (Dunbar and Skinner)
    Pseudoschwagerina cf. *P. texana* Dunbar and Skinner
    Stewartina laxissima (Dunbar and Skinner)

706i. *Monodiexodina linearis* (Dunbar and Skinner)

706p. *Triticites pinguis* Dunbar and Skinner
    T. ventricosus (Meek and Hayden)?
    T. uddeni Dunbar and Skinner

706q. *Triticites comptus* Ross

706v. *Paraschwagerina plena* Ross
    Pseudoschwagerina parabeedei Ross [pebbles]
    Schwagerina crebrisepta Ross
    S. emaciata (Beede) [pebbles]
    S. pugunculus Ross [pebbles]

    [Mostly reworked specimens of *Triticites* cf. *T. uddeni* Dunbar and Skinner and *Pseudoschwagerina* sp.]

706x. *Pseudoschwagerina gigantea* (White)
    P. texana Dunbar and Skinner
    P. uddeni Dunbar and Skinner
    Schwagerina pugunculus Ross

707j. *Pseudoschwagerina parabeedei* Ross

707m. *Chalaroschwagerina? nelsoni* (Dunbar and Skinner)
    Pseudoschwagerina robusta (Meek)
    Schwagerina crebrisepta Ross

707o. *Schwagerina crebrisepta* Ross
    S. laxissima Dunbar and Skinner

708g. *Chalaroschwagerina? nelsoni* (Dunbar and Skinner)

708h. *Chalaroschwagerina? nelsoni* (Dunbar and Skinner)
    Stewartina laxissima (Dunbar and Skinner)

708i. *Schubertella melonica* Dunbar and Skinner

708k. *Chalaroschwagerina? nelsoni* (Dunbar and Skinner)

Monodiexodina linearis (Dunbar and Skinner)
Schwagerina diversiformis Dunbar and Skinner

708n. *Triticites burgessae* Burma

718q. *Schwagerina emaciata* (Beede)
    S. pugunculus Ross

Age Relations of Fusulinaceans from the
Gaptank, Neal Ranch, Lenox Hill, and Skinner Ranch Formations

BY CHARLES A. ROSS

The species of fusulinaceans listed above and also in Dunbar and Skinner (1937), and Ross (1959, 1963, 1965, and 1975), indicate the following ages. The "*Uddenites*-bearing" shale and the limestone beneath it have *Triticites secalicus, T. cullomensis,* early *T. ventricosus, Dunbarinella* sp., and *Waeringella* sp. and, therefore, are older than the Thrifty Formation of northcentral Texas and are close to, or the same age as, the Ivan Limestone Member and superjacent beds in the Graham Formation in northcentral Texas. In terms of the Russian Platform and pre-Ural sections, these fusulinaceans compare well with those in the middle to upper part, but not the highest part, of the Carboniferous Gzhel'ian Stage.

"Bed 2 of the Gray Limestone Member" has a meager fusulinacean fauna of three or four species in the Wolfcamp Hills and laterally equivalent beds have only a few additional species to contribute to this fauna. Most of the species are the same as or similar to those in the underlying "*Uddenites*-bearing" shale. *Triticites capaxoides* Ross, a species with a wide range of prolocular sizes, and *T. nealensis* Ross are probably characteristic of "Bed 2." Wilde (1971) has reported *Schwagerina* species from this bed and considered it equivalent to the lowest zone of the McCloud, which also is difficult to correlate with other late Paleozoic sections. Bostwick (1962) illustrated and identified a number of fusulinaceans from the "*Uddenites*-bearing" shale and higher beds at two places along the Glass Mountains escarpment. His illustrated specimens identified as *Schwagerina* from the "*Uddenites*-bearing" shale and "Bed 2" should be assigned to *Triticites*. Four of the illus-trated specimens that he assigned to *Schwagerina* (Bostwick, 1962, pl. 164: figs. 4, 14; pl. 166: figs. 11, 13) are probably *Triticites confertoides* (Ross, 1965), an advanced species with folded septa in which the chomata adjacent to the tunnel in later volutions become more or less discontinuous (pseudo-chomata). This set of features is similar to features found in *Daixina,* a Russian Platform and pre-Ural genus, which ranges through the upper part of the Gzhel'ian Stage and into the Asselian. One species of *Daixina* (not very similar to *T. confertoides* in other features) and species of *Pseudofusulina* form an important zone at the top of the Gzhel'ian marking the "Orenburgian Stage" of some Soviet authors. The top few decimeters of "Bed 2" commonly are a limestone conglomerate and may contain a mixed fusulinacean fauna.

The Neal Ranch and Lenox Hills formations constitute the Zone of *Pseudoschwagerina* in the Glass Mountains, which includes *Triticites (Leptotriticites), Paraschwagerina, Pseudofusulina, Schwagerina, Stewartina, Eoparafusulina,* and *Schubertella* along with *Triticites (Triticites).* This fusulinacean fauna compares well with that from the Asselian; however, several differences also are apparent. The Asselian "Zone of *Schwagerina,*" because of taxonomic confusion and disagreement, is not based on the same genus as the North American Zone of *Schwagerina* or the Zone of *Pseudoschwagerina* for reasons that are too involved to explore here. The species on which the Soviet "Zone of *Schwagerina*" is based have been assigned to *Sphaeroschwagerina,* a genus that many Soviet workers do not accept and which is not known from West Texas. Primitive species of *Pseudoschwagerina,* similar to those in the Neal Ranch fauna, occur with *Sphaeroschwagerina* in the Asselian, so it seems reasonably certain that the Asselian and Neal Ranch faunas

Charles A. Ross, Department of Geology, Western Washington State College, Bellingham, Washington 98225.

are correlative. The Sakmarian, Tastubian, and Sterlitamakian beds of the Ural region lack both *Sphaeroschwagerina* and *Pseudoschwagerina*, but have species of *Schwagerina* (North American sense) and *Pseudofusulina* that are similar to those from the Lenox Hills. The "Hess Ledge" and the Decie Ranch Member of the Skinner Ranch Formation have fusulinacean faunas that are similar to those of the lower part of the Artinskian Stage and include primitive *Parafusulina* and *Eoparafusulina*.

Corrigenda

Corrections to Localities

(appearing in Part I, pages 135–165)

Page

138   AMNH 813: *should read* AMNH 843.

142   USNM 702r (first 702r that follows 702m): *should read* USNM 702n.

145   USNM 706b: *should read* (lower thin lens between Willis Ranch and Appel Ranch members).

150   USNM 711d: *for* N 20° W *read* N 2° W.

157   USNM 722g: *should read* 1.45 mi S 72° W of hill 4910, 1.25 mi N 9° E of hill 4920, Altuda quadrangle.

158   USNM 722z: *should read* 50 ft above top of Decie Ranch Member in ravine 3.1 mi S 10° E of Sullivan Peak, 1.03 mi N 73° E of hill 5300, Lenox Hills Formation, Altuda quadrangle.

158   USNM 723u: *for* S 70° E *read* S 70° W.

158   USNM 724a: *for* N 56° W *read* S 56° W.

159   USNM 726i: *for* Hess Ranch quadrangle *read* Hess Canyon quadrangle.

161   USNM 728e: *for* 2.15 miles *read* 2.45 mi.

163   USNM 733j: *for* (hill 5191) *read* (hill 5195).

164   USNM 740-l: *should read* Capitan Formation: About 7300 ft elev., 0.9 mi S 58° E of Guadalupe Peak, 0.8 mi N 51° E of El Capitan, Guadalupe Peak quadrangle.

Additions to Localities

Abbreviations used in these locality designations now added to the lists appearing in Part I, pages 135–165, are:

A = American Museum of Natural History [abbreviated elsewhere herein: AMNH]

N = National Museum of Natural History, formerly United States National Museum [abbreviated elsewhere herein: USNM]

Additions to the list of United States Geological Survey Localities (Part I, page 135) are included in the faunal list of brachiopods arranged by USGS localities.

A323. Phosphoria Formation (Bed 13) [about 6 mi NE of Indian Pass (hill 5970), just E of hill 7200, Confusion Range, Fish Springs Quad., Utah]

A351. Bell Canyon Formation (Lamar Member) [N side of mouth of McKittrick Canyon, 5/16 mi SE of hill 7059 just beyond margin of Lamar Limestone, Guadalupe Mts.]

A390. Hueco Formation [1.1 mi NE of BM 5325 ft, Rancheria Mt., Hueco Mts., El Paso and Hudspeth counties, Texas Oil and Gas Preliminary Sheet No. 36, No. 1]

A397. Bell Canyon Formation (probably Pinery Member) [on promontory of spur approximately 0.2 mi E of Hegler Ranch house on N side of road, Guadalupe Peak Quad.]

A402. Cherry Canyon Formation (Manzanita Member) [gulch immediately W of southern promontory of Rader Ridge, approximately 1 mi SW of Nickel Creek station]

A409. Bell Canyon Formation (McCombs Member) [head of ridge to S of Rader Ridge and between it and Smith Spring (N of Juniper Spring), Guadalupe Peak Quad.]

A633. Bone Spring Formation [180 ft below top of northeasternmost hill of Bone Spring Limestone in Baylor Mts.]

A653. Hueco Formation [hill SE of hill 4978, N of drainage divide in Red Tank Canyon, Baylor Mts.]

A661. Bone Spring Formation [small reef at entrance to Bone Spring Canyon about 100 ft below Brushy Canyon base]

A663. Bone Spring Formation (Victorio Peak Member) [silicified blocks, top of highest cliff on S side of Pure-Hunter oil well canyon, 0.4 mi due E of well site, Guadalupe Mts.]

A799. Capitan Formation (= Lamar Member) [N side of McKittrick Canyon at mouth; base of first cliff S 40° E of triangulation station 6500]

N513c. Graham Formation [Road to Barton Chapel, 4.8 mi S of Texas 24, 0.5 mi N of Stradley School, Jack County]

N518v. Gunsight Formation [SE 1/4 SW 1/4 plot S1, 2.2 mi N 80° W of 36th Division State Park Headquarters, 100 yards north of Park road 15, 5.5 mi S 80° E of Grosvenor, Brown Co.]

N700b. Gaptank Formation [small nob 1/4 to 1/2 mi S of locality 700]

N700e. Gaptank Formation [*Prouddenites* bed, in gully, 1.9 mi S 5° W of Arnold Ranch, Monument Spring Quad.]

N700i. Gaptank Formation (*Uddenites* zone) [0.2 to 0.3 mi NE of hill 5060, Wolf Camp Hills, Hess Canyon Quad.]

N701j. Neal Ranch Formation [float, Wolf Camp Hills, Hess Canyon Quad.]

N701n. Neal Ranch Formation (bed 14 of P. B. King) [on W side of canyon at head, center of Wolf Camp Hills, Hess Canyon Quad.]

N701o. Gaptank Formation (*Uddenites*-bearing Shale Member) [patch of shale on E side of Geologist Canyon mouth, 0.55 mi S 71° W of hill 5060 ft, W end of Wolf Camp Hills, Hess Canyon Quad.]

N701s. Gaptank Formation (*Uddenites*-bearing Shale Member) [along road 0.32 mi S 18° E of hill 4815, 3 mi W of Conoly Brooks Ranch, at 4460 ft, Hess Canyon Quad.]

N701w. Gaptank Formation (*Uddenites*-bearing Shale Member) [edge of hill just SE of knob, 0.33 mi S 75° W of hill 5060, Wolf Camp Hills, Hess Canyon Quad.]

N702i. Gaptank Formation [just above limestone bed 2 of P. B. King (not equal to Gray Limestone Member of P. B. King) 0.5 mi SW of Gaptank, W of Stockton Pass, 4 mi NE of Montgomery Ranch, Hess Canyon Quad.]

N702n. Gaptank Formation (*Uddenites*-bearing Shale Member) [E slope of W side of Amphitheater, 0.8 mi N 40° E of hill 5060, Wolf Camp Hills, Hess Canyon Quad.]

N704z. Leonard Formation [near top of hill 5200, 1/4 mi SSW of hill 5300, Altuda Quad.]

N705c. Gaptank Formation [Ammonites from near head of ravine at 5075 ft on E side of SE nose of Leonard Mtn., 0.28 mi S 64° E of BM 5860, Hess Canyon Quad.]

N705i. Gaptank Formation [under large cedar tree in ravine in SE nose of Leonard Mtn., near top of shale, 0.28 mi S 64° E of BM 5860, Hess Canyon Quad.]

N708v. Skinner Ranch Formation (Sullivan Peak Member) [long dip slope of hill 5021, at stream and road crossing, N end of hill, 1.5 mi WNW of hill 5021, Altuda Quad.]

N709b. Moran Formation [quarry on E side of U.S. 283, 5 mi SE of Moran]

N711s. Road Canyon Formation [7 ft above 15 foot limestone, 1.6 mi S 32° E of BM 4973, Gilliland Canyon, Altuda Quad.]

N712d. Hueco Formation [1/2 mi NNE of Hueco Inn, E of road, Hueco Mts.]

N713h. Neal Ranch Formation (= beds 5–8 of P. B. King) [E end of canyon in Wolf Camp Hills, Hess Canyon Quad.]

N713v. Cathedral Mountain Formation [10–15 ft above Leonard Limestone No. 1; SE nose of hill 4920, Altuda Quad.]

N714z. Skinner Ranch Formation [0.25 mi S 43° W of hill 5021, E of Sullivan Ranch Road, Altuda Quad.]

N715-l. Lenox Hills Formation [near base of hill just W of Slick-Urschell well, Decie Ranch, Altuda Quad.]

N715o. Skinner Ranch Formation (Sullivan Peak Member) [0.25 mi S 30° W of hill 4920, Altuda Quad.]

N715p. Skinner Ranch Formation (Sullivan Peak Member) [loose on slope under cliff of Leonard Limestone Number 1 in section 0.95 mi N 79° E of hill 5300, Lenox Hills, Altuda Quad.]

N715q. Hess Formation [0.48 mi N 81° E of BM 5652, E of Old Word Ranch, Hess Canyon Quad.]

N715u. Skinner Ranch Formation (Sullivan Peak Member) [W side Sullivan Ranch Road, 0.77 mi S 33° E of hill 4920, 1.48 mi N 61° E of hill 5300, Lenox Hills, Altuda Quad.]

N716b. Hess Formation [at 4940 ft in long section 0.6 mi due N of hill 4952 in mountain front N of Wolf Camp Hills, Hess Canyon Quad.]

N716c. Hess Formation [at 4972 ft in section 0.6 mi due N of hill 4952 in mountain front N of Wolf Camp Hills, Hess Canyon Quad.]

N716g. Hess Formation [at 5188 ft in long section 0.6 mi due N of hill 4952, in mountain front N of Wolf Camp Hills, Hess Canyon Quad.]

N718g. Cathedral Mountain Formation [on slope above saddle, 0.6 mi S 80° W of hill 5021, at about 4890 ft, Altuda Quad.]

N718r. Neal Ranch Formation [ledge of brown limestone 20–25 ft below Lenox Hills conglomerate, center of hill just W of main canyon, 0.65 mi N 76° W of hill 5060, Wolf Camp Hills, Hess Canyon Quad.]

N718t. Skinner Ranch Formation (Decie Ranch Member) [near base of "Wolfcamp" of P. B. King just S of second knob of spur at E end of Lenox Hills, 0.5 mi W of Sullivan (Yates) Ranch road, 1.2 mi N 78° E of hill 5300, N of Decie Ranch, Altuda Quad.]

N718u. Hess Formation [100 ft below Taylor Ranch Member at locality 702d]

N718v. Skinner Ranch Formation (Poplar Tank Member) [0.53 mi N 86° E of hill 5300 at about 4875 ft elevation, Altuda Quad.]

N720h. Skinner Ranch Formation (Decie Ranch Member) [1.28 mi S 80° W of hill 5816, W side of Hess Ranch Horst, Hess Canyon Quad.]

N720i. Skinner Ranch Formation (Decie Ranch Member: *Scacchinella* beds) [0.65 mi N 17° W of Hess Ranch house, Hess Canyon Quad.]

N720k. Skinner Ranch Formation (Decie Ranch Member: *Scacchinella* beds) [0.63 mi N 8° W of Hess Ranch house, Hess Canyon Quad.]

N720-l. Neal Ranch Formation [base of section about 4820 ft, 2.42 mi S 87.5° W of hill 5060, W of Wolf Camp Hills, Hess Canyon Quad.]

N720m. Hess Formation [at 4932 ft elevation in hill 2.42 mi S 87.5° W of hill 5060, W of Wolf Camp Hills, Hess Canyon Quad.]

N720n. Hess Formation [at 4943 ft elevation in hill 2.42 mi S 87.5° W of hill 5060, W of Wolf Camp Hills, Hess Canyon Quad.]

N720o. Hess Formation [5040 ft in hill, same as locality 720m]

N720p. [5051 ft in hill, same as locality 720m]

N720q. Hess Formation [5102 ft in hill, same as locality 720m]

N720r. Hess Formation [5106 ft in hill, same as locality 720m]

N720s. Hess Formation [5160 ft in hill, same as locality 720m]

N720t. Hess Formation [5251 ft in hill, same as locality 720m]

N720u. Hess Formation [5262 ft in hill, same locality as 720m]

N720v. Lenox Hills Formation [5746 ft elevation in hill 5816, Hess Ranch Horst, W side of hill above saddle at 5600 ft, Hess Canyon Quad.]

N720w. Lenox Hills Formation [5801 ft elevation on W side of hill 5816, Hess Ranch Horst, Hess Canyon Quad.]

N720y. Lenox Hills Formation [0.44 mi N 8° W of hill 5816, Hess Ranch Horst, Hess Canyon Quad.]

N720z. Lenox Hills Formation [SE nose of Leonard Mtn., Hess Canyon Quad.]

N721c. Lenox Hills Formation [27 ft above base of "white" limestone on knob in pass, 0.55 mi due W of hill 5816, Hess Ranch Horst, Hess Canyon Quad.]

N721d. Lenox Hills Formation [31 ft above base of "white" limestone in knob pass, 0.55 mi S 87.5° W of hill 5816, Hess Ranch Horst, Hess Canyon Quad.]

N721e. Lenox Hills Formation [crest of knob in pass, 0.55 mi S 87.5° W of hill 5816, Hess Ranch Horst, Hess Canyon Quad.]

N721f. Cathedral Mountain Formation [loose, 86 ft below Word Limestone, slope facing Leonard Mtn., Hess Canyon Quad.]

N721h. Gaptank Formation (*Uddenites*-bearing Shale Member) [dip slope on S side of canyon, 0.4 mi up from mouth, upper *Uddenites* zone slope between hill 5060 and canyon, Hess Canyon Quad.]

N721n. Neal Ranch Formation (probably Gray Limestone Member = Bed 2 of P. B. King) [loose on NW slope of knob on S side of *Uddenites* saddle, Wolf Camp Hills, Hess Canyon Quad.]

N721qc. Road Canyon Formation [at 5297–5313 ft elevation, 1.83 mi N 83° W of Hess Ranch, Hess Canyon Quad.]

N722i. Skinner Ranch Formation (Sullivan Peak Member) [0.35 mi S 15° W of hill 4920, Altuda Quad.]

N722k. Skinner Ranch Formation (Sullivan Peak Member) [1.7 mi S 15° E of Old Payne Ranch, W flank of Dugout Mtn., Monument Spring Quad.]

N722r. Skinner Ranch Formation (lower Sullivan Peak Member) [ravine 3.1 mi S 10° E of Sullivan Peak, 1.03 mi N 73° E of hill 5300, Lenox Hills, Altuda Quad.]

N722u. Skinner Ranch Formation (Decie Ranch Member) [*Scacchinella* beds 2.35 mi N 22° E of Hess Ranch house, Hess Canyon Quad.]

N722y. Skinner Ranch Formation (Poplar Tank Member) [30 ft above Decie Ranch Member, same as location 722r]

N723b. Hess Formation [0.3 mi N 11° W of BM 5860, Leonard Mtn., Hess Canyon Quad.]

N723e. Skinner Ranch Formation (Poplar Tank Member) [ravine 3.1 mi S 10° E of Sullivan Peak, 1.03 mi N 73° E of hill 5300, Lenox Hills, Altuda Quad.]

N723f. Cibolo Formation [250 ft up slope, W end Permian, narrows of Cibolo Creek, Shafter Quad.]

N723g. Hueco Formation [100 ft above divide in Red Tank Canyon, Baylor Mts., Van Horn Quad.]

N725q. Cibolo Formation [thin-bedded limestone 265 ft vertical up slope, narrows of Cibolo Creek, Chinati Peak Quad.]

N725u. Cibolo Formation [260 ft vertical in thin-bedded limestone, narrows of Cibolo Creek, Chinati Peak Quad.]

N726m. Lenox Hills Formation [0.65 mi S 30° W of hill 5816, 1.78 mi S 68° E of Willis Ranch site, Hess Ranch Horst, Hess Canyon Quad.]

N728u. Capitan Formation [1 mi NW of Frijole P.O., first ledge of limestone above Delaware Sandstone]

N728x. Graham Formation (Wayland Shale Member) [1.2 mi S of Gunsight]

N728y. Hueco Formation (near base) [Permian foothills about 4 mi E of highway U.S. 80–85, at White Spur, 9 mi N of El Paso, Texas (in Franklin Mts.)]

N728z. Copacabana Formation [hillside 2.5 km S 40° E of Apillapampa, S of Capinota, Bolivia]

N729f. Skinner Ranch Formation (Poplar Tank Member) [slope on S end of Lenox Hills, just W of hill 4801, Monument Spring Quad.]

N729m. Skinner Ranch Formation (Sullivan Peak Member) [type section of member, hill 5300, Lenox Hills]

N729u. Hess Formation [slope of hill, 0.65 mi S 50° W of hill 5021, Altuda Quad.]

N729z. Cathedral Mountain Formation [N side of road to Split Tank, 3.35 mi N 49° E of Hess Ranch House, Texas]

N730a. Lenox Hills Formation [loose on conglomerate slope SE nose of Leonard Mtn., Hess Canyon Quad.]

N730c. Neal Ranch Formation (= King bed 8) [Hogback N of Geologist Canyon, Wolf Camp Hills, Hess Canyon Quad.]

N730e. Skinner Ranch Formation (Dugout Mountain Member) [about middle of Third Limestone of the Leonard, 1.6 mi S 87° W of Dugout Mtn. (5195), 1.4 mi S 50° W of Old Payne Ranch site, Monument Spring Quad.]

N730f. Skinner Ranch Formation (Dugout Mountain Member) [upper part of Third Limestone of the Leonard, same as locality 730e]

N730g. Skinner Ranch Formation (Dugout Mountain Member) [1.15 mi N 74° W of Dugout Mtn. (hill 5195), 1.05 mi S 20° E of Old Payne Ranch site, Monument Spring Quad.]

N730i. Skinner Ranch Formation (Dugout Mountain Member) [top of Third Limestone of the Leonard, 0.87 mi N 64° W of Dugout Mtn. (5195), 1.17 mi S 37° E of Old Payne Ranch site, Monument Spring Quad.]

N730j. Skinner Ranch Formation (Dugout Mountain Member) [fourth Limestone of the Leonard, 1.08 mi N 55° W of Dugout Mtn. (5195), 0.9 mi S 36° E of Old Payne Ranch site, Monument Spring Quad.]

N730–l. Skinner Ranch Formation (Sullivan Peak Member) [on top of largest bioherm at S end of Lenox Hills in hill 4801, Monument Spring Quad.]

N730p. Skinner Ranch Formation [base of heavy beds in fault block, 1.6 mi N 54° E of Hess Ranch, 0.52 mi N 75° W of hill 5726, Hess Canyon Quad.]

N730t. Skinner Ranch Formation (Bed C) [siliceous shale with fusulinids, fault block 1.55 mi N 40° E of Hess Ranch, Hess Canyon Quad.]

N730w. Word Formation (Willis Ranch Member) [0.53 mi N 75° E of BM 4973, 1.25 mi N 32° E of BM 4869, Gilliland Canyon, Altuda Quad.]

N730x. Hess Formation [0.7 mi N 30° W of hill 5725, 1.1 mi N 70° W of hill 5767, Hess Canyon Quad.]

N730y. Hess Formation [3.15 mi N 58° E of Hess Ranch, 1.1 mi S 59° E of hill 5816, Hess Canyon Quad.]

N730z. Word Formation [1.55 mi N 13° W of hill 4910, 0.9 mi S 29° W of hill 5939, Altuda Quad.]

N731c. Skinner Ranch Formation [upper *Scacchinella* beds, 0.9 mi N 74° W of hill 5816, 1.5 mi S 76° E of Willis Ranch site, Hess Ranch Horst, Hess Canyon Quad.]

N731f. Skinner Ranch Formation (Poplar Tank Member) [W saddle of "Windmill" hill, E side of Sullivan Ranch Road, hill 5021, Altuda Quad.]

N731g. Skinner Ranch Formation (Sullivan Peak Member) [loose on outcrop at locality 707o]

N731h. Word Formation (Willis Ranch Member) [0.5 mi N of hill 5611, Hess Canyon, Glass Mts.]

N731i. Neal Ranch Formation [float on Dugout Mtn., Monument Spring Quad.]

N731n. Cathedral Mountain Formation [0.9 mi S 74° E of hill 4910, 1.95 mi N 27° E of hill 5021, Altuda Quad.]

N731s. Cathedral Mountain Formation [0.9 mi S 4° W of hill 4920, 1.73 mi S 70° W of hill 5021, Altuda Quad.]

N731v. Word Formation [0.57 mi S 28° E of Sullivan Peak (BM 6125), 1.07 mi S 5° E of Sullivan (Yates) Ranch, Altuda Quad.]

N731w. Road Canyon Formation (top bed) [0.65 mi S 30° E of Sullivan Peak (BM 6125), 1.18 mi S 80° E of Sullivan (Yates) Ranch, Altuda Quad.]

N731x. Word Formation (Bed C); possibly Road Canyon [1.1 mi S 39° W of hill 5935, Altuda Quad.]

N731y. Word Formation (Bed A) = Road Canyon Formation [1.1 mi S 39° W of hill 5935, Altuda Quad.]

· N732g. Road Canyon Formation [3 ft below top of A in section, 0.62 mi S 69° W of Old Payne Ranch site, 0.4 mi N 80° E of hill 4806, Monument Spring Quad.]

N732h. Road Canyon Formation (Bed C) [0.65 mi S 69° W of Old Payne Ranch site, 0.35 mi N 80° E of hill 4806. Monument Spring Quad.]

N732–l. Cathedral Mountain Formation [ammonites at 4637 ft on conical hill 0.25 mi N 28° W of Old Payne Ranch site, Monument Spring Quad.]

N732n. Road Canyon Formation [middle bioherms in conical hill 0.25 mi N 28° W of Old Payne Ranch site, Monument Spring Quad.]

N732o. Road Canyon Formation [10 ft above the base of the bioherms in conical hill 0.25 mi N 28° W of Old Payne Ranch site, Monument Spring Quad.]

N732p. Road Canyon Formation [very top of conical hill 0.25 mi N 28° W of Old Payne Ranch site, Monument Spring Quad.]

N732r. Road Canyon Formation [*Coscinophora*, 10 ft below top of conical hill, 0.25 mi N 28° W of Old Payne Ranch, Monument Spring Quad.]

N732x. Road Canyon Formation (base) [1.32 mi N 52° W of Old Payne Ranch site, 1.15 mi N 4° W of hill 4806. Monument Spring Quad.]

N732y. Road Canyon Formation(?) [1.35 mi N 53° W of Old Payne Ranch site, 1.15 mi N 6° W of hill 4806, Monument Spring Quad.]

N732z. Road Canyon Formation (upper) [1.36 mi N 50° W of Old Payne Ranch site, 1.2 mi N 2° W of hill 4806, Monument Spring Quad.]

N733b. Road Canyon Formation (Bed B) [in section 1.55 mi N 64° W of Old Payne Ranch, Monument Spring Quad.]

N733c. Road Canyon Formation (Bed D) [1.55 mi N 64° W of Old Payne Ranch site, Monument Spring Quad.]

N733d. Road Canyon Formation (Bed H) [fusulinid limestone, 1.55 mi N 64° W of Old Payne Ranch site, Monument Spring Quad.]

N733e. Road Canyon Formation (Bed J) [1.55 mi N 64° W of Old Payne Ranch site, Monument Spring Quad.]

N733f. Road Canyon Formation (Bed L) [crumbly shale with ammonites, in section 1.55 mi N 64° W of Old Payne Ranch site, Monument Spring Quad.]

N733i. Skinner Ranch Formation (Sullivan Peak Member) [1.33 mi N 39° E of Dugout Mtn. (BM 5195), 2.0 mi N 53° E of BM 4190, Monument Spring Quad.]

N733k. Skinner Ranch Formation (Sullivan Peak Member) [*Coscinophora* bioherm, same locality as 733j; Fusulinids from 30 ft below *Coscinophora*]

N733o. Road Canyon Formation [17 ft under bioherm on nose of hill in a 2 ft lens, 0.83 mi S 70° W of Old Word Ranch site, 1.15 mi S 12° E of hill 5507, Hess Canyon Quad.]

N733p. Road Canyon Formation [about 15 ft above locality 733o]

N733s. Skinner Ranch Formation [1.2 mi S 46° E of Willis Ranch site, 0.35 mi N 48° W of hill 5305, Hess Canyon Quad.]

N733t. Road Canyon Formation [1.82 mi N 84° W of Hess Ranch, 0.27 mi S 28° E of hill 5674, Hess Canyon Quad.]

N733u. Road Canyon Formation (Bed H) [1.82 mi N 84° W of Hess Ranch, 0.27 mi S 28° E of hill 5674, Hess Canyon Quad.]

N733v. Road Canyon Formation (Bed D) [same locality as 733u]

N733w. Cibolo Formation (exact level indefinite) [2 mi NW of Ojo Bonito, Chinati Peak Quad.]

N733x. Cibolo Formation [thin, dark, platy limestone of upper Cibolo, 2 mi NW of Ojo Bonito, Chinati Peak Quad.]

N733y. Cibolo Formation [1.7 mi N 47° W of Ojo Bonito, Chinati Peak Quad.]

N734. Bell Canyon Formation (middle Pinery Member) [0.5 mi south of Hegler Ranch, Guadalupe Peak Quad.]

N734b. Cibolo Formation (upper) [40 ft below top of D, section 2 mi N 49° W of Ojo Bonito, Chinati Peak Quad.]

N734c. Cibolo Formation (Bed E) [2 mi N 49° W of Ojo Bonito, Chinati Peak Quad.]

N734d. Cibolo Formation (upper) [50 ft below base of Word-type rock, 1.9 mi N 26° W of Ojo Bonito, Chinati Peak Quad.]

N734e. Bone Spring Formation [75 ft above the Hueco Formation, northernmost hill of Baylor Mts., W side of Texas 54, E side of hill 4402, 0.6 mi S 22.5° W of BM 3806, Van Horn (30′) Quad.]

N734j. Road Canyon Formation (Leonardian) [1.37 mi S 4° W of Willis Ranch house, 0.98 mi N 68° E of hill 5801, Hess Canyon Quad.]

N735a. Road Canyon Formation [Old Word Ranch, Hess Canyon Quad.]

N735c. Word Formation (Willis Ranch Member) [Hess Canyon, NE of Hess Ranch, same as locality 706e, Hess Canyon Quad.]

N735e. Road Canyon Formation [0.35 mi N 82° W of Old Payne Ranch site, 0.8 mi S 46° E of hill 4861, Monument Spring Quad.]

N735f. Skinner Ranch Formation (Sullivan Peak Member) [Hill 5300, Lenox Hills, Altuda Quad.]

N735i. Cathedral Mountain Formation [sandstone bed below Road Canyon Formation, just E of A7-2, 0.3 mi NNW of Old Payne Ranch, Monument Spring Quad.]

N735j. Capitan Formation [canyon N of Pine Canyon, Guadalupe Mts.]

N735w. Road Canyon Formation [1.48 mi S 64.5° W of Old Word Ranch house, 0.67 mi S 48° E of hill 5611, Hess Canyon Quad.]

N736b. Skinner Ranch Formation (Sullivan Peak Member) [0.08 mi S 56° E of hill 4801, S end of Lenox Hills, Monument Spring Quad.]

N736c. Skinner Ranch Formation (Sullivan Peak Member) [fusulinids from E end of faulted block, 1 ft below top of massive Sullivan Peak, same locality as 736b]

N736d. Skinner Ranch Formation (Sullivan Peak Member) [0.35 mi S 2° E of hill 4801, S end of Lenox Hills, 1.05 mi N 51° E of Lenox, Monument Spring Quad.]

N736e. Cathedral Mountain Formation [small hill 0.55 mi S 75° W of hill 4861, 1.6 mi N 72° W of Old Payne Ranch site, Monument Spring Quad.]

N736f. Road Canyon Formation (Bed H) [massive ledge, same locality as 736e]

N736g. Road Canyon Formation (Bed F) [massive 6 ft of fusulinid limestone; same locality as 736e]

N736h. Cathedral Mountain Formation [ammonites in conglomerate, 0.6 mi S 66° W of hill 4861, 1.55 mi N 76° W of Old Payne Ranch site, Monument Spring Quad.]

N736j. Word Formation [0.67 mi S 17° W of hill 4861, 1.2 mi S 85° W of Old Payne Ranch site, Monument Spring Quad.]

N736o. Road Canyon Formation [92 ft below top, 0.75 mi S 32° E of Sullivan Peak (BM 6125), 2.15 mi S 72° W of hill 4910, Altuda Quad.]

N736p. Road Canyon Formation (near top) [same locality as 736o]

N736q. Word Formation [fusulinid limestone near base of Word, 0.57 mi S 32° E of Sullivan Peak (BM 6125), 2.23 mi S 76° W of hill 4910, Altuda Quad.]

N736r. Road Canyon Formation [ammonite in Road Canyon near top of hill, E slope of spur S of Sullivan Peak, in bed C of section 4/1/66, Altuda Quad.]

N736v. Road Canyon Formation [from lowest bioherm, in face of hill 5801, 1.45 mi N 55° W of Hess Ranch, 0.25 mi S 67° E of hill 5801, Hess Canyon Quad.]

N736w. Word Formation (Willis Ranch Member) [float on Road Canyon outcrop, same locality as 736v]

N737c. Road Canyon Formation (Ammonite Bed) [1.65 mi N 76° W of Old Payne Ranch site, 0.7 mi S 73° W of hill 4861, Monument Spring Quad.]

N737f. Cathedral Mountain Formation (Bed J) [1.6 mi N 78° W of Old Payne Ranch, 0.68 mi S 63° W of hill 4861, Monument Spring Quad.]

N737g. Road Canyon Formation (Ammonite Bed) [2.15 mi N 82° W of Old Payne Ranch, 1.23 mi S 73° W of hill 4861, Monument Spring Quad.]

N737h. Road Canyon Formation [on road 230 ft SW of house, 2.1 mi N 82° W of Old Payne Ranch site, Monument Spring Quad.]

N737i. Road Canyon Formation (lower) [Road just NW of house, 2.1 mi N 82° W of Old Payne Ranch site, Monument Spring Quad.]

N737j. Skinner Ranch Formation (originally listed as Cathedral Mountain Formation) [1.4 mi N 70° W of point 4269, 1.37 mi S 52° W of point 4386, Monument Spring Quad.]

N737m. Road Canyon Formation (Bed B) [with small *Enteletes exiguus* Cooper and Grant, 2.25 mi S 60° W of Old Payne Ranch site, 2.1 mi N 59° W of point 4386, Monument Spring Quad.]

N737o. Road Canyon Formation (Bed F) [same locality as 737m]

N737p. Road Canyon Formation (topmost layer of Bed H) [same locality as 737m]

N737q. Road Canyon Formation (Bed H) [fourth limestone layer below top of Bed H, same locality as 737m]

N737r. Road Canyon Formation (Ammonite Bed) [1.22 mi S 55° W of hill 4861, 1.96 mi S 89° W of Old Payne Ranch site, Monument Spring Quad.]

N737s. Cathedral Mountain Formation (*Perrinites* Bed) [due W of new house, 1.85 mi S 87° W of Old Payne Ranch, 1.15 mi S 52° W of hill 4861, Monument Spring Quad.]

N737t. Gaptank Formation (*Prouddenites* Zone), Missourian [0.58 mi S 45° E of hill 5300, 1.37 mi N 70° E of hill 4902, Altuda Quad.]

N737x. Road Canyon Formation (Ammonite Bed) [1.4 mi N 80° W of point 4386, 2.5 mi S 38° W of Old Payne Ranch site, Monument Spring Quad.]

N737z. Word Formation [same locality as 737x]

N738e. Cibolo Formation (Breccia Zone of Udden) [boulder from breccia bed just under bioherm at 728-1, 0.8 mi N 83° E of Cibolo Ranch, Chinati Peak Quad.]

N738k. Cibolo Formation (Thin-bedded Zone) [25 ft below *Liosotella* bed, slope above largest bioherm, 1.3 mi N 75° E of Cibolo Ranch, Chinati Peak Quad.]

N738m. Cibolo Formation (Thin-bedded Zone) [about middle of thin-bedded member, 1.3 mi N 72° E of Cibolo Ranch, Chinati Peak Quad.]

N738q. Cibolo Formation [basal spicule bed, W side of largest bioherm, 1.3 mi N 75° E of Cibolo Ranch, Chinati Peak Quad.]

N738x. Cibolo Formation (Thin-bedded Zone) [50 ft stratigraphically below the base of the yellow dolomite zone, on hill, W side of largest bioherm, 1.3 mi N 75° E of Cibolo Ranch, Chinati Peak Quad.]

N738y. Cibolo Formation (Thin-bedded Zone) [170 ft below yellow dolomite and 10 ft below top of a thick limestone; same locality as 738x]

N738z. Cibolo Formation (Thin-bedded Zone) [fusulinids from a thick limestone in midst of thin-bedded zone in hill above largest bioherm; locality same as 738x]

N739a. Road Canyon Formation or Word Formation (China Tank Member) [mouth of canyon, 0.4 mi N 29° W of Old James Ranch, 2.7 mi N 71° W of Altuda, King brothers map of Glass Mts. (P. B. King, 1931); lowest fusulinid bed]

N739b. Word Formation (Willis Ranch Member) [upper fusulinid bed, same locality as 739a]

N739d. Road Canyon Formation (Ammonite Bed) [1.4 mi N 80° W of point 4386, 2.5 mi S 38° W of Old Payne Ranch site, Monument Spring Quad.]

N739e. Road Canyon Formation (Ammonite Bed) [same locality as 737x]

N739f. Road Canyon Formation? [low hill at base of Del Norte Mts., 0.95 mi due W of point 4386, Monument Spring Quad.]

N739i. Hess Formation [75 ft below top of hill closed by 5750 ft contour, 0.3 mi SW of hill 5821, and 0.2 mi SE of hill 5767, Hess Canyon Quad.]

N739j. Cibolo Formation (Spicule Zone of Udden) [ravine 1.5 mi NE of volcanic plug, one mile S of E end of Permian outcrop along Sierra Alta Creek, Chinati Peak Quad.]

N739m. Cibolo Formation (Breccia Zone) [bioherm E of

biggest bioherm, 1.6 mi NE of Cibolo Ranch, on Sierra Alta Creek, Chinati Peak Quad.]

N740m. Capitan Formation [1.55 mi N 75° E of Pratt Lodge, 2.12 mi S 83° E of hill 6560, NE corner of Guadalupe Peak Quad.]

N740o. Capitan Formation [about same level as locality 740n but on SW side of Yucca Canyon, Carlsbad Caverns West (15') Quad., New Mexico–Texas]

N741h. Hueco Formation [S side of gully S of reef, 0.3 mi S 17° W of Alacran Mt., 2.2 mi N of Hueco Inn, Hueco Mts. (15') Quad.]

N741i. Road Canyon Formation [approximately equal to locality 741a]

N742a. Hess Formation [5675 ft on SW side of knob, 0.18 mi S 50° E of hill 5767, 0.3 mi S 54° W of hill 5821, NW of Wolf Camp Hills, Hess Canyon Quad.]

N742d. Lenox Hills Formation [shale between conglomerate and Decie Ranch Member, hill on front of mountains, 2 mi NE of Lenox, Monument Spring–Altuda quadrangles]

N768. Permian (Kaibab) [Camp 73 in Canyon of Cascade River, Grand Canyon of the Colorado River, Arizona]

N768a. Kaibab [Canyon of Diamond River, Grand Canyon of the Colorado, Arizona]

N776. Permian [Union Range, 20 mi NW of Nebraska City, Nebraska]

N776a. Upper Carboniferous = Permian (Phosphoria) [Long Valley, Nevada]

N814. Word Formation equivalent (*Waagenoceras* Zone) [Palo Quemado, NW end of Las Delicias Valley, Coahuila, Mexico]

N3361. (Bowsher loc.) Bursum Formation [100 ft below the level of the Tularosa Clay Pit fauna, shale and limestone in round hill above microgranite sill, NW ¼ NE ¼ sec. 2, T. 15 S., R. 10 E., Otero County, New Mexico]

Glass Mountains Localities by Formation (Revised)

(cf. Part I, pages 165–166)

Capitan Limestone Formation: USNM 732q.

Cathedral Mountain Formation: AMNH 500, 504; Moore 23; USNM 702, 702a, 702a[1], 702b, 702ent, 702inst, 702-low, 702un, 703a[1], 703b, 703bs, 704z, 707q, 708, 708c, 708u, 708x, 709, 709o, 710b, 711q, 711r, 711w, 712o, 713p, 713t, 713v, 713w, 717g, 721f, 721u, 721v, 723k, 723n, 723p, 723u, 723y, 724i, 724k, 724m, 724n, 724r, 724s, 724t, 726o, 726u, 726v, 726w, 726x, 726y, 727o, 727q, 727w, 727x, 729r, 729z, 730q, 730u, 731b, 731n, 731q, 731t, 732u, 733m, 735b, 735g, 735i, 736t, 737f, 737j, 737s, 737v, 741s.

(Wedin Member): USNM 700-l, 700x, 710d, 714v, 714w, 714wa, 717e, 723v, 727p.

Gaptank Formation: USNM 700, 700a, 700b, 700e, 700f, 700g, 701y, 704d, 705ca, 705f, 705i, 705q, 705v, 708p, 713e, 715z, 716k, 730m.

(*Uddenites*-bearing Shale Member): USNM 700i, 701e, 701f,

701p, 701q, 701r, 701t, 701u, 701v, 701x, 702j, 702k, 702n, 702q, 702r, 703–l, 703o, 703p, 703x, 705h, 713a, 713b, 713g, 713o, 713u, 721h, 721i, 721–l, 721m, 730n.

Hess Formation: USNM 709g, 709h, 713x, 715q, 716a, 716g, 719q, 722p, 723b, 726n, 729e, 729u, 742a.

(Taylor Ranch Member): USNM 702d, 702e, 702f, 702m, 716n, 716o.

Lenox Hills Formation: USNM 704f, 704q, 704r, 705, 705k, 705m, 705s, 706g, 707j, 707ja, 707m, 707n, 707o, 707s, 709t, 709w, 710w, 713j, 713q, 713y, 715, 715b, 715–l, 716r, 718y, 719r, 720z, 723d, 723r, 724x, 727i, 730a, 731k, 737u, 742d.

Neal Ranch Formation: USNM 701, 701a, 701a[1], 701a[2], 701a[3], 701b, 701c, 701d, 701g, 701h, 701j, 701k, 701–l, 702h, 702t, 706x, 708b, 708w, 708y, 712w, 712z, 713h, 713k, 713–l, 715e, 718e, 719a, 721g, 721k, 721n, 722w, 722x, 727d, 727e, 730c, 731i, 731–l, 742c.

Road Canyon Formation: AMNH 501, 503, 507, 509; USNM 700v, 702c, 703, 703a, 703c, 703d, 706f, 707e, 709c, 710h, 710i, 710u, 710z, 712q, 712t, 716x, 716xa, 716z, 719w, 719x, 720d, 721j, 721o, 721r, 721s, 721t, 721w, 721x, 721y, 721z, 722e, 722f, 722g, 722v, 723a, 723x, 724a, 724b, 724c, 724d, 724j, 726c, 726d, 726e, 726f, 726z, 726za, 731e, 732i, 732j, 732m, 732r, 732t, 732w, 733a, 733b, 733n, 734j, 735a, 735w, 736x, 737n, 737q, 737y, 741a, 741i.

Skinner Ranch Formation: AMNH 520; USNM 705a, 705b, 705–l, 705n, 705o, 705r, 707h, 707u, 707z, 709a, 709u, 709v, 709z, 711d, 711i, 711k, 711o, 711p, 711z, 712n, 712p, 713n, 714p, 714q, 714z, 715n, 716q, 716t, 717v, 719y, 720e, 720f, 720g, 720j, 722m, 722o, 723h, 723–l, 723o, 723q, 723s, 724–l, 724p, 724q, 726h, 726j, 726–l, 727b, 727f, 727h, 727m, 727n, 729j, 729–l, 730o, 730r, 730s, 730v, 731o, 733r, 739–l.

(Decie Ranch Member): USNM 707a, 707g, 707–l, 707v, 707w, 707x, 708q, 708z, 713s, 714e, 714t, 715a, 715c, 715v, 716p, 717i, 719s, 727t, 727u, 729i, 732b, 733h.

(Dugout Mountain Member): USNM 700o, 700p, 700r, 700s, 700t, 732d, 732e, 733–l.

(Poplar Tank Member): USNM 703y, 707ha, 707i, 708a, 708e, 710x, 713r, 718v, 729f, 729q, 731f, 741k.

(Sullivan Peak Member): USNM 700y, 704y, 707, 707b, 707c, 707d, 707t, 708v, 709–l, 710r, 710y, 713c, 713d, 713i, 713m, 713z, 714y, 715f, 715h, 715j, 715m, 715o, 715p, 715u, 717a, 718z, 722h, 722j, 722k, 722–l, 723e, 727a, 729h, 729m, 729o, 729p, 730k, 731g, 733j, 735f, 739g.

Word Formation: USNM 719e, 731p, 731u, 732s, 737b.

(Appel Ranch Member): USNM 704, 706d, 714o, 715i, 716v, 719z, 722t, 726t, 727j, 731z.

(China Tank Member): USNM 703e, 706a, 706c, 706z, 713, 721p, 726r, 726s, 733q.

(Lenses between Willis Ranch and Appel Ranch members): USNM 706b, 732c, 737w, 741p, 741q, 742b.

(Willis Ranch Member): AMNH 505, 506; USNM 706, 706e, 718d, 723t, 723w, 724u, 731h, 731m, 735c.

Guadalupe Mountains and Sierra Diablo
Localities by Formation (Revised)
(cf. Part I, page 166)

Bell Canyon Formation

(Hegler Member): AMNH 635; USNM 731, 732a, 740c, 740d.

(Lamar Member): AMNH 25, 37, 38, 39, 40, 347, 348, 351, 373, 384, 430; USNM 725e, 728i, 728p, 728q, 728r, 728s, 738, 738b.

(McCombs Member): AMNH 385, 409.

(Pinery): AMNH 33, 375, 397, 398, 401, 435, 437, 524, 528, 537, 636; Moore 30; USNM 725h, 725n, 733, 734, 736, 736a, 748.

(Rader): AMNH 388, 389, 403, 404, 410; USNM 725f, 725g, 725o, 735, 740a, 740g, 740h, 740i, 740j.

Bone Spring Formation: AMNH 46, 369, 492, 497, 591, 592, 624, 625, 628, 629, 631, 632, 633, 634, 655, 658, 660, 661, 663, 696, 697, 699; USNM 725c, 725s, 725y, 728e, 728f, 728g, 728h, 728t, 728v, 729, 741, 742, 744, 745, 746.

(Cutoff Member): AMNH 678; USNM 747.

Capitan Formation: AMNH 475, 725, 774, 799, 801, 803, 804, 806, 817, 820, 830, 837, 840, 843, 847, 853; USNM 725i, 725j, 725k, 725–l, 725m, 725p, 728u, 731j, 735j, 737a, 738a, 739, 740, 740k, 740–l, 740m, 740n, 740o, 748a, 750, 750a, 750b, 750e, 750f, 750g.

Carlsbad Formation: AMNH 417.

Cherry Canyon Formation

(Getaway Member): AMNH 21, 28, 496, 512, 519, 547, 585, 600, 652; Moore 31; USNM 728, 728w, 730, 732.

(Manzanita Member): AMNH 402.

(South Wells Member): AMNH 414.

Hueco Group: AMNH 390, 626, 653, 700; USNM 499b, 712d, 712e, 712m, 719, 720a, 720b, 720c, 725a, 725b, 725z, 728d, 728y, 741h.

Chinati Mountains Localities by Formation (Revised)
(cf. Part I, page 166)

Cibolo Formation

(Brecciated Zone): AMNH 703; USNM 728j, 728k, 728–l, 728m, 738c, 738r, 738s, 739m.

(Spicule Zone): USNM 725v, 738f, 738o, 738q, 739k.

(Thin-bedded Zone): USNM 738g, 738–l.

(Transition Zone): USNM 738d, 738h, 738n, 738t.

Ross Mine Formation: USNM 733z.

Concluding Remarks

This study of the brachiopods of West Texas and their stratigraphic setting does not exhaust these subjects. Our sampling of the strata of the Glass Mountains, although extensive, was not exhaustive. Any bioherm not sampled by us is a possible source of new taxa. Many thin beds and some lenticular bands not previously sampled offer attractive possibilities for further study. Still greater opportunities appear in the Guadalupe Mountains and the Delaware Basin. Our sampling in these areas was cursory and designed to help us understand the Girty species so that we could more accurately identify Glass Mountains materials. The Delaware Basin has never been thoroughly collected and offers promise because there is considerable silicification of the brachiopods.

The Capitan Limestone in the Guadalupes has only been cursorily collected. This will involve sledge hammer work and the breaking of great quantities of rock to produce an adequate collection, but the reward should be great for the effort.

The Sierra Diablo, Hueco, and Baylor Mountains have not been well collected. Our collections and Stehli's come from only a narrow, although critical, part of the Sierra Diablo. None of the higher beds has been more than scratched.

In the Marathon region three problems needing to be studied are outstanding: (1) the stratigraphic sequence in the Sierra del Norte; (2) more detailed study of the Road Canyon fauna; and (3) further environmental studies based on sediments and fossils—a cooperative venture.

SIERRA DEL NORTE.—In the part of these mountains embraced by the Monument Spring quadrangle, a long Word sequence with higher beds has been mapped but not collected. The lower part of this sequence is now known to consist of Cathedral Mountain and Road Canyon formations. A Cretaceous limestone is included in the sequence. To the south, the Word Formation thins and some beds of the Skinner Ranch Formation, tilted at a high angle, appear at the base of the mountains west of Dugout Mountain (locality 737j). This entire area needs detailed mapping and/or collecting.

ROAD CANYON FAUNA.—We had no problems with the Road Canyon fauna until we started work on the hills (5801 and 5453) northwest of the Hess Ranch. On the east side of hill 5801 (locality 706f) exposures are excellent, the sequence fairly well provided with bioherms at the base and near the top. Here we noted some brachiopods with Word affinities such as *Echinosteges, Costispinifera, Spiriferella,* and *Paucispinifera.*

We suspected a possibility of having collected float blocks from the Word (Willis Ranch Member) higher on the hill but a close search of the slopes revealed no blocks. Furthermore, here and on the west side of this hill we found lenses in the shaly beds immediately above the Road Canyon (locality 720d). The shaly beds are like the Word and would be mapped with it but the fossils of the lenses are unusual forms not readily identified with either Word or Road Canyon formations.

In the sequence of Road Canyon and Word formations leading up to Sullivan Peak, Ross (1962a:1732) found the "Third Limestone Member of the Word" of P. B. King at the top of the Road Canyon Formation. In the same sequence, far above the Road Canyon (locality 731u), we found brachiopods and ammonites characteristic of the Word Number 3 (= Willis Ranch Member).

In the foothills of the Sierra del Norte, the Road Canyon consists of thin limestones, often a sand or gravel of fusulinids, intercalated in shaly beds of Word Formation type. Here too, a mixture of characteristic Road Canyon forms was found with some Word fusulinids and brachiopods (see Garner Wilde's comments herein on locality 732j in the faunal list of fusulinids that he identified). West of Sullivan Peak the Road Canyon appears to fray out into thin limestone beds by intercalation of yellowish shale suggestive of the Word. Close collecting and tracing of Road Canyon strata from the site of the Old Word Ranch to and into the foothills of the Sierra del Norte is greatly needed because of the critical position of the Road Canyon in correlation. It has obvious affinities with the Cutoff Shale of the Guadalupe Mountains and part of the San Andres Mountains of New Mexico.

PALEO-ENVIRONMENTAL STUDIES.—It is interesting to note that studies of the sediments of the Glass Mountains and Chinati Mountains have led sedimentologists to conclude that these deposits were formed in deep water and that the included limestone lumps ("bioherms") are the result of submarine slide and reef talus. Rigby (1958:308) interpreted the *Scacchinella* bioherms of the Brecciated Zone of the Cibolo Formation of the Chinati Mountains as reef talus. The Decie Ranch Member of the Skinner Ranch Formation is a similar deposit but differently interpreted. Bioherms of the Glass Mountains sequence are interpreted as slide blocks (Rogers, 1972). Paleontologists, on the other hand, regard the so-called slide masses as bioherms in place. The bioherms contain fossils that are believed to have been shallow water types; algae and some corals are also present. We have stated our views on these structures in part I, and they need not be repeated here. A cooperative study by practitioners of the two disciplines is needed.

Literature Cited

Newell, N. D., and D. W. Boyd.
  1975. Parallel Evolution in Early Trigoniacean Bivalves. *American Museum of Natural History Bulletin,* 154(2):55–162, 98 figures, 31 tables.

Rogers, W. B.
  1972. Depositional Environments of the Skinner Ranch and Hess Formations (Lower Permian), Glass Mountains, West Texas. 392 pages, 28 plates. Doctoral dissertation, University of Texas.

Ross, C. A.
  1975. Base of the Permian System in the Glass Mountains, Texas. *West Texas Geological Society and Permian Basin Section, Society of Economic Paleontologists and Mineralogists,* Publication 75–65:43–50.

Smith, A. G.
  1976. Two New Permian Chitons from West Texas (Mollusca: Polyplacophora). *The Veliger,* 18(3):281–288, 34 figures, 4 tables.

Wilde, G. L.
  1971. Phylogeny of *Pseudofusulinella* and Its Bearing on Early Permian Stratigraphy. *In* J. T. Dutro, Jr., editor, Paleozoic Perspectives: A Paleontological Tribute to G. Arthur Cooper. *Smithsonian Contributions to Paleobiology,* 3:363–379.

Index

Names of new taxa and page numbers of principal entries in italics; pagination by Part: 1–231 (I), 233–793 (II), 795–1921 (III), 1923–2607 (IV), 2609–3159 (V); plates are referenced by the numbers of the pages on which they occur; see "Introduction" (Part VI) for delineation of corrections and additions to the data of Parts I–V that are included in Part VI but are not covered by this Index

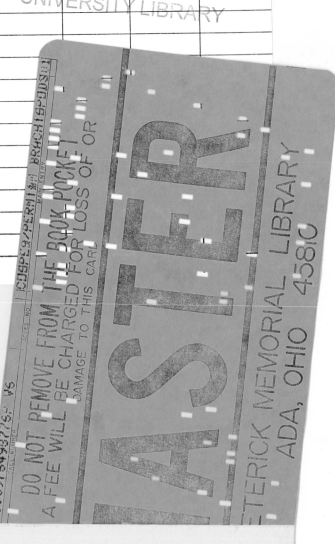